Introduction to Engineering Business Management
Custom Edition

Custom Edition for University of Warwick
School of Engineering

Compiled by Ian Tuersley and Nigel Denton

ISBN 13: 9781307064308

McGraw-Hill Custom Publishing

http://create.mheducation.com/uk/

Published by McGraw-Hill Education, 2 Penn Plaza, New York, NY 10121.

Cover image: ©iStock

ISBN: 9781307064308

Introduction to Engineering Business Management
ES194
CUSTOM EDITION

Contents

Chapter 2 page 34 - 49 and page 61

Credits

Chapter 1

What is the Business Environment?

Suppose you had a million pounds to invest and wanted to achieve the maximum return on your investment over the next ten years. Where would you invest? How would you go about deciding on the best opportunities? In the past, visionary entrepreneurs have been able to read trends in the business environment, and have made goods and services that were just right for the new emerging opportunities. Billy Butlin spotted a trend for more paid holidays and achieved great success in the 1930s with his new holiday camps. The Hoover company successfully foresaw that with more women going out to work, there would be greater demand for automated household appliances such as the vacuum cleaner. In recent years, internet entrepreneurs have spotted the great desire of people to extend their circles of friends from offline to online, and the result has been the tremendous growth of social network websites such as Facebook and Twitter. Even ten years before the launch of these innovatory products, the entrepreneurs behind them might have been laughed at as unrealistic idealists, but they succeeded through a combination of good luck and good reading of the dynamic, changing environment. Looking back is easy, but predicting the next ten years is much more difficult. What opportunities will foreseeable changes in the business environment present you with? How will lots of individual changes combine with one another to influence the types of goods and services that we want to buy and the ability of firms to supply them? This chapter introduces the basic building blocks of the business environment and how organizations can make sense of its complexity so that they can improve their preparedness for the future.

✓ Learning Objectives

This chapter will explain:

✓ The elements that make up an organization's macro-, micro- and internal environments.

✓ The complex interdependencies that exist in the business environment.

✓ The concept of a value chain.

✓ Models for viewing the business environment as a system.

1.1 Defining the business environment

What do we mean by the term business environment? In its most general sense, an environment can be defined as everything that surrounds a system. The environment of a central heating system, for example, comprises all of those phenomena that impact on the system's ability to operate effectively. The environment would therefore include such factors as the external air temperature, the insulation properties of the rooms being heated, the quality and consistency of fuel supplied, etc. A business organization can similarly be seen as a system, whose performance is influenced by a whole range of phenomena in its environment. However, while a central heating system may be said to be a *closed* system, the business organization and its environment is an *open* system. For the central heating system, all elements of the system can generally be identified, but for business organizations, it can be difficult to define what makes up the system, and even more difficult to define the elements of their environment. Some elements may seem quite inconsequential today, but may nevertheless have potential to affect critically a business organization in future years. The test of a good business leader is to be able to read the environment and to understand not only how business systems and their environments work today, but also how they will evolve in the future. Society's rising expectations with regard to the ethical behaviour of business organizations is an example of an environmental factor that has emerged as an increasingly critical factor to the survival of business organizations. After studying this book, you should have a better idea of the complexity of the business environment.

Business organizations exist to turn inputs from their environment (e.g. materials, labour and capital) into goods and services that customers in the environment want to purchase. This transformation process adds value to the inputs, so that buyers are prepared to pay more to the business organization than the cost of resources that it has used up in the production process. This is the basis of a simple model of the organization in its environment, illustrated in Figure 1.1. This transformation process within the organization cannot be seen as a steady state, because external environmental influences have a tendency to be continually shifting, having the effect of undermining the current balance within the system. Just as the central heating thermostat has to react constantly to ensure a balance between its inputs (the energy source) and its outputs (the required amount of heat), so too organizations must constantly ensure that the system continues to transform inputs into higher-value outputs.

Of course, the organizations that form the centre of this transformation process take many shapes and forms, from a small sole trader through to a large multinational organization. The nature of the organization greatly affects the way in which it can adapt to its external environment. We will explore the great diversity of organizational types later, in the context of their ability to respond to environmental change.

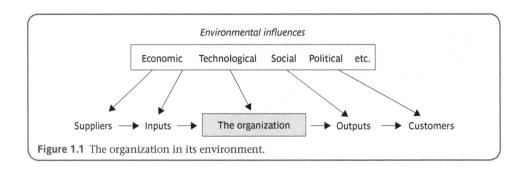

Figure 1.1 The organization in its environment.

Throughout this book, we are going to disaggregate a business organization's environment into a number of components. For now, we will introduce three important groups of components, which we will classify under the following headings:

- the macroenvironment
- the microenvironment
- the internal environment.

These are introduced schematically in Figure 1.2.

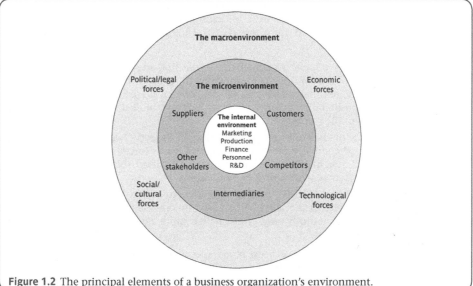

Figure 1.2 The principal elements of a business organization's environment.

The external environment comprises all those forces and events outside the organization that impinge on its activities. Some of these events impinge directly on the firm's activities – these can be described as forming an organization's **microenvironment**. Other events that are beyond the immediate environment nevertheless affect the organization and can be described as the **macroenvironment**. As well as looking to the outside world, managers must also take account of factors within other functions of their own firm. This is referred to as the **internal environment**.

The macroenvironment comprises a whole set of factors that can indirectly affect an organization's relationship to its markets. The organization may have no direct relationships with legislators as it does with suppliers, yet their actions in passing new legislation may have profound effects on the markets that the organization is able to serve, as well as affecting its production costs. The macroenvironmental factors cover a wide range of nebulous phenomena. They represent general forces and pressures rather than institutions with which the organization relates.

The microenvironment, by contrast, is concerned with actual individuals and organizations (such as customers, suppliers and intermediaries) that a company deals with. It may currently deal directly with some of these, while others exist with whom there is currently no direct contact, but who could nevertheless influence its policies. An organization's competitors could have a direct effect on its market position and form part of its microenvironment.

1.2 Why study the business environment?

History is full of examples of organizations that have failed to understand their operating environment, or simply failed to respond to change in the environment. The result has been a gradual decline in their profitability, and eventually they may cease to exist as a viable business unit. Theodore Levitt called this 'marketing myopia' and cited the example of railway companies that focused their vision on providing railway services, but failed to take account of the development of road transport (Levitt 1960). Consider the following more recent examples.

- The retailer Marks & Spencer assumed that its position was unassailable, but by the 1990s had failed to take account of the great improvements in value being offered by its competitors. The result was that many of Marks & Spencer's loyal customers deserted it, leading to a sharp fall in profitability, before a thwarted takeover bid led to new management bringing a new vision to the company.
- Healthy eating has become an important issue in the early twenty-first century. The profits of the fast-food company McDonald's fell and it was forced to close branches worldwide as consumers sought more healthy convenience food, before the company belatedly responded to change with healthier menu items.
- Music retailers such as HMV and EMI were accused of 'putting their head in the sand' and ignoring the threat to the sale of CDs posed by downloadable music sites. They adopted new distribution methods only after smaller, more aggressive companies had developed the online music market.

On the other hand, there have been many spectacular successes where organizations have spotted emerging trends in their business environment, and capitalized on these with new goods and services, or new ways of operating their business, in order to meet the new opportunities presented within the environment. Consider the following examples.

- In the airline market, companies such as Ryanair and easyJet spotted the opportunities represented by government deregulation and offered profitable low-cost 'no frills' air services, often aimed at people who would not previously have flown.
- Many supermarkets and farmers have noted consumers' concern for the purity of the food we eat, and this, combined with rising incomes, has led them successfully to develop ranges of organic foods.
- Many of the UK's pub operators have identified changing social behaviour, with fewer people using pubs as a regular venue primarily for beer drinking, but much greater levels of dining out for social purposes. This has led pub operators to increase their profits by reconfiguring their pubs as restaurants.

There is every indication that the pace of change in most organizations' business environment is speeding up and it is therefore increasingly important for organizations to have in place systems for monitoring their environment and, just as importantly, for responding appropriately to such change. There is evidence that successful organizations are not so much those that deliver value to customers today, but those that understand how definitions of value are likely to change in the future. A company may have been very good at creating value through the typewriters that it made, but it may nevertheless have failed to deliver value into the future had it not understood the impacts of information technology. In the eyes of customers, the company's traditional products would no longer represent good value when compared with the possibilities presented by the new technologies.

Of course, it is much more difficult to predict the future than to describe the past. A stark indication of the rewards of looking forwards rather than backwards is provided by an analyst who studied stock-market performance. If a cumulative investment of $1 had been invested from 1900 on 1 January each year in the stock that had performed best in the *previous* year, and then reinvested the following year, the accumulated value in 2000 would have been just $250. However, if it had been invested each year in the stock that performed best in the *year ahead*, the accumulated value would be over $1 billion. Successful companies have often been those that understand their business environment and have invested in growth areas, while cutting back in areas that are most likely to go into decline. Being first to market when trends are changing can be much more profitable than simply reacting to a market trend. However, predicting future trends can be very difficult and can involve a lot of risk. The aim of this book is to provide frameworks for making well-informed judgements about the likely future state of the business environment, based on a sound analysis of emerging trends.

1.3 The macroenvironment → Out of your hands

While the microenvironment comprises individuals and organizations with whom a company interacts, the macroenvironment is more nebulous. It comprises general trends and forces that may not immediately affect the relationships that a company has with its customers, suppliers and intermediaries but, sooner or later, macroenvironmental change will alter the nature of these relationships. As an example, change in the population structure of a country does not immediately affect the way in which a company does business with its customers but, over time, it may affect the numbers of young or elderly people with whom it is able to do business.

Most analyses of the macroenvironment divide the environment into a number of areas. The principle headings, which form the basis for chapters of this book, are described below. It must, however, be remembered that the division of the macroenvironment into subject areas does not result in watertight compartments. The macroenvironment is complex and interdependent, and these interdependencies will be brought out in later chapters. The subheadings of the sections that follow are also those that are commonly used in macroenvironmental analysis.

⟳ Thinking around the subject

Big Mac, big business, big problem?

Business leaders have come under increasing levels of scrutiny from governments, the media and the public in general. Some people have held grudges against particular companies, and others against the system of big business in general. In 2009, anti-globalization protesters damaged a Royal Bank of Scotland (RBS) building during a G20 summit of world leaders in London; the object of the protestors was as much the world business environment in general as RBS in particular. The advent of social networking media has made it easier for groups of disenchanted individuals to connect with one another and to voice their concerns about the business environment.

Large, successful companies, it seems, just have to accept that they will never please those people who hold large corporate organizations responsible for all of the world's problems. But just how hostile is the environment to business organizations?

A report by the Future Foundation appeared to challenge the idea that young people are becoming more hostile towards big business than their parents (Future Foundation). According to a 2001 study by the organization, 16–24-year-olds have more positive feelings towards multinationals than older groups, particularly those who came of age in the 1960s, a period commonly associated with protest movements. Now in their forties and fifties, this group seemed to be the most critical of big business. The research revealed that younger generations are less inclined towards direct action than their parents and grandparents. Nearly half of all 16–34 year olds claimed they would not demonstrate if a multinational company had done something wrong. Further confounding the myth of young people wanting to change the world was the statistic that fewer than one in twenty strongly agreed that they 'would not buy the products of a large multinational company that had done something wrong'. A third of teens and twentysomethings agreed to preserving the power of multinational companies, and a further one in ten believed that multinationals are 'ultimately for the good of consumers' and should be encouraged to grow. By contrast, two-thirds of their grandparents – those aged 55 and above – claimed they would boycott goods to punish companies they considered guilty of corporate crimes. Even the issue of genetic engineering failed to provoke a strong response from young people, with only four in ten mistrusting the claims of the multinationals, compared to six in ten of their parents and grandparents.

Does this research indicate the ultimate supremacy for big business, where the golden arches of McDonald's and the Nike 'swoosh' are symbols of its global sovereignty? Should such organizations feel safe in the knowledge of this study, or do they still need to be alert to possible trouble in the future? And even if a high proportion of young people support the idea of capitalism and big business, can such firms afford to ignore the vociferous and extreme minority whose direct action and boycotts can do costly and long-lasting harm to a firm's image?

1.3.1 The political environment

Politicians are instrumental in shaping the general nature of the external environment as well as being responsible for passing legislation that affects specific types of organization. The political environment can be one of the less predictable elements in an organization's marketing environment, and businesses need to monitor the changing political environment for a number of reasons.

- At the most general level, the stability of the political system affects the attractiveness of the business environment. Companies are likely to be reluctant to invest in a country with an unstable government, for fear that the law would not protect their investment.
- Governments pass legislation that directly and indirectly affects firms' business opportunities.
- There are many examples of the direct effects on business organizations – for example, laws giving consumers rights against the seller of faulty goods. At other times, the effects of legislative changes are less direct, as where legislation outlawing anti-competitive practices changes the nature of competition between firms within a market.
- In its broadest sense, the political environment includes pressure groups and trade associations that can be influential in changing government policy.

- Government is responsible for formulating policies that can influence the rate of growth in the economy and hence the total amount of spending power. It is also a political decision as to how this spending power should be distributed between different groups of consumers and between the public and private sectors.

- Governments are responsible for protecting the public interest at large, imposing further constraints on the activities of firms (for example, controls on pollution, which may make a manufacturing firm uncompetitive in international markets on account of its increased costs).

- Increasingly, the political environment affecting business organizations includes supranational organizations that can directly or indirectly affect companies. These include trading blocs (e.g. the EU, ASEAN and NAFTA) and the influence of worldwide intergovernmental organizations (e.g. the World Trade Organization) and pressure groups (e.g. Greenpeace).

1.3.2 The social, demographic and cultural environment

Business organizations are concerned with the structure and values of the societies in which they operate. It is crucial for businesses to appreciate fully the cultural values of a society, especially where an organization is seeking to do business in a country that is quite different to its own. Attitudes to specific products change through time and at any one time can differ between groups in society.

Even in home markets, business organizations should understand the processes of gradual change in values and attitudes and be prepared to satisfy the changing needs of consumers. The 2010 edition of *Social Trends*, published by the UK's Office for National Statistics, highlighted a number of changes that had occurred during the previous 40 years:

- in 1971, the average household size in Great Britain was 2.9 people, with single-person households accounting for 18 per cent of all households; by 2009, the average household size had fallen to 2.4, with the proportion of single-person households rising to 29 per cent

- in 1970, life expectancy at birth for males in the UK was 68.7 years and for females 75.0 years; by 2008, life expectancy at birth for males had risen to 77.8 years and for females 81.9 years

- in 1970, there were 340,000 first marriages in England and Wales, but this had fallen to 143,000 by 2007

- attitudes to healthy living have changed – for example, in 1974, 26 per cent of men and 13 per cent of women in Great Britain who smoked regularly were classed as heavy smokers, but by 2008 these figures had fallen to 7 per cent and 5 per cent respectively.

These are just a few examples of detail changes that can have direct and indirect impacts on the business environment. To take the example of the decline in the number of heavy smokers, this has encouraged many governments around the world to ban smoking in public spaces. Such legislation might have been difficult to agree and implement if smokers were still a dominant group in society, but with declining numbers, the legislation has been passed. Some business sectors have been significantly affected by this, especially the hospitality and entertainment sector. As an example, in 2008 a UK-based bingo operator blamed a fall in profits on the smoking ban as many clients decided to smoke at home rather than visit a smoke-free bingo hall.

A number of general social trends with potential impacts on business can be observed in most developed economies, as the following examples illustrate.

- Leisure is becoming a bigger part of many people's lives, and businesses have responded with a wide range of leisure-related goods and services.

- Attitudes to debt have changed and there is a tendency for increasing numbers of people to buy products for experiential values rather than to satisfy basic utilitarian needs.

- The role of women in society has changed – although, worldwide, big differences in the role of women and men remain. For example, a report to the World Economic Forum in 2010 noted that, in Nordic nations, women live longer, have high employment rates, high levels of participation in higher education, and often enjoy generous maternity and paternity schemes. At the other end of the scale, Pakistan, Chad and Yemen perform poorly. In the case of India, it was noted that women suffered from persistent health, education and economic participation gaps.

- Growing concern with the environment among many groups in society is reflected in a variety of 'green' consumer products.
- Greater life expectancy is leading to an ageing of the population and a shift to an increasingly 'elderly' culture. This is reflected in product design that emphasizes durability rather than fashionability. New services have emerged to meet the aspirations of this growing group – for example, adventure holidays and 'gap years' for older people.
- Many western European countries are becoming ethnically and culturally much more diverse. In the UK, the large number of Polish people who entered the country from 2004 has led to the development of many retail and financial services aimed specifically at this group.

In Chapter 3 we look in detail at consumers' values, attitudes and lifestyles, and the processes of gradual change in these. That chapter also explores the issue of 'cultural convergence', referring to an apparent decline in differences between cultures.

1.3.3 The technological environment

The pace of technological change is becoming increasingly rapid and marketers need to understand how technological developments might affect them in four related business areas.

1 New technologies can allow new goods and services to be offered to consumers – internet banking, mobile internet and new anti-cancer drugs, for example.

2 New technology can allow existing products to be made more cheaply, thereby widening their market through being able to charge lower prices. In this way, more efficient aircraft have allowed new markets for air travel to develop.

3 Technological developments have allowed new methods of distributing goods and services (for example, Amazon.com used the internet to offer book buyers a new way of browsing and buying books).

4 New opportunities for companies to communicate with their target customers are continuing to emerge, with many companies using computer databases to target potential customers and to maintain a dialogue with established customers. The internet, '3G' mobile phone networks and global positioning systems (GPS) have opened up new communication opportunities for many companies.

1.3.4 The economic environment

Businesses need to keep an eye on indications of a nation's prosperity. There are many indicators of a nation's economic health, of which two of the most common are measures of gross domestic product (GDP) and household disposable income. Many of these indicators tend to follow cyclical patterns related to a general economic cycle of expansion followed by contraction.

Throughout the economic cycle, the consumption of most goods and services tends to increase during the boom period and decline during recessionary periods. The difficulty in forecasting the level of demand for a firm's products is therefore often quite closely linked to the difficulty of forecasting future economic prosperity. This difficulty is compounded by the problem of understanding the relationship between economic factors and the state of demand – most goods and services are positively related to total available income, but some, such as bus services and insolvency practitioners, are negatively related. Furthermore, while aggregate changes in spending power may indicate a likely increase for goods and services in general, the actual distribution of spending power among the population will influence the pattern of demand for specific products. In addition to measurable economic prosperity, the level of perceived wealth and confidence in the future can be an important determinant of

Figure 1.3 Changing family structures and growing career orientation among women have led many people to seek outside childcare services, rather than caring for children entirely within the family unit. Some cultures may regard childcare as central to family life, and would therefore provide few opportunities for a commercial childcare service. Attitudes in western countries have changed, and a growing proportion of people would regard it as quite normal to buy in professional help to look after their children. Many service providers, such as this one, have emerged to satisfy this growing market. (Photo reproduced with permission of Cheeky Chums Nursery.)

demand for some high-value goods and services. The economic cycle also affects competition for resources, with peak prices for resources such as oil and metals being reached during periods of boom, and much lower prices during periods of economic recession.

Understanding the economic environment can become particularly difficult during periods of great turbulence. During 2008, a 'credit crunch' led to the collapse of several banks and many commentators predicted that established economic patterns would change for ever. Just the existence of turbulence led many individuals and organizations to be much more cautious in the lending and borrowing decisions they made, which in turn had knock-on effects elsewhere in the economy.

⟳ Thinking around the subject

The consumer culture is dead – long live the consumer?

In September 2008 it seemed that the business environment had changed for ever, as cherished institutions collapsed, one after another. In the space of a few months, banks around the world had gone bankrupt, from the mighty Lehman Brothers down to the small savings and loans institutions that ran out of cash. Mighty retailers such as Woolworths – just one year short of its hundredth birthday in the UK – were laid to ruin. A generation had been brought up on the idea that 'greed is good' and that big end-of-year bonuses were to

⟳

be celebrated, not condemned. But now greedy bonus seekers were seen as the cause of so many problems. In many circles, 'ostentatious consumption' was eclipsed by a new age of 'ostentatious utilitarianism'. At dinner parties, people who once would have boasted about how much they had paid for their Prada handbag or Jimmy Choo shoes now revelled in telling their friends how they had been so clever in 'discovering' good-value bargains in the likes of Poundland and Lidl. This coincided with a period of growing concern for the ecological environment, so any self-respecting socialite could now save their dwindling pennies and acquire street cred by convincing their friends that, by shopping at Poundland, they were helping to help save the environment. Where would all this lead? Some pundits saw an inexorable trend to an anti-materialistic world in which people felt guilty about earning bonuses (at least those who still had a job), and those who had the money felt bad about spending it. Surely the world would never be the same again and the business environment would grind to a halt as consumers' new-found values resulted in them spending less with companies, which would in turn lead to fewer people with well-paid jobs and therefore even fewer consumers able and willing to keep the economy afloat.

Reports of the death of the capitalist, consumer-led culture turned out to be premature. Some wealthy groups never stopped spending – for example, the profits of upmarket auction house Sotheby's remained strong following the financial crisis. Others appeared to have been laying low and soon came out spending again. By 2010 the profits of many upmarket retailers had begun to rise as shoppers rediscovered luxury.

Even the 'bonus culture' that had been so much maligned during the financial crisis seemed to be making a strong comeback. In February 2010, Royal Bank of Scotland, which had been brought close to bankruptcy partly as a result of its own bonus culture, announced that it would be paying £1.3 billion in bonuses to its staff.

Trying to predict the future business environment can be fraught with difficulty. In the eye of a crisis, we might think that the world has changed for ever but, as this example illustrates, systems can be resilient and the business environment, seen as a complex system, may have great self-correcting characteristics. A difficult challenge for business leaders is to distinguish transient, self-correcting changes from these that bring about fundamental change in the relationship between elements of the business environment. Maybe some things are quite constant – for example, consumers' need to adapt to the norms of their peer group – and this was just manifested in different ways at the depths of the recession, but when the peer groups' values changed, was it simply a case of back to 'business as usual'?

1.4   The microenvironment

The microenvironment of an organization can best be understood as comprising all those other organizations and individuals who directly or indirectly affect the activities of the organization. The microenvironment comprises actual people and organizations. The company may be dealing with these organizations today, or may potentially deal with them in the future. It may have no intention of dealing with other companies in its microenvironment (such as competitors), but these can nevertheless have a major impact on the activities of an organization. Also, many of these other companies and individuals may feel that they have such a keen interest in the activities of the organization that they become **stakeholders** in it. We will return to the subject of stakeholders in organizations later. The following key groups can be identified in most companies' microenvironments.

1.4.1 Customers

Customers are a crucial part of an organization's microenvironment. Quite simply, in a competitive environment, no customers means no business. An organization should be concerned about the changing requirements of its customers and should keep in touch with these changing needs by using an appropriate information-gathering system. In an ideal world, an organization should know its customers so well that it is able to predict what they will require next, rather than wait until it is possibly too late and then react.

But we need to think beyond this simplistic model of customers expressing their preferences and businesses then satisfying them. First, the people who buy a company's products are not necessarily the same people as those who consume them. Any good book on consumer behaviour will describe a range of influencers, users, deciders and 'gatekeepers' who have a bearing on whether a company's product is bought.

Second, does the customer always know what is best for them, and should organizations take a wider view of their customers' long-term interests? There have been many examples of situations where customers' long-term interests have been neglected by companies, including the following:

- fast-food companies, who have been accused of contributing to an 'epidemic' of obesity among young people by their promotion of high-fat food
- manufacturers of baby milk that failed to make mothers aware of the claimed long-term health benefits of using breast milk rather than manufactured milk products
- car manufacturers that add expensive music systems to cars as standard equipment but relegate vital safety equipment such as passenger airbags to the status of optional extras.

In each of these cases, most people might agree that, objectively, buyers are being persuaded to make a choice against their own long-term self-interest. Consumer groups have an increasing tendency to highlight the mis-selling of products that are against the best long-term interests of customers, and the results of such actions range from bad publicity to expensive product recalls and litigation. We will return to the issue of ethical behaviour in Chapter 5.

1.4.2 Suppliers

Suppliers provide an organization with goods and services that are transformed by the organization into value-added products for customers. Very often, suppliers are crucial to an organization's marketing success. This is particularly true where factors of production are in short supply, and the main constraint on an organization selling more of its product is the shortage of production resources. For example, in 2007, world steel prices rose following an increase in demand – especially from China – relative to the available capacity. Some businesses in the engineering sector were forced to reduce their production because of difficulties in obtaining supplies of steel. For companies operating in highly competitive markets where differentiation between products is minimal, obtaining supplies at the best possible price may be vital in order to be able to pass on cost savings in the form of lower prices charged to customers. Where reliability of delivery to customers is crucial, unreliable suppliers may thwart a manufacturer's marketing efforts.

Globally, many commentators have predicted shortages of key natural resources, as the demands of the rapidly growing 'BRIC' countries (Brazil, Russia, India and China) consume ever increasing resources to satisfy their growing domestic demand. This has led Chinese government agencies to seek to protect the country's future supply of scarce resources through collaborative development projects with less developed countries in Africa and South America.

There is an argument that companies should act in a socially responsible way towards their suppliers. Does a company favour local companies rather than buying from lower-priced overseas producers? (For example, many UK supermarkets have gone out of their way to highlight locally grown farm produce, which supports local farmers and has not incurred a high level of 'food miles'.) Does it use its dominant market power unfairly over small suppliers (an accusation that has been made against UK supermarkets for their treatment of their small farm suppliers)? Does it divide its orders between a large number of small suppliers, or place the bulk of its custom with a small handful of preferred suppliers? Does it favour new businesses or businesses representing minority interests when it places its orders?

Taking into account the needs of suppliers is a combination of shrewd business sense and good ethical practice. In business-to-business marketing, one company's supplier is likely to be another company's customer, and it is important to understand how suppliers, manufacturers and intermediaries work together to create value. The idea of a value chain is introduced later in this chapter.

1.4.3 Intermediaries

These often provide a valuable link between an organization and its customers. Large-scale manufacturing firms usually find it difficult to deal with each one of their final customers individually, so they choose instead to sell their products through **intermediaries**. The advantages of using intermediaries are discussed below. In some business sectors, access to effective intermediaries can be crucial for marketing success. For example, food manufacturers who do not get shelf-space in the major supermarkets may find it difficult to achieve large volume sales.

Channels of distribution comprise all those people and organizations involved in the process of transferring title to a product from the producer to the consumer. Sometimes, products will be transferred directly from producer to final consumer – a factory selling specialized kitchen units direct to the public would fit in to this category. Alternatively, the producer could sell its output through retailers or, if these are considered too numerous for the manufacturer to handle, it could deal with a wholesaler that in turn would sell to the retailer. More than one wholesaler could be involved in the process.

Intermediaries may need reassurance about the company's capabilities as a supplier that is capable of working with intermediaries to supply goods and services in a reliable and ethical manner. Many companies have suffered because they failed to take adequate account of the needs of their intermediaries (for example, Body Shop and McDonald's have faced protests from their franchisees where they felt threatened by a marketing strategy that was perceived as being against their own interests).

The internet has added to the complexity of channels of distribution. In the early days of the internet, it was widely predicted that many companies would be able to dispense with intermediaries and distribute their goods and services direct to the customer. The growth of direct-selling intermediaries such as Direct Line Insurance appeared to confirm the ability to cut out intermediaries, who were often portrayed as parasitic and delaying middlemen. The inelegant term 'disintermediation' has been used to describe the process of removing intermediaries from a distribution channel and developing direct communications. However, the reality has in many cases being quite different, with the proliferation of new types of internet-based intermediaries. Companies providing search engine optimization, affiliate marketing sites and price comparison sites, among others, have made the task of companies getting through to their final customer more complex. Some retailers have closed branches or reduced their salesforce and instead offer customers access to their product range via a website. Several UK suppliers of books, music, computer games and flowers have the logistical support to develop their business on the internet.

1.4.4 Competitors

In highly competitive markets, keeping an eye on competitors and trying to understand their likely next moves can be crucial. Think of the manoeuvring and out-manoeuvring that appears to take place between competitors in such highly competitive sectors as soft drinks, budget airlines and mobile phones. But who are a company's competitors? *Direct* competitors are generally similar in form and satisfy customers' needs in a similar way. *Indirect* competitors may appear different in form, but satisfy a fundamentally similar need. It is the indirect competitors that can be the most difficult to identify and to understand. What is a competitor for a cinema? Is it another cinema? A home rental movie? A telephone company offering videos on demand through smartphones? Or some completely different form of leisure activity that satisfies similar underlying needs?

1.4.5 Government

The demands of government agencies often take precedence over the needs of a company's customers. Government has a number of roles to play as stakeholder in commercial organizations.

- Commercial organizations provide governments with taxation revenue, so a healthy business sector is in the interests of government.
- Government is increasingly expecting business organizations to take over many responsibilities from the public sector – for example, with regard to the payment of sickness and maternity benefits to employees. In 2010, the newly elected coalition government in the UK announced its 'Big Society' programme, by which it actively sought community-based groups to take over many functions traditionally undertaken by government.
- It is through business organizations that governments achieve many of their economic and social objectives – for example, with respect to regional economic development and skills training.

Given the role of such regulators, which impact on many aspects of business activity, companies often go to great lengths in seeking favourable responses from such agencies. In the case of many UK private-sector utility providers, promotional effort is often aimed more at regulatory bodies than final consumers. In the case of the water industry, promoting greater use of water to final consumers is unlikely to have any significant impact on a water utility company, but influencing the disposition of the Office of Water Regulation, which sets price limits and service standards, can have a major impact.

1.4.6 Pressure groups

Pressure groups form part of the broadly defined political environment. Members of pressure groups may never have been customers of a company and are probably never likely to be. Yet a pressure group can detract seriously from the image that the company has worked hard to develop. Many businesses have learned to their cost that they cannot ignore pressure groups. It seems that, in Britain, fewer people may be voting in elections, but this is more than offset by a greater willingness of people to make their voice heard through pressure groups.

1.4.7 The financial community

This includes financial institutions that have supported, are currently supporting or may support the organization in the future. Shareholders – both private and institutional – form an important element of this community and must be reassured that the organization is going to achieve its stated objectives. Many market expansion plans have failed because the company did not adequately consider the needs and expectations of potential investors.

Following the 'credit crunch' of 2008, financial institutions became increasingly important in the lives of many individuals and organizations, with reports of banks' unwillingness or inability to lend money to small businesses.

1.4.8 Local communities

Society at large has rising expectations of organizations, and market-led companies often try to be seen as a 'good neighbour' in their local communities. Such companies can enhance their image through the use of charitable contributions, sponsorship of local events and being seen to support the local environment. Again, this may be interpreted either as part of a firm's genuine concern for its local community, or as a more cynical and pragmatic attempt to buy favour where its own interests are at stake. If a fast-food restaurant installs improved filters on its extractor fans, is it doing it genuinely to improve the lives of local residents, or merely in an attempt to forestall prohibition action taken by the local authority?

1.5 The internal environment

The structure and politics of an organization can affect the manner in which it responds to environmental change. We are all familiar with lumbering giants of companies that, like a supertanker, have ploughed ahead on a seemingly predetermined course and had difficulty in changing direction. Well-respected companies such as Sainsbury's and Marks & Spencer have in the past been accused of having internal structures and processes that were too rigid to cope with a changing external environment. Simply having a strong marketing department is not necessarily the best way of ensuring adaptation to change. Such companies may in fact create internal tensions that make them less effective at responding to changing consumer needs than where marketing responsibilities in their widest sense are spread throughout the organization. Sainsbury's and Marks & Spencer eventually adapted and subsequently prospered. Others such as Woolworths either went out of business or were taken over by a more agile predator.

The internal culture of an organization can greatly affect the way it responds to organizational change. In the case of Sainsbury's, its culture was probably too much based on hierarchy and tradition, which can be a weakness in a rapidly changing external environment. **Organizational culture** concerns the social and behavioural manifestation of a whole set of values that are shared by members of the organization. Cultural values can be shared in a number of ways, including: the way work is organized and experienced; how authority is exercised and delegated; how people are rewarded, organized and controlled; and the roles and expectations of staff and managers.

For many organizations, employees are the biggest item of cost and potentially the biggest cause of delay in responding to environmental change. Having the right staff in the right place at the right time can demand a lot of flexibility on the part of employees. Many organizations have sought to improve the effectiveness of their employees by increasing their level of engagement with the organization. When the external environment calls for change, employees who share a sense of engagement with the organization are more likely to share in the threats and opportunities that environmental change presents, compared with employees who feel alienated from the organization. Change can be facilitated by a sense of teamwork, and effective communication between different groups of employees within an organization.

It is not uncommon to find organizations where communication between these different groups is characterized by distrust, and even hostility, making it difficult for the organization to respond to environmental change in a rapid and coordinated manner. In Chapter 10 we will look in more detail at the effects of internal management structures and processes on an organization's ability to respond to external environmental change.

1.6 Contextual issues in a dynamic environment

So far in this introductory chapter, we have broken down the business environment into a number of component parts. These are the basic building blocks that we will come back to throughout the book. However, the key to analysing the business environment is to see the links between these component parts. A number of these linkages have already been mentioned – for example, how the political environment affects the nature of the economic environment that the business faces. Within the microenvironment, members of the local community may also be customers of an organization. Community groups may influence government agencies, which in turn affect the activities of business organizations.

As well as taking a snapshot of the interdependency between elements of the business environment, we also need to consider their dynamic interaction. Successful business organizations have spotted trends, especially the interaction between trends in the different environments. For example, one trend in the social environment has been an increasing fear of crime, especially against children. Another trend in the technological environment has been the falling cost and increasing sophistication of mobile phones. By putting these two trends together, businesses have developed novel products – for example, mobile phones that can track children and automatically send warning messages if they stray beyond a predetermined zone.

We have introduced the main levels of the business environment in a manner that provides a foundation for the structure of this book. We will begin by looking at the macroenvironment before moving on to the micro- and internal environments. But the point cannot be stressed enough that the different elements of an organization's environment are very much interrelated and, in order to stress this interrelatedness, we will now briefly examine some common themes that run through all levels of the environment. We will focus on information and communication as two crucial elements that run through an organization's environment. We will then consider some simple frameworks that integrate the elements of the business environment, beginning with identification of the members of an organization's 'environmental set'. We will then integrate these within the concept of a 'value chain', and move on to take a dynamic look at these relationships and the emergence of power within them.

1.6.1 The interdependency of organizations in the business environment

No organization exists in a vacuum, and a crucial aspect of understanding the business environment lies in understanding the networks of formal and informal relationships that exist between a firm and its various stakeholders.

The people and organizations within a particular company's business environment that are of particular relevance to it are sometimes referred to as its **environmental set**. An example of an environmental set for a car manufacturer is shown in Figure 1.4.

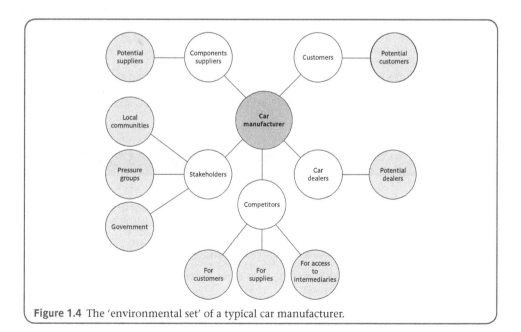

Figure 1.4 The 'environmental set' of a typical car manufacturer.

Some of these relationships between members of an organization's environmental set will be latent rather than actual – for example, a company may currently have no dealings with a prospective customer, but knows that one day they could become an actual customer. Some actual relationships with set members may be casual, infrequent and relatively unimportant for the company, whereas others will be crucial and the company will seek to develop long-term relationships, rather than rely on casual transactions. It may have power over some set members, but other set members may have considerable power over it. Although the environmental set shown in Figure 1.4 depicts a network focused on one organization, in fact networks can bring together these individual set members – for example, suppliers may have developed strategic alliances with the focal company's key competitors.

The relationship between set members is likely to be complex and constantly changing. Change can take a number of forms, including:

- a tendency for firms to seek the stability of long-term relationships with key members of their environmental set, rather than treating them all on a fairly casual basis
- shifts in the balance of power between members of the environment (e.g. retailers becoming more dominant relative to manufacturers)
- the emergence of new groups of potential customers or suppliers
- fringe pressure groups may come to represent mainstream opinions, in response to changes in social attitudes.

Understanding the relationship between members of an organization's environmental set is a crucial part of environmental analysis, and in Chapter 8 we will return to look in more detail at the nature of relationships that bring companies together.

1.6.2 Value chains

It was noted at the beginning of this chapter that a purpose of organizations is to transform inputs bought from suppliers into outputs sold to customers. In carrying out such a transformation, organizations add value to resources. In fact, the buyer of one firm's output may be another firm that treats the products purchased as inputs to its own production process. It in turn will add value to the resources and sell on its outputs to customers. This process can continue as goods and services pass though several organizations, gaining added value as they change hands. This is the basis of a **value chain**.

An illustration of the principles of a value chain can be made by considering the value-added transformation processes that occur in the process of making ice cream available to consumers. Table 1.1 shows who may be involved in the value-adding process and the value that is added at each stage.

Table 1.1 Value chain for ice cream.

Value chain member	Functions performed
Farmer	Produces a basic commodity product – milk
Milk merchant	Adds value to the milk by arranging for it to be collected from the farm, checked for purity and made available to milk processors
Ice cream manufacturer	By processing the milk and adding other ingredients, turns raw milk into ice cream. Through promotion, creates a brand image
Wholesaler	Buys bulk stocks of ice cream and stores in warehouses close to customers
Retailer	Provides a facility for customers to buy ice cream at a place and time that is convenient to them rather than the manufacturer

The value of the raw milk contained in a block of ice cream may be no more than a few pennies, but the final product may be sold for over £1. Customers are happy to pay £1 for a few pennies' worth of milk because it is transformed into a product that they value, and it is made available at a time and place where they want it. In fact, on a hot sunny day at the beach, many buyers would be prepared to pay even more to a vendor that brings ice cream to them. Value – as defined by customers – has been added at each stage of the transformation process.

Who should be in the value chain? The ice cream manufacturer might decide that it can add value at the preceding and subsequent stages better than other people are capable of doing. It may, for example, decide to operate its own farms and produce its own milk, or sell its ice cream direct to the public. The crucial question to be asked is whether the company can add value more cost-effectively than other suppliers and intermediaries. In a value chain, it is only value in the eyes of customers that matters. If high value is attached to having ice cream easily available, then distributing it through a limited number of company-owned shops will not add much value to the product.

The process of expanding a firm's activities through the value chain is often referred to as vertical integration where ownership is established. Backward vertical integration occurs where a manufacturer buys back in to its suppliers. Forward vertical integration occurs where it buys in to its outlets. Many firms expand in both directions.

With service being used as an increasingly important basis for differentiation between competing products, it is important that an organization looks not only outwards at the value chain, but also inwards at its own service–profit chain. The concept of the service–profit chain is based on the idea that employee satisfaction and productivity feed in to customer satisfaction and loyalty, thereby improving profitability. Profitability in turn can help create a more productive and satisfying work environment (see Figure 1.5).

The growth of the internet has led to the development of a modified form of 'virtual value chain' to try to explain how information-based industries operate a value chain that is distinct from traditional models based on raw materials, production and distribution. Getting access to web surfers can be a big challenge for many internet-based companies, such as motor insurance and electricity suppliers, who are selling a fairly generic product. Many have therefore chosen

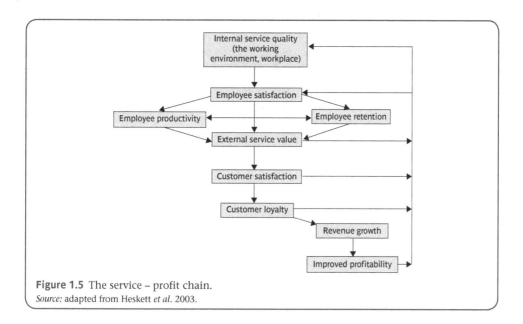

Figure 1.5 The service – profit chain.
Source: adapted from Heskett *et al.* 2003.

to pay a range of affiliate sites, price comparison sites and 'cash back' sites to help them in the task of bringing potential customers to their site.

The traditional manufacturer to customer distribution channel has also been challenged by the existence of peer-to-peer social networking websites. In many cases, a buyer's choice is strongly influenced by what their peers are saying through blogs and review sites. In this way, the peer group can create value by providing advice to buyers and information to the seller about how it could improve its product offer. The idea of 'co-creation of value' between consumers is at the heart of 'service dominant logic' (Vargo and Lusch 2008).

1.6.3 The information environment

Information represents a bridge between the organization and its environment, and is the means by which a picture of the changing environment is built up within the organization. The amount of information available to organizations seems to grow every year, as previous paper-based systems for collecting and distributing information are replaced by real-time electronic systems. Instead of a monthly printed sales report, retailers can now get real-time analysis of their sales disaggregated by type of product, time of sale, place of sale, or a seemingly endless permutations of analyses. In an age where there is a lot of information available, the key to business success is turning lots of little bits of information into actionable knowledge. It is not unknown for companies to be sitting on mountains of data, but to have no real insight into the markets they serve, the changing needs of their customers or the changing nature of the competition. Knowledge is one of the greatest assets of most organizations and its contribution to sustainable competitive advantage has been noted by many. In 1991, Ikujiro Nonaka began an article in the *Harvard Business Review* with the simple statement: 'In an economy where the only certainty is uncertainty, the one sure source of lasting competitive advantage is knowledge' (Nonaka 1991).

Information about the current state of the environment is used as a starting point for planning future strategy, based on assumptions about how the environment will change. It is also vital to monitor the implementation of an organization's corporate plans, to note the causes of any deviation from plan, and to identify whether these are caused by internal or external environmental factors. Information allows management to improve its strategic planning, tactical implementation of programmes, and its monitoring and control. In turbulent environments, having access to timely and relevant information can give a firm a competitive advantage. This can be manifested, for example, in the ability to spot turning points in the business cycle ahead of competitors; to respond more rapidly to customers' changing preferences; and to adapt manufacturing schedules more closely to demand patterns, thereby avoiding a build-up of stocks.

The internet has generated a huge amount of new information, and has challenged the assumption that an organization is at the centre of its information environment. The proliferation of Web 2.0 blogs, customer review sites and other social media allows customers, local communities and competitors to talk about the organization and its competitors. 'Viral marketing' has been seen by many companies as an opportunity for spreading its message rapidly, but at other times harmful messages have spread rapidly, which companies may find difficult to control. In terms of information available for planning their future strategies and operations, many companies have turned to various forms of social network 'mining' to try to build knowledge from what other people are saying in blogs and review sites. With the proliferation of information, attention is moving away from who is able to collect the most information, to who is able to most effectively turn it into actionable knowledge.

Large organizations operating in complex and turbulent environments often use information to build models of their environment, or at least sub-components of it. Some of these can be quite general, as in the case of the models of the national economy that many large companies have developed. From a general model of the economy a firm can predict how a specific item of government policy (for example, increasing the rate of value added tax on luxury goods) will impact directly and indirectly on sales of its own products.

We look in more detail in Chapter 4 at the ways in which information technology influences firms' business environment, and explore the implications of information for firms' responses to environmental change in Chapter 13.

⟳ Thinking around the subject

The tiny spy that follows you home?

Many inventions come along that have the potential to change the business environment, but the excitement of a launch may be matched with scepticism. RFId (radio frequency identification) is one new development that has taken some time in achieving widespread acceptance, while simultaneously raising concerns among many groups about its privacy implications.

RFId involves placing a small radio transmitter on a product so that its movement can be tracked remotely. So far, RFID has mainly been applied to pallets and case loads of goods, rather than individual consumer goods. The cost of tags, as well as the equipment needed to read them and process the data, means that item-level tagging may still be some way off. But the prospect of rapidly falling costs and greater miniaturization has alerted companies to the opportunities, and some consumer groups to the potential threats. However, a report for the EU in 2008 talked about the 'hype cycle' that has affected RFId, like many new technology-based products (Schmitt and Michahelles 2008). The initial excitement is eventually seen as unrealistic and, eventually, adoption of the new technology settles down at a much more modest level than the previous hype might have led us to believe.

In addition to the technical issues of reducing the costs of producing RFId tags is the issue of privacy. RFId would seem like a blessing to companies keen to find out more about their products after they have left their shelves. But is its use ethical? In 2007, the EU's Information Society Commissioner called for a debate about the security and privacy issues surrounding RFId. Consumer groups and privacy campaigners have expressed concern that RFId tags could be used to build up massive databases of individuals' shopping, leisure and travel habits. These databases could be exploited by unscrupulous businesses and also become a target for cybercriminals. The fact that RFId tags track the actual items that people buy has led to fears that RFId data could be much more intrusive than the information retailers typically collect through bar code data and loyalty card programmes. As the cost of RFId tags falls and their versatility increases, they have the potential to be read at a distance without a consumer's knowledge. Would you want a bookshop 'spying' on how and where you read a book that you recently bought from it?

Not to be outdone, proponents of RFId have gone on the offensive to present the positive elements of the technology, such as its use in preventing counterfeit drugs reaching consumers; or in aviation, where tags have been fixed to aircraft spares and safety equipment. Retailers have attached RFId tags to goods to monitor thefts, and have argued that honest customers would have nothing to fear and would benefit from the lower prices resulting from reduced shoplifting.

⟩

If you were a commercial organization contemplating the use of RFId, which way do you think the privacy debate will go? Are pressure groups being paranoid about the data that companies can keep on an individual when, in reality, government agencies routinely collect much more information about us – for example, through vehicle number plate recognition? Will consumers be won over by the safety and security aspects of RFId, in much the same way as many people would readily accept the necessity for 'sinister' monitoring of their movements by CCTV? Would the most likely outcome of the EU review of RFId be a compromise, perhaps limiting how long RFId data could be kept and who would be allowed access to it?

1.6.4 The communication environment

Communications bring together elements within a firm's environmental set. With no communication, there is no possibility for trading to take place. Although we talk today about a communications 'revolution', businesses in previous centuries have faced the challenge of rapid developments in communication. Improved communication through canals, railways and steamships was an underlying foundation of the Industrial Revolution of nineteenth-century England. Today, internet-based communication technologies can be crucial for regional and national economic development. Towns and villages without access to high-speed internet services have often been passed by for economic development in much the same way as an office or factory might consider the absence of a main road or railway to be a disadvantage in terms of location.

The communication environment is changing rapidly and firms need to understand how it is likely to emerge in future. Will communication through mobile phones replace traditional landlines? What will be the business benefits of location-based mobile communication technologies that can allow communication at specific times and specific places? With the proliferation of communication media, how does a company ensure that its message stands out above the mountain of spam and unwanted communication?

More fundamentally, the question has been raised whether companies can ever again be in control of their communication in an environment of peer-to-peer social networking media. In an environment of only basic communication technologies, most of what the customer knows about a company may be based on communication from the company. Today, a customer or potential customer may rely much more on their peer groups to establish whether a prospective seller is reliable and suitable for them.

The development of social media is having profound effects on patterns of communication in the environment. We have already seen how viral marketing can rapidly build or undermine a company's position in the markets it serves. Actions taken by customers are increasingly likely to be affected by peer group communication rather than 'official' communication from the company. There are many creative examples of this effect – for example, Pledgebank is an online platform, active in 60 countries, that helps groups of like-minded people to take action. One person would sign a pledge to do something if others agree to take the same action – for example, 'I will stop eating junk food if 100 people in my town agree to do the same.' The creator of the pledge then publicizes their pledge and encourages other people to sign up.

Peer-to-peer social networks have also helped organizations in their research and development and to find answers to operational problems. It is also reported that both the EU and the White House have used social networks to generate ideas about how to solve problems such as global warming and obesity.

Thinking around the subject

Firms face up to Facebook

In the old days, companies had research departments that listened to customers, and advertising departments that sent messages to them. Although customers may have learned about a company through word of mouth, this communication channel was essentially limited to small groups of friends. The communication environment has changed rapidly in recent years and the development of 'Web 2.0' technologies has facilitated communication between customers themselves, as well as between companies and their customers. So-called 'social networking' sites, such as Facebook and YouTube, have led to many widely publicized problems for companies. For example, in 2005, the computer manufacturer Dell was hit by influential blogger Jeff Jarvis complaining about its poor customer service. Fellow consumers, no longer passive in their dissatisfaction, joined in with comments of their own, and stories of 'Dell Hell' rapidly became mainstream news. The company was rudely awoken to the power of social media and realized that simply trying to silence one individual or sue them for libel was never going to be effective. It subsequently put a lot of effort into engaging with social media, including the appointment of a 'coordinator of customer messages'.

Increasingly, companies have been mingling on social networking sites, and have sometimes created their own sites as community forums. Dell, for example, established the Dell2Dell blog, in an attempt to gain some control over communication about it. But on other occasions, companies have sponsored blogs without declaring their involvement. The retailer Wal-Mart covertly sponsored a blog that was supposedly operated by a couple camping in the store's car parks. It had hoped to manipulate content to show the company in a good light, but eventually the exercise turned into a PR disaster when news broke that the company had in fact been controlling the blog.

A significant challenge for companies is the sometimes blurred distinction between communication that is internal and external to company. Social networking sites allow employees to spread stories of dissent about the company they work for among their circle of friends. Using simpler communication technologies, a slanderous comment about a bad employer might have gone no further than a small circle of friends and family. But with their large numbers of friends linked through sites such as Facebook, dissent can spread much more widely. For example, there have been many reported cases of disgruntled restaurant workers who have told the world about the disgusting kitchens that they work in, but which customers do not ordinarily get to see. Some websites, such as www.wikileaks.com make a point of publicizing business and government policy documents that they would rather keep secret. Previously a document marked 'Top Secret' would have to have been physically stolen and copied to have an impact. Today a disgruntled employee can upload the document and have it on the screens of millions of people within hours.

1.6.5 The financial environment

There is an old saying that 'money makes the world go round', and this simple statement has continuing relevance for analysing the business environment. One important factor behind the Industrial Revolution in nineteenth-century Britain – in addition to the development of new manufacturing technologies – was the availability of finance. Financial institutions had previously been local, and largely incapable of financing the big factories and transport infrastructure that were a feature of the Industrial Revolution. Financial institutions were also needed for the transmission of money between manufacturers and their customers, who were no longer based in the local town and paid cash, but may have been located hundred of miles away and needed efficient payment systems that followed the changing patterns of trade. Financial institutions operating on a national and international level fuelled the Industrial Revolution. Today, these institutions continue to have enormous importance in the business environment. Without an efficient payment system that buyers and sellers can trust, world trade would become more costly and risky. Without funds available for investment, the construction of new infrastructure and investment in stocks would be reduced, with subsequent reduction in 'multiplier' effects on the economy. In September 2008 there was a fear that the world's banking system was in meltdown as the once mighty Lehman Brothers bank went bankrupt, and many banks around the world, including Lloyds TSB and Royal Bank of Scotland, either went bankrupt or had to be rescued by governments. Banks found themselves depleted of capital, and unwilling or unable to take risks in their lending decisions, therefore businesses found it increasingly difficult to borrow money to invest in capacity that would generate jobs and wealth. Consumers were hit not only by the effect of this on jobs and earnings, but also by banks' increasing wariness of lending to consumers to buy houses and cars, among other things. With firms and consumers unable to spend more, it seemed that, through a 'vicious circle', the economy would be in 'meltdown'.

Governments throughout the world realized that having money flowing through the system was vital for a vibrant economy, therefore on the basis that 'money makes the world go round', they resorted to creating new money and putting it into circulation through a process often referred to as 'quantitative easing'. We will return to the principles and practice of this in Chapter 13.

1.6.6 The ethical environment

All systems need rules if they are to operate efficiently and effectively. This can be observed in any marketplace, whether it is a fruit and vegetable market or a stock market. The market only functions because all participants conduct their actions according to a shared set of rules. These rules can either be informal or based on formal regulation. In many less developed economies, the dominant basis for rules is focused on embedded codes of trust. Increasingly in western societies, commercial relationships are governed by formality and regulation. Of course, informal rules in a market may not always be in consumers' best interests, as sometimes happens when suppliers have formal or informal understandings about how they can restrict the level of competition between themselves.

In western societies there is increasing concern that relationships between members of the environmental set should be conducted in an ethical manner. Ethics is essentially about the definition of what is right and wrong. However, it can be difficult to agree just what is right and wrong – no two people have precisely the same opinion. Culture has a great effect in defining ethics, and what is considered unethical in one society may be considered perfectly acceptable in another.

It can also be difficult to distinguish between ethics and legality. For example, it may not yet be strictly illegal to exploit the gullibility of children in advertisements, but it may nevertheless be unethical.

Today, ethical considerations are present in many business decisions. An example of a current issue is whether soft drinks and confectionery manufacturers should sponsor school activities – is it ethical to expose children to subconscious positive messages about junk food at a time of increasing obesity?

With expanding media availability and an increasingly intelligent audience, it is becoming easier to expose examples of unethical business practice. Moreover, many television audiences appear to enjoy watching programmes that reveal the alleged unethical practices of household-name companies. To give one example, the media have on many occasions focused attention on the alleged exploitative employment practices of suppliers used by some of the biggest brand names in sportswear.

We return to the subject of ethics in Chapter 5.

Figure 1.6 Like many bars, this one loudly promotes a 'happy hour' period during which alcohol is sold at a reduced price. For pub operators, such promotions may be vital to boost margins, especially if all bars in the area are offering equally low prices. Unfortunately, one consequence of cheap alcohol and 'buy one, get one free' offers is to increase 'binge drinking', with many town centres becoming noisy and violent areas at night time, fuelled by excessive drinking. For any individual pub, how does it balance the need for aggressive price promotion to customers with the need to appear socially responsible, for fear of further government regulation of the sector? Adverts for alcohol now routinely include warnings about the consequences for the customer of excessive drinking, but often in much smaller print than the main price information. Should a pub simply stop '2 for 1' offers and earn a higher margin on a smaller volume of sales? Although this may seem to be a responsible and profitable approach, it is unlikely to work if other pubs continue with their 2 for 1 offers – determined drinkers will simply make their way to the cheapest pub that has communicated the best offers. To illustrate the complexity of the task facing the sector, bar owners in some towns have voluntarily got together to try and agree collectively to stop price promotions that many believe lead to binge drinking. Agreement of all bar owners would be crucial, because otherwise drinkers would simply find out the cheapest outlet, and

© lillisphotography

other bars would be forced defensively to cut their prices to retain business. But did government see this as a benign example of socially motivated co-operation? Not the Office of Fair Trading, which gave a veiled threat to a group of Essex bar owners that they could be prosecuted for operating a cartel and illegally fixing prices.

1.6.7 The ecological environment

Issues affecting our natural ecology have captured the public imagination in recent years. The destruction of tropical rainforests, and the depletion of the ozone layer leading to global warming, have serious implications for our quality of life – not necessarily today, but for future generations. Business organizations are often seen as being in conflict with the need to protect the natural ecology. It is very easy for critics of commercial organizations to point to cases where greed and mismanagement have created long-lasting or permanent ecological damage. Have rainforests been destroyed partly by our greed for more hardwood furniture? More locally, is our impatience for getting to our destination quickly the reason why many natural habitats have been lost to new road developments?

Only a few years ago, most business organizations in western developed economies could have dismissed ecological concerns as something that only fanatical, minority groups in the population were concerned about. In the 1970s and 1980s, 'environmentalists' might have been ridiculed and associated with unrealistic dreams of the 'good life'. Today, the situation is very different, and just about all business organizations need to take the ecological environment seriously.

There are many good reasons why the ecological environment is rising up the agenda of business organizations.

- At its simplest, many organizations face segments of customers who prefer to make purchases that they believe to be ecologically responsible. For a variety of underlying psychological and sociological reasons, some consumers may feel better about their purchase if it is perceived to be 'good' for the planet. Of course, whether it is actually good or not may be another factor, and sometimes peer-group pressure may be at variance with the technical reality. As an example, the *Independent* newspaper reported in 2007 a case, probably not an isolated one, of a London home owner who had installed a solar panel on the north side of their house. Technically, the panel would be useless, because of the lack of direct sunlight, but for the house owner, the north side of the house could be seen by everybody. A panel on the south side of the house would not be visible, and would therefore be less able to make a statement about their 'green' credentials.

- Business organizations are dependent on the ecological environment for natural resources. If ecosystems are not carefully managed, resources that are affordable today, and taken for granted, may no longer be available, and firms will have to pay higher prices for possibly inferior substitutes. As an example, the fishing industry in Britain has been greatly reduced in size through the overfishing of the North Sea. Even companies further down the value chain of fish have been affected by this depletion of the ecological environment – for example, fish and chip shops have had to find alternative types of fish to replace increasingly expensive cod.

- Firms can gain advantage in a market by leading in the use of alternative natural resources ahead of competitors, giving them a competitive advantage when the alternative becomes the only, or most cost-effective, source available. However, it may be difficult for firms to evaluate not only what is going to be a better use of resources for the planet, but also one that is going to be better for their organization specifically. To illustrate this difficulty, many firms have been advocating a greater use of 'biofuels', which are derived from renewable crops, rather than fossil fuels. However, there is argument about the relative size of the ecological and social impacts of fossil fuels and renewable energy sources. The dilemma for business was illustrated in July 2007, when the Virgin Group, never an organization to miss an opportunity for good publicity, announced that it would be greatly increasing the use of biofuels for its fleet of trains. However, just a few weeks later, National Express Group, another UK operator of trains and buses, announced that it was abandoning its previous plan for the increased use of biofuels. It had thought through the implications of farmers growing an increasing proportion of their crops for fuel rather than food, which could be expected to lead to progressively higher prices for biofuels and sharply increasing food prices. The consumer appeal of biofuels was also wearing thin, with the scene set for the rich western countries to benefit from this new source of fuel, while less developed countries could no longer afford basic food items because crops were diverted to fuel the West's appetite for energy. In this scenario, biofuels became less cost-effective and socially acceptable.

- Similarly, ecological concerns may spur the development of completely new technologies, often with the support of government. Wind turbines presented a new opportunity in the early twenty-first century, which was exploited by aircraft manufacturing companies, among others. UK companies were relatively late to the scene, by which time competitive advantage had been gained by overseas manufacturers, and the one remaining large-scale wind turbine manufacturer based in the UK faced closure in 2009. However, the UK government saw advantages in being first to market with innovative 'carbon capture' technologies, and in 2010 increased funding for research and development in this area.

- Markets are often incapable collectively to alleviate pending problems in ecosystems, and political intervention may be necessary to prevent a complete failure of the ecosystem. In the example above, individual fishermen may have had no incentive to limit their own fishing, until they reached the point where only government intervention could protect fish stocks from their own individual activities, and ultimately preserve long-term employment for companies and availability of supplies for consumers. Business organizations should be able to read the political environment and be prepared for politically imposed change in their business plans. See the case study at the end of this chapter – if you were running an airline, what level of future government taxation or restrictions on air travel would you factor in to your future development plans, given current concerns about the effects of aircraft emissions?

We will return to the ecological environment in Chapter 5.

1.6.8 Systems theory, complexity and chaos

Systems theory was proposed in the 1940s by the biologist Ludwig von Bertalanffy. It is the interdisciplinary study of the abstract organization of phenomena, and investigates both the principles common to all complex entities and the models that can be used to describe them. More recently it has been applied to mathematics, computing and ecological systems. Some elements of systems theory have been applied to the modelling of relationships within the environmental sets of business organizations that we discussed earlier.

Although a number of attempts have been made to apply the principles of systems theory to the business environment, there are major differences between scientific models and the business environment. Very often, the natural sciences deal with closed systems in which all the parameters are known, and each can be monitored and controlled. Admittedly, this is not always true – for example, in some ecological studies it may not be possible to identify all life forms that might possibly migrate into a system. By contrast, the business environment is essentially an open system in which it is very difficult to place a boundary round the environment and to identify the complete set of components within the system. Elements may come or go from the system, and a researcher generally has no control over these elements in the way that a laboratory-based scientist could carry out controlled experiments.

Two developments of systems theory are complexity theory and chaos theory. Complexity theory is concerned with the behaviour over time of certain kinds of complex system. The systems of interest to complexity theory, under certain conditions, perform in regular, predictable ways; under other conditions they exhibit behaviour in which regularity and predictability is lost. Almost undetectable differences in initial conditions lead to gradually diverging system reactions until, eventually, the evolution of behaviour is quite dissimilar.

Chaos theory describes the dynamics of sensitive systems that are mathematically deterministic but nearly impossible to predict, due to their sensitivity to initial conditions. The weather is an example of a chaotic system. In order to make long-term weather forecasts it would be necessary to take an infinite number of measurements, which would be impossible to do. Also, because the atmosphere is chaotic, tiny uncertainties would eventually overwhelm any calculations and defeat the accuracy of the forecast. One of the most widely quoted examples of chaos theory is the butterfly that flaps its wings and in doing so creates destabilizing forces that trigger subsequent events, resulting in a hurricane on the other side of the world.

Many business environments may be considered as chaotic in that it can be very difficult to predict the sequence of events following an initial disturbance to equilibrium. In Chapter 15 we return to the subject of risk and turbulence in the business environment.

1.6.9 Business cycles

The business environment is rarely in a stable state, and many phenomena follow a cyclical pattern. After a lengthy period of economic prosperity during the early twenty-first century, the boom came sharply to an end in 2008 when rising levels of manufacturing output, employment levels and consumer confidence, among other things, suddenly went into reverse. Companies are particularly interested in understanding business cycles and in predicting a cycle as it affects their sector. We return to the subject of business cycles in Chapter 13. Although the business cycle is widely talked about, there are other cyclical factors evident in the business environment. The interaction between supply and demand can result in a cycle of high prices, leading to new entrants coming into the market, which leads to lower prices, which makes the market less attractive, so companies leave the market, so prices begin to rise, which attracts new entrants to the market, and the cycle repeats itself.

As well as cycles affecting tangible resources, it is also possible to identify cycles in *ideas* about how the business environment operates. There have been many studies of how ideas grow to become mainstream and the critical factors involved in this process. Chaos theory and the study of mimetics have offered an explanation of how, through random events, a small local idea can develop into a global paradigm. An analysis by Gladwell discusses how reaching a critical point is facilitated by the existence of 'connectors', 'mavens' and the 'stickiness' of an idea (Gladwell 2000). One such idea that took hold in the 1990s was 'relationship marketing' as a method of conducting exchanges between a company and its customers. It followed a long series of 'big new ideas' that have risen and fallen over time.

1.6.10 Risk and uncertainty

The business environment for most organizations is rarely in a stable state. There is no certainty that the future will follow the pattern of the recent past. For companies operating in a low-tech, low-scale environment, adaptation to change may be quite easy. But for a large organization that has to invest heavily for the future, the risks can be enormous. For very large projects, such as the construction of the European Airbus 'super jumbo' A380 aircraft, the risk and uncertainty was too large not only for one company to take upon itself, but for the consortium of companies that makes up Airbus. Apart from uncertainty about the technology, and the risk of cost overruns, there is considerable risk concerning the business environment of airlines that would be customers for the Airbus. Will passengers want to fly between a small number of very large airports in very large aircraft? Or would they prefer the alternative model of the future, which sees larger numbers of smaller aircraft flying between a much bigger network of smaller airports? What will happen to fuel prices? Will long-term real increases in fuel prices put up air fares to the point where the long-term growth rate in passenger traffic is slowed down? Will governments introduce new taxation on aviation fuel, again possibly slowing down demand for air travel? And there is always the threat of terrorism, which caused such uncertainty following 11 September 2001, and which could recur at any time.

All aspects of the business environment that have been introduced in this chapter carry an element of uncertainty. Within the microenvironment, what is the risk of a new, well-resourced competitor emerging? What if a strategic supplier goes out of business or is acquired by your competitor? What happens if government introduces new legislation or imposes new taxation? Within the macroenvironment, there is continual uncertainty for most companies about the future state of the economy and the impact of changes in disposable income on consumer expenditure. What would happen if a new government were elected with a radically different political agenda? And, in the internal environment, what is the risk of not being able to recruit the skilled employees the company needs? What would be the effect of new legislation on the recruitment and payment of employees?

There are many models for trying to comprehend the complexity of the business environment, and to attach risk levels to the different elements of it. In Chapter 15, we will look in more detail at some of these methods, including cross-impact analysis, and environmental threat and opportunity profiles. We will also discuss the development of scenarios, which is an attempt to paint a picture of the future. It may be possible to build a small number of alternative scenarios based on differing assumptions. This qualitative approach is a means of handling environmental issues that are hard to quantify because they are less structured, more uncertain and may involve very complex relationships. Scenarios may paint a picture of a major crisis or source of turbulence facing a company. For an airline, this could be a renewed terrorist threat elsewhere in the world, or the crash of one of its own aircraft. Although it may not be possible to predict the exact detail of the event, the company could establish a set of guidelines for what it should do in the event that such a scenario occurs. For example, following the abrupt collapse in confidence in the world economy in September 2008, the airline Virgin Atlantic downsized its fleet and laid off staff. It had seen a future scenario in which demand was likely to remain low for some time, and it would be better to make a rapid and decisive decision to cut capacity and costs sooner, rather than just drifting on.

1.7   The globalized business environment

Globalization has become a dominant theme for many business organizations. The number of companies that can regard their markets purely in terms of their home country is rapidly diminishing. Airlines, commercial banks and consulting engineers have for a long time seen their markets in world terms. Companies operating in sectors such as electricity supply, office cleaning and bus services would, only a few years ago, have most likely considered globalization to be something that concerned only other sectors and not theirs. However, all of these sectors have seen companies expanding outside of their domestic market.

It may be fair to say that 'going global' is no longer an additional activity that companies may decide to become involved in. The reality for more and more companies is that they are already part of the globalized business environment. Even if they are not taking their products to overseas customers, they are quite likely to be facing competition from companies that are based abroad.

At some point, many business organizations recognize that their growth can continue only if they exploit overseas markets. However, entering overseas markets can be extremely risky, as evidenced by examples of recent failures where companies failed to foresee all the problems involved.

- The mobile phone company O_2 invested over £1.5 billion in the Dutch mobile phone operator Telfort but failed to achieve higher than fifth ranking in the Dutch market. In April 2003, it admitted defeat and sold the entire Dutch operation for just £16 million.
- The grocery retailer Sainsbury's pulled out of Egypt in 2001, only two years after investing in a chain of 100 supermarkets. Sainsbury's had gone out on a limb in Egypt, which had no tradition of supermarket shopping, and the company was not helped by persistent rumours of links with Jewish owners. The supermarket's two years of involvement in the Egyptian market incurred a loss of over £100 million.
- Even the fast-food retailer McDonald's initially failed to make profits when it entered the UK market in the 1970s and had to rapidly adjust its service offer in order to achieve viability.

Nevertheless, a company that has successfully developed its business strategy should be well placed to extend this development into overseas markets. There are many examples of companies that have successfully developed overseas markets, including the following.

- The retailer Tesco successfully reduced its dependence on the saturated UK grocery market by developing outlets in the Far East and eastern Europe.
- The mobile phone company Vodafone has expanded from its UK base and now provides service in 30 countries, reducing the company's unit costs through economies of scale, and offering seamless, added-value services to international travellers.

- The Irish airline Ryanair started life with a route network that focused on Dublin. With successful expansion of this network, most of its services now do not call at its Irish base.
- Carphone Warehouse was the brainchild of entrepreneur Charles Dunstone and, after a small-scale start in London, it has successfully expanded to more than 1100 stores throughout Europe, operating under the Carphone Warehouse banner in the UK, and the Phone House in France, Spain, Germany, Sweden and the Netherlands.

Although the focus of this book is on the UK and European environment, it should never be forgotten that UK organizations increasingly have to co-exist with a global business environment. Frequent reference is made throughout this book to the global context of business.

Case study:
A war of words over green airline claims

© David Joyner

A key issue on the mind of many businesses during the first decade of the twenty-first century has been global warming. Initially, awareness of the causes and consequences of global warming was confined to a small part of the population, but linkages with the destructive Tsunami of 2004 and Hurricane Katrina in 2005 brought home to many people the possible long-term harmful consequences of excessive emissions of CO_2 to the atmosphere. Global warming was no longer a humorous subject where people in the developed countries of northern Europe and the US focused on the benign consequences of mild winters and the exotic new plants that they would be able to grow. Destructive winds, rising sea levels and the devastation of low-lying areas were increasingly coming to be seen as consequences of our prodigious use of fossil fuels. What will be the direct impacts on business? What might be the indirect impacts caused by increasingly restrictive government regulation? How will a company's customers expect it to act?

One industry sector that has more to be concerned about than most is civil aviation. The reduction of CO_2 emissions had already been taken on board by many manufacturing companies, the largest of which had seen reductions through a system of carbon trading initiated by the Kyoto Treaty. But civil aviation had been quite notable for its failure to embrace the principles of reducing carbon emissions. Critics of the sector pointed out that, as a result of worldwide agreements, aviation fuel was not taxed, in contrast to the steep taxation on most other forms of fuel. Although

aircraft had become more efficient in their use of fuel during the 1990s, this was more than offset by the booming demand for flights with 'no-frills' airlines such as easyJet and Ryanair.

Actually assessing the ecological impacts of flying is more problematic than it might appear at first sight. The low-cost airlines have spotted an opportunity to present themselves as ecologically more friendly than the 'full service' airlines from whom they had been gradually taking business. According to analysis by Liligo.co.uk, a flight-comparison website, a couple making a return flight with Ryanair from London to Venice have a carbon footprint of 410 kg, while the equivalent journey on Alitalia would produce 977 kg. A return flight from London to Zurich with easyJet has a carbon footprint of 277 kg per couple, compared with 688 kg with Aer Lingus. Ryanair was quick to boast of its 'green' credentials, just in case potential flyers were feeling a sense of guilt as they hovered over the 'buy' button for one of its bargain tickets. The ecological benefits of low-cost airlines are based on a number of factors. First, they tend to fly with more seats occupied: according to the Association of European Airlines, in 2009 the average occupancy for an easyJet flight was 86 per cent and for Ryanair 82 per cent, compared with 73 per cent for British Airways and an average of 68 per cent on Europe's full-service airlines, Second, low-cost airlines squeeze more seats into an aircraft than their full-service rivals. For example, easyJet ('squeezyJet' to some of its passengers) fits 156 seats into an Airbus A319, whereas the average full-service airline has just 124 seats. The carbon footprint per passenger is correspondingly lower. Finally, low-cost airlines promoted the fact that they tended to fly direct between a wide range of dispersed airports, without the need to change planes at a central 'hub' airport, again reducing carbon emissions during take-off and landing.

It seemed that the budget airline companies were very effective in communicating their low price message to customers, who filled their planes, often giving more thought to a cheap weekend break by the Mediterranean than the unknown and remote possibilities of global warming. Indeed, the general public seemed to be somewhat hypocritical about the effects of global warming. Surveys had suggested that there can be a big difference between what people said and what they did - they may agree that flying was bad for the environment, but could not resist the £29.99 flight to Spain. In one survey conducted in 2007 consumers' consideration of greenhouse gas emissions came way behind other evaluation criteria when choosing a holiday, including the ease of getting a sun lounger, proximity to the beach and the range of nightlife available. Furthermore, it seemed that many people were tiring of claims about climate change and saw this as just an excuse for government to raise taxes. A survey carried out in February 2010 by the polling organization Populus for the BBC showed that 25 per cent of those questioned did not think global warming was happening, an increase of 10 per cent since a similar poll was conducted three months earlier. More people seemed to be thinking that the problem would just go away, and may have recalled previous 'scares'such as the imminent depletion of fossil fuels and the effects of 'acid rain', neither of which had really affected most people's lives, and had subsequently slipped down the news agenda.

How should airlines respond to the apparent threat to their business model that had been thrown up by the issue of global warming? Should they put their head in the sand and hope that the problem would go away? Should they concentrate on giving customers what they have repeatedly said they wanted – cheap flights – and hope that human hedonism would win out over feelings of social responsibility? Or should airlines be on their guard against possible government intervention that could undermine their business model. How could they prevent new legislation? And if it were introduced, how could they respond to it?

Politicians were becoming increasingly frustrated by the airlines' seeming lack of willingness to address issues of climate change. Already, the Bishop of London had described air travel as 'immoral', for the way that wealthy western travellers could inflict harm on people in the less developed world through climate change. Could a significant number of airline passengers really begin to feel guilty about flying away for a cheap weekend break, and cut back their purchases?

In January 2007, the communications battle was stepped up when a UK government minister described Ryanair as 'the irresponsible face of capitalism'. He had argued that while other industries and consumers were cutting down their emissions, Ryanair had expanded at a phenomenal rate, churning out more CO_2 into the atmosphere at a time when other industry sectors were reducing their emissions. Friends of the Earth, in a report entitled 'Aviation and global climate change', noted that commercial jets were adding 600 million tonnes of CO_2 a year to global warming, almost as much as for the whole of Africa. With such negative communication, would Ryanair suffer as people felt guilty about flying, and governments increasingly moved to regulate civil aviation and make it more expensive, especially for the price-sensitive segments that the no-frills airlines had been targeting?

Rarely known to be quiet, the chief executive of Ryanair, Michael O'Leary, went on a communications offensive. Dismissing the minister as 'knowing nothing', he presented Ryanair as a friend rather than an enemy of global warming. He argued that travellers should feel reassured that Ryanair used one of the world's most modern and fuel-efficient fleets of aircraft. Moreover, Ryanair's business model of filling seats at the lowest price really meant that the carbon emissions per passenger were much lower than those of traditional full-service airlines, which often flew half-empty planes. And then there was the fact that budget airlines operated an extensive point-to-point network, avoiding the costly and environmentally harmful effects of taking two indirect flights via a central hub airport.

The war of words that has ensued over airlines' contribution to global warming demonstrates the difficulty that many ordinary consumers have in evaluating rival claims. Many may have taken to heart governments' and church leaders' claims that made them feel guilty about flying. But even if hypocritical consumers were happy to carry on flying and not backing their expressed concerns for climate change with changes in their behaviour, there was certainly a possibility that governments would intervene, Both the UK government and the EU Commission had floated the idea of taxing aviation fuel, and bringing aircraft emissions within the scope of the EU Emissions

Trading Scheme. Some airlines, such as Ryanair, continued to sound off against the government, positioning them as the consumer's champion. But others, including easyJet, sensed the change in mood of the public and government bodies, and openly supported the idea of bringing aircraft emissions into the carbon trading regime. Was easyJet being philanthropic? Was it simply putting out a message that it thought its customers would want to hear, helping them salve their consciences and giving easyJet a better image than arch-rival Ryanair? Or was there a shrewd underlying commercial advantage, in which the modern, efficient easyJet fleet may use less than its allotted share of carbon emissions, which it could then sell on to less efficient 'legacy' carriers? Should the company begin planning for higher taxes on flying, and be prepared for reducing its growth plans if some marginal customers decided that a weekend break by the Mediterranean was no longer a luxury that they could afford?

Source: based on Ben Hall and Kevin Done, 'Pearson brought to earth in airline row', *Financial Times*, 6 January 2007; Charles Starmer-Smith, 'Green travel: the winners and losers', *Daily Telegraph*, 12 January 2008; Jimmy Lee

Shreeve, 'Green skies?', *Daily Telegraph*, 26 June 2007; Friends of the Earth (2000), '*Aviation and global climate change*', London; 'Climate scepticism "on the rise"', BBC poll shows, *BBC News Online*, 7 February 2010, http://news.bbc.co.uk/1/hi/8500443.stm, accessed 10 October 2010

QUESTIONS

1 Discuss the possible policy options open to government to curb aircraft emissions, and assess their likely effects on 'budget' airlines.

2 The case study refers to the apparent hypocrisy of consumers who may claim to be concerned about the environment, but nevertheless continue to fly. What might bring about a narrowing of this gap between what consumers think and what they actually do? How could a company such as easyJet measure and monitor consumers' attitudes?

3 What might be the consequences for a budget airline of government policy measures that have the effect of doubling air fares in real terms? Critically discuss how a budget airline might respond.

Summary

This chapter has reviewed the complex nature of an organization's business environment. The environment can be analysed at three levels: the microenvironment, comprising firms and individuals that an organization directly interacts with (or that directly affect its activities); the macroenvironment, comprising general forces that may eventually impact on the microenvironment; and the internal environment, comprising other functions within the organization.

This chapter has stressed the interrelatedness of all elements of the business environment. Although the social environment and technological environment are identified as separate elements, the two are closely linked (for example, technology has resulted in mass ownership of cars, which has in turn affected social behaviour).

Subsequent chapters pay attention to each of the elements of the business environment, but the complexity of linkages must never be forgotten. **Chapter 15** seeks to integrate these elements within dynamic analytical frameworks, which can be used to develop holistic forecasts of the future business environment.

Key Terms

Channels of distribution (14)	Microenvironment (5)
Closed system (27)	Open system (27)
Credit crunch (15)	Organizational culture (16)
Environmental set (17)	Stakeholders (12)
Information environment (20)	Strategic alliances (18)
Intermediaries (14)	Transformation process (4)
Internal environment (5)	Value chain (18)
Macroenvironment (5)	

Online Learning Centre

To help you grasp the key concepts of this chapter, explore the extra resources posted on the Online Learning Centre at **www.mcgraw-hill.co.uk/palmer**. Among other helpful resources there are chapter-by-chapter test questions, revision notes and web links.

Chapter review questions

1 Discuss what you understand by the term 'business environment'.

2 Suppliers and intermediaries are important stakeholders in the microenvironment of the business. Discuss the evolving role and functions of stakeholders in business organizations.

3 Members of an organizational set are becoming increasingly interdependent. Identify examples of this interdependency, and discuss the reasons why it is happening.

Activities

1 Develop a checklist of points that you consider to be important indicators of whether an organization is responsive to changes in its business environment. Why did you choose these indicators? Now apply your checklist to three selected organizations: one a traditional manufacturing industry, the second a service-based commercial organization, and the third a government organization that serves the public. What, if anything, should your chosen organizations do to become more responsive to changes in their business environment?

2 Go back to Figure 1.4, which shows an environmental set for a car manufacturer. If you are studying at a college or university, repeat this diagram, but show the environmental set for your university/college.

3 Choose an industry sector with which you are familiar (e.g. mobile phones, grocery retail). Identify the elements in firms' macroenvironment that may affect their profitability during the next ten years.

Further reading

A good starting point for understanding the competitive advantage of firms and the role of value chains in achieving this is provided in Michael Porter's frequently cited book:

Porter, M.E. (1985) *Competitive Advantage: Creating and Sustaining Superior Performance*, New York, Free Press.

There is now an extensive literature on the development of close buyer–seller relationships. A good summary of the principles can be found in the following texts.

Buttle, F. D. (2008) *Relationship Marketing* (2nd edn), London, Butterworth-Heinemann.

Egan, J. (2008) *Relationship Marketing: Exploring Relational Strategies in Marketing* (3rd edn), Harlow, Pearson Education Ltd.

Donaldson, W.G. and O'Toole, T. (2007) *Strategic Market Relationships: From Strategy to Implementation* (2nd edn), Chichester, John Wiley.

This chapter has provided a general overview of the components that make up the business environment. Suggestions for further reading on each of these components are given in later chapters.

References

Gladwell, M. (2000) *The Tipping Point: How Little Things Can Make a Big Difference*, New York, Little Brown & Co.

Heskett, J. L., Sasser, W. E. Jr. and Schlesinger, L.A. (2003) *The Value Profit Chain: Treat Employees like Customers and Customers like Employees*, New York, The Free Press.

Levitt, T. (1960) 'Marketing myopia', *Harvard Business Review*, July–August, pp. 45–56.

Nonaka, I. (1991) 'The knowledge-creating company', *Harvard Business Review*, Vol. 69, No. 6, pp. 96–104.

Office for National Statistics (2010) *Social Trends*, 40, London, Office for National Statistics (available online at http://www.statistics.gov.uk/socialtrends/).

Schmitt, P. and Michahelles, F. (2008) *Economic Impact of RFID Report*, Zurich, ETH.

Vargo, S.L. and Lusch, R.F. (2008) 'Service-dominant logic: continuing the evolution', *Journal of the Academy of Marketing Science*, Vol. 36, 1–10.

CHAPTER 4

Planning and Strategic Management

> Manage your destiny, or someone else will.
> —JACK WELCH, FORMER CEO, GENERAL ELECTRIC

LEARNING OBJECTIVES

After studying Chapter 4, you will be able to:

LO 1   Summarize the basic steps in any planning process.

LO 2   Describe how strategic planning should be integrated with tactical and operational planning.

LO 3   Identify elements of the external environment and internal resources of the firm to analyze before formulating a strategy.

LO 4   Define core capabilities and explain how they provide the foundation for business strategy.

LO 5   Summarize the types of choices available for corporate strategy.

LO 6   Discuss how companies can achieve competitive advantage through business strategy.

LO 7   Describe the keys to effective strategy implementation.

CHAPTER OUTLINE

An Overview of Planning Fundamentals

The Basic Planning Process

Levels of Planning

Strategic Planning

Tactical and Operational Planning

Aligning Tactical, Operational, and Strategic Planning

Strategic Planning

Step 1: Establishment of Mission, Vision, and Goals

Step 2: Analysis of External Opportunities and Threats

Step 3: Analysis of Internal Strengths and Weaknesses

Step 4: SWOT Analysis and Strategy Formulation

Step 5: Strategy Implementation

Step 6: Strategic Control

Management in Action

HOW WALT DISNEY COMPANY SCRIPTS ITS OWN SUCCESS

Mickey Mouse, mascot of the Walt Disney Company, may be a tiny creature, but the company he represents might be better portrayed as the massive and many-tentacled giant squid. With revenues approaching $49 billion per year, the company is one of the largest in the entertainment industry, competing with Comcast, News Corp, and others.

Walt Disney is not merely huge in terms of sales volume; it has five business divisions, involved in nearly every kind of commercial entertainment. It all began with Walt Disney Studios, which today produces movies, music, and stage shows under the banners of Disney, Pixar, Marvel Studios, Lucasfilm, Touchstone Pictures, and Hollywood Records. The Media Networks group covers publishing, radio, and broadcast and cable television, including Disney/ABC Television and ESPN. The Parks and Resorts group encompasses 11 theme parks and 44 resorts around the world as well as a cruise line. Disney Interactive offers entertainment on digital platforms, including console games and the Internet. And Disney Consumer Products extends the business value of characters and story lines by operating Disney Stores and licensing its creations for use on toys, clothing, art objects, and a wide variety of other consumer goods.

The man in charge of keeping the magic alive through activities carried out by more than 175,000 employees is Disney's chief executive officer, Robert Iger. Iger and his executive team must define an overall direction and goal for the company and keep an eye on how well each business group is contributing to achievement of that goal. Iger does this by spotting

© Photos 12/Alamy

opportunities for growth in the industry—hence the expansion into cable television and, more recently, into interactive entertainment. He also looks for characters and brands Disney can make more valuable because of its access to more channels. For example, Disney could pay generously for Pixar and Marvel because those companies' characters generate sales in products as diverse as theme parks, videogames, and sweatshirts. Another coup for Iger was the purchase of ESPN, the most valuable cable channel in terms of revenues.

Iger meets weekly with the heads of the business units. Although he keeps an eye on the company's overall direction, he gives each unit's head wide latitude. This pattern was evident when he planned the purchase of Pixar in 2006. Acknowledging that Pixar had become the dominant animation studio, he not only left its executives in charge after the acquisition but also placed them at the helm of the Disney animation studios. *Frozen,* the highest grossing animated film of all time, and sales of movie-themed toys, contributed to a 19 percent increase in profits in first quarter 2015. However, challenges remain for Iger. Disney Interactive is struggling to turn a profit. Somehow, the CEO from the television era has to ensure that Mickey remains a star of the Internet age.[1]

As you read this chapter, think about the challenge of providing direction to a massive enterprise offering entertainment to all ages around the globe. What planning methods could help managers at all levels zero in on the best opportunities?

To imagine Disney—or any organization—dealing with the significant challenges it faces without developing a plan beforehand is almost impossible. Planning describes what managers decide to do and how they will do it. It provides the framework, focus, and direction required for a meaningful effort. Without planning, any improvements in an organization's innovation, speed, quality, service, and cost will be accidental, if they occur at all. This chapter examines the most important concepts and processes involved in planning and strategic management. By learning these concepts and reviewing the steps outlined, you will be on your way to understanding the current approaches to the strategic management of today's organizations.

An Overview of Planning Fundamentals

The importance of formal planning in organizations has grown dramatically. Until the mid-1900s, most planning was unstructured and fragmented, and formal planning was restricted to a few large corporations. Although management pioneers such as Alfred Sloan of General Motors instituted formal planning processes, planning became a widespread management function only during the past few decades. Initially, larger organizations adopted formal planning, but today even small firms operated by aggressive, opportunistic entrepreneurs engage in formal planning.[2]

As discussed in Chapter 1, planning is the conscious, systematic process of making decisions about goals and activities that an individual, group, work unit, or organization will pursue in the future. Planning is not an informal or haphazard response to a crisis; it is a purposeful effort that is directed and controlled by managers and often draws on the knowledge and experience of employees throughout the organization. Planning provides individuals and work units with a clear map to follow in their future activities; at the same time, this map may be flexible enough to allow for individual circumstances and changing conditions.

  ## The Basic Planning Process

Because planning is a decision process—you're deciding what to do and how to go about doing it—the important steps followed during formal planning are similar to the basic decision-making steps we discussed in Chapter 3. Exhibit 4.1 summarizes the similarities between decision making and planning—including the fact that both move not just in one direction but in a cycle. The outcomes of decisions and plans are evaluated, and if necessary, they are revised.

We now describe the basic planning process in more detail. Later in this chapter, we will discuss how managerial decisions and plans fit into the larger purposes of the organization—its ultimate strategy, mission, vision, and goals.

situational analysis

A process planners use, within time and resource constraints, to gather, interpret, and summarize all information relevant to the planning issue under consideration.

Step 1: Situational Analysis   As the contingency approach advocates, planning begins with a **situational analysis.** Within their time and resource constraints, planners should gather, interpret, and summarize all information relevant to the planning issue in question. A thorough situational analysis studies past events, examines current conditions, and attempts to forecast future trends. It focuses on the internal forces at work in the organization or work unit and, consistent with the open-systems approach (see Chapter 2), examines influences from the external environment. The outcome of this step is the identification and diagnosis of planning assumptions, issues, and problems.

A thorough situational analysis will provide information about the planning decisions you need to make. For example, if you are a manager in a magazine company considering the launch of a sports publication for the teen market, your analysis will include such factors as the number of teens who subscribe to magazines, the appeal of the teen market to advertisers, your firm's ability to serve this market effectively, current economic conditions, the level of teen interest in sports, and any sports magazines already serving this

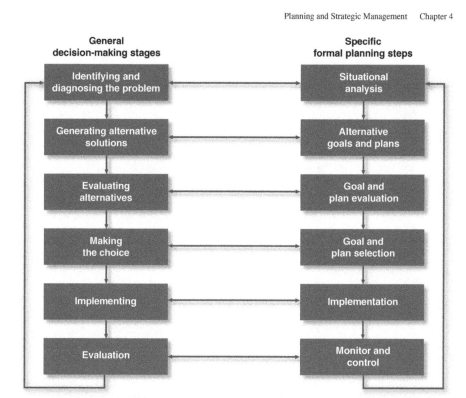

General decision-making stages	Specific formal planning steps
Identifying and diagnosing the problem	Situational analysis
Generating alternative solutions	Alternative goals and plans
Evaluating alternatives	Goal and plan evaluation
Making the choice	Goal and plan selection
Implementing	Implementation
Evaluation	Monitor and control

EXHIBIT 4.1

Decision-Making Stages (Chapter 3) and Formal Planning Steps (Chapter 4)

market and their current sales. Such a detailed analysis will help you decide whether to proceed with the next step in your magazine launch.

Step 2: Alternative Goals and Plans   Based on the situational analysis, the planning process should generate alternative goals that may be pursued in the future and the alternative plans that may be used to achieve those goals. This step in the process should stress creativity and encourage managers and employees to think in broad terms about their jobs. Once a range of alternatives has been developed, the merits of these different plans and goals will be evaluated. Continuing with our magazine publishing example, the alternatives you might want to consider could include whether the magazine should be targeted at young men, young women, or both groups, and whether it should be sold mainly online, through subscriptions, or on newsstands.

Goals are the targets or ends the manager wants to reach. As shown in Exhibit 4.2, effective goals tend to have certain qualities, which can be remembered by the acronym SMART.

Starbucks is applying several of these criteria as it plans to open 3,400 stores in China by 2020. To date, the specialty coffee retailer has opened 1,400 stores in 84 cities with more than 3 million transactions per week.[3] Belinda Wong, president of Starbucks China, is leading the charge. At the recent opening of the company's flagship three-story building in the city of Chengdu, Wong linked the event to Starbucks' goals in China: "This is a reflection of our continued focus to highlight our coffee passion and create a locally-relevant Starbucks Experience through each moment of connection for our customers."[4] Ideally, SMART goals not only point individual employees in the direction they should be going but also tend to be accepted by the managers and employees who are charged with achieving them. Thus they both direct employees and motivate them. (For more on the importance of motivation, see Chapter 13.)

Plans are the actions or means the manager intends to use to achieve goals. At a minimum, planning should outline alternative actions that may lead to the attainment of each

goal

A target or end that management desires to reach.

plans

The actions or means managers intend to use to achieve organizational goals.

110   Part Two   Planning: Delivering Strategic Value

Specific	• Describe precisely what behavior and outcomes are desired so employees can direct their efforts. • *Example: Increase sales by landing 3–4 new clients from companies with more than 500 employees.*
Measurable	• Quantify what the goal should achieve. • *Example: Increase sales revenue by 5% or $50,000.*
Attainable (but challenging)	• The goal should challenge employees to work hard and creatively, but not be so difficult that they become discouraged. • *Example: Last year's increase in sales revenue was 4% or $40,000. An increase of 5% this year is achievable.*
Relevant	• Each goal should contribute to the organization's overall mission while being consistent with its mission, values, and ethical standards. Goals are relevant when they are consistent among and within teams and groups. • *Example: To support the organization's mission to help more customers each year, all sales units are asked to increase revenue by 5%.*
Time-bound	• Effective goals have a deadline or target date for completion. • *Example: Each sales employee needs to achieve the 5% increase in sales by December 31.*

EXHIBIT 4.2
SMART Goals Are Motivational

Bottom Line

Contingency plans that keep service levels high during a crisis can seal a company's reputation for caring about customers. But this commitment requires highly dedicated and creative employees, and access to the necessary resources can be expensive. Managers must decide how crucial service is to their strategy—and how willing customers will be to forgive them for service lapses under pressure. *During a major storm, what services do you expect to be able to receive without interruption? Would you pay more to make these services more reliable?*

goal, the resources required to reach the goal through those means, and the obstacles that may develop. After General Motors declared bankruptcy and borrowed billions from the U.S. government in 2009, management made plans for a return to profitability. The plans included reducing costs by producing fewer trucks, eliminating several brands, introducing smaller vehicles, keeping fewer vehicles in inventory, and closing hundreds of dealerships. So besides cutting costs, GM introduced cars it hoped would be more popular, including the Cruze compact and the Sonic subcompact. Despite obstacles such as difficulty meeting demand with a reduced workforce and the lower profitability of smaller vehicles, the company moved back into the black a year after the bankruptcy, and in two years it reported its strongest financial performance in over a decade.[5]

In this chapter, we will talk about various types of plans. Some plans, called *contingency plans,* might be referred to as "what if" plans. They include sets of actions to be taken when a company's initial plans have not worked well or if events in the external environment require a sudden change. Disasters of recent years, including the 2001 terrorist attacks and Hurricanes Katrina, Rita, and Sandy, have reminded many businesses how important contingency planning can be. Wal-Mart stores in the United States, with over 140 million customer visits per week, has several crisis plans in place to keep stores open and stocked with food, water, pharmaceutical supplies, and so forth in the aftermath of natural disasters.[6]

Most major corporations now have contingency plans in place to respond to a major disaster—to make sure vital data are backed up and can be recovered in an emergency, for instance, or that employees know what to do when a crisis occurs. But contingency plans are important for more common situations as well. For example, many businesses are affected by snowstorms, increases in gasoline prices, computer breakdowns, or changes in consumer tastes. JetBlue initially achieved success as an airline that would "bring humanity back to air travel" by caring about its customers and employees. But the airline was humiliated by its inability to cope with a February snowstorm during which at least one plane notoriously sat on a runway for 10 hours; the company took days to recover, canceling a thousand flights.[7]

Step 3: Goal and Plan Evaluation

Next, managers will evaluate the advantages, disadvantages, and potential effects of each alternative goal and plan. They must prioritize those goals and even eliminate some of them. Also, managers will consider carefully the implications of alternative plans for meeting high-priority goals. In particular, they will pay a great deal of attention to the cost of any initiative and the investment return that is likely to result. In our magazine publishing example, your evaluation might determine that newsstand sales alone wouldn't be profitable enough to justify the launch. Perhaps you could improve profits with an online edition supplemented by podcasts. To decide, you would estimate the costs and expected returns of such alternatives, trying to follow the decision steps advised in Chapter 3.

The Hard Rock Café carries its strategy—to be identified with rock 'n' roll—through to its hotel signs.

© Richard Cummins/Corbis

Step 4: Goal and Plan Selection

Once managers have assessed the various goals and plans, they will select the one that is most appropriate and feasible. The evaluation process will identify the priorities and trade-offs among the goals and plans. For example, if your plan is to launch a number of new online publications, and you're trying to choose among them, you might weigh the different up-front investment each requires, the size of each market, which one fits best with your existing product line or company image, and so on. Experienced judgment always plays an important role in this process. However, as you will discover later in the chapter, relying on judgment alone may not be the best way to proceed.

Typically, a formal planning process leads to a written set of goals and plans that are appropriate and feasible for a particular set of circumstances. In some organizations, the alternative generation, evaluation, and selection steps generate planning **scenarios,** as discussed in Chapter 2. A different contingency plan is attached to each scenario. The manager pursues the goals and implements the plans associated with the most likely scenario. However, the manager will also be prepared to switch to another set of plans if the situation changes and another scenario becomes relevant. This approach helps the firm anticipate and manage crises and allows greater flexibility and responsiveness.

scenario

A narrative that describes a particular set of future conditions.

Step 5: Implementation

Once managers have selected the goals and plans, they must implement the plans designed to achieve the goals. Even the best plans are useless if they are not implemented properly. Managers and employees must understand the plan, have the resources to implement it, and be motivated to do so. Including employees in the previous steps of the planning process paves the way for the implementation phase. As we mentioned earlier, employees usually are better informed, more committed, and more highly motivated when a goal or plan is one they helped develop.

Finally, successful implementation requires a plan to be linked to other systems in the organization, particularly the budget and reward systems. If the manager does not have a budget with financial resources to execute the plan, the plan is probably doomed. Similarly, goal achievement must be linked to the organization's reward system. Many organizations use incentive

> Even the best plans are useless if they are not implemented properly.

Social Enterprise

Novo Nordisk Monitors Progress Regarding Its Triple Bottom Line

While some companies discuss the importance of operating in a more socially and environmentally conscious manner, others like Novo Nordisk put this philosophy into action. Headquartered in Denmark, Novo Nordisk is a leading global provider of diabetes care solutions. The firm follows a Triple Bottom Line (TBL) strategy, meaning decisions are based on the belief that "a healthy economy, environment, and society are fundamental to long-term business success." Novo Nordisk's goal is to operate its business so that diabetes solutions benefit both the business and patients, while meeting societal expectations in the process. To ensure that the TBL philosophy would stick, Novo Nordisk took the uncommon step of incorporating it into its company bylaws.[8]

In addition to standard financial performance measures, Novo Nordisk monitors multiple short- and long-term goals within the social and environmental areas. The 2014 Integrated Annual Report Emphasizing Long-term Thinking highlights the company's social and environmental performance:[9]

Social impact	• Diabetes care products reached 24.4 million people with the disease. • Over 3,000 new jobs were added in the company.

Environmental impact	• Continued to reduce CO_2 emissions from energy consumption for production (45 percent reduction since 2004). • Decreased energy consumption by 1 percent over previous year.

Novo Nordisk is breaking with traditional profit-only business models by setting and monitoring meaningful social and environmental goals. The TBL model seems to be working. With the diabetes drug market expected to reach $58 billion by 2018, the company is positioned to perform well financially while making a significant, multilevel impact.[10]

Questions

- According to Novo Nordisk, only four companies have incorporated Triple Bottom Line goals into their bylaws. Why do you think so few companies take this step?
- Assume you want your employer to consider adopting a Triple Bottom Line philosophy. How would you pitch the idea? With whom would you speak?

programs to encourage employees to achieve goals and to implement plans properly. Commissions, salaries, promotions, bonuses, and other rewards are based on successful performance.

New York Community Bancorp (NYCB) looked at the possible ways to compete for customers: convenient locations, interest rates on savings, and customer service. With branches expensive to open and interest rates highly competitive, NYCB decided it would become known for exceptional customer service. NYCB's training department used service standards to create a classroom training program that teaches employees how to deliver excellent service. The trainers also visit NYCB's business units to practice the jobs and see firsthand what issues are important to success, using these experiences to make improvements to the employee training program. NYCB reinforces the program with coaching, and it has a system of rewards and recognition for meeting the service standards. Since implementing the goal-oriented training, coaching, and rewards, NYCB has seen its overall score for customer service rise from 89.5 percent to 97.5 percent.[11]

Step 6: Monitor and Control   Although it is sometimes ignored, the sixth step in the formal planning process—monitoring and controlling—is essential. Without it, you

Bottom Line

Tying plans to a firm's financials is a key element of success.

How might a plan to improve employees' job satisfaction be tied to a company's financial measures?

will never know whether your plan is succeeding. As we mentioned earlier, planning works in a cycle; it is an ongoing, repetitive process. Managers must continually monitor the actual performance of their work units against the units' goals and plans. They also need to develop control systems to measure that performance and allow them to take corrective action when the plans are implemented improperly or when the situation changes. The nearby "Social Enterprise" box discusses how Novo Nordisk monitors progress toward achieving important organizational goals. We will discuss the important issue of control systems in greater detail later in this chapter and in Chapter 16.

Levels of Planning

In Chapter 1, you learned about the three major types of managers: top-level (strategic managers), middle-level (tactical managers), and frontline (operational managers). Because planning is an important management function, managers at all three levels use it. However, the scope and activities of the planning process at each level of the organization often differ.

 LO 2

Strategic Planning

Strategic planning involves making decisions about the organization's long-term goals and strategies. Strategic plans have a strong external orientation and cover major portions of the organization. Senior executives are responsible for the development and execution of the strategic plan, although they usually do not formulate or implement the entire plan personally.

Strategic goals are major targets or results that relate to the long-term survival, value, and growth of the organization. Strategic managers—top-level managers—usually establish goals that reflect both effectiveness (providing appropriate outputs) and efficiency (a high ratio of outputs to inputs). Typical strategic goals include growth, increasing market share, improving profitability, boosting return on investment, fostering both quantity and quality of outputs, increasing productivity, improving customer service, and contributing to society.

Organizations usually have a number of mutually reinforcing strategic goals. For example, a computer manufacturer may have as its strategic goals the launch of a specified number of new products in a particular time frame, of higher quality, with a targeted increase in market share. Each of these goals supports and contributes to the others.

A **strategy** is a pattern of actions and resource allocations designed to achieve the goals of the organization. As Exhibit 4.3 illustrates, an effective strategy provides a basis for answering five broad questions about how the organization will meet its objectives.[12] Former Procter & Gamble CEO A. G. Lafley and consultant Roger Martin emphasize that the answers to the "where" and "how" questions should be aimed at winning (question 3), which requires offering a better "value proposition" than the competition. Merely matching the competition, they say, is neither strategic nor a path to success. For example, P&G gave new life to its Oil of Olay skin care brand by addressing the concerns of middle-aged women and by improving the active ingredients in its product. In addition, P&G used its strength in selling to mass-market retailers to persuade them to set up attractive displays

strategic planning

A set of procedures for making decisions about the organization's long-term goals and strategies; see also *planning*.

strategic goals

Major targets or end results relating to the organization's long-term survival, value, and growth.

strategy

A pattern of actions and resource allocations designed to achieve the organization's goals.

1. Where will we be active?
2. How will we get there (e.g., by increasing sales or acquiring another company)?
3. How will we win in the market (e.g., by keeping prices low or offering the best service)?
4. How fast will we move and in what sequence will we make changes?
5. How will we obtain financial returns (low costs or premium prices)?

EXHIBIT 4.3

Effective Strategies Answer Five Questions

for Oil of Olay. With the value proposition of an affordable, attractive, widely available product serving a previously ignored market segment, P&G could meet its strategic goal of leadership in the skin care market.[13]

In setting a strategy, managers try to match the organization's skills and resources to the opportunities found in the external environment. Every organization has certain strengths and weaknesses, so the actions, or strategies, the organization implements should help build on strengths in areas that satisfy the wants and needs of consumers and other key factors in the organization's external environment. Also, some organizations may implement strategies that change or influence the external environment, as discussed in Chapter 2.

Tactical and Operational Planning

tactical planning

A set of procedures for translating broad strategic goals and plans into specific goals and plans that are relevant to a distinct portion of the organization, such as a functional area like marketing.

Once the organization's strategic goals and plans are identified, they serve as the foundation for planning done by middle-level and frontline managers. As you can see in Exhibit 4.4, goals and plans become more specific and involve shorter periods of time as they move from the strategic level to the tactical level and then to the operational level. A strategic plan will typically have a time horizon of from three to seven years—but sometimes even decades, as with the successful plan to land a probe on Titan, Saturn's moon. Tactical plans may have a time horizon of a year or two, and operational plans may cover a period of months.

operational planning

The process of identifying the specific procedures and processes required at lower levels of the organization.

Tactical planning translates broad strategic goals and plans into specific goals and plans that are relevant to a definite portion of the organization, often a functional area like marketing or human resources, as discussed in Chapter 10. Tactical plans focus on the major actions a unit must take to fulfill its part of the strategic plan. For example, if the strategy calls for the rollout of a new product line, the tactical plan for the manufacturing unit might involve the design, testing, and installation of the equipment needed to produce the new line.

Operational planning identifies the specific procedures and processes required at lower levels of the organization. Frontline managers usually focus on routine tasks such as production runs, delivery schedules, and human resource requirements, as we discuss in Chapters 16 and 17.

Bottom Line

Ideally, strategic plans integrate all the bottom-line practices of the firm. *What could be the consequences if a company's innovation practices were not aligned with its strategy?*

The planning model we have been describing is a hierarchical one, with top-level strategies flowing down through the levels of the organization into more specific goals and plans and an ever-more-limited timetable. But in today's complex organizations, the planning sequence is often not as rigid as this traditional view. As we will see later in this chapter, managers throughout an organization may be involved in developing the strategic plan and contributing critical elements to it. Also, in practice, lower-level managers may be making decisions that shape strategy, whether or not top executives realize it. When Intel senior adviser Andy Grove suggested that the company exit the computer memory business, Intel

EXHIBIT 4.4
Hierarchy of Goals and Plans

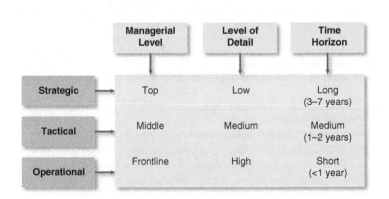

	Managerial Level	Level of Detail	Time Horizon
Strategic	Top	Low	Long (3–7 years)
Tactical	Middle	Medium	Medium (1–2 years)
Operational	Frontline	High	Short (<1 year)

was directing about one-third of its research dollars to memory-related projects. However, on a practical level, the company had already been exiting the business; only 4 percent of its total sales were for computer memory products. Why was this occurring if it wasn't yet a defined strategy? Manufacturing managers had been directed by finance executives to set up factories in a way that would generate the biggest margins (revenues minus costs) per square inch of microchips produced. As computer memory became a money-losing commodity, manufacturing made fewer of those products. So when Intel announced it would get out of the memory business, its strategy was catching up with its operational planning, which had been driven by tactical plans.[14] The lesson for top managers is to make sure they are communicating strategy to all levels of the organization *and* paying attention to what is happening at all levels in the organization.

Aligning Tactical, Operational, and Strategic Planning

To be fully effective, the organization's strategic, tactical, and operational goals and plans must be aligned—that is, they must be consistent, mutually supportive, and focused on achieving the common purpose and direction. Whole Foods Market, for example, links its tactical and operational planning directly to its strategic planning. The firm describes itself on its website as a mission-driven company that aims to set the standards for excellence for food retailers. The firm measures its success in fulfilling its vision by "customer satisfaction, team member excellence and happiness, return on capital investment, improvement in the state of the environment, and local and larger community support."

Whole Foods' strategic goal is "to sell the highest-quality products that also offer high value for our customers." Its operational goals focus on ingredients, freshness, taste, nutritional value, safety, and appearance that meet or exceed its customers' expectations, including guaranteeing product satisfaction. Tactical goals include store environments that are "inviting, fun, unique, comfortable, attractive, nurturing, and educational" and safe and inviting work environments for its employees.

One method for aligning the organization's strategic and operational goals is a *strategy map*. A strategy map provides a tool managers can use to communicate their strategic goals and enable members of the organization at every level to understand the parts they will play in helping to achieve them. The map illustrates the four key drivers (or "balanced scorecard") of a firm's long-term success: the skills of its people and their ability to grow and learn; the effectiveness of its internal processes; its ability to deliver value to customers; and ultimately its ability to grow its financial assets. The map shows how specific plans and goals in each area link to the others and can generate real improvements in an organization's performance.

Whole Foods has operational goals that focus on high quality and appearance among other qualities.

© Rubberball/Getty Images

Exhibit 4.5 shows how a strategy map might be built and how the various goals of the organization relate to each other to create long-term value for the firm. As an example, let us assume that a company's primary financial goal is "to increase revenues by enhancing the value we offer to existing customers by making our prices the lowest available." (Target and Walmart might be good examples of companies with this kind of strategy.) The company will then have corresponding goals and plans in the other sections of the map to support that strategy. Its learning and growth goals might include bringing in the most efficient production technologies or work processes and training the staff to use them. These in turn will lead to the internal goals of improved production speed and lower cost, which in turn lead to the customer goal of competitive pricing, making the original financial goal feasible. On the other hand, a financial strategy of revenue growth through new products might lead to people and technology goals that speed up product design, to internal processes that lead to innovation, and to a customer goal of perceived product leadership. Whatever the strategy, the strategy map can be used to develop the appropriate measures and standards in each operational area for that strategy and to show how they are all linked.[15]

Bottom Line

The strategy map shows the relationship between a firm's practices and its long-term success.
Where do a company's quality practices show up in the strategy map (Exhibit 4.5)?

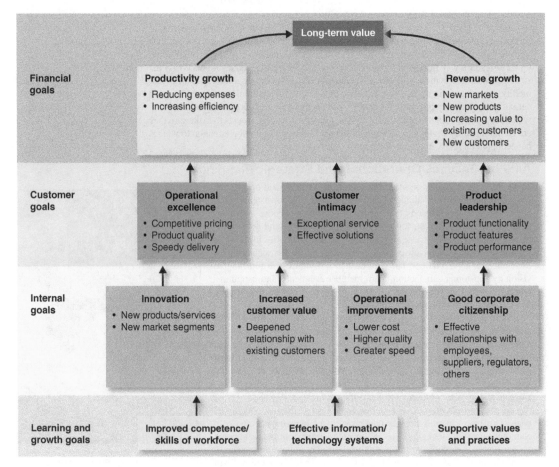

EXHIBIT 4.5   The Strategy Map: Creating Value by Aligning Goals

SOURCE: Adapted from R. Kaplan and Norton, "Plotting Success with Strategy Maps," *Optimize*, February 2004, online; and R. Kaplan and Norton, "Having Trouble with Your Strategy? Then Map It," *Harvard Business Review*, September–October 2000.

As you read "Management in Action: Progress Report," consider how well tactical, operational, and strategic planning are aligned at Walt Disney Company, particularly with regard to its Disney Interactive unit.

Strategic Planning

Strategic decision making is one of the most exciting and controversial topics in management today. In fact, many organizations currently are changing the ways they develop and execute their strategic plans.

Traditionally, strategic planning emphasized a top-down approach—senior executives and specialized planning units developed goals and plans for the entire organization. Tactical and operational managers received those goals and plans, and their own planning activities were limited to specific procedures and budgets for the units.

Management in Action

PLANNING A TURNAROUND FOR DISNEY INTERACTIVE

Walt Disney Company's corporate strategy is to lead in providing entertainment and information. The company's top ranking in the industry and recent profits of $9 billion suggest it is succeeding. Despite years of operating at a loss and recent layoffs, Disney Interactive Media is the fastest growing business segment in the company's portfolio.

Disney Interactive, founded in 2008, has as its ambitious goal to "entertain kids, families, and Disney enthusiasts everywhere with world-class products that push the boundaries of technology and imagination." Its tactical plans include development of games for every digital media platform, including mobile and social media as well as the major gaming consoles.

Measured by those standards, performance has been less than stellar. The slow pace at which it crafts movies is unsuitable for game creation. The six years required to go from concept to release of Epic Mickey, created only for the Nintendo Wii, meant the release came in 2010, after that console's popularity had peaked. At one point, Disney ran six development studios creating games for consoles, which became a problem when players switched to online games and began using mobile devices.

A basic element of Disney's digital strategy has been its entertainment website, Disney.com, successor to the Go.com web portal, which closed in 2001. However, the company has struggled to make it relevant. One challenge is that the brand aims to serve the diverse interests of toddlers and parents as well as game players of all ages in between. Mostly, the site has focused on cross-promoting its entertainment and licensed merchandise.

James A. Pitaro, president of Disney Interactive Media, is pivoting the unit in two significant ways. First, it is focusing more on mobile gaming that can be played on tablets and smartphones. In Japan, the mobile game Tsumu Tsumu is a big hit with over 8 million downloads. And second, Disney Interactive Media is seeking brand sponsors for its Disney Online website that has grown in popularity to nearly 53 million unique visitors per month.[16] Pitaro believes that brand sponsors will generate more revenue than the website advertising model currently being used.

- At which steps of the planning process would you say Disney Interactive most needs improvement? Why?
- How can Pitaro ensure that strategic, tactical, and operational management are well aligned?

Over the years, managers and consulting firms innovated with a variety of analytical techniques and planning approaches, many of which have been critical for analyzing complex business situations and competitive issues. In many instances, however, senior executives spent too much time with their planning specialists to the exclusion of line managers in the rest of the organization. As a result, a gap often developed between strategic managers and tactical and operational managers, and managers and employees throughout the organization became alienated and uncommitted to the organization's success.[17]

Today, however, senior executives increasingly are involving managers throughout the organization in the strategy formation process.[18] The problems just described and the rapidly changing environment of the past 25 years have forced executives to look to all levels of the organization for ideas and innovations to make their firms more competitive. Although the CEO and other top managers continue to furnish the strategic direction, or "vision," of the organization, tactical and even operational managers often provide valuable inputs to the organization's strategic plan. In some cases, these managers also have substantial autonomy to formulate or change their own plans. This authority increases flexibility and responsiveness, critical requirements for success in today's organizations.

Because of these trends, firms often use the term *strategic management* to describe the process. **Strategic management** involves managers from all parts of the organization in the formulation and implementation of strategic goals and strategies. It integrates strategic planning and management into a single process. Strategic planning becomes an ongoing activity in which all managers are encouraged to think strategically and focus on long-term, externally oriented issues as well as short-term tactical and operational issues.

Bottom Line
New ideas from managers throughout the organization can contribute to a plan's effectiveness.
What experiences might give frontline managers ideas that top-level executives haven't thought of?

strategic management

A process that involves managers from all parts of the organization in the formulation and implementation of strategic goals and strategies.

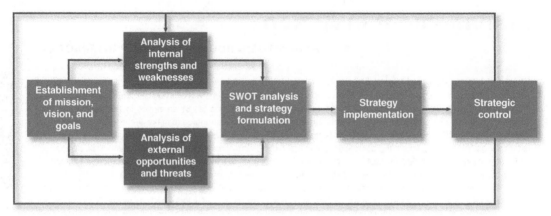

EXHIBIT 4.6

The Strategic Management Process

As shown in Exhibit 4.6, the strategic management process has six major components:

1. Establishment of mission, vision, and goals.
2. Analysis of external opportunities and threats.
3. Analysis of internal strengths and weaknesses.
4. SWOT (strengths, weaknesses, opportunities, and threats) analysis and strategy formulation.
5. Strategy implementation.
6. Strategic control.

Because this process is a planning and decision process, it is similar to the planning framework discussed earlier. Although organizations may use different terms or emphasize different parts of the process, the components and concepts described in this section are found either explicitly or implicitly in every organization. Even a small entrepreneurial firm can benefit from the kind of planning framework we describe here.

Step 1: Establishment of Mission, Vision, and Goals

mission

An organization's basic purpose and scope of operations.

The first step in strategic planning is establishing a mission, a vision, and goals for the organization. The **mission** is a clear and concise expression of the basic purpose of the organization. It describes what the organization does, for whom it does it, its basic good or service, and its values. Here are some mission statements from firms you will recognize:[19]

McDonald's: "To be our customers' favorite place and way to eat."
Uber: "Evolve the way the world moves."
United Way: "Improve lives by mobilizing the caring power of communities around the world to advance the common good."

Smaller organizations, of course, may have missions that aren't as broad as these. For example, the local bar found next to most campuses has this implicit mission: "to sell large quantities of inexpensive beer to college students in a noisily enjoyable environment."

strategic vision

The long-term direction and strategic intent of a company.

The mission describes the organization as it currently operates. The **strategic vision** points to the future—it provides a perspective on where the organization is headed and what it can become. Ideally, the vision statement clarifies the long-term direction of the company and its strategic intent. Here are some actual vision statements:[20]

NASA Armstrong Flight Research Center: "To fly what others only imagine."
City of Redmond, Washington: "Together we create a community of good neighbors."
Samsung: "Inspire the world. Create the future."

The most effective vision statements inspire organization members. They offer a worthwhile target for the entire organization to work together to achieve. Often these statements are not strictly financial because financial targets alone may not motivate all organization members. For example, NASA's Armstrong Flight Research Center focuses on the future of flight and exploration. Similarly, Samsung's vision refers to inspiring the world and creating the future.

> The strategic vision points to the future—where the organization is headed and what it can become.

Strategic goals evolve from the mission and vision of the organization. The chief executive officer of the organization, with the input and approval of the board of directors, establishes the mission, vision, and major strategic goals. The concepts and information within the mission statement, vision statement, and strategic goals statement may not be identified as such, but they should be communicated to everyone who has contact with the organization. Large firms generally provide public formal statements of their missions, visions, goals, and even values. For example, in support of its vision that "creating a community of good neighbors" is best done "together" with all sectors of the community, the City of Redmond has established goals such as these:

- Enhance citizen engagement in city issues.
- Sustain the natural systems and beauty of the community.
- Sustain a safe community with a coherent, comprehensive, cohesive approach to safety.
- Maintain economic vitality.

Different city departments would contribute to various aspects of this vision in the way they carry out their operational plans with an emphasis on collaborating with local businesses and residents.

Lofty words in a vision and mission statement cannot be meaningful without strong leadership support. At McDonald's, the commitment of past and present CEOs has played a large role in the success of the company's strategy implementation. Several years ago, the company was floundering as it lost sight of its commitment to quality, value, speed, and convenience. Under the leadership of James Cantalupo, the company created the mission statement quoted earlier, which placed the emphasis on the customer's experience. In a "Plan to Win," strategic goals such as revamping restaurants for a better drive-through experience and improving the quality of the menu supported the mission. When Jim Skinner took the job of chief executive, he enthusiastically backed the mission statement and its supporting Plan to Win, not hesitating to share credit for the company's continued success.[21]

Where leadership is strong, statements of visions and goals clarify the organization's purpose to key constituencies outside the organization. They also help employees focus their talent, energy, and commitment in pursuit of the organization's goals. When the time comes for you to seek employment with a firm, reviewing the firm's statements of mission, vision, and goals is a good first step in determining whether the firm's purposes and values will be compatible with your own.

Step 2: Analysis of External Opportunities and Threats

The mission and vision drive the second component of the strategic management process: analysis of the external environment. Successful strategic management depends on an accurate and thorough evaluation of the competitive environment and macroenvironment. The various components of these environments were introduced in Chapter 2.

The important activities in an environmental analysis include the ones listed in Exhibit 4.7. The analysis begins with an examination of the industry. Next, organizational stakeholders are examined. **Stakeholders** are groups and individuals who affect and are affected by the achievement of the organization's mission, goals, and strategies. They include buyers, suppliers, competitors, government and regulatory agencies, unions and employee groups, the financial community, owners and shareholders, and trade associations. The environmental analysis provides a map of these stakeholders and the ways they influence the organization.[22]

stakeholders

Groups and individuals who affect and are affected by the achievement of the organization's mission, goals, and strategies.

EXHIBIT 4.7
Environmental Analysis

Industry and Market Analysis
Industry profile: major product lines and significant market segments in the industry.
Industry growth: growth rates for the entire industry, growth rates for key market segments, projected changes in patterns of growth, and the determinants of growth.
Industry forces: threat of new industry entrants, threat of substitutes, economic power of buyers, economic power of suppliers, and internal industry rivalry (recall Chapter 2).

Competitor Analysis
Competitor profile: major competitors and their market shares.
Competitor analysis: goals, strategies, strengths, and weaknesses of each major competitor.
Competitor advantages: the degree to which industry competitors have differentiated their products or services or achieved cost leadership.

Political and Regulatory Analysis
Legislation and regulatory activities and their effects on the industry.
Political activity: the level of political activity that organizations and associations within the industry undertake (see Chapter 5).

Social Analysis
Social issues: current and potential social issues and their effects on the industry.
Social interest groups: consumer, environmental, and similar activist groups that attempt to influence the industry (see Chapters 5 and 6).

Human Resources Analysis
Labor issues: key labor needs, shortages, opportunities, and problems confronting the industry (see Chapters 10 and 11).

Macroeconomic Analysis
Macroeconomic conditions: economic factors that affect supply, demand, growth, competition, and profitability within the industry.

Technological Analysis
Technological factors: scientific or technical methods that affect the industry, particularly recent and potential innovations (see Chapter 17).

Since some states require the use of renewable sources to generate power, it is up to these companies to turn the negative aspect of higher costs into an overall positive outcome.

© Kim Steele/Getty Images

The environmental analysis also should examine other forces in the environment, such as economic conditions and technological factors. One critical task in environmental analysis is forecasting future trends. As noted in Chapter 2, forecasting techniques range from simple judgment to complex mathematical models that examine systematic relationships among many variables. Even simple quantitative techniques outperform the intuitive assessments of experts. Judgment is susceptible to bias, and managers have a limited ability to process information. Managers should use subjective judgments as inputs to quantitative models or when they confront new situations.

Frequently, the difference between an opportunity and a threat depends on how a company positions itself strategically. For example, some states have required electric utilities to get a certain share of their power from renewable sources such as wind and solar energy rather than from fossil fuels, including coal, oil, and natural gas. This requirement poses an obvious threat to utilities because the costs of fossil fuel energy are less, and customers demand low prices. However, some companies see strategic opportunities in renewable power. For over 10 years, Ocean Renewable Power Company (ORPC) has been developing technology that uses "ocean and river currents to produce clean, predictable electricity to power our homes and businesses while protecting the environment." At the Bay of Fundy on the border between Maine and Canada, ORPC operates the first commercial tidal power system in the United States. The system converts ocean energy to electricity that is then delivered to the public electricity grid. ORPC's goal is to increase output to the point where the system will power approximately 2,000 homes and businesses in Maine with clean tidal energy. ORPC has similar renewable energy generation projects under way in Alaska and Nova Scotia.[23] Similarly, overflowing landfills are an expensive challenge for many municipalities, but a growing number are seeing an opportunity in the form of energy generation. As garbage decomposes, it produces methane gas, which is used as a fuel to power generators. In East Brunswick, New Jersey, for example, the Edgeboro landfill generates electricity that powers the county's wastewater treatment plant.[24]

In some environments, it takes an especially creative mind to see opportunities among severe threats. For Farif Ali Abood, who opened a shop to make commercial signs in his hometown of Najaf, Iraq, the difficulties have included sporadic electrical service, lack of funds to borrow, and even occasional sniper fire in the area. Despite these challenges, Abood has managed to keep the business running by using a generator when the power goes out. As conditions in the city have stabilized, business has grown enough for Abood to hire several full-time employees and earn a modest profit.[25] The brave few who, like Abood, can fill needs amidst such difficult threats are well positioned to benefit from the business relationships they create with loyal customers.

Step 3: Analysis of Internal Strengths and Weaknesses

As managers conduct an external analysis, they will also assess the strengths and weaknesses of major functional areas inside their organization. Exhibit 4.8 lists some of the major components of this internal resource analysis. For example, is your firm strong enough financially to handle the lengthy and costly investment new projects often require? Can your existing staff carry out its part of the plan, or will additional training or hiring be needed? Is your firm's image compatible with the strategy, or will it have to persuade key

Financial Analysis
Examines financial strengths and weaknesses through financial statements such as a balance sheet and an income statement and compares trends to historical and industry figures (see Chapter 18).
Marketing Audit
Examines strengths and weaknesses of major marketing activities and identifies markets, key market segments, and the competitive position (market share) of the organization within key markets.
Operations Analysis
Examines the strengths and weaknesses of the manufacturing, production, or service delivery activities of the organization (see Chapters 9, 16, and 17).
Other Internal Resource Analyses
Examine, as necessary and appropriate, the strengths and weaknesses of other organizational activities, such as research and development (product and process), management information systems, engineering, and purchasing.
Human Resources Assessment
Examines strengths and weaknesses of all levels of management and employees and focuses on key human resources activities, including recruitment, selection, placement, training, labor (union) relationships, compensation, promotion, appraisal, quality of work life, and human resources planning (see Chapters 10 and 11).

EXHIBIT 4.8
Internal Resource
Analysis

122   Part Two   Planning: Delivering Strategic Value

stakeholders that a change in direction makes sense? This kind of internal analysis gives strategic decision makers an inventory of the organization's existing functions, skills, and resources as well as its overall performance level. Many of your other business courses will prepare you to conduct an internal analysis.

 Resources and Core Capabilities   Without question, strategic planning has been strongly influenced in recent years by a focus on internal resources. **Resources** are inputs to production (recall systems theory) that can be accumulated over time to enhance the performance of a firm. Resources can take many forms, but they tend to fall into two broad categories: (1) tangible assets such as real estate, production facilities, raw materials, and so on, and (2) intangible assets such as company reputation, culture, technical knowledge, and patents as well as accumulated learning and experience. The Walt Disney Company, for example, has developed its strategic plan on combinations of tangible assets (e.g., hotels and theme parks) as well as intangible assets (brand recognition, talented crafts-people, culture focused on customer service).[26]

resources

Inputs to a system that can enhance performance.

Effective internal analysis provides a clearer understanding of how a company can compete through its resources. Resources are a source of competitive advantage only under certain circumstances. First, if the resource is instrumental for creating customer value—that is, if it increases the benefits customers derive from a good or service relative to the costs they incur—the resource can lead to a competitive advantage.[27] For example, Amazon's powerful search technology and its ability to track customer preferences and offer personalized recommendations each time its site is accessed, as well as its quick product delivery system, are clearly valuable resources that enhance Amazon's competitiveness.

Second, resources are a source of advantage if they are rare and not equally available to all competitors. Even for extremely valuable resources, if all competitors have equal access, the resource cannot provide a source of competitive advantage. For companies such as W.L. Gore, Intel, DuPont, Dow Chemical, and others, patented formulas represent important resources that are both rare and valuable. Amazon, too, sought a patent for its one-click shopping technique.

Third, if resources are difficult to imitate, they provide a source of competitive advantage. Online retailer Zappos.com seeks a competitive advantage in the form of service that makes customers say "Wow!" The company hires customer service employees based on their match with its values, gives them seven weeks of training, and empowers them to do whatever it takes to delight a customer, whether that be spending hours on the phone, issuing a refund, or sending a package of free cookies. Zappos frees reps from using scripted replies, promotes positive relationships with colleagues through mentoring programs and fun activities, and provides on-site coaching to help employees achieve their career and personal goals.[28] As in this example, where success relies on a combination of hiring, training, motivation, and job design, not just a policy of free returns, resources tend to be harder to imitate if they are complex, with many interdependent variables and no obvious links between easily explained behaviors and desired outcomes.[29]

Bottom Line

Amazon's key customer benefits are speed and excellence of service. *What are some resources Amazon needs to deliver these benefits?*

Finally, resources can enhance a firm's competitive advantage when they are well organized. For example, Coca-Cola's well-organized and global network of bottlers allows the company to introduce a new soft drink worldwide quickly and to distribute it more efficiently than any competitor. IBM, known primarily for computer hardware until it became more of a commodity than a source of competitive advantage.

As shown in Exhibit 4.9, when resources are valuable, rare, inimitable, and organized, they can be viewed as a company's core capabilities. Simply stated, a **core capability** (also referred to as "competence") is something a company does especially well relative to its competitors. Honda, for example, has a core competence in small engine design and manufacturing; Netflix has a core competence in delivering Internet TV and movies; and Federal Express has a core competence in logistics and customer service. As in these examples, a core competence typically refers to a set of skills or expertise in some activity rather than physical or financial assets.

core capability

A unique skill and/or knowledge an organization possesses that gives it an edge over competitors.

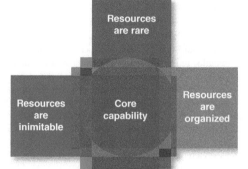

EXHIBIT 4.9
Resources and Core
Capability

Benchmarking   To assess and improve performance, some companies use benchmarking, the process of assessing how well one company's basic functions and skills compare with those of another company or set of companies. The goal of benchmarking is to understand the "best practices" of other firms thoroughly and to undertake actions to achieve both better performance and lower costs.

According to consulting firm Accenture, benchmarking consists of four stages:[30]

1. Decide what needs to be measured and which metrics will be used.
2. Collect and validate the data; compile initial findings.
3. Assess initial findings to see if additional data need to be collected.
4. Analyze results and make final recommendations to key stakeholders.

Benchmarking programs have helped a myriad of companies, such as Ford, Corning, Hewlett-Packard, Xerox, and Anheuser-Busch, make great strides in eliminating inefficiencies and improving competitiveness.

Depending on how it is applied, benchmarking may be of limited help in that it only helps a company perform as well as its competitors; strategic management ultimately is about surpassing those companies. Besides benchmarking against leading organizations in other industries, companies may address this problem by engaging in internal benchmarking. That approach involves benchmarking their different internal operations and departments against one another to disseminate the company's best practices throughout the organization and thereby gain a competitive advantage.

One company that has experienced the pros and cons of benchmarking is AXA Canada, an insurance company. The company turned to benchmarking as a way to identify how it could improve its processes and lower its costs. AXA Canada used internal benchmarking to compare results among its regions. However, employees objected that in a country as vast as Canada, the differences among regions were so great that performance couldn't really be compared. More energy went to arguing about the numbers than looking for ways to close performance gaps. The company made similar efforts to compare Canadian performance with insurers in other countries, and it ran into even greater difficulty making comparisons. The most success came from an arrangement with the Ward Group to gather performance data from several insurance companies, analyze it, and report on areas of strength and weakness. Using this benchmarking information, AXA Canada has found areas where it can operate more efficiently by applying other companies' practices. The company uses the benchmarking data primarily for cutting costs and identifying potential new markets.[31]

Bottom Line

Aligning a firm's bottom-line practices with best practices can improve its competitiveness.
In some famous benchmarking examples, businesses have learned from pit crews for race car teams. What kinds of bottom-line practices could such an organization demonstrate?

Step 4: SWOT Analysis and Strategy Formulation

Once managers have analyzed the external environment and the internal resources of the organization, they will have the information they need to assess the organization's strengths, weaknesses, opportunities, and threats. Such an assessment normally is referred to as a **SWOT analysis.** Strengths and weaknesses refer to internal resources. For example, an organization's strengths might include skilled management, positive cash flow, and well-known and highly regarded brands. Weaknesses might be lack of spare production capacity and the absence of reliable suppliers. Opportunities and threats arise in the macroenvironment and competitive environment. Examples of opportunities are a new technology that could make the supply chain more efficient and a market niche that is currently underserved. Threats might include the possibility that competitors will enter the underserved niche once it has been shown to be profitable.

SWOT analysis helps managers summarize the relevant, important facts from their external and internal analyses. Based on this summary, they can identify the primary and secondary strategic issues their organization faces. The managers then formulate a strategy that will build on the SWOT analysis to take advantage of available opportunities by capitalizing on the organization's strengths, neutralizing its weakness, and countering potential threats.

To take an example, David Handmaker enjoyed several years of unfettered growth since opening his printing company, Next Day Flyers, in Los Angeles in 2004. However, over time he noticed that his competitors were more adept at finding and serving online customers. Handmaker needed a plan to restore healthy business growth by migrating parts of his marketing and printing services online before it was too late. But, Next Day Flyers originally aimed at local customers, which raised questions about whether the company could serve the needs of geographically dispersed customers.

Handmaker and his team need to analyze what the firm does well and in what areas it needs improvement relative to the printing marketplace. Exhibit 4.10 summarizes these points in a format commonly used for a basic SWOT analysis. The company's strategy

SWOT analysis

A comparison of strengths, weaknesses, opportunities, and threats that helps executives formulate strategy.

EXHIBIT 4.10

Sample SWOT Analysis:
Next Day Flyers

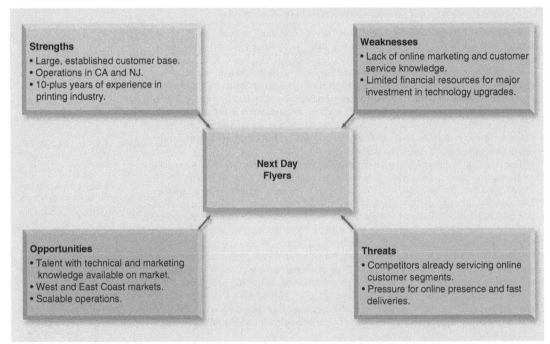

Strengths
- Large, established customer base.
- Operations in CA and NJ.
- 10-plus years of experience in printing industry.

Weaknesses
- Lack of online marketing and customer service knowledge.
- Limited financial resources for major investment in technology upgrades.

Next Day Flyers

Opportunities
- Talent with technical and marketing knowledge available on market.
- West and East Coast markets.
- Scalable operations.

Threats
- Competitors already servicing online customer segments.
- Pressure for online presence and fast deliveries.

SOURCE: Based on information from R. Myers, "That Sounds Like a Plan," *Inc.*, no. 36 (2014), pp. 90–92; and Next Day Flyers company website, "About Next Day Flyers," http://www.nextdayflyers.com.

Multiple Generations at Work

Perceived Strengths and Weaknesses of Each Generation

Ernst & Young, an accounting and consulting firm, recently asked managers and employees across multiple generations and industries to describe the strengths and weaknesses commonly associated with workers from other generational cohorts. The following exhibit includes some of the findings:

Baby Boomers	Gen Xers	Millennials
Strengths • Loyal • Mentoring others • Hardworking **Weaknesses** • Slower to adapt to change and collaborate with others	**Strengths** • Revenue generators • Adaptable • Problem-solvers **Weaknesses** • Displaying executive presence and being cost effective	**Strengths** • Tech savvy • Skilled at leveraging social media • Enthusiastic **Weaknesses** • Team player and hardworking

The results reflect respondents' perceptions of the strengths and weaknesses of different generations at work. Of course, caution is advised when generalizing to all members of a given generation of workers. However, when individuals do a self-SWOT analysis, they may want to compare their results to those of the stereotypical traits identified above. This information may prove useful for overcoming or leveraging stereotypes. If a Millennial has a track record of being hardworking (e.g., working full-time while in college to pay for tuition), then the individual should highlight this fact during interviews. Gen Xers who want to advance into executive positions may want to observe how current executives dress, communicate, plan, and make decisions. A Boomer can overcome the stereotype of being slow to adapt to change by embracing new technology at work.[32]

calls for it to hire talent with the skills, knowledge, and experience to help Next Day Flyers establish a professional presence on the web, including simple online ordering; free online design services; free printing templates; blog with design and marketing tips; and customer support by phone, e-mail, and live chat.[33]

In the real world, as a company is formulating strategy, so are its competitors. As a result, the process must be continually evolving through contingency planning. The more uncertainty that exists in the external environment, the more the strategy needs to focus on building internal capabilities through practices such as knowledge sharing and continuous process improvement.[34] Yet at a basic level, strategy formulation moves from analysis to devising a coherent course of action. In this way, the organization's online customer engagement will keep Next Day Flyers competitive.

Before we continue our strategy discussion, we note that many individuals seeking a job or a career change can find a self-SWOT analysis helpful. What are you particularly good at? What weaknesses might you need to overcome to improve your employment chances? What firms offer the best opportunity to market your skills to full advantage? How are individuals from your generation perceived in the workplace (see the nearby "Multiple Generations at Work" box)? Will you have a lot of competition from other job seekers? As with companies, this kind of analysis can be the beginning of a plan of action and can improve the plan's effectiveness.

corporate strategy

The set of businesses, markets, or industries in which an organization competes and the distribution of resources among those entities.

Corporate Strategy   A **corporate strategy** identifies the set of businesses, markets, or industries in which the organization competes and the distribution of resources among those businesses. Exhibit 4.11 shows four basic alternatives for a corporate strategy,

126   Part Two   Planning: Delivering Strategic Value

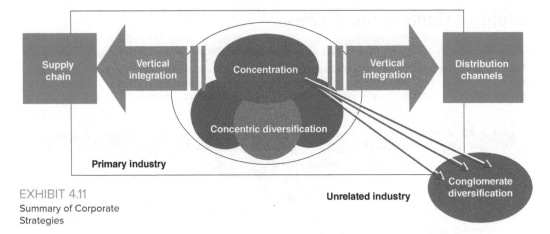

EXHIBIT 4.11
Summary of Corporate
Strategies

concentration

A strategy employed
for an organization that
operates a single business
and competes in a single
industry.

vertical integration

The acquisition or
development of new
businesses that produce
parts or components of the
organization's product.

concentric diversification

A strategy used to add new
businesses that produce
related products or are
involved in related markets
and activities.

**conglomerate
diversification**

A strategy used to add new
businesses that produce
unrelated products or
are involved in unrelated
markets and activities.

ranging from very specialized to highly diverse. A **concentration** strategy focuses on a single business competing in a single industry. In the food retailing industry, Kroger, Safeway, and A&P all pursue concentration strategies. Frequently, companies pursue concentration strategies to gain entry into an industry when industry growth is good or when the company has a narrow range of competencies. An example is C. F. Martin & Company, which pursues a concentration strategy by focusing on making the best possible guitars and guitar strings, a strategy that has enabled the family-owned business to operate successfully for more than 150 years.

A **vertical integration** strategy involves expanding the domain of the organization into supply channels or to distributors. At one time, Henry Ford had fully integrated his company from the ore mines needed to make steel all the way to the showrooms where his cars were sold. Vertical integration generally is used to eliminate uncertainties and reduce costs associated with suppliers or distributors.

A strategy of **concentric diversification** involves moving into new businesses that are related to the company's original core business. William Marriott expanded his original restaurant business outside Washington, DC, by moving into airline catering, hotels, and fast food. Each of these businesses within the hospitality industry is related in terms of the services it provides, the skills necessary for success, and the customers it attracts. Often companies such as Marriott pursue a strategy of concentric diversification to take advantage of their strengths in one business to gain advantage in another. Because the businesses are related, the products, markets, technologies, or capabilities used in one business can be transferred to another. Success in a concentric diversification strategy requires adequate management and other resources for operating more than one business. Guitar maker C. F. Martin once tried expanding through purchases of other instrument companies, but management was stretched too thin to run them all well, so the company eventually divested the acquisitions and returned to its concentration strategy.[35]

In contrast to concentric diversification, **conglomerate diversification** is a corporate strategy that involves expansion into unrelated businesses. For example, General Electric Corporation has diversified from its original base in electrical and home appliance products to such wide-ranging industries as health, finance, insurance, truck and air transportation, and even media with its ownership of NBC (now owned with Comcast). Typically, companies pursue a conglomerate diversification strategy to minimize risks due to market fluctuations in one industry.

The diversified businesses of an organization are sometimes called its business *portfolio*. One of the most popular techniques for analyzing a corporation's strategy for managing its portfolio is the BCG matrix, developed by the Boston Consulting Group. The BCG matrix is shown in Exhibit 4.12. Each business in the corporation is plotted on the matrix

EXHIBIT 4.12

Mapping GE's Business Units and Product Lines to the BCG Matrix

		Strong	Weak
Market growth	**High**	**Stars** Energy Health care Transportation	**Question marks** Wind farms
	Low	**Cash cows** Turbines Jet engines	**Dogs** NBC Universal GE Capital

Relative competitive position

on the basis of the growth rate of its market and the relative strength of its competitive position in that market (market share). The business is represented by a circle whose size depends on the business's contribution to corporate revenues.

High-growth, weak-competitive-position businesses are called *question marks.* They require substantial investment to improve their position; otherwise divestiture is recommended. High-growth, strong-competitive-position businesses are called *stars.* These businesses require heavy investment, but their strong position allows them to generate the needed revenues. Low-growth, strong-competitive-position businesses are called *cash cows.* These businesses generate revenues in excess of their investment needs and therefore fund other businesses. Finally, low-growth, weak-competitive-position businesses are called *dogs.* The remaining revenues from these businesses are realized, and then the businesses are divested.

The BCG matrix is not intended as a substitute for management judgment, creativity, insight, or leadership. But it is a tool that can, along with other techniques, help managers of the firm as a whole and of its individual businesses evaluate their strategy alternatives.[36] This approach can help a company such as General Electric that needs to weigh the relative merits of many business units and product lines. When GE struggled to generate acceptable returns in some of its widely diversified businesses, such as NBC Universal and GE Capital, the company refocused on its strength as a manufacturer, targeting three industries: energy, health care, and transportation. Not only do these industries offer significant growth potential, but GE already dominates the markets for electric turbines and jet engines. Therefore, besides selling the NBC unit and scaling back the financial business, GE has acquired wind farms in Europe and purchased Avio, an Italian aerospace company with jet engine expertise and customers beyond the aviation industry.[37]

Trends in Corporate Strategy   Corporate America is periodically swept by waves of mergers and acquisitions (M&As). The targets chosen for mergers and acquisitions depend on the organization's corporate strategy of either concentrating in one industry or diversifying its portfolio. Many recent deals have been aimed at helping companies expand their market share and product offerings within related industries. For example, General Electric's acquisition of France-based Alstom gives the American company access to nuclear plant servicing technology and renewable energy assets in Europe. By purchasing DirecTV, AT&T gained 38 million customers in the United States and Latin America. Holcim's acquisition of Lafarge will create the largest cement manufacturer in the world.[38]

Bottom Line

Companies that integrate vertically often do so to reduce their costs. *Why might buying from a division of your company be less costly than buying on the open market?*

128   Part Two   Planning: Delivering Strategic Value

The value of implementing a diversified corporate strategy depends on individual circumstances. Many critics have argued that unrelated diversification hurts a company more often than it helps it. In recent years, many diversified companies have sold their peripheral businesses so they could concentrate on a more focused portfolio. In contrast, the diversification efforts of an organization competing in a slow-growth, mature, or threatened industry often are applauded.

Within the various types of corporate strategies, other trends are shaping the ways that today's companies are seeking growth. One major trend affecting almost every company's strategy is the degree to which business today takes place across national boundaries. Today, there is hardly any organization that does not buy at least some of its supplies and equipment from, or sell at least some of its products to, individuals and organizations in other countries. In terms of strategy, companies are often finding the best opportunities for growth where economies are expanding the fastest, as in Brazil, India, and China. Chapter 6 explores this trend, known as globalization.

Other trends are related to the business arrangements used to carry out the strategy. Rather than expanding through organic growth—that is, adding employees, equipment, offices, and so on—an organization can find a partner that already has the expertise it needs in a particular market, technology, or product. Choosing such partners in support of a strategy and entering a business arrangement with them can be called a joint venture, strategic partnership, or strategic alliance, depending on the details of the arrangement. Chapter 9 describes how some organizations use strategic alliances to become more agile, and Chapter 17 tells how joint ventures can give companies quick access to new technology.

business strategy

The major actions by which a business competes in a particular industry or market.

Business Strategy   After the top management team and board make the corporate strategic decisions, executives must determine how they will compete in each business area. **Business strategy** defines the major actions by which an organization builds and strengthens its competitive position in the marketplace. A competitive advantage typically results from one of two generic business strategies introduced here and elaborated in Chapter 7.[39]

First, organizations such as Walmart and Southwest Airlines pursue competitive advantage through **low-cost strategies.** Businesses using a low-cost strategy attempt to be efficient and offer a standard, no-frills product. Walmart Stores expresses its low-price strategy with the slogan "save money, live better." The company uses the power of its giant size to negotiate favorable prices from suppliers, enabling it to sell at prices below those of most competing retailers. Recently, when gasoline prices soared, the company promoted its stores as a place where consumers can save on transportation costs by purchasing everything they need at low prices in one trip.[40] Companies that succeed with a low-cost strategy often are large and try to take advantage of economies of scale in production or distribution. In many cases, their scale allows them to buy and sell their goods and services at a lower price, which leads to higher market share, volume, and ultimately profits. To succeed, an organization using this strategy generally must be the cost leader in its industry or market segment. However, even a cost leader must offer a product that is acceptable to customers compared with competitors' products.

Second, an organization may pursue a **differentiation strategy.** With a differentiation strategy, a company attempts to be unique in its industry or market segment along some dimensions that customers value. This unique or differentiated position within the industry often is based on high product quality, excellent marketing and distribution, or superior service.

Nordstrom's commitment to quality and customer service in the retail apparel industry is an excellent example of a differentiation strategy. For example, Nordstrom's personal shoppers are available online, by phone, or in stores to select items for shoppers' consideration at no charge. Innovation, too, is an important ingredient of a differentiation strategy. In the market for toilet paper, Scott Paper Company once determined that it could not afford to compete for institutional sales based on price. Instead, the company began

low-cost strategy

A strategy an organization uses to build competitive advantage by being efficient and offering a standard, no-frills product.

differentiation strategy

A strategy an organization uses to build competitive advantage by being unique in its industry or market segment along one or more dimensions.

Bottom Line

Low-price strategies usually require low production costs. *How do you think Walmart keeps costs low?*

offering institutions a free dispenser that would hold larger rolls of paper, saving its customers the labor cost of replacing empty rolls more frequently. Scott initially was the only company selling the larger rolls, so it gained market share while competitors scrambled to catch up.[41]

Whatever strategy managers adopt, the most effective strategy is one that competitors are unwilling or unable to imitate. If the organization's strategic plan is one that could easily be adopted by industry competitors, it may not be sufficiently distinctive or, in the long run, contribute significantly to the organization's competitiveness. For example, a strategy to gain market share and profits by being the first mover to offer an innovative product may or may not succeed, depending in part on competitive responses. In some industries, such as computers, technology advances so fast that the first company to provide a new product is quickly challenged by later entrants offering superior products.[42]

Functional Strategy   The final step in strategy formulation is to establish the major functional strategies. **Functional strategies** are implemented by each functional area of the organization to support the business strategy. The typical functional areas include production, human resources, marketing, research and development, finance, and distribution. For example, Bloomin' Brands, the parent company of restaurant chains including Outback Steakhouse, Bonefish Grill, and Carrabba's Italian Grill, recently set a business strategy with targets for aggressive growth and greater efficiency built on the chains' reputation for offering good food at affordable prices. To achieve this, functional strategies include creation of a lunch menu, methods aimed at improving the productivity of its employees, and deals signed in advance for large purchases of beef, a major expense for the Outback restaurants. Another functional strategy is the use of a team of data analysts to keep an eye on consumer behavior, environmental trends, and other information that can support informed decisions about menu items, new restaurant locations, and more.[43]

Functional strategies typically are developed by functional area executives with input of and approval from the executives responsible for business strategy. Senior strategic decision makers review the functional strategies to ensure that each major department is operating consistently with the business strategies of the organization. For example, automated production techniques—even if they saved money—would not be appropriate for a piano company like Steinway, whose products are strategically positioned (and priced) as high-quality and handcrafted. At companies that compete based on product innovation, strategies for research and development are especially critical. But in the recession of 2001, General Electric cut back on research in lighting technology just as other companies were making advances in LED lighting. When the economy recovered, customers were looking for innovative lighting, but GE had fallen behind. Based on that experience, GE committed itself to an R&D strategy of maintaining budgets even when sales slow down. In the latest economic downturn, the company continued to fund a project in which it developed new aircraft engines with Honda Motor Company.[44]

functional strategies

Strategies implemented by each functional area of the organization to support the organization's business strategy.

Employees at Bonefish Grill strive to meet the company's business strategy to achieve greater efficiency.
© *Mark Gail/The Washington Post/ Getty Images*

Step 5: Strategy Implementation

As with any plan, simply formulating a good strategy is not enough. Strategic managers also must ensure that the new strategies are implemented effectively and efficiently. Recently, corporations and strategy consultants have been paying more attention to implementation. They realize that clever techniques and a good plan do not guarantee success. This greater appreciation is reflected in two major trends.

First, organizations are adopting a more comprehensive view of implementation. Successful strategy execution depends on building human and organizational resources

130   Part Two   Planning: Delivering Strategic Value

EXHIBIT 4.13
4 A's Model of Execution
Capability

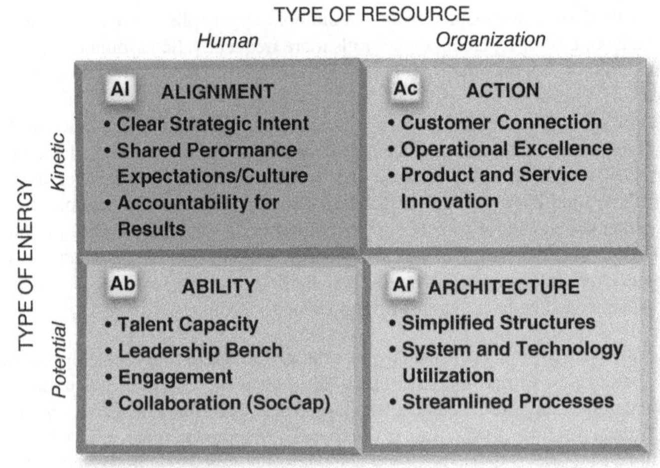

SOURCE: Carrig, Snell, and Onozuka (2014).

that can be energized to achieve organizational goals. Exhibit 4.13 suggests that energy is either potential or kinetic (in motion) in nature. When applied to human or organizational resources, four "A's" result: ability and architecture are sources of potential energy, while alignment and activation are sources of kinetic energy that sparks performance.[45]

Second, many organizations are extending the more participative strategic management process to implementation. Managers at all levels are involved with formulating strategy and identifying and executing ways to implement it. Senior executives still may oversee the implementation process, but they are placing much greater responsibility and authority in the hands of others. In general, strategy implementation involves four related steps:

Step 1: Define strategic tasks. Articulate in simple language what a particular business must do to create or sustain a competitive advantage. Define strategic tasks to help employees understand how they contribute to the organization, including redefining relationships among the parts of the organization.

Step 2: Assess organization capabilities. Evaluate the organization's ability to implement the strategic tasks. A task force typically interviews employees and managers to identify specific issues that help or hinder effective implementation. Then the results are summarized for top management. In the course of your career, you will likely be asked to participate in a task force. We discuss working effectively in teams in Chapter 14.

Step 3: Develop an implementation agenda. Management decides how it will change its own activities and procedures; how critical interdependencies will be managed; what skills and individuals are needed in key roles; and what structures, measures, information, and rewards might ultimately support the needed behavior. A philosophy statement, communicated in terms of value, is the outcome of this process.

Step 4: Create an implementation plan. The top management team, the employee task force, and others develop the implementation plan. The top management team then monitors progress. The employee task force continues its work by providing feedback about how others in the organization are responding to the changes.

This process, though straightforward, does not always go smoothly. Exhibit 4.14 shows six barriers to strategy implementation and provides a description of some key principles for overcoming these silent killers. By paying closer attention to the processes by which strategies are implemented, executives, managers, and employees can make sure that strategic plans are actually carried out.[46]

EXHIBIT 4.14

Attacking the Six Barriers to Strategy Implementation

Change starts with the leader	
The Silent Killers	**Principles for Engaging and Changing the Silent Killers**
Top-down or laissez-faire senior management style	With the top team and lower levels, the CEO/general manager creates a partnership built around the development of a compelling business direction, the creation of an enabling organizational context, and the delegation of authority to clearly accountable individuals and teams.
Unclear strategy and conflicting priorities	The top team, as a group, develops a statement of strategy, and priorities that members are willing to stand behind are developed.
An ineffective senior management team	The top team, as a group, is involved in all steps in the change process so that its effectiveness is tested and developed.
Poor vertical communication	An honest, fact-based dialogue is established with lower levels about the new strategy and the barriers to implementing it.
Poor coordination across functions, businesses, or borders	A set of businesswide initiatives and new organizational roles and responsibilities are defined that require "the right people to work together on the right things in the right way" to implement the strategy.
Inadequate down-the-line leadership skills and development	Lower-level managers develop skills through newly created opportunities to lead change and drive key business initiatives. They are supported with just-in-time coaching, training, and targeted recruitment. Those who still are not able to make the grade must be replaced.

SOURCE: From M. Beer and R. A Eisenstat, "The Silent Killers of Strategy Implementation and Learning Barriers," *MIT Sloan Management Review*, Summer 2000, Vol. 4 #4, pp. 29–40. Copyright © 2000 by Massachusetts Institute of Technology. All rights reserved. Distributed by Tribune Media Services.

Step 6: Strategic Control

The final component of the strategic management process is strategic control. A **strategic control system** is designed to support managers in evaluating the organization's progress with its strategy and, when discrepancies exist, taking corrective action. The system must encourage efficient operations that are consistent with the plan while allowing flexibility to adapt to changing conditions. As with all control systems, the organization must develop performance indicators, an information system, and specific mechanisms to monitor progress. Spirit Airlines has a low-cost strategy, captured in the "Bare Fare" flights slogan, that depends on cutting costs wherever possible so the airline can remain profitable while winning passengers with the lowest fare. According to Spirit's CEO, Ben Baldanza, this makes productivity a key performance indicator for every function. For example, the company purchases airplanes with the maximum number of seats allowed by the Federal Aviation Administration, so it minimizes the amount of fuel required to transport each passenger. In marketing, Spirit relies heavily on e-mail advertising because that medium costs relatively little, yet recipients will pass along messages they find funny or thought-provoking.[47]

strategic control system

A system designed to support managers in evaluating the organization's progress regarding its strategy and, when discrepancies exist, taking corrective action.

Management in Action

WALT DISNEY COMPANY'S STRATEGY UNDER ROBERT IGER

Reportedly, Walt Disney Company's mission statement once was "Make people happy." The corporate website now offers a longer statement: "to be one of the world's leading producers and providers of entertainment and information, using its portfolio of brands to differentiate its content, services and consumer products." The statement adds, "The company's primary financial goals are to maximize earnings and cash flow, and to allocate capital toward growth initiatives that will drive long-term shareholder value."

In pursuit of this two-part objective, Disney has made decisions about its large portfolio of businesses. As it repositions itself for a global marketplace and a social, mobile Internet, it continues making strategic decisions about where to invest and what to divest.

Disney's largest sources of revenues are cable networks and theme parks, with cable providing by far the greatest profits. ESPN alone delivers 45 percent of operating income. Recently, Disney entered into a media rights contract with the NFL and a deal to air NBA games on ESPN and ABC. The company has rolled out apps based on WatchESPN to let cable subscribers watch programming on mobile devices. In the theme park arena, profitability during a sluggish economy lets Disney build when construction costs are low, so it has renovated Disney California Adventure, expanded Hong Kong Disneyland, and added a cruise ship to its fleet. In 2016, it plans to open a theme park in Shanghai, China.

Disney Interactive is by far the smallest business unit in terms of revenues and has not been profitable. Still, it

matters because children are spending ever more time online, and winning the hearts of children has been the basis for the company's growth. Disney Interactive will continue to engage fans through mobile games like Frozen Free Fall and Disney Tsum Tsum, as well as connect with parents via Disney.com.

Disney's movie studios, though a relatively small unit, are a core business. To increase the brand's appeal with teenage boys, this unit purchased Lucasfilm, producer of *Star Wars*. Disney also signed a deal giving Netflix the right to stream movies soon after release on DVD, when cable channels air movies. Dealing directly with Netflix signals that movie streaming is an important trend for Disney. And Disney created Keychest, which gives buyers of its DVDs and Blu-ray discs automatic access to streamed versions.

China is a huge growth market, so Iger is heavily investing in a new theme park, Shanghai Disney. The venture is risky; Disney's resort in Hong Kong is just breaking even after a 2005 opening. But it offers access to a billion consumers, and the effort is supported by use of the Disney Channel to build consumer relationships in China and 166 other countries.[48]

- How clear is Walt Disney Company's mission? How well does its strategy support the mission?
- In the BCG matrix (see again Exhibit 4.12), where would you place Disney's main businesses? How well is Disney matching its strategic moves to businesses' positions in the matrix?

Bottom Line

Firms that follow low-cost strategies exert downward pressure on competitors' prices.
What is the best way to compete against a low-cost strategy so that a firm can continue to charge higher prices for its products or services?

Most strategic control systems include a budget to monitor and control major financial expenditures. In fact, as a first-time manager, you will most likely confront your work unit's budget—a key aspect of your organization's strategic plan. Your executive team may give you budget assumptions and targets for your area, reflecting your part in the overall plan, and you may be asked to revise your budget once all the budgets in your organization have been consolidated and reviewed.

The dual responsibilities of a control system—efficiency and flexibility—often seem contradictory with respect to budgets. The budget usually establishes spending limits, but changing conditions or the need for innovation may require different financial commitments during the period. To solve this dilemma, some companies have created two budgets: strategic and operational. For example, managers at Texas Instruments control two budgets under the OST (objectives–strategies–tactics) system. The strategic budget is used to create and maintain long-term effectiveness, and the operational budget is tightly monitored to achieve short-term efficiency. In "Management in Action: Onward," consider the significance of budgets and budgetary controls to Disney's decisions about its portfolio of businesses. The topic of control in general—and budgets in particular—is discussed in more detail in Chapter 16.

KEY TERMS

RETAINING WHAT YOU LEARNED

In Chapter 4, you learned that managerial planning is a conscious, systematic process of deciding which goals and activities the organization will pursue in the future. Directed and controlled by managers, this purposeful effort draws on the experience and knowledge of employees throughout the organization. As shown in Exhibit 4.1, general decision making is linked closely to the formal planning process. Strategic planning should be integrated with tactical and operational planning. Before formulating a strategy, managers should analyze the external environment and internal resources, such as core capabilities. Corporate strategies can be narrow, or include suppliers and buyers. A firm may broaden its strategy via related or unrelated diversification. Companies can achieve competitive advantage by being unique and differentiated, or by focusing on efficiency and lower prices. Effective implementation is critical to the success of any strategy.

LO 1 **Summarize the basic steps in any planning process.**

- The planning process begins with a situation analysis of the external and internal forces affecting the

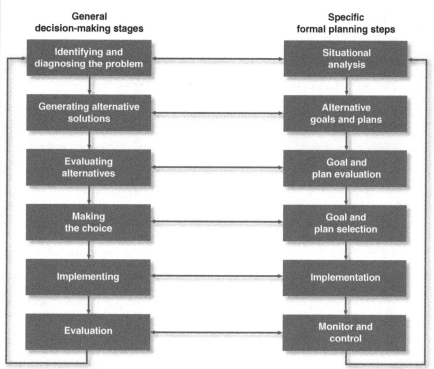

General decision-making stages

- Identifying and diagnosing the problem
- Generating alternative solutions
- Evaluating alternatives
- Making the choice
- Implementing
- Evaluation

Specific formal planning steps

- Situational analysis
- Alternative goals and plans
- Goal and plan evaluation
- Goal and plan selection
- Implementation
- Monitor and control

EXHIBIT 4.1

Decision-Making Stages (Chapter 3) and Formal Planning Steps (Chapter 4) organization. This examination helps identify and diagnose issues and problems and may bring to the surface alternative goals and plans for the firm.

- The advantages and disadvantages of these goals and plans should be evaluated against one another.
- Once a set of goals and a plan have been selected, implementation involves communicating the plan to employees, allocating resources, and making certain that other systems such as rewards and budgets support the plan.
- Planning requires instituting control systems to monitor progress toward the goals.

LO 2   Describe how strategic planning should be integrated with tactical and operational planning.

- Strategic planning is different from operational planning in that it involves making long-term decisions about the entire organization.
- Tactical planning translates broad goals and strategies into specific actions to be taken within parts of the organization.
- Operational planning identifies the specific short-term procedures and processes required at lower levels of the organization.

LO 3   Identify elements of the external environment and internal resources of the firm to analyze before formulating a strategy.

- Strategic planning is designed to leverage the strengths of a firm while minimizing the effects of its weaknesses.
- It is difficult to know the potential advantage a firm may have unless external analysis is done well. For example, a company may have a talented marketing department or an efficient production system.
- However, the organization cannot determine whether these internal characteristics are sources of competitive advantage until it knows something about how well the competitors stack up in these areas.

LO 4   Define core capabilities and explain how they provide the foundation for business strategy.

- A core competence is something a company does especially well relative to its competitors.
- When this competence, say, in engineering or marketing, is in some area important to market success, it becomes the foundation for developing a competitive advantage.
- It can provide a sustainable advantage if it is valuable, rare, difficult to imitate, and well organized.

LO 5   Summarize the types of choices available for corporate strategy.

- Corporate strategy identifies the breadth of a firm's competitive domain.
- Corporate strategy can be kept narrow, as in a concentration strategy, or can move to suppliers and buyers via vertical integration.
- Corporate strategy also can broaden a firm's domain via concentric (related) diversification or conglomerate (unrelated) diversification.

LO 6   Discuss how companies can achieve competitive advantage through business strategy.

- Companies gain competitive advantage in two primary ways. They can attempt to be unique in some way by pursuing a differentiation strategy, or they can focus on efficiency and price by pursuing a low-cost strategy.

LO 7   Describe the keys to effective strategy implementation.

- Many good plans are doomed to failure because they are not implemented correctly.
- Strategy must be supported by structure, technology, human resources, rewards, information systems, culture, leadership, and so on.
- Ultimately, the success of a plan depends on how well employees at low levels are able and willing to implement it.
- Participative management is one of the more popular approaches executives use to gain employees' input and ensure their commitment to strategy implementation.

DISCUSSION QUESTIONS

1. This chapter opened with a quote from former CEO of GE Jack Welch: "Manage your destiny, or someone else will." What does this mean for strategic management? What does it mean when Welch adds, "or someone else will"?

2. List the six steps in the formal planning process. Suppose you are a top executive of a home improvement chain and you want to launch a new company website. Provide examples of activities you would carry out during each step to create the site.

3. Your friend is frustrated because he's having trouble selecting a career. He says, "I can't plan because the future is too complicated. Anything can happen, and

there are too many choices." What would you say to him to change his mind?

4. How do strategic, operational, and tactical planning differ? How might the three levels complement one another in an organization?

5. How might an organization such as Urban Outfitters use a strategy map? With your classmates and using Exhibit 4.5 as a guide, develop a possible strategy map for the company.

6. What accounts for the shift from strategic planning to strategic management? In which industries would you be most likely to observe these trends? Why?

7. Review Exhibit 4.7, which lists the components of an environmental analysis. Why would this analysis be important to a company's strategic planning process?

8. In your opinion, what are the core capabilities of Harley-Davidson Motor Company motorcycles? How do these capabilities help Harley-Davidson compete against foreign competitors such as Yamaha and Suzuki?

9. How could SWOT analysis help newspaper companies remain competitive in the new media environment?

10. What are the key challenges in strategy implementation? What barriers might prevent strategy implementation?

EXPERIENTIAL EXERCISES

4.1 BUSINESS STRATEGIES NEED ADJUSTING

OBJECTIVE

To study why and how a company adjusts its business strategy to adapt to changing external environments.

INSTRUCTIONS

Using an Internet browser or a college's library research portal, identify a recent article from such business news outlets as *The Wall Street Journal, Bloomberg Business, Forbes,* or *Fast Company* that describes a company that is changing its short-and long-term business strategies. Please read the article and provide answers the following questions:

1. How would you describe the company's former business strategy?

_____

_____

_____

_____

_____

_____

_____

_____

2. Why is the company changing its strategy? What external forces are encouraging it to change?

_____

_____

_____

_____

_____

_____

_____

_____

3. How would you describe the new business strategy?

_____

_____

_____

_____

_____

_____

_____

_____

4. What strategic goals or major targets does the company hope to achieve?

_____

_____

_____

_____

_____

_____

_____

5. How does the company intend to translate its new strategic goals into tactical or operational plans? Which levels of management will carry out these plans?

_____

_____

_____

_____

_____

_____

_____

6. To what extent do you think the new strategy will be successful in addressing or adapting to the external forces? Explain.

_____

_____

_____

_____

_____

_____

_____

_____

SOURCE: Adapted from R. R. McGrath Jr., *Exercises in Management Fundamentals*, 1st, p. 15.

CONCLUDING CASE

WISH YOU WOOD TOY STORE

Wish You Wood is a toy boutique located in the main shopping strip of a resort town near Piney Lake. People who own cabins near the lake or come to visit the local state park enjoy browsing through the town's stores, where they pick up pottery, landscape paintings, and Wish You Wood's beautifully crafted wooden toys. For these shoppers, Wish You Wood is more than a store; it is a destination they associate with family and fun.

The store's owners, Jim and Pam Klein, personally select the toys from craftspeople and toymakers around the world. They enjoy their regular customers but believe selling mostly to vacationers has limited the company's growth.

They decided that the lowest-cost way to expand would be to sell toys online. However, after several years, they had to admit that traffic to the store's website was unimpressive. Thanks to e-mail and Facebook reminders, they were luring some of their loyal in-store shoppers to the site to make off-season purchases, but few other people looking for toys ever found Wish You Wood online.

Jim and Pam concluded that the next-best way to sell online would be to partner with Amazon.com. Amazon's Marketplace service lets other retailers sell products on Amazon. The Kleins signed an agreement to list the store's most popular items with Amazon. For example, if a shopper is searching for wooden dollhouses, Wish You Wood's doll-houses will be included in the search results. A customer who chooses to buy from Wish You Wood places the order right on Amazon's website. Under Amazon's participation agreement, the listings must be honest and may not link to Wish You Wood's own website or invite phone calls from customers. In exchange for giving the products exposure on the site, Amazon charges a monthly fee plus a commission on each sale.

Initially, Jim and Pam were thrilled about their decision to partner with Amazon. They tracked each month's sales and compared them with in-store sales. In the first five months, sales jumped 45 percent, mainly because of sales on Amazon. Then, suddenly, sales of popular toy train sets, which were particularly profitable, stopped alto-gether. Puzzled, Jim visited Amazon to make sure the train sets were still listed. To his surprise, he found that the train set was there, at the usual price of $149, listed right after the same set available directly from Amazon, at $129. He and Pam concluded that shoppers were now buying the product directly from Amazon. It appeared that their store had helped Amazon identify a product consumers value.

The Kleins worried that they needed a new strategy. If they matched Amazon's price, they would lose most of the profit on their most popular items. Wish You Wood was too small of a business to negotiate better prices from its suppliers. If the store didn't match Amazon's price, it would continue to lose sales at the Amazon site. Jim and Pam won-dered whether they should pull out of Amazon altogether or find a way to continue working with the partner that had become a competitor. They also considered rethinking which toys to offer on Amazon.

DISCUSSION QUESTIONS

1. Prepare a SWOT analysis for Wish You Wood, based on the information given.
2. Using the SWOT analysis, what general corporate strat-egy would you recommend for Wish You Wood? Should the store continue or change its current approach?

CHAPTER 14

Marketing

Chapter contents

❖ LEARNING OBJECTIVES

After reading this chapter you should understand some of the purposes and the position of the marketing function within organisations. You should be familiar with ways of analysing markets and understand the ideas behind the marketing mix. You should also be familiar with some of the general criticisms of the marketing function. In particular you should be able to:

* ❖ **define** both markets and marketing and explain key terms such as size, niches, segmentation and relationship marketing

* ❖ **explain** concepts such as competition, barriers to entry and exit and market dynamism

* ❖ **discuss in detail** market strategy and market positioning

* ❖ **contrast** briefly markets research and marketing research

* ❖ **list** seven uses and four methods of market research

* ❖ **discuss in detail** each of the five main components of the marketing mix

* ❖ **differentiate** between marketing and public relations

* ❖ **outline** some of the techniques and methods used in advertising

* ❖ **evaluate** at least four criticisms of marketing

In theory at least, marketing has prime place in the sequence of management functions because it identifies needs an organisation can exploit with a product or service. Once this need has been recognised, the other functions – operations, human resource management (HRM), finance function, etc. – can work together to produce the product or service. In fact, the marketing function also plays an important part at the end of the process – selling the finished product. Some people find it difficult to distinguish between marketing and sales. As a simplification, marketing is "having something you can get rid of" while selling is "getting rid of what you have!"

CASE 14.1: *Marketing Red Bull*

You are late for a lecture, and feeling exhausted after last night's party. What you need is a pick-me-up. You pop into the nearest corner shop and scan the fridge which is full of cans of various fizzy drinks. You soon see that the shop has a promotion on a brand of cola (buy one get one free), but it's not your preferred choice. Luckily, it does sell your favourite energy drink which you eagerly buy, even though the smaller can represents relatively poor value. After a few swigs, the caffeine kicks in and you're feeling almost human again.

When you're shopping like this, do you ever wonder why does this shop sell one type of fizzy drink but not another? Do you wonder why they packaged the drinks in that way, or why one costs more than another? All these decisions have been made as part of somebody's marketing strategy, involving a complex mix of pricing, competition, promotion and positioning. And Red Bull is an excellent example of this.

In the early 1980s, Dietrich Mateschitz came across products known as "tonic drinks" while travelling in the Far East, including one, from Thailand which local workers used to stay awake during their shifts. It was called Krating Daeng or "Red Bull". Mateschitz bought the foreign licensing rights and decided to target young professionals, rather than factory workers, as they were more affluent and open to trendy marketing campaigns. The firm focused on "buzz marketing" or word of mouth, and the brand image was linked to youth culture and extreme sports, such as motor sports, mountain biking, snowboarding and dance music. Red Bull's target consumer segment began to adopt nicknames for the product such as "liquid cocaine" or "speed in a can", thus spreading its "left-field" appeal. Red Bull is now a leading player in the energy drinks field, yet still maintains an anti-corporate image.

The marketing of Red Bull involves a lot more than spotting a gap in the market and then developing an excellent brand image. It also included developing a marketing strategy based upon a great deal of market research. A sophisticated marketing mix was also developed to make Red Bull a competitive product. Last, but by no means least, it needed a large and well-motivated salesforce to get the product "on the shelves" so that the ultimate consumers could make their purchases. This chapter gives a greater understanding of all these aspects of marketing.

Source: based on: http://www.bized.co.uk/compfact/redbull/redbullindex.htm

14.1 Definition of marketing

Typical definitions assert that marketing is:

> An organisational function and set of processes for creating, communicating and delivering value to customers and for managing customer relationships in ways that benefit the organisation and its stakeholders.
>
> *(American Marketing Association, 2004)*

> Responsible for identifying, anticipating and satisfying customer requirements profitably.
>
> *(Hannagan, 2005)*

> The management process responsible for identifying, anticipating and satisfying customer requirements profitably.
>
> *(Chartered Institute of Marketing [UK], 2010)*

Each of the definitions has disadvantages. The first is so megalomanic that it includes practically everything in an organisation. It does not differentiate between marketing and other essential functions such as production or finance. Two of the definitions imply, quite wrongly, that marketing only applies to commercial, profit-making, organisations. A definition which escapes these problems and which commands some consensus is:

> A product or service's conception, pricing, promotion and distribution in order to create exchanges that satisfy consumers, organisational objectives and the interest of other stakeholders.
>
> *(See, for example, Health Advantage, 2004; Pride and Farrell, 2000; Quintessential Careers, 2004)*

This definition has a number of key features:

- It centres on the exchange relationship between consumers (in the broadest sense) and organisations.
- It emphasises that these exchanges should be satisfactory to all parties.
- It specifies the activities which constitute marketing.
- It implicitly accepts that other functions in the organisation play an important part in a satisfactory exchange.

Many writers emphasise the importance of adopting a marketing orientation where everyone in an organisation has a marketing role. For example, when a driver of a company van parks discourteously it tarnishes the company's image and affects its relationship with a customer. Similarly, an operative making a poor-quality product, an off-hand customer service assistant, a tardy accounts clerk and an arrogant chief executive all affect an organisation's relationship with customers and clients. The management guru, Peter Drucker (1999) takes the view that:

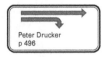

Peter Drucker
p 496

> 66 The purpose of business is to create and keep customers . . . it has only two functions – marketing and innovation. The basic function of marketing is to attract and retain customers at a profit. 99

This view is overstated. It makes marketing synonymous with everyone in an organisation so the term is therefore redundant. Further, there are many non-profit organisations where customer satisfaction is not the only organisational objective (e.g. the prison service). Nevertheless, most organisations need to have a **market orientation**. This is also called being "consumer centred" or being "consumer driven".

14.2 Successive views of the marketing function

Robert Keith (1960) argued that marketing functions had experienced a revolution. His ideas have been updated: current "periodisation" divides the marketing revolution into five phases (see below), and plentiful examples of of each phase still exist. Petkus (2010) suggests that practical outcomes can arise from a study of marketing history:

- **Production** orientation was the first phase – at its height from, say, 1870–1950. This marketing strategy emphasised producing as much of any product as cheaply as possible so that as many people as possible would buy it. This orientation is appropriate when a large, under-supplied market exists and where consumer tastes do not alter very quickly. A classic example would be Sunlight Soap, developed in 1884. There was a huge market but incomes were low. Further, there was not an over-supply of soap; there was a credo that "cleanliness is next to godliness" and smoke-filled skies guaranteed continuing demand. The manufacturers, Lever Brothers, only had to make huge quantities of soap at a low price and get it to the shops. They and their workers in Port Sunlight were "well off".

- **Product** orientation was very prominent from, say, the 1920s until the 1960s. This strategy emphasised the quality of a product in the belief that well-made products would dominate. This strategy is appropriate when a market is aspirational, incomes are rising and where other products are of dubious quality. A classic example would be the Hoover vacuum cleaner whose quality features included a "beater bar" and a headlight.

- **Selling** orientation was important during the 1950s and 1960s. It emphasised high sales and promoting products as much as possible – with relatively little attention to product design. It required good salespeople, advertising and points of display. A classic example would be the selling of washing powders where there was little difference between the products but they were heavily advertised in order to gain brand recognition and to encourage consumers to perceive the differences.

- **Marketing** in its current form gained importance in the 1970s. It is the dominant orientation today. It focuses on detecting and satisfying consumer needs. It is characterised by high levels of market research and good customer services. *Societal marketing* is now considered a major aspect of the marketing orientation. It emerged in the 1960s and is based on the idea that products should meet the needs of customers and also promote the well-being of society by refraining from products or selling methods that would be harmful. A good example of societal marketing would be the development of the Fair Trade organisation and the development of investments that are ethical. Much of the rest of this chapter is based on this orientation. However, the next edition of this text will probably need to include a section on academic advances in galactic marketing!

■ **Relationship marketing** stresses satisfying, and preferably long-lasting, links with customers. Quality products which satisfy customer needs remain important, but consultants and academics advise that a positive customer experience engendered by close attention to customers and good customer service is paramount. The aim is to develop customer loyalty so they repeat their purchases. A classic example of relationship marketing is Marks & Spencer's emphasis on good quality products, which used to be made in Britain for use by British people, at a sensible price and with good customer service which would not make exchanges or refunds difficult. Marks & Spencer's ubiquitous phrase "Your M&S" clearly exemplifies *they* have "bought into" relationship marketing. It is often thought that relationship marketing emerged during the 1970s but it has been present longer (see, Tadajewski and Saren, 2009).

CRITICAL THINKING 14.1 *Are "stages" marketing's own QWERTY keyboard?*

The stages of the marketing "revolution" are reproduced in most contemporary textbooks. Yet, decades ago, Fullerton (1988) and Hollander (1986) disputed them. A recent analysis by Jones and Richardson (2007) shows that the other marketing orientations were clearly in existence during the period known as the production era. Jones and Richardson attribute the persistence of periodisation to "sloppy scholarship to plagiarising the work of other textbook authors". Perhaps there is an analogy with keyboard production. As noted earlier, while it is known that the QWERTY keyboard is very inefficient, it is so familiar that no manufacturer would dare to be the first to market something better – what a pity for us all!

14.3 Markets

A market (in contrast to *marketing*) may be defined as:

> The actual or potential buyers of a product.

This means a market is wider than individuals: it includes private and public sector organisations, supplier groups and purchasing groups. It is also wider than present or past buyers: it includes anyone or any organisation that is reasonably likely to buy a product in the future. Kotler (1986) defined a product broadly as:

> anything that can be offered to a market for attention, acquisition, use or consumption that might satisfy a want or need. It includes physical objects, services, persons, places, organisations and ideas.

An organisation that hopes to sell its product needs to study its market very carefully and may commission extensive market research. It needs to examine the characteristics of its market such as:

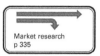

Market research
p 335

- the *people* and *organisations* that make up the market
- the *product* or *service* it offers
- the *purpose* for which the product is bought and the *needs* it satisfies
- the *times* and *occasions* (e.g. birthdays, setting up a new home or everyday purchases) when the product is bought
- the *method used to buy* the product (e.g. retail outlet, regular order, telephone order or Internet shopping)

People and organisations do not buy products for their own sake. Products are bought because they *solve a problem* or confer *benefits* upon their owners. For example, organisations do not purchase a car for a sales representative because they want to own a car. It will be purchased because the organisation believes it will benefit from the sales representative's ability to visit more customers and it can be sure its image will not be damaged by its representative arriving in a clapped-out old banger.

Markets can differ in many ways. The main differences are size, competition, barriers and dynamism.

Size, niches and market segmentation

Markets differ markedly in size. Some markets, such as detergents and cleaning materials, are vast and international. Global companies such as Proctor and Gamble have developed to meet the needs of such markets. In principle, large markets are good and lead to very cost-effective products because development costs are shared among millions of customers. However, these benefits accrue only if the large market is *homogeneous* (every consumer is quite similar and has comparable needs). It is difficult to mount an effective marketing campaign for a large, *heterogeneous* market (where there are distinctive groups with distinctive needs). It is usually better to target a smaller, more homogeneous group. by focusing upon a restricted range of products or consumers, i.e. a niche market.

A **niche market** is "a portion of a market whose needs are met by a restricted range of specialised products". A classic example is the Tie Rack chain. It operates within a wider market for clothing, but it sells only ties, scarves, handkerchiefs and other accessories. Appropriately, many of Tie Rack's outlets occupy physical niches at airports or railway stations. WesternGeco, a subsidiary of the American company Schlumberger, also operates within a niche market. It provides technically sophisticated seismic imaging services for oil companies. Catering for a niche market means an organisation can develop highly specialised expertise and project a distinctive image.

Another way to produce a homogeneous market is *market segmentation* where a wider market is divided into subgroups whose members have similar needs. Typical methods of market segmentation divide customers according to factors such as loyalty, age, gender, neighbourhood or social economic status.

328   Part 3: Management functions

Perhaps the most important way to segment a market is to divide it into *past customers* (i.e. loyal customers) and *new customers*. In the late 1990s there was a craze to focus upon past customers. The craze arose because, with the development of the Internet, customers had a much greater ability to "shop around" and become "promiscuous consumers". Many organisations therefore concentrated on establishing a dedicated base of existing customers and developing a long-term relationship that would prevent loyal customers switching to other suppliers. This is called "relationship marketing". It was supported by claims such as:

- Costs of acquiring a new customer are 10 times higher than keeping an existing customer.
- Loyal customers spend more than new customers.
- Past, satisfied customers tell others about their satisfaction.
- Past customers are more profitable because they are willing to pay a premium for a service they know.

The principles of relationship marketing were embraced by organisations trading with other organisations. For example, a computer software company would develop a close marketing relationship with its customers. Specific programmers would be devoted to specific clients so personalised assistance would be available if needed and they would help establish a deep, long-term and profitable relationship. Initially these concepts were applied to business organisations (**B2B transactions**). However, their relevance to retail transactions was quickly appreciated. Very successful examples of **customer management** and relationship marketing include the Tesco Clubcard scheme and Airmiles. A fundamental aspect of customer management is the concept of **client life-cycle**. A new client needs to be welcomed, perhaps by email, and assured that they have made the correct choice. An established customer needs to be told that they are important and that the organisation wishes to attend to their needs. A long-established client needs to be made aware of new products.

B2B transactions
p 450

Some of these basic beliefs have not withstood scrutiny. Werner and Kumar (2002) suggest that loyalty is not as profitable as the gurus of the 1990s suggested. For example, long-term customers tend to demand more favourable contracts. Further, many long-term customers make disproportionate demands in terms of customer support.

Market segmentation by *age* is also very common. Classic examples are the UK travel organisation Club 18–30 which markets lively Mediterranean holidays to youthful consumers, and the SAGA Group which markets holidays and financial products to people aged over 50 years. Market segmentation by age is widespread in the fashion and entertainment industries.

Market segmentation by *gender* is widespread in the publishing industry. For example magazines such as *Woman's Weekly* and *Cosmopolitan* are marketed for women, while *FHM* and *What Car* are marketed for men. Similarly, cars offered by major manufacturers will include some cars designed to appeal to women and other cars designed to appeal to men.

Market segmentation by *neighbourhood* is very common. For example, billboards in prosperous areas will depict luxury goods purchased out of discretionary income, while billboards in less affluent areas will advertise basic products. Probably the most extensive classification of residential areas is the ACORN system (CACI, 2010). Readers in the UK can obtain the ACORN classification of where they live by visiting the Internet site http://www.caci.co.uk/acorn-classification.aspx. The ACORN classification starts with five major categories:

1 wealthly achievers

2 urban prosperity

3 comfortably off

4 moderate means

5 hard-pressed

These are then subdivided into 17 major groups. For example, the wealthy achievers are subdivided into three groups: wealthy executives, affluent greys and flourishing families. The hard-pressed are divided into four groups: struggling families, burdened singles, high-rise hardship and inner-city adversity. The groups are further divided into subgroups. For example, the affluent greys, who comprise 7.7 per cent of the British population, are subdivided into older affluent professionals (1.8 per cent), farming communities (2.0 per cent), old people in detached homes (1.9 per cent) and mature couples (2.0 per cent). A manager marketing sophisticated financial products such as shares or annuities would target neighbourhoods containing many affluent greys, while a government department trying to ensure proper take-up of welfare benefits might target neighbourhoods containing many people experiencing high-rise hardship.

Markets are often segmented by *socio-economic status*. This system classifies markets according to the work performed by the head of the household. The categories are:

- A upper middle-class (e.g. directors, senior managers and senior civil servants)
- B middle-class (e.g. lawyers, doctors, middle managers and higher professional workers)
- C1 lower middle-class (e.g. teachers, nurses, junior managers and lower professional workers)
- C2 skilled workers including technologists and many engineering workers
- D working class
- E subsistence workers and unemployed people

Market segmentation by socio-economic status groups consumers who have similar spending power and preferences. This discussion covers only the most popular ways of dividing a large market into homogeneous groups. Many other methods exist. Markets are often segmented by lifestyle using categories with cute acronyms such as "YUPPIES" (young upwardly mobile persons), "DINKIES" (dual income no kids) or "GRUMPIES" (grown-up mature persons).

Competition

In a captive market customers must purchase from a single supplier or do without. For a supplier a captive market is ideal because very little effort is needed to sell products. But, captive markets are like magnets to other organisations that set up in competition. Captive markets are very rare. A market is generally regarded as being a captive when there are fewer than four suppliers. Sometimes captive markets are called **monopolies** or **duopolies**. A market which has, say, more than 12 suppliers is generally called a "fluid market".

Barriers to entry and exit

Captive markets exist in situations when it is difficult for competitors to enter. For example, in the aerospace industry there are often only one or two suppliers (e.g. Boeing or Airbus). Few organisations can afford the immense costs of setting up huge and complicated factories or build up the technical knowledge and expertise. **Barriers to entry** also exist in the form of laws and regulations such as patent laws, copyright laws and planning permissions. Distribution channels can also constitute entry barriers. Commercial practices by competitors may present further entry barriers – especially the practice of **predatory pricing** (OECD, 1989), whereby a large, established business cuts its price below its costs so that new competitors must sell at a loss and therefore eventually be driven out. **Exit barriers** prevent organisations withdrawing from markets. Usually they wish to exit because a market because it is unprofitable or it is no longer fits an organisation's strategy. Typical exit barriers include losing the capital already invested, the costs of making staff redundant, loss of prestige or government pressure.

CASE 14.2: *Rockefeller's predatory pricing*

A classic case of predatory pricing is given by John D. Rockefeller's oil interests (Tarbell, 1950). A new entrant, the Pure Oil Company, was driven out of business when Rockefeller's Standard Oil Company drastically lowered its price, knowing that its vast reserves could survive a short-term loss in order to reap a long-term benefit of having the market to itself. Another example of predatory pricing is the way established airlines cut the price of their air fares in the 1970s to force a new entrant, Laker Airways, out of the transatlantic passenger market.

Dynamism

A growing market is called an "expanding market". A market that is shrinking is called a "declining market" and one that stays the same is called a "static" or "stagnant market". It is generally easiest to operate in an expanding market. Organisations operating in a declining market need to pay very close attention to costs in the hope that they will be able to drive out less efficient competitors.

These characteristics are not the only factors that differentiate markets. In order to predict and anticipate markets it is necessary to understand six further influences such as those indicated by a PESTLE analysis. **Cultural factors** are also important characteristics of markets. For example, the French culture and traditions made it much more difficult for the McDonald's hamburger chain to enter the French market.

PESTLE
p 96

14.4 Market strategy and market positioning

Organisations often consciously decide, the type of market they prefer to serve. This is called "**market strategy**", "**market positioning**" or "**portfolio planning**". PESTLE analysis was developed to aid market positioning. Other schemes include the Boston matrix, the General Electric matrix and the Anscoff matrix.

The **Boston Consulting Group Matrix** (**BCG matrix**) focuses on two aspects of a market, its *dynamism* (growth rate) and relative *share of a market*. This allows products or services to be categorised into the four types shown in Figure 14.1.

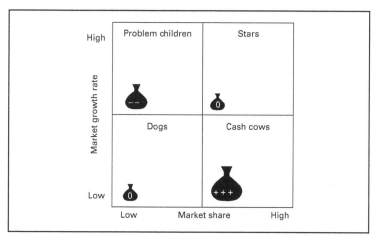

FIGURE 14.1 The BCG matrix

If a product has a low market share in a slow-growing market, the product is classified as "a dog" because it is doing poorly in a weak market. The outlook is poor and an organisation might be well advised to consider eliminating the product from its range – preferably by selling it to someone else or, in the worst case, shutting it down. If the product has a low market share but operates in an expanding market, the organisation has a "problem child" because the outlook is mixed. The expanding market bodes well but the low market share implies a struggle to keep up with market leaders who will be able to obtain greater economies of scale. In these situations an organisation must decide whether to inject substantial resources. This may be risky. Sometimes, products categorised as "problem children" are called "cash hogs" because, like some adolescents, their potential is uncertain but they require large and frequent injections of cash. A product which commands a high share of a slowly growing market is categorised as a "cash cow". Its high market share means that economies of scale are achieved and a lot of money is generated. This money can be used to promote other projects such as "a problem child" or a "star". Organisations may become complacent about their "cash cows" and pay more attention to new products. Because of lack of investment the "cash cows" lose their competitiveness and turn into "dogs". A "star" is a product that has a high share of an expanding market. Generally, it will generate most of the funds needed for its own development and promotion but, from time to time, this may need supplementing by injections of resources from a "cash cow".

CRITICAL THINKING 14.2 *What is wrong with the Boston matrix?*

The Boston matrix provides a reasonable basis for the allocation of development funds. However, it has its disadvantages (Morrison and Wensley, 1991). It oversimplifies markets by focusing upon just two aspects: market growth and market share. This may lead an organisation to ignore other important aspects (Haspeslagh, 1982). Moreover, the Boston matrix simplifies the two dimensions into just two crude categories; high and low.

The **General Electric matrix** is also known as "The Industry Attractiveness/ Business Strength" matrix or the "Directional Policy" matrix. It overcomes some of the disadvantages of the Boston matrix by incorporating *more factors* and allowing *three levels* for each dimension. The General Electric matrix has two composite dimensions: "industry attractiveness" and "business strength". **Industry attractiveness** is an amalgam of five characteristics, resembling PESTLE:

PESTLE
p 96

- *market forces* – size, growth, price sensitivity and bargaining position
- *competition* – as types of competitors or substitution by new technology
- *financial and economic factors* – economies of scale, profits, entry and exit barriers
- *technology* – market maturity, patents, copyrights and manufacturing technology
- *socio-political factors* – pressure groups, legal constraints and unionisation

The General Electric matrix then evaluates on factors reflecting **business strength**. Using these two dimensions an appropriate strategy is determined. In practice, this process is quite complicated because an intricate system of weights is applied to the characteristics of the industry and the strengths of the business or product. Figure 14.2 indicates appropriate strategy for products or sevices in each cell.

For example, a weak product in an unattractive market should be discontinued, preferably by its sale to another organisation. A strong product in a similarly unattractive market should be milked for all the cash it can generate. The case of a weak product in an attractive market is interesting. The organisation should either quit or take a gamble and invest many resources in the hope the product or service can be a market leader. It is similar to the "problem child" category of the BCG matrix.

Unfortunately, even a system as sophisticated as the General Electric matrix does not capture the full complexity of product positioning. For example, an established market leader can be positioned in a number of ways. It could try to obtain an even greater market

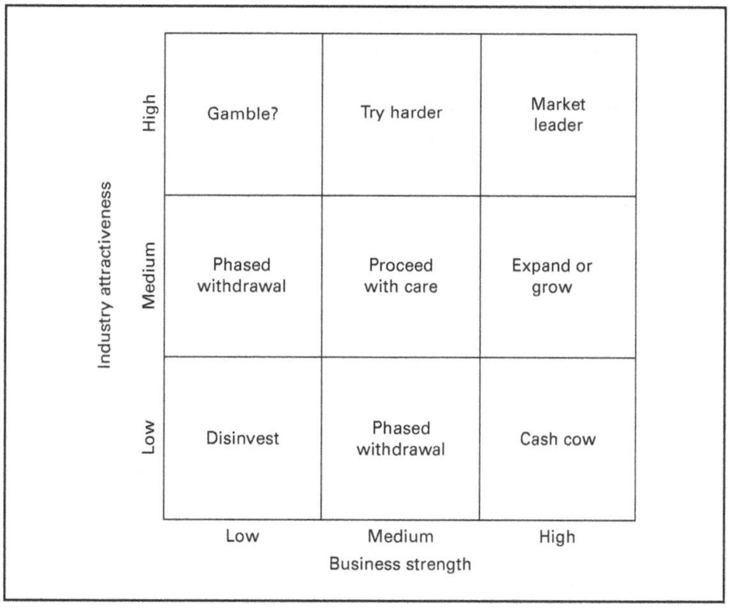

FIGURE 14.2 The General Electric matrix

share. Alternatively, the product can be adjusted so that it appeals to a new market. Ansoff (1989) developed a matrix to aid these decisions. An Ansoff matrix focuses upon whether both the markets and the products are new or established. Figure 14.3 shows Anscoff's recommendation for each combination.

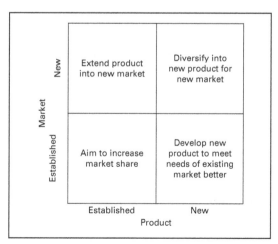

FIGURE 14.3 The Ansoff matrix

334   Part 3: Management functions

Once a suitable market has been identified it is necessary to decide the organisation's position. It is often assumed that organisations should be market leaders or **pioneers** – devising new methods, opening up new markets and devising new products (Pettinger, 1997). They frequently have a high esteem. However, being a pioneer can be risky. There may be unknown difficulties. Pioneers carry substantial development costs. If the ideas are successful they can be copied, at less cost, by other organisations. An alternative, often more successful, marketing strategy is to adopt a "follow the leader" approach: keeping a keen eye on developments and maintaining a capability to quickly exploit the advances made by others. Other organisations adopt a strategy of building up a competitive advantage through **technical excellence**, or quality.

A marketing function must consider the maturity of their organisation's products or services and try to ensure their portfolios contain goods at different stages of the product life cycle. In general, product life cycles have five main phases, as shown in Figure 14.4.

The continuous line shows the "natural" progression of sales. When a new product or service is introduced, there is a period of slow growth of sales, followed by a rapid increase as the product or service is adopted by opinion leaders and then a wider range of consumers. At maturity, growth is either slow or there is a small decline as the product loses some of its "novelty value". At this point the product has wide acceptance. During the saturation phase, sales may decline because, although the market may be expanding, new competitors emerge. Finally, the product declines and sales generate little cash. This pattern varies greatly. In fashion items and children's toys, the whole life cycle is less than a year. In other cases such as "big ticket" items (e.g. televisions) the life cycle can be more than a decade. Organisations try to predict the life cycle of their products or services to ensure that they have new products "in the pipeline" to replace saturated or declining products. The life cycle

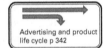

Advertising and product life cycle p 342

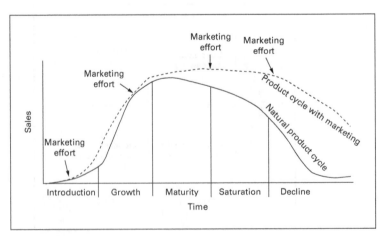

FIGURE 14.4 Product life cycle

of products is particularly important in industries such as pharmaceuticals where it can take decades to develop new medicines. Marketing functions monitor the life cycles of products for a second reason. By mounting a marketing effort, such as advertising, new packaging or restyling at key times, sales can be boosted to extend the product life cycle. The effect of a marketing effort on a product life cycle is demonstrated by the dotted line in Figure 14.4.

14.5 Understanding markets (market research)

Market research is defined by the American Marketing Association (2004) as:

> the function that links the consumer, customer and public to the marketer through information – information used to identify and define marketing opportunities and problems; generate, refine and evaluate marketing actions; monitor marketing performance; and improve understanding of marketing as a process.

The terms "market research", "markets research" and "marketing research" sound very similar. **Market research** refers to *any* information about markets. **Markets research** is looks at the characteristics of markets. **Marketing research** looks at information concerning a specific product or service. It is useful to divide market research into two main activities: *markets research* and *marketing research*.

Markets research

Research on markets is sometimes called "market intelligence". It obtains information, usually quantitative, on the size of a market, its growth, its use of technology, its dynamism and the level of competition. Often markets research is based on existing (secondary) data compiled by government and industry sources such as census figures, the retail price index and the value of imported goods. It may also use journal and newspaper articles to build up a picture of competitors.

Marketing research

Marketing research is information that will be useful to organisations who wish to sell specific products. It is the research which, say, the brand manager for Coca-Cola uses to devise an advertising campaign. Marketing research overlaps with research on markets but its focus is narrower and is closer to the point of sale. Marketing research can, perhaps, best be considered under two headings: usage and methods.

Uses of marketing research

Marketing research can play a vital role in bringing to market a product valued by customers and which is presented to them in an enjoyable way. Marketing research's main uses include:

- *Product generation* – identifying new products by listening to consumers, brainstorming sessions with designers and marketing executives.
- *Product improvement and embellishment* – again, the source of suggestions can be consumers or brainstorming. Ideas may also be generated by examining competitors' products or even products and services in other markets.
- *Product testing and refinement* – prototypes of products and services can be tested on small groups of consumers. Their reactions and comments are usually incorporated in a modified product.
- *Consumer targeting* – pinpointing the people who are most likely to buy the product or use a service.
- *Sales forecasting.*
- *Packaging and advertising design* – various suggestions for packaging or adverts can be tested on consumers and the most effective chosen.
- *Point-of-sale displays and procedures* – developing and then refining point of sale displays, brochures, etc.

Marketing research methods

The main sources of marketing research are:

- **Existing internal data** – sales records, call reports and especially quotations that have been not been taking up by customers. Customer loyalty schemes routinely gather vast amounts of information on consumers. **Surveys** have many forms. The simplest is a questionnaire returned by a purchaser when she or he registers a guarantee. Many organisations also use **questionnaire surveys**. Questionnaire surveys are administered by market researchers who approach customers, who fit their **quotas**, as they visit shopping malls, etc. Alternatively, they may be administered in a more rigorous way to a **random sample** of people. Random samples are much more expensive than quota samples. Questionnaires *may also* be distributed via the post but this method may result in a very poor response rate. The telephone and the Internet are also used to administer questionnaires. However, the sample of respondents may be very unrepresentative.
- Questionnaires need to be constructed to ensure that questions are "neutral". A series of questionnaires administered to the same group of people is called **consumer panel**. Consumer panels have the advantage that they can track changes in customer preferences. Unfortunately, repeated questioning of the same people can sensitise them to issues so that they gradually become unrepresentative. Some unscrupulous organisations use questionnaires as a way of introducing themselves to people, getting them to divulge information and then attempting to sell them a product. This is called "SUGGING" (selling under the guise). Charities also use surveys as a ruse to raise funds. This is called "FRUGGING" (fund-raising under the guise). Both practices are unethical.
- **Focus groups** or **group discussions** are frequently used in market research – especially when customers' underlying attitudes to new or changing situations are relevant. Focus groups consist of, say, 12 people representing different types of consumers plus a leader who ensures they cover the required topics. Focus groups may attempt to assess "emotions" and "deep attitudes". Some techniques are exotic and perhaps

silly. Partricipants, might be asked to nominate a type of tree that they associate with a certain public figure. In better situations, a focus group is asked to taste a new drink and compare it to existing drinks. **Experiments** are used infrequently. Usually they are employed to study the impact of advertisements and packaging and they often take the form of observing consumer behavior. For example, a supermarket may stock shelves in a different ways and videotape the behaviour of customers. The videotape will be analysed to establish which shelf layout generates most purchases.

14.6 The marketing mix

Successful marketing involves an appropriate combination of five main factors. This combination is called the **marketing mix** and is based on the "5 Ps": **p**roduct or service, **p**rice, **p**ackaging, **p**romotion and **p**lace of purchase.

Products

A product can be either a physical entity or a service. Ownership of a physical entity changes hands when a *product* is purchased. When a *service* is purchased ownership is not transferred. From a marketing viewpoint, the most important feature of either is the *benefit* it bestows upon the customer. An engineer, a technologist, and a design specialist may eulogise about the product's features or its technical sophistication. However, these are only important if the consumer believes that they confer some benefit. Benefits may be a saving of time, enabling a previously impossible task, a feeling of well-being and attractiveness or an increase in status. In other words a product or service must solve or ease a problem for the consumer. For example, consumers do not buy computers because they can add up numbers quickly or because they are high technology. They buy computers because the machines solve problems such as communicating with others, writing assignments, keeping accounts or storing information. If a product or service confers benefits its competitors do not, the product has a "**unique selling-point**".

Consumers frequently judge products on the basis of their **quality** – freedom from imperfections and an implication of exclusivity or "class". Marketeers imply quality when they offer "fine wines", "prime beef", "select cheeses", "high-calibre education", and so on. Generally products must also offer **durability** – functioning satisfactorily for an acceptable time. However, in some products (razors, pens, live entertainment, etc.) durability is not expected.

Brand is important. Marketing functions give their brands close attention. Brands started when farmers burnt distinctive marks into the flesh of their cattle so that they could be identified should they stray or be stolen. Farmers who produced good cattle were particularly keen on branding because their brand would be recognised at market and their cattle would command a higher price. In the early days of mass production good producers of products such as cornflakes (Kelloggs) or soap (Pears) would mark their products with a distinctive mark. As the brands of cornflakes or soap became better known, manufacturers took steps to ensure other people could not use the same mark. They also promoted brands via advertising that made them instantly recognisable and invoked positive associations in consumer's minds. Kellogg's, for example, developed a brand which is associated with freshness, sunshine and vitality. Today, most major products carry brands, some of which are so well known that they are very valuable. Some of the most famous brands in the USA include Coca-Cola, Ford, McDonald's, Microsoft and GAP. Other world-famous brands include BP, Cadbury, IKEA, Nintendo, Qantas and Rip Curl.

The major advantage of brands is that they add benefits to a product. A classic experiment by Penny, Hunt and Twyman as long ago as 1974 neatly demonstrates the point. They asked consumers who normally used brand B to try two products without knowing their brand. A majority (61 per cent) preferred brand A while 39 per cent preferred brand B. Another group also tried the same two products. For this group the brands were known. 35 per cent were found to prefer brand A while 65 per cent preferred brand B. A brand may be defined as:

> ❝ A symbolic construct created by a marketeer to represent a collection of information about a product or group of products. This symbolic construct typically consist of a name, identifying mark, logo, visual images or symbols or mental concepts which distinguish the product or service. ❞

A brand projects a product's "promise" and differentiates it from competitors, and may attempt to give a product a "personality". To be successful, a brand must have several characteristics (see iboost, 2005). These include:

- *Simple, clear messages*. A campaigning message or one which seems to go against the "Establishment" (e.g. the themes of the Benetton and FCUK branding) are often a "cheap" way to success.
- *Credibility* – so claims are believed.
- *Motivation of customers* which increases the enjoyment of purchasing products with the brand. This makes it more likely that purchases will actually take place.
- *Creation of strong user loyalty*. This is, perhaps, the most important aspect of branding.

Once a brand has been established, it can be extended to other products. This reduces the cost of a new project gaining a place in the market. However, extension to weak or inappropriate new products can cause significant damage to a brand image.

Price

As a broad generalisation, a marketing function will set the price of its goods at a *level* above its costs and as much as the product or service can command.

Exceptions to this rule are almost as many as adherents. The ability and willingness of consumers to pay for a product is important. It is pointless marketing a product or service at a price beyond the means of customers. The variation in supermarket and petrol prices from region to region or town to town is a clear example of how the ability of the consumer to pay influences prices: in affluent areas prices are usually higher than in poorer areas. Luxury goods are a classic example where people are willing to pay substantially more than the production costs. The price of diamonds, for example, has, for over a century, been maintained at an artificially high level. Superb branding (a diamond is forever) and a superb cartel (DeBeers) meant that the price of diamonds could be controlled so that the very affluent and starry-eyed men would pay high prices (*see* Economist, 2004).

Sales of some products respond very quickly to changes in price while the sales of other products change very little if the price increases or decreases (this is called **price sensitivity** or **elasticity of demand**). The price of vegetables such as broccoli is very price sensitive because people will switch to another vegetable such as cauliflower if there is a small price increase. On the other hand, many medicines are price insensitive. People will cut back on other purchases in order to have money to buy medicines that might save their life. If a product or service has an inelastic demand, the marketing function of an organisation can engage in **price-skimming** – supplying only the upper fraction (those who can afford high prices) of the market. They can charge very high prices which quickly recover development and production costs. Price-skimming enables an organisation to build a considerable surplus so that, should a competitor enter the market, they can afford to engage in predatory pricing. Branding can also raise prices. Classic examples are the pharmaceutical industry where branded, well-advertised products supported by an excellent sales force can cost several times more than an equally effective generic medication. For example, the painkiller Neurofen costs more than the equally effective generic drug Ibuprofen. However, the generic drug Ibuprofen does not have to bear the marketing, sales and advertising costs incurred by the branded version.

The price of products is heavily influenced by marketing strategy. For example, new products, such as plasma screen televisions, are introduced at a very high price to establish an aspirational position at the top of the market. This confers prestige that will help sustain a higher price among naive and impressionable consumers.

The price of a product or service may be concealed. For example, people can visit many tourist attractions such as museums, parks or educational "lectures" without any fee. However, someone, somewhere, will be paying higher taxes to sustain their enjoyment. In fact, a marketing function's dream is to separate the person who uses the product from the person or organisation that pays – that way the demand will stay high despite high prices.

Packaging

Packaging is not often considered as a separate aspect of the marketing mix and it is usually subsumed under the heading of "promotion". In practice, the marketing function of most organisations will pay considerable attention to the way goods are packaged because it can make a very substantial difference to sales. Further, packaging has the important purpose of ensuring a product is delivered in prime condition. Packaging can also be used to increase the perceived benefit. For example, some items are packaged in an oversized box in an attempt to make the customer believe that the product is bigger than its actual size. Similarly, some products such as jewellery, are packaged in grossly expensive cases made of embossed leather and silk in order to enhance the perceived value of their contents.

The characteristics of good packaging include:

- *It is distinctive* from its competitors.
- *The colours are appropriate to the product's benefits.* For example, the packaging of a valuable item is likely to be coloured in gold and silver, while the packaging of a fun item is likely to be coloured in vivid reds, oranges and yellows.

- It *displays the brand name* in a prominent position.
- It contains a *flattering picture of the product* where happy people (sometimes, animals) clearly enjoy the benefits of a purchase.

Promotion

Promotion is also called "**marketing communications**" and may be defined as:

> 66 Any type of persuasive communication between the marketing function and one or more of its present customers, potential customers or stakeholder groups which aims, directly or indirectly, to increase the likelihood that time, product or service will be purchased. 99

This definition has four important components. *First*, it emphasises the central concept of persuasive communication. *Second*, the aim of communication is to increase purchases. *Third*, communications are directed at a target that is wider than the organisation's present customers. *Finally*, some communications may be closely linked to the sales process in the short term, while other communications may be designed to have an indirect, longer-term effect.

Public relations

Public relations (PR) is also known as "**perception management**" and critics such as Chomsky (2002) have called it "manufacturing consent", "media control" or "spin". It may be defined as:

> 66 A part of the promotional mix that communicates with stakeholders, the media and the public in general in order to achieve broadly favourable and supportive attitudes towards a product, organisation or cause. 99

A shorter and less technical definition for public relations might be "the management of an organisation's image". Both definitions emphasise that public relations is a general activity and is only loosely tied to the sale of a specific product. It aims to obtain a generally favourable attitude so that subsequent, more specific communications are likely to succeed. Often, an organisation's marketing function will employ specialist public relations consultants to maintain its image. Public relations experts use six main methods:

- **Press conferences** are public or quasi-public events where speakers provide information on newsworthy items. They are stage-managed and attended by selected journalists and television reporters.
- **Press releases** are also called "news releases" and may consist of short fax statements sent to the media.
- **Publicity events** are contrived situations designed to attract media attention. Outrageous publicity events are sometimes called "**guerrilla marketing**".
- **The circuit** refers to the "talk-show circuit" where public relations consultants attempt to get their clients or spokespersons to appear on these programmes.

- **Books, brochures** and other writings are sometimes commissioned and published on behalf of clients.
- **Press contacts** are developed assiduously so that they can be fed information about the organisation in the hope that the reporter will write a favourable story.

Public relations experts often identify opinion leaders and powerful people ("movers and shakers"). They then attempt to develop friendships by offering corporate hospitality at events such as the Chelsea Flower Show, the Happy Valley racecourse in Hong Kong or Australia's prestigious Telstra motor rally.

Sometimes public relations organisations engage in "cause-related marketing" – giving a proportion of their profits to a good cause in the hope that their generosity will reflect positively on them.

CASE 14.3: *Cause-related marketing*

A classic example of cause-related marketing is given by Christmas card manufacturers who hope to promote their sales by promising to give 10 per cent of their profits to charities. A clever and ingenious example of this is provided by Tesco's "Computers for Schools" campaign in which shoppers are given vouchers to pass to their local school. However, cause-related marketing can backfire. In 2003 Cadbury sold chocolate bars with tokens which a school could exchange for sports equipment. The scheme caused uproar. It was criticised by the Food Commission for encouraging obesity rather than a healthy, sporty lifestyle.

Internal promotion

Internal promotion aims to alter the attitudes of the organisation's own workforce. It is particularly relevant when new products are being launched. Internal communications tend to foster the "team spirit" within an organisation. Further, staff become an unofficial salesforce who talk about the new product with their relatives, friends and acquaintances.

CASE 14.4: *Guerrilla marketing*

A good example of guerrilla publicity occurred in August 2002 when Vodafone arranged for two men to "streak" at an international rugby game with the Vodafone logo painted on their backsides. The men's magazine *FHM* provides another good example of guerrilla marketing. The magazine cover featured a nude photograph of a former children's television presenter. After doctoring the photograph to preserve her modesty, *FHM* projected it onto one of the towers of the Houses of Parliament. Both stunts earned considerable free publicity. World Cup authorities take guerrilla marketing very seriously indeed. Perhaps

▶

they do not wish to endanger the money earned by official sponsorship. The official beer sponsor for the 2010 World Cup was Budweiser. However, a Dutch brewery, mystifyingly called Bavaria, decided to impinge with some very mild guerrilla publicity. Thirty-six blonde beauties attended a match wearing orange tops and miniskirts – no slogans, just the colour of the Dutch team. The FIFA marketing police were enraged. The orange-clad blonde beauties were escorted from the terraces and two of them were arrested, carted off to jail and arraigned with criminal charges. Of course they were subsequently released. The Dutch brewery must have been over the moon because comparable publicity would have cost a lot of money. FIFA officials and the South African police did their own reputation some harm.

In 2010 the British Conservative Party anticipated the route that the outgoing prime minister would take on the way to seek the Queen's approval for a general election. They also anticipated that the media would film his progress from helicopters. So, they arranged supporters to be along the route. They held aloft big placards promoting the Conservative cause. Few television newscasts could resist the images.

Advertising

Advertising *promotes specific goods and services*. It may be defined as:

> Attracting public attention to a product, service or issue using non-personal methods of communication with a view to persuading the targets to adopt certain behaviours or thought patterns. Usually the desired behaviour is to purchase a product and the advertising organisation usually pays for the advertisement to be put before the target audience.

It should be noted that advertising is impersonal. There is no one-to-one contact between buyer and seller. This distinguishes advertising from selling. Moreover, advertising concerns specific products or services. This distinguishes it from public relations.

An advertising campaign can have a number of objectives depending upon a product's position in the product life cycle. If the product is new, the campaign is likely to focus on making target customers aware that the product exists. It may also try to establish the new product's position in the market and its brand. Advertising a new product will also emphasise its unique benefits and appeal to people's needs for novelty and the status from being an early adopter. During the growth stage, advertising may seek to reassure tentative purchasers and boost confidence in the product.

Product life cycle
p 342

In the maturity and saturation stages, advertising will seek to differentiate one brand from another. At this stage the main objective will be to increase, or at least preserve, market share. Organisations may engage in either defensive or offensive advertising. Offensive advertising ("knocking copy") points out weaknesses of competitors' products.

Advertisers use many media including: **billboards** ("poster hoardings") (lorries, taxis or buses); **leaflets** (also known as "flyers") (distributed in the street); **direct mail** (magazines) newspapers, skywriting, Web-banners; **radio, cinema** and **television**. The exact choice depends on the product and target audience. For example, luxury goods are unlikely to be advertised using leaflets distributed in the street. They are more likely to be advertised in upmarket magazines.

An advertisements first job is to **a**ttract attention, then develop the **d**esire for the product and finally to encourage consumers to take **a**ction and purchase the product (ADA). Methods may include:

- *Repetition* – very important with new products where the aim is to make people remember the name.

- *Bandwagon campaigns* implying everyone is purchasing the product or service and to be without it would be odd. This tactic is frequently used during a product's growth stage.

- *Testimonials* appeal to people's propensity to obey authority. They may quote sources of authority such as "five out of six doctors eat product X".

- *Pressure campaigns* often take the form of "buy now, before stocks are gone" or "buy now, before a tax increase". This tactic is frequently used during a product's maturity stage.

- *Association campaigns* try to link products with desirable things and attractive or famous people. Association campaigns are often used in conjunction with testimonials.

CASE 14.5: *Misleading advertisements*

In 2002 the Chinese State Drug Administration estimated that 89 per cent of advertisements for drugs and medical services were illegal. Specific examples of misleading advertisements are found throughout the world. In 2003 the American Federal Drug Agency (FDA) ordered Purdue Pharma to withdraw advertisements for a painkiller, OxyCotin, because they failed to mention a fatal side effect. A rather different criticism was levelled against the American milk industry's campaign "got milk" featuring celebrities with "milk moustaches". Physicians complained that the advertisements ignored data linking high milk consumption with heart disease and prostate cancer. Their complaints were supported by the Department of Agriculture (USDA).

Place

Place is the fifth and final component of the marketing mix. It is the location where ownership of goods is transferred or where a service is performed. The place where a product is marketed depends on two main factors: distribution channels and customer expectations.

Distribution and place

Transporting goods to market, storing them until requested by a customer, employing sales staff and providing a setting which the customer finds conducive can cost as much as the production of an article or service. Few organisations can afford to provide these facilities on a national or regional basis; hence they need to rely on other people, wholesalers and retailers. Since wholesalers and retailers act on behalf of many producers the costs can be shared. Moreover, wholesalers and retailers develop specialist expertise so distribution costs are minimised. Historically, the location of the transfer of goods and services happened in marketplaces at the centre of towns and cities. Then it took place in shops in the centre of towns and cities. Now, with motor transport, goods and services are exchanged for money in an often purpose-built **shopping mall** or **retail park** on a motorway circling a large town.

However, a traditional *shop* or a *department store* is not always appropriate or convenient. **Catalogue sales**, for example, are more convenient for people in isolated communities or those who are confined to homes by disability. Some organisations have deliberately developed alternatives to the traditional chain of retail distribution. Tupperware developed a new distribution structure by *selling its products in people's homes* at Tupperware parties. This reduced costs and used social pressures. **Catalogue showrooms**, pioneered by Argos, reduce the need for space to display merchandise. Consequently catalogue showrooms offer a wider range of products at a keen price. However, they require superb logistics to ensure that a replacement article is sent from a central store on the same day one is sold. With the Internet a growing number of transactions take place in *cyberspace*.

E-commerce p 446

Customer experience and place

Customers have clear images and expectations about where they will buy goods. If these expectations are not met they do not buy. They expect to buy cabbages at a greengrocer and not at a newsagent. They expect to buy expensive jewellery in a plush setting where they receive a great deal of personal attention. Consequently, a marketing function will pay great attention to the image of the place where its goods or services are exchanged, This is known as the "**merchandise assortment**". The merchandise assortment must be consistent with the ideas of the consumer otherwise they are unlikely to enter the store to find a suitable article. Another important factor image is *location*. People expect stores to be located among other stores selling similar or complementary products. For example, it is expected that a store selling chairs and tables will be near a store that sells carpets, which in turn will be near a store that sells curtains. Stores arranged in a line next to a large parking area are called a "strip". Stores that are arranged around a central area designed for sitting, strolling and perhaps taking light refreshments are called, especially in America, a "mall".

The interior of a store will be laid out so it gives a customer an experience which is consistent with the image of the organisation. The physical characteristics such as decor, displays and layout are called "atmospherics" or "ambiance". Most important, the exterior atmospherics, which indicate the type of things a store will sell, exert a strong influence on a customer's willingness to enter. Interior atmospherics, which may include music, influence a customer's movement and mood. A primary concern will be to draw potential consumers to the back of a store by using a particularly attractive display or moving image. Once drawn to the back of a store a customer will be encouraged, perhaps by appropriate music or exotic displays, to tarry. As they tarry, they are more likely to make a purchase. A way for supermarkets to draw customers to the further reaches of their stores is to place essential items such as bread at the furthest distance from the entrance. Supermarkets have long appreciated the importance of layout. For example, sales are increased if essential items are positioned either on high shelves or on low ones. Discretionary items are placed on shelves at eye level. As consumers reach for essential items they are likely to see, and purchase, discretionary products. Similarly, supermarkets know that the ends, between aisles, are positions where products are most likely to be selected.

CRITICAL THINKING 14.3   *The charges against marketing*

Marketing is more controversial than other management functions. Its intentions – to interpret and fulfil customer demand – are impeccable. It also plays an undeniable role in creating mass markets which bring economies of scale that in turn drive prices down to the benefit of most people. However, its critics also have a strong case. Their indictment includes misleading advertisements, manipulation, encouragement of antisocial behaviour, creation of false markets and dumbing down.

Use of *misleading advertisements* is a frequent criticism. The malpractice seems to be particularly prevalent in the pharmaceutical and food industries where advertisements may claim spurious health benefits. In some countries the problem seems endemic. The marketing function is often accused of *underhand manipulation*. Advertisements may not openly state a product's benefits. They may be implied by information of which the consumer is unaware. In other words, consumers are induced to buy products by messages outside their awareness or logical control. This reflects an imbalance in power and resources. A consumer buying an everyday product can only devote seconds to their choice. A multinational organisation marketing the same product to millions of individuals can devote a team of a dozen or more experts for several months to devise ways to induce a consumer to make a purchase. One tactic is to target people with fewer evaluative powers. For example, makers of a breakfast cereal may *target adverts at children* knowing that, in turn, they will pressurise their parents.

Another tactic might be **subliminal advertising,** which involves projecting a message at a very low level so that people are not conscious of the message being there. For example, an advertiser might project a very faint advertisement during a soap opera programme. The advert is so faint that the viewer does not realise it is there but the message is registered subconsciously. Initial experiments showing subliminal advertising could be effective were seriously flawed. Modern research shows that subliminal advertising does not work. Subliminal advertising is illegal in many countries. Underhand manipulation is not limited to the use of children or subliminal adverts. It can arise from non-verbal messages. An advertisement may not explicitly state that a product will bring wealth and power. It may, however, imply these benefits by including images of wealthy and powerful people. For example, a business school prospectus might include photographs of successful business people boarding an aeroplane en route to a meeting on international strategy. However, it may know, full well, that most of its MBAs work within the domestic economy. One of the first people to note manipulation by the marketing function was Packard (1957).

Criticisms of the marketing function for using misleading advertisements are by no means restricted to the pharmaceutical or food industries. The travel industry, especially companies selling air fares, is frequently admonished for misleading, bait and switch tactics. Hectares of Sunday newspapers are covered with offers of cheap flights. Yet, when even the nimblest consumer telephones, there are no remaining seats at the cheapest rates. They are encouraged to switch to more expensive, and presumably more profitable, flights.

Some people criticise marketing for *encouraging antisocial behaviour*. Attracting attention is a major problem. There is so much advertising and so much media coverage that an organisation's message may get lost. An easy solution is shock tactics. But many shock tactics involve antisocial behaviour. For example, an organisation producing crisps (chips) might draw attention to its product with an advertisement depicting a pupil successfully deceiving a teacher during a mathematics lesson to eat crisps. The advertisements would probably increase the sales of the crisp manufacturer. However, it would make classroom discipline more difficult. It might mean the skills of a future generation are impaired so that a country has a reduced ability to provide social goods such as transport or health care.

The marketing function will usually seek to maximise the benefit for its own organisation rather than the community. It may benefit the organisation to develop and market a new product that is unnecessary and which will, in the long term, damage people and their society. In essence, this criticism accuses the marketing function of *developing and exploiting unnecessary and dangerous consumer needs*. For example, the market research of the company Masterfoods (MARS) revealed a marketing opportunity for a large wafer, chocolate caramel cream confectionary bar for women. It developed a product, Mars Delight, which was launched in Ireland. A marketing spend of £15 million was devoted to promoting this product. However, in the light of increasing obesity in the developed world, Mars was criticised for developing a needless and, possibly dangerous, product.

Perhaps the most important criticism against the marketing function is its *impact on society*. Because of its economic power and its expertise, the influence of the marketing is very widespread and pervasive. This leads to two further criticisms. First, it promulgates a capitalist, market ethos which ignores other social, cultural and aesthetic considerations. Probably more important is the impact on intellectual standards – *dumbing down*. The marketing function will wish to appeal to as many people as possible. This behaviour might lead to a society with low standards.

Many of these criticisms may be unfair because they are directed at the image of the marketing function. The marketing function may be partly responsible as a victim of its own hype. Further, many countries have enacted legislation that curb marketing's worst excesses.

14.7 The sales function

The sales function is ignored by many textbooks. However, practising managers such as Henry Ford knew the value of the sales function. He is reported to have said that *nothing* has value until it is actually sold. Strategy can be superb, production can be lean, finance can be sophisticated and the human resources function can be inspirational, but a commercial organisation will die unless it sells its products or services.

CRITICAL THINKING 14.4 *Why do textbooks shun sales?*

Most management textbooks wax lyrical about marketing and marketing strategy and devote endless chapters to them, but sales is all but ignored except for a brief mention of sales promotion. This is clearly unbalanced since many of the top organisations such as Marks & Spencer, Tesco, B&Q, Amazon, John Lewis, IKEA, Carphone Warehouse and DSG (formerly Dixons) are predominantly sales organisations. How does this imbalance come about? Why do academics and researchers tend to shun the sales function? There are at least three possible reasons:

1 Academics and researchers work in universities and colleges where income is provided by the state and the sales function, if any, is small. They are unaware of its importance.

2 They have a negative view of sales as the mere pursuit of profit and lucre – this, they believe, is so much less worthy than the pursuit of truth, knowledge and learning.

3 The topic of sales is less congenial to academic study. An understanding of sales requires more than reading a few books and research papers. It may need some actual experience. Further, sales requires more than analysis and contemplation. It requires practical, emotional and social skills.

A cynic might maintain that people who are interested in sales avoid academic life, with its writing and research, because so much more money can be earned working in sales than writing about it.

The sales function covers a huge range of situations – from someone on a street corner selling the *Big Issue* to a very high-powered executive selling an inter-continental computer system. There are many instances of heinous sales methods. The techniques to sell timeshares and the methods employed by consultants and advisers in the finance and pension industries are sometimes very questionable indeed. Often, the common link in bad sales is a highly geared bonus or commission system. Nevertheless, these examples of sales give an inaccurate caricature. The vast majority of sales staff are oriented to providing a service to provide a benefit to the community. For example, without the activities of pharmaceutical company's sales representatives many GPs would remain ignorant of medications that would be good for their patients.

Most sales situations can be fitted into one of two categories: B2C (business to customer) and B2B (business to business) sales There are at least two general approaches to **B2C sales**. At the lower end, where the product is worth less than, say, £2, or where local enthusiasts for a charity aim to raise contributions, a pushy approach may yield benefits. People will contribute £1 or £2 to avoid hassle. However, a pushy sales approach soon reaches its limits. Sales people selling big-ticket items need to adopt a much more thoughtful approach. Within seconds, they need to evaluate the best way to approach a customer and to elicit their likely needs. It is often said that a good salesperson sells with their ears, not with their mouths! When needs are clarified a salesperson needs to suggest appropriate purchases and the **benefits** that the purchases will provide. Inexperienced sales staff often make the mistake of pointing out the technical features of a purchase such as a television screen with a faster refresh rate. An experienced salesperson, on the other hand, emphasises the benefits of a better viewing experience of, say, a soccer match where a football in flight is smooth rather than juddering. The sales function will be responsible for training sales staff. Much of this training will be on-the-job training but most sales staff will attend a course on selling techniques. Many different approaches are available. Perhaps the best known is the AIDA method which has four stages:

E-commerce B2C and B2B p 450

- First, **Attract** the customer's attention in a pleasant and civilised way.
- Second, **Interest** the customer in a product.
- Third, develop the customers **Desire** to own the product (anticipating the benefits).
- Finally, induce the customer to take a vital **Act** of making the purchase.

Business-to-business sales can be very sophisticated. In essence, a sales representative will aim to establish a long-term relationship where they are regarded as a trusted adviser. Again there are many methods and training courses. Perhaps the best known is "**the seven steps of the sale**" which is also known as PSS – professional selling. The seven steps are:

1 *Plan the approach carefully*. The larger the organisation the greater the need for research about its structure, suppliers and the organisation's strategy, etc. Gaining access can be a major problem. It is usually vital to establish a good rapport with a decision-maker's personal assistant since they can grant or deny access. They can also provide information that is very useful at a later stage.

2 *Prepare a friendly, professional and confident introduction* to the first meeting and set the scene by asking how much time is available and if it is acceptable to start by asking questions and taking notes. In some situations a *brief* description of your own organisation and its capabilities might be appropriate at this stage.

3 *Use thoughtful questions* to determine the needs of the organisation. Often there is a major need plus subsidiary ones. Questioning should be done with empathy and the responses should be listened to most carefully. Body language is important. Questions should also cover how the organisation might prefer to develop your relationship. *Make a presentation* which focuses upon how the benefits of the product match the needs of the organisation. The presentation should also show an understanding of the organisation. *Overcome* objections and comments. Often the first response should be to clarify the issue by asking questions such as "what makes you say that?" Many objections are merely requests for further information. Use questions and objections to develop a constructive discussion.

4 *Close the sale* – but not too early! A standard closing is, "Are you happy that we've covered everything and would you like to go ahead?" – but many other ploys exist.

5 *Follow-up* depends on the type of product or service. At the very least it should be a call to confirm that they customer is happy with the product and its delivery. Follow-up may provide good opportunities for extending a network of contacts.

Business-to-business sales may involve other activities. It may, for example, include advising customers how to display your products. It may involve explaining the product to your customer's staff and perhaps training them to use it. Above all else, sales representatives gather a great deal of intelligence about the market – its trends and opportunities – which the marketing function and the organisation as a whole might exploit.

14.8 The marketing plan

Many marketing functions formalise their intentions into a marketing plan for the next three or more years. The process is a special version of planning in general, which was explained in Chapter 4. Typically, the plan starts with the corporate mission which is translated into a future strategy incorporating customer needs and the resources, especially financial technological and human, available. Marketing strategy is usually formed after reviewing:

Planning
p 89

- the marketing environment
- the organisation's marketing mix
- the organisation's marketing function – its experience and capabilities

This information is used to devise an appropriate marketing mix which will contain specific targets for major objectives. Tactical plans are constructed to enable the achievement of the major objectives. They will include goals such as advertising campaigns, sales efforts and, say, point-of-sale material. Finally, there will be operational plans to determine, for example, exactly which advertisements will be placed in which magazines on what dates. The process is rarely so linear. For example, a strategic marketing plan is revised when operational plans make it apparent that there is no realistic prospect of achieving a strategic objective.

CASE 14.6: *Sleigh Bells' marketing plan*

Sleigh Bells is a new American duo who specialise in noise, dance punk and lo-fi. The contract is with Columbia Studios which are owned by Sony. In 2010 they released their debut album, *Treats*. Marketing is a vital component in the success of performers. A label will have a strategic marketing plan that involves maintaining existing stars and launching a number of new performers each year (launch pipeline).

The marketing department at Columbia devised a tactical marketing plan for Sleigh Bells – only parts of which are public. The department went into top gear to implement its front-line tactical marketing. A lead single was planned to step up publicity in preparation for the release of an album. The next tactical event was a campaign in the UK where the awareness of the duo was thought to be strong – partly because the plan had staged a series of events and articles with *NME*, *Sunday Times Culture* and *Q*. Specialist radio support was scheduled to include John Kennedy at XFM, Zane Lowe and and Huw Stephens at Radio One. A whole year was a careful marketing plan.

Marketing plans and, indeed, the whole of the marketing function are useless unless they are properly implemented and the product or service is formed. This can be a complicated operation. The next chapter therefore gives details of the operations function.

Activities and further study

Essay plans

Write essay plans for the following questions:

1 How might markets differ?
2 What models might organisations use to locate a profitable market? To what extent are these models consistent with each other and how useful might they be in practice?
3 Why do organisations undertake market research? What methods could they use?
4 What is meant by "the marketing mix"?
5 What are the main criticisms against marketing? To what extent are these criticisms valid?

Web activities

1 Look up the websites of:
Chartered Institute of Marketing – http://www.cim.co.uk/home.aspx
   Marketing Week – http://www.marketingweek.co.uk/
   Marketing Institute Singapore – http://www.mis.org.sg/
   Marketing Association of Australia and New Zealand – http://www.marketing.org.au/

2 Look up postgraduate courses in marketing such as:
   http://www.prospects.ac.uk/
   http://www.whatuni.com/degrees/courses/Postgraduate-list/Marketing
   http://www.masterstudies.com/MBA-MSc-Masters-Degree/Business-Economics-and-Administration/Marketing/Sweden/

Experiential activities

1 It is possible to gain some first-hand experience of marketing or sales with vacation work or, perhaps, a management training scheme with short periods of work in different functions ("Cooks Tours").
2 Talk to a manager who works in marketing or sales. Try to get detailed answers to the following questions: what type of organisation is it? What are its goals? What is its basic

transformation process? What are the future challenges marketing and sales functions are likely to face?

Recommended reading

1 Smith, M. (2002) "Derrick's Ice Cream Company: applying the BCG matrix in customer profitability analysis" *Accounting Education*, **11** (4), 365–376. A practical example of how the BCG matrix can be used.

2 Friel, M. (1999) "Marketing practice in small tourism and hospitality firms", *International Journal of Tourism Research*, **1**, 97–109. A description of the way small firms in the English tourist industry market themselves.

3 Cooper, L. (2010) "Small business digs in deep into marketing mix", *Marketing Week*, **33** (28), 26–29. Discusses the marketing activities of small and medium-sized businesses.

CHAPTER 11
Value Through Innovation

You learn more from failure . . . but the key is to fail early, fail cheaply, and not to make the same mistake twice.
A. G. LAFLEY, CEO, PROCTER & GAMBLE

LEARNING OBJECTIVES

After reading this chapter, you should be able to:

1 define the different types of new products that can be launched
2 describe how to create and nurture an innovative culture
3 discuss the organizational options that apply to new product development
4 identify the methods of reducing time to market
5 explain how marketing and R&D staff can work together effectively
6 describe the stages in the new product development process
7 explain how to stimulate the corporate imagination
8 discuss the six key principles of managing product teams
9 describe the innovation categories and their marketing implications
10 discuss the key ingredients in commercializing technology quickly and effectively

Arguably, innovation is the lifeblood of corporate success, but it is increasingly important to consider how new products can add value. Changing customer tastes, technological advances and competitive pressures mean that companies cannot afford to rely on past product success. Companies must look closely at the needs of customers and other stakeholders and the impact on the wider environment if they are to develop new products that add value.

New product development is a risky activity as most new products fail. But new product development should not be judged in terms of the percentage of failures, as this could stifle the spirit of innovation. The acid test is the number of successes. Failure has to be tolerated.

To fully understand new product development, we need to distinguish between invention and innovation. Invention is the discovery of new ideas and methods. Innovation occurs when an invention is commercialized by bringing it to market. Not all countries have the same capacity for invention. The UK has a history of being inventive from the steam engine, the bicycle, to the television, the computer, and the jet engine. The Japanese are equally inventive but also have the ability to successfully market products by constantly seeking to improve and develop using a process called *Kaizen* (sometimes *Kaisan*) (Pearson, 1993). The classic example is the Sony Walkman, which was not an invention in the sense that it was fundamentally new; rather its success (over 75 million have been sold worldwide) was based on the innovative marketing of existing technologies. In Scandinavia many businesses were built on a local invention. For example, Tetra Pak was founded by a person who conceived of 'pouring milk into a paper bag'. Lego bricks revolutionized toys, and IKEA's invention of a new way to deliver furniture was central to its phenomenal growth. In these cases, the key was not just the invention, but the capability to innovate by bringing the product successfully to market (Richard, 1996).

The USA is a major source of innovation. The Internet is dominated by US companies such as Microsoft, Apple, Amazon, Google and eBay. Table 11.1 shows the world's most innovative companies and their country of origin (McGregor, 2006).

A key point to remember is that the focus of innovation should be on providing new solutions that better meet customer needs. Innovative solutions often do not require major breakthroughs in technology. For example, the growth of Starbucks was not fuelled by technological breakthroughs but by redefining what city-centre coffee drinking meant, and Ryanair has built its success by creating a different consumer appeal from that of traditional airlines, based on low prices and strict cost control (Doyle, 1997).

Because many innovations fail, it is important to understand the key success factors. Research into the key success factors in innovation identified the following (Kashami and Clayton, 2000).

- *Creating and delivering added value is important.* Innovations that produce large improvements in value perform much better than those that fail to deliver improved benefits. Radical innovation has greater potential for enhancing marketing performance but is inherently more risky than incremental innovations that deliver small improvements.
- *Speed to market counts.* The most successful new products tend to be those that are launched quickly. There are two reasons for this. First, delay increases the risk of others getting to market first; second, consumer priorities may change.
- A *product's inferior perceived value cannot be compensated for with high communications spending.* High expenditures on advertising and promotion only have a significant effect on performance where the product is already perceived to have high consumer value. High expenditures for inferior products actually worsen the performance: advertising makes bad products fail more quickly.

In this chapter we shall ask the question 'What is a new product?' and examine three key issues in new product development: 1) organization, 2) developing an innovation culture, 3) new product development process. Then we examine the strategies involved in product replacement and the most common form of new product development. Finally, we look at the consumer adoption process, which is how people learn about new products, try them, and adopt or reject them. Throughout this chapter reference will be made to research that highlights the success factors in new product development.

TABLE 11.1 The top 10 most innovative companies

Company	Headquarters—industrial sector	Innovative products
Apple	USA—technology and telecommunication	iPad, iPhone, MacBook Air, iWatch
Google	USA—technology and telecommunication	Google search, Google Maps, Google+, Gmail
Samsung	S. Korea—technology and telecoms	Galaxy S6, Smart Camera, virtual reality headsets, Smart televisions

Company	Headquarters—industrial sector	Innovative products
Microsoft Facebook	USA—technology and telecommunication USA—technology and telecommunication	Microsoft Office, Windows 10 operating system, Bing, Microsoft SQL, Xbox Social network, social marketplace, customized advertising; the 'Like' button
IBM Sony Haier	USA—technology and telecommunication Japan—technology and telecommunication China—consumer and retail products	PureSystems, SmartCloud computing, Watson Analytics LCD televisions; SmartWear-wearable technology 3D refrigerators, Smart Home products and domestic appliances
Amazon.com Hyundai	USA—consumer and retail S. Korea—automotive	Online retail store, Kindle, MP3 player Blue Drive carbon reduction; eco-friendly cars; electric vehicles

Source: a 2012 survey of 2,700 senior executives by the Boston Consulting Group (Boston Consulting Group, 2012)

What is a New Product?

Some new products are so fundamentally different from products that already exist that they reshape markets and competition; for example satellite navigation systems, which have created a new market for digital navigation devices and reduced the sale of printed road maps significantly. Publisher HarperCollins said sales of maps and atlases declined from £13.5 million in 2006 to £9.7 million in 2010 (Geoghegan, 2011).

At the other extreme, a shampoo that is different from existing products only by means of its brand name, fragrance, packaging and colour is also a new product. In fact, four broad categories of new product exist (Booz, Allen and Hamilton, 1982).

1 *Product replacements*: these account for about 45 per cent of all new product launches, and include revisions and improvements to existing products, for example repositioning (existing products such as Lucozade Sport being positioned as a 'body fuel' to access new market segments) and cost reductions (existing products being reformulated or redesigned to cost less to produce). Dyson releases new products based on improvement to an existing product. Its new vacuum cleaner has an innovative ball to improve manoeuvrability, and is smaller and more flexible than previous models.

2 *Additions to existing lines*: these account for about 25 per cent of new product launches and take the form of new products that add to a company's existing product lines. This produces greater product depth. Chocolate Weetabix is an extension that enables the well-known cereal brand to compete with chocolate cereals. Another example is the addition to the Crest toothpaste brand of Crest Pro-health whitening toothpaste.

3 *New product lines*: these total around 20 per cent of new product launches, and represent a move into a new market. For example, in Europe Volvic introduced the 'Touch of Fruit' range of bottled waters, and Evian brought out a facial spray—both targeted at different audiences. This strategy widens a company's product mix.

4 *New-to-the-world products*: these total around 10 per cent of new product launches, and create entirely new markets. For example, netbooks, tablet computers and smartphones have created new markets because of the highly valued customer benefits they provide.

Clearly, the degree of risk and reward varies according to the new product category. New-to-the-world products normally carry the highest risk since it is often very difficult to predict consumer reaction. Effective new product development is based on creating and nurturing an innovative culture, organizing effectively for new product development and managing the new product development process. We shall now examine these three issues.

Creating and Nurturing an Innovative Culture

The foundation for successful new product development is the creation of a corporate culture that promotes and rewards innovation. Unfortunately, many marketing managers regard their company's corporate culture as a key constraint to innovation (Matthews, 2002). Managers, therefore, need to pay more attention to creating a culture

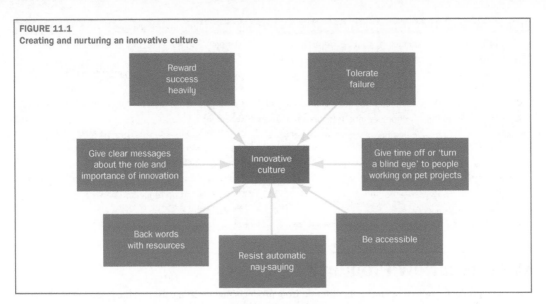

FIGURE 11.1
Creating and nurturing an innovative culture

that encourages innovation. Figure 11.1 shows the kinds of attitudes and actions that can foster an innovative culture. People in organizations observe those actions that are likely to lead to success or punishment. The surest way to kill innovative spirit is to conspicuously punish those people who are prepared to create and champion new product ideas through to communication when things go wrong, and to reward those people who are content to manage the status quo. Such actions breed the attitude 'Why should I take the risk of failing when by carrying on as before I will probably be rewarded?' Research has shown that those companies that have supportive attitudes to rewards and risk, and a tolerant attitude towards failure, are more likely to innovate successfully (see Gupta and Wileman, 1990; Koshler, 1991; Shrivastava and Souder, 1987). Read Marketing in Action 11.1 to find out more.

MARKETING IN ACTION 11.1
Investing in Innovation at 3M

3M produces innovative products for many different industrial sectors, from healthcare to transport. With over $30 billion in global sales and operations in more than 65 countries the company has had a constant stream of innovation in its 100-year history. Innovations that have helped the company grow are: waterproof sandpaper, Scotch pressure-sensitive tape, Cellophane tape, Scotchgard fabric protector, Post-it notes, Privacy Plus filter, optical film for LCD televisions and Scotch-Brite cleaning products. Indeed, there are over 55,000 products in the company's portfolio.

3M has an innovative culture, set in place by former CEO William McKnight. He believed that if the company was going to continue to grow and make the innovative products then it needed to employ the right employees and then give them freedom to explore and to get things wrong. 3M has a programme known as '15 Percent Time', which allows employees to use part of their time at work to develop their own ideas. Although it may take years for this approach to bear fruit, the results of this programme have been some of the company's most innovative products, including the Scotch® Brand tapes, Post-it® notes, Scotchgard™ Fabric Protector and silicon adhesive systems for transdermal drug delivery. The firm also has a policy that each of its divisions must bring in 30 per cent of its revenues from products that are less than four years old.

Innovation development is well organized across the world. 3M has a global science and technical community which fosters a culture of cooperation, communication and cross-pollination of ideas. There are rewards for innovators and scientists and managers alike can progress up the career ladder. 3M also invests in supporting education and development beyond the walls of the business in order to promote industry standards and develop national workforces.

Based on: 3M (2012); Kovacs (2012); Govindarajan and Srinivas (2013)

An innovation culture can also be nurtured by senior management visibly supporting new product development in general and high-profile projects in particular (see Booz, Allen and Hamilton, 1982; Maidique and Zirger, 1984). Besides sending clear messages about the role and importance of new product development, senior management should reinforce their words by allowing time off from their usual duties to people who wish to develop their own ideas, make available funds and resources for projects, and make themselves accessible when difficult decisions need to be taken (see Bergen, Miyajima and McLaughlin, 1988; Hegarty and Hoffman, 1990; Cooper, 1979; Johne and Snelson, 1988).

Finally, management at all levels should resist the temptation of automatic 'nay-saying'—that is, whenever a new idea is suggested, there is a tendency for doubters in a firm to make negative comments and question the feasibility of the new idea. This does not mean that all ideas should immediately be developed as each will be scrutinized and have to pass through many stages of development before becoming a reality. The point is that stifling new ideas at conception only serves as a constraint on innovation. Managers need to seek ways to create an innovative culture.

Creative leadership is required to release the passions, imagination and energy needed for outstanding innovation. Such leadership encourages staff to reject the status quo and operate in a productive discomfort zone, has a clear vision of the future, and provides support for exploration (e.g. Apple, Google, Haier, 3M, Hyundai).

Arguably, there is an underlying assumption that all innovation by commercial profit-based businesses is for affluent markets, where customers will eventually pay for the research, development and marketing of new products and deliver surplus profits by paying high prices for such goods and services. On the one hand, perhaps this is a reasonable assumption as over half the world's population survives on less than $2.50 dollars a day and therefore are deemed to be uninterested in or unable to purchase innovative products (Shah, 2012). On the other hand, is it a classic example of marketing myopia as suggested by Theodore Levitt in the 1960s (Levitt, 1960), whereby companies are short-sighted about growth opportunities in the market? Read Mini Case 11.1 to find out more about how a shift towards frugal innovation is creating innovative products for billions of under-served consumers.

MINI CASE 11.1
Frugal Innovations: From Clay Fridges to Cardboard Splints

Historically, over half the world's population has been ignored by global corporations as a segment capable of being interested in innovation. However, Eric von Hippel, a professor of technological innovation, has argued for many years that the key to innovation comes from customers, not corporate thinking, and that everyone has *needs* that can be satisfied by new products and services.

Sustained global recession has affected many areas of business, and governments around the world have taken to using austerity as a watchword for managing national and regional affairs. This shift in emphasis has profound implications for marketers. For example, the engineers in India won the day with the Tata Nano when Renault-Nissan asked its engineers in France, India and Japan to come up with some cost-saving ideas. The Haier Group, a Chinese consumer electronics manufacturer, has undercut western competitors by producing goods from air conditioners and washing machines to wine coolers, often at half the usual cost. The result has been that Haier has taken significant percentages of US and European markets. However, the shift towards frugal innovation is more far-reaching than just producing goods for western markets more cheaply. According to Prahalad and Mashelkar (2010), a form of new product development called *frugal innovation* or *reverse innovation* specifically engineers products to meet the needs of developing countries—for example, a rough-terrain wheelchair, or a $20 prosthetic knee that can be assembled in an hour.

In the developing world the various champions of frugal innovations include Anil Gupta, who is an academic at one of India's top business schools, the Indian Institute of Management. Anil is a champion of individuals who are deemed to be 'knowledge-rich yet economically poor'. Anil believes that there is a solution to world poverty, but it requires a different approach: a bottom-up one. He established the Honey Bee Network in the

»

»

1980s with the aim of nurturing innovation, knowledge and creativity at a grassroots level. This initiative led to the development of a village-to-government approach towards innovation. Innovation scouts go to rural villages in India looking for potential products to develop. Mansukhbhai Prajapati is an example of a successful entrepreneur who has emerged from this initiative. He developed the Mitti cool brands, which include clay pans, pressure cookers and non-electric refrigerators, which are making a difference to local communities' health through better-kept and better-cooked food.

Jugaad is an example of a company that began creating products from recycled material in 1997 through a Delhi-based children's home that organized work for disadvantaged children. 'Jugaad' is a unique Hindi word that refers to the practice of getting required results by using whatever limited resources are available. People Tree (a retailer) provided outlets and supported Jugaad until it became an independent brand in 2004. This creative manufacturer now provides employment and training and helps members of its workforce to become independent entrepreneurs.

The Tata Nano may not have changed the world, but frugal innovation will!

Questions:

1 What are 'frugal' innovations and how might they change the world?
2 If you worked for a large multinational, suggest how you would incorporate frugal innovations into your marketing strategy.

Based on: Day (2012); The Economist (2012); Jugaad (2012); Kadri (2010); Duggan (2012); Honey Bee (n.d.); Prahalad and Mashelkar (2010)

Organizing Effectively for New Product Development

The second building block of successful innovation is an appropriate organization structure. Most companies use one or a combination of the following methods: project teams, product and brand managers, new product departments and new product committees.

Project teams

Project teams involve the bringing together of staff from such areas as research and development (R&D), engineering, manufacturing, finance and marketing to work on a new product development project. Research has shown that assigning the responsibility of new product development to such cross-functional teams has a positive effect on new product performance (Joshi and Sharma, 2004). Specialized skills are combined to form an effective team to develop the new product concept. Furthermore, if the members of the team remain stable for the duration of a project there is greater potential to foster better decision-making, engender shared responsibility, and leverage advantage from the collective expertise. Ultimately, this approach helps develop better new product advantage. Working together in stable teams can also help to avoid 'tunnel vision and inflexibility in problem solving', up to a point.

Slotegraaf and Atuahene-Gima (2011) discuss how stable teams benefit from better decision-making. However, a key challenge associated with developing a new product is that innovation requires the conversion of knowledge into something tangible, and the stability of a product team can help the process. However, there is a certain point where the benefits begin to diminish. So, long-term stability beyond a particular project may be less successful. Google supported new product development by allowing employees 20 per cent of their work time to spend on innovative projects. Gmail, AdSense and Google+ have all been developed in this manner (*The Marketers*, 2008). However, ensuring the productivity of this approach for everyone in the company has proved challenging.

Product and brand managers

Product and brand management entails the assignment of product managers to product lines (or groups of brands within a product line) and/or brand managers to individual brands. These managers are then responsible for their success and have the task of coordinating functional areas (e.g. production, sales, advertising and marketing research). They are also often responsible for new product development, including the creation of new product ideas, improving existing products and designing brand extensions. Product managers may be supported by a team of assistant brand managers and a dedicated marketing researcher. In some companies, a new product development manager may help product and brand managers in the task of generating and testing new product concepts. This form of organization is common for high-volume, relatively low-value products such as groceries and toiletries, and in the drinks industries.

New product departments and committees

The review of new product projects is normally in the hands of high-ranking functional managers, who listen to progress reports and decide whether further funds should be assigned to a project. They may also be charged with deciding new product strategies and priorities. No matter whether the underlying structure is venture team, product and brand management or new product department, a new products committee often oversees the process and services to give projects a high corporate profile through the stature of its membership.

The importance of teamwork

Whichever method (or combination of methods) is used, effective cross-functional teamwork is crucial for success (see Hise, O'Neal, Parasuraman and McNeal, 1990; Johne and Snelson, 1988; Walsh, 1990) and there has to be effective communication and teamwork between R&D and marketing (Fred, 1991). Although all functional relationships are important during new product development, the cultural differences between R&D and marketing are potentially the most harmful and difficult to resolve. The challenge is to prevent technical people developing only things that interest them professionally, and to get them to understand the realities of the marketplace.

The role of marketing directors

A study by Gupta and Wileman (1991) asked marketing directors of technology-based companies what they believed they could do to improve their relationship with R&D and achieve greater integration of effort. Six major suggestions were made by the marketing directors.

1 *Encourage teamwork*: marketing should work with R&D to establish clear, mutually agreed project priorities to reduce the incidence of pet projects. Marketing, R&D and senior management should hold regular joint project review meetings.

2 *Improve the provision of marketing information to R&D*: one of the major causes of R&D rejecting input from marketing was the lack of quality and timely information. Many marketing directors admitted that they could do a better job of providing such information to R&D. They also believed that the use of information would be enhanced if R&D personnel were made part of the marketing research team so that the questions on their minds could be incorporated into studies. They also felt that such a move would improve the credibility and trust between marketing and R&D.

3 *Take R&D people out of the lab*: marketing should encourage R&D staff to be more customer aware by inviting them to attend trade shows, take part in customer visits and prepare customer materials.

4 *Develop informal relationships with R&D*: they noted that there were often important personality and value differences between the two groups, which could cause conflict as well as being a stimulus to creativity. More effort could be made to break down these barriers by greater socializing, going to lunch together, and sitting with each other at seminars and presentations.

5 *Learn about technology*: the marketing directors believed that improving their 'technological savvy' would help them communicate more effectively with R&D people, understand various product design trade-offs, and comprehend the capabilities and limits of technology to create competitive advantages and provide solutions to customer problems.

6 *Formalize the product development process*: they noted that marketing people were often preoccupied with present products to the neglect of new products, and that the new product development process was far too unstructured. They advocated a more formal process, including formal new project initiation, status reports and review procedures, and a formal requirement that involvement in the process was an important part of marketing personnel's jobs.

The role of senior management

The study also focused on marketing directors' opinions of what senior management could do to help improve the marketing/R&D relationship. We have already noted, when discussing how to create an innovative culture, the crucial role that senior management staff play in creating the conditions for a thriving new product programme. Marketing directors mentioned six major ways in which senior management could play a part in fostering better relations.

1 *Make organizational design changes*: senior management should locate marketing and R&D near to each other to encourage communication and the development of informal relationships. They should clarify the roles of marketing and R&D in developing new products and reduce the number of approvals required for small changes in a project, which would give both R&D and marketing greater authority and responsibility.

2 *Show a personal interest in new product development*: organizational design changes should be backed up by more overt commitment and interest in innovation through early involvement in the product development process, attending product planning and review meetings, and helping to coordinate product development plans.

3 *Provide strategic direction*: many marketing directors felt that senior management could provide more strategic vision regarding new product/market priorities. They also needed to be more long term with their strategic thinking.

4 *Encourage teamwork*: senior management should encourage, or even demand, teamwork between marketing and R&D. Specifically, they should require joint R&D/marketing discussions, joint planning and budgeting, joint marketing research and joint reporting to them.

5 *Increase resources*: *some* marketing directors pointed to the need to increase resources to foster product development activities. The alternative was to reduce the number of projects. Resources should also be provided for seminars, workshops and training programmes for R&D and marketing people. The objective of these programmes would be to develop a better understanding of the roles, constraints and pressures of each group.

6 *Understand marketing's importance*: marketing directors complained of senior management's lack of understanding of marketing's role in new product development and the value of marketing in general. They felt that senior management should insist that marketing becomes involved with R&D in product development much earlier in the process so that the needs of customers are more prominent.

This research has provided valuable insights into how companies should manage the marketing/R&D relationship. It is important that companies organize themselves effectively since cross-functional teamwork and communication has proved to be a significant predictor of successful innovation in a number of studies (see Dwyer, 1990; Gupta and Wileman, 1990; Adler, Riggs and Wheelwright, 1989).

Managing the New Product Development Process

There are three inescapable facts about new product development: it is expensive, risky and time-consuming. For example, Gillette spent in excess of £100 million over more than 10 years developing its Sensor razor brand. The new product concept was to develop a non-disposable shaver that would use new technology to produce a shaver that would follow the contours of a man's face, giving an excellent shave (through two spring-mounted, platinum-hardened, chromium blades) with fewer cuts. This made commercial sense, since shaving systems are more profitable than disposable razors and allow more opportunity for creating a differential advantage. Had the brand failed, Gillette's position in the shaving market could have been damaged irreparably. Nike is another company that invests heavily in new product development to maintain its lead in the specialist sports shoe market. Read Marketing in Action 11.2 to discover how innovation drives the Decathlon service brand.

Managing the process of new product development is an important factor in reducing cost, time and risk. Studies have shown that having a formal process with review points, clear new product goals and a strong marketing orientation underlying the process leads to greater success, whether the product is a physical good or a service (Brentani, 1991; Johne and Storey, 1998).

An eight-step new product development process to provide these characteristics is shown in Figure 11.2 and consists of setting new product strategy, idea generation, screening, concept testing, business analysis, product development, market testing and commercialization. Although the reality of new product development may resemble organizational chaos, the discipline imposed by the activities carried out at each stage leads to a greater likelihood of developing a product that not only works, but also confers customer benefits. We should note, however, that new products pass through each stage at varying speeds; some may dwell at a stage for a long period, while others may pass through very quickly (Cooper and Kleinschmidt, 1986).

New product strategy

As we have already seen, marketing directors value strategic guidance from senior management about their vision and priorities for new product development. By providing clear guidelines about which products/markets the company is interested in serving, senior management staff can provide a focus for the areas in which idea generation should take place. Also, by outlining their objectives (e.g. market share gain, profitability, technological leadership) for new products they can provide indicators for the screening criteria that should be used to evaluate those ideas. A key issue in new product strategy is where to allocate resources. A company may have several divisions and a multitude of product lines so the company has to decide where funds should be invested.

Idea generation

One of the benefits of developing an innovative corporate culture is that it sparks the imagination (see Marketing in Action 11.2). The objective is to motivate the search for ideas so that salespeople, engineers, top management, marketers and other employees are all alert to new opportunities. Interestingly, questioning Nobel Prize winners about the time and circumstances when they had the important germ of an idea that led them to great scientific discovery revealed that it can occur at the most unexpected time: just before going to sleep, on waking up in the morning, at a place of worship. The common factor seems to be a period of quiet contemplation, uninterrupted by the bustle of everyday life and work.

Successful new product ideas are not necessarily based on technological innovation. Often they are based on novel applications of existing technology (e.g. Velcro poppers on disposable nappies). The iPhone created a need for a place to buy 'portable music' which led to the development of the iTunes store.

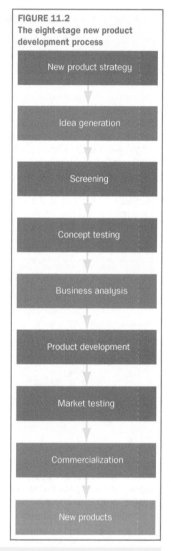

FIGURE 11.2
The eight-stage new product development process

- New product strategy
- Idea generation
- Screening
- Concept testing
- Business analysis
- Product development
- Market testing
- Commercialization
- New products

 Scan the QR code to find out how the mobile provider EE is launching its new product EE TV.

The sources of new product ideas can be internal to the company: scientists, engineers, marketers, salespeople and designers (as at 3M). Some companies use **brainstorming** as a technique to stimulate the creation of ideas, and use financial incentives to persuade people to put forward the ideas they have had. At Royal Dutch Shell, virtual teams meet via the Internet to share ideas. These sessions have generated many ideas for ways to reduce paperwork to using sophisticated laser sensors to find oil (Viklund, 2015).

The prediction by Hamel and Prahalad (1991) that global competitive battles will be won by those companies that have the corporate imagination to build and dominate fundamentally new markets has been proved right, especially in high-tech markets.

Often, fundamentally new products/markets are created by small businesses that are willing to invent new business models or radically redesign existing models. Sources of new product ideas can also be external to the company. Examining competitors' products may provide clues to product improvements. Competitors' new product plans can

MARKETING IN ACTION 11.2
Innovation Drives Passion Brands and Builds Sporting Universes at Decathlon

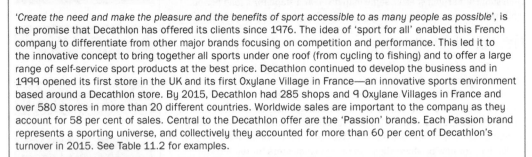

'*Create the need and make the pleasure and the benefits of sport accessible to as many people as possible*', is the promise that Decathlon has offered its clients since 1976. The idea of 'sport for all' enabled this French company to differentiate from other major brands focusing on competition and performance. This led it to the innovative concept to bring together all sports under one roof (from cycling to fishing) and to offer a large range of self-service sport products at the best price. Decathlon continued to develop the business and in 1999 opened its first store in the UK and its first Oxylane Village in France—an innovative sports environment based around a Decathlon store. By 2015, Decathlon had 285 shops and 9 Oxylane Villages in France and over 580 stores in more than 20 different countries. Worldwide sales are important to the company as they account for 58 per cent of sales. Central to the Decathlon offer are the 'Passion' brands. Each Passion brand represents a sporting universe, and collectively they accounted for more than 60 per cent of Decathlon's turnover in 2015. See Table 11.2 for examples.

TABLE 11.2 Examples of Passions, sporting universes and innovative products

Passion Brand	Sporting universe	Examples of products
Geologic	Darts, archery and boules	Soft archery kit, totally safe to use anywhere T-light, a safe dartboard
Newfeel	Walking	Propulse Walk 400, shoes that aid fitness Fullwalk 540 design shoes, with lightness in mind
Oxelo	Urban skate sport	Town 7 Easyfold scooter – easy to assemble anywhere Sneak-in inline skates to be worn with own shoes
Tribord	Nautical water sports	Easybreathe full-face snorkel; see and breathe underwater Izeber 50 floating system lifejacket to aid buoyancy

Each Passion brand conceives the products, exclusively distributed by Decathlon stores. The own-brand offer is due to Decathlon placing innovation at the heart of its activities. With a very advanced internal R&D department composed of researchers, engineers and designers, Decathlon's international design network is prolific, producing about 40 patents and nearly 3,000 products each year. Decathlon rewards excellence in innovation at an annual award-giving event, the Oxylane Awards.

Domyos is another Passion brand (dedicated to fitness) and is the best example of the firm's willingness to immerse the employees amongst its customers. Who better than sportspeople know what they need to improve their game? Decathlon provides them with a website, Openoxylane (http://www.openoxylane. com), dedicated to the co-creation of new products. Anyone can put forward ideas and participate in projects submitted by members of the community. At each stage of the creative process – from defining functions to selecting materials or colours and choosing a name and even the price—users can submit proposals, interact and give their opinion. Prototype workshops are also available for teams to observe the behaviour and test the components of finished products; they help speed up the design process. Organising this innovation culture allows the group to compete with major brands such as Nike and Adidas, who traditionally highlight their innovation and design.

Based on: http://www.decathlon.co.uk

be gleaned by training the salesforce to ask distributors about new activities. Distributors can also be a source of new product ideas directly, since they deal with customers and have an interest in selling improved products.

Another source of externally generated new product ideas is the millions of scientists, engineers and other companies globally. By collaborating with them, a firm can gain access to innovative solutions. Procter & Gamble leads the way by using online networks to get in touch with thousands of experts, as Marketing in Action 11.3 explains.

MARKETING IN ACTION 11.3
Connect + Develop

Anyone anywhere can connect with Procter & Gamble (P&G) through the web and share ideas. P&G taps into a vast well of expertise through its Connect + Develop programme. It practises open innovation, which is a means of accessing externally developed intellectual property while allowing its internally developed assets and know-how to be used by others. This two-way process has led to innovation in such areas as technology, engineering, marketing, packaging, design and business services. For example, Bounce, the world's first dryer-aided softener, was created by an independent Canadian inventor. By P&G and the inventor working together, this innovative product was patented and licensed and sold throughout the world. The Internet has enabled the creation of Connect + Develop hubs, joining together innovators as far and wide as China, Japan, Europe and North and South America. Febreze, which has become a billion-dollar brand for P&G, is another example of an innovation developed through the Connect + Develop programme.

The consumer is at the heart of innovation, and Bruce Brown, Chief Technology Officer for P&G, invites all innovators to submit their ideas. Through Connect + Develop, P&G actively seeks collaboration with external partners to generate and develop new product ideas. As Nabil Sakkab, global leader of its fabric and homecare research and development, commented, 'I pay 7,000 scientists to work for me at P&G but there are 1.5 million scientists out there who do not work for P&G. I want to make my R&D department 1,507,000 strong.' This attempt to 'unsource' ideas is working: 45 per cent of the new ideas he is working on have come from outside the company. Across P&G as a whole, external collaboration plays a key role in nearly 50 per cent of its products.

An example of external collaboration is the launch of Pringle Prints in North America. The product is a line of potato crisps printed with entertaining pictures and words, and was developed in record time and at a fraction of the usual cost. Instead of looking internally for solutions to the problem of how to print images on crisps, P&G searched its global networks of individuals and institutions. It discovered a small bakery in Italy, owned by a university professor who had invented an ink-jet method of printing edible images on cakes and biscuits. P&G adapted the method for crisps, and the result was double-digit growth for its North American Pringles business.

Based on: Procter & Gamble (2012); Huston and Sakkab (2006); Mitchell (2005)

A major source of good ideas is consumers themselves. Their needs may not be satisfied by existing products and they may be genuinely interested in providing ideas that lead to product improvement. Sometimes, traditional marketing research techniques such as focus groups can be useful. Other companies require a less traditional approach. Procter & Gamble, for example, has used ethnographic research to observe consumers using its products, in order to develop new and improved products. Philips has employed anthropologists and cognitive psychologists to gather insights into the needs and expectations of consumers around the world. Online, researching blogs and social community sites can reveal ideas for new products and give insights into the strengths and weaknesses of existing products, which can lead to improved product replacements.

 Scan the QR code to see the approach used by Kenco Coffee to product innovation.

In organizational markets, keeping in close contact with customers who are innovators and market leaders in their own marketplace is likely to be a fruitful source of new product ideas (Parkinson, 1982). These *lead customers* are likely to recognize required improvements ahead of other customers as they have advanced needs and are likely to face problems before other product users. For example, GE's healthcare division researches 'luminaries', who tend to be well-published doctors and research scientists from leading medical institutions. Up to 25 luminaries are brought together at regular medical advisory board sessions to discuss developments in GE's technology. GE then shares some of its advanced technology with a subset of these people. The result is a stream of new products that emerge from collaboration with these groups. Marketing research can play a role in providing feedback when the product line is familiar to customers. However, for radically new products customers may be unable to articulate their requirements and so conventional marketing research may be ineffective as a source of ideas. In this situation, as can be seen in Marketing in Action 11.4, companies need to be proactive in their search for new markets rather than rely on customer suggestions (Johne, 1992).

MARKETING IN ACTION 11.4
Creating Radical Innovation

Many new products are incremental, such as Diet Coke from Coca-Cola, or Persil Bio Action laundry capsules from Unilever; others fundamentally change the nature of a market and may be based on technological breakthroughs such as the wearable technologies like the iWatch from Apple, or the invention of new business models such as that of Google, which freely gives away its core search product for free, or Starbucks' reinvention of city-centre coffee drinking. Radical innovation is risky but can bring huge rewards, creating new markets and destroying old ones. The focus is on making the competition irrelevant by creating a leap in value for customers, and entry into new and uncontested market space.

Avoiding an incremental approach to new product development involves a sharpening of the corporate imagination to become more alive to new market opportunities. Five factors can aid this development.

1 *Escaping the tyranny of served markets*: looking outside markets that are currently served can be assisted by defining core competences and looking at products/markets that lie between existing business units. For example, Motorola's core competences in wireless technology led it to look beyond current products/markets (e.g. mobile phones) and towards global positioning satellite receivers.

2 *Searching for innovative product concepts*: this can be aided by viewing markets as a set of customer needs and product functionalities. This has led to adding an important function to an existing product (e.g. Yamaha's electronic piano), creating a new way to deliver an existing function (e.g. electronic notepads), or creating a new functionality (e.g. web browsers, search engines).

3 *Weakening traditional price–performance assumptions*: traditional price–performance assumptions should be questioned. For example, the price of drone technology, or unmanned aerial vehicles (UAVs), used to provide satellite signals to inaccessible parts, has fallen dramatically. Originally, this highly sophisticated technology cost thousands of dollars, but firms like Google and Facebook have been developing low-flying solar-powered drones to widen Internet access in remote locations, and in doing so have significantly reduced the cost. 3D Robotics is selling UAVs at less than $700.

4 *Leading customers*: a problem with developing truly innovative products is that customers rarely ask for them. Successful innovating companies lead customers by imagining unarticulated needs rather than simply following them. They gain insights into incipient needs by talking in-depth to and observing closely a market's most sophisticated and demanding customers. For example, Gillette held focus groups with female customers to find out how often they used their razors. In their focus groups, the women said they changed their razor blades regularly. However, Gillette carried out an ethnographic study by going to the homes of the women in the survey. The researchers found that the women regularly forgot to keep a supply of spare blades close to their shower. The outcome was the launch of the Venus razor with an in-shower blade dispenser making it more convenient for consumers. This also sold many more razor blades to women.

5 *Building a radical innovation hub*: a hub is a group of people who encourage and oversee innovation. It includes idea hunters, idea gatherers, internal venture capitalists, members of project evaluation committees, members of overseeing boards and experienced entrepreneurs. The hub's prime function is to nurture hunters and gatherers from all over the company to foster a stream of innovative ideas. Innovation hubs, which foster innovation and enterprise, have developed across the globe from Silicon Valley to Zurich and Helsinki.

The attitudes and practices within innovative firms are also important and help create a culture that assists in driving radical innovation. Attitudes include a tolerance for risk-taking and a future market focus that encourages managers to seek customer needs through strategic futures research. Key practices are the empowerment of product champions, which encourages them (supported by resources) to explore research and build on promising, but uncertain, future technologies, and the use of generous financial and non-financial (e.g. recognition and autonomy) rewards for innovative employees.

Based on: Belton (2015); Nadworny (2014); Moules (2013); Moosmayer and Koehn (2011); Tellis, Prabhu and Chandy (2009)

Screening

Having developed new product ideas, they need to be screened to evaluate their commercial worth. Some companies use formal checklists to help them judge whether the product idea should be rejected or accepted for further evaluation. This ensures that no important criterion is overlooked. Criteria may be used that measure the attractiveness of the market for the proposed product, the fit between the product and company objectives, and the capability of the company to produce and market the product.

Concept testing

Once the product idea has been accepted as worthy of further investigation, it can be framed into a specific concept for testing with potential customers. In many instances the basic product idea will be expanded into several product concepts, each of which can be compared by testing with target customers. For example, a study into the acceptability of a new service—a proposed audit of software development procedures that would lead to the award of a quality assurance certificate—was expressed in eight service concepts depending on which parts of the development procedure would be audited (e.g. understanding customer needs, documentation, benchmarking, and so on). Each concept was evaluated by potential buyers of the software to gauge which were the most important aspects of software development that should be audited (Jobber et al., 1989). Concept testing thus allows the views of customers to enter the new product development process at an early stage.

Group discussion can also be used to develop and test product concepts. The concept may be described verbally or pictorially so that the major features are understood. Potential customers can then state whether they perceive any benefits accruing from the features. A questionnaire is used to ascertain the extent of liking/disliking what is liked/disliked, the kind of person/organization that might buy the product, how/where/when/how often the product would be used, its price acceptability, and how likely they would be to buy the product.

Online marketing research is being used increasingly to test concepts, partly because of its relatively low cost. Companies such as Lego, BA, Philips and P&G have set up their own digital communities where they can test consumers' reactions to new product concepts. Considerable ingenuity is needed to research new product concepts. Some companies, such as Diageo, have developed their own highly innovative centres for concept testing. Shop Direct's user experience lab (UX lab) has been designed to help develop better understanding of online shoppers at its websites; for example very.co.uk, isme.co.uk and littlewoods.co.uk. Many innovations have emerged and contributed to Shop Direct's online success.

Often a consideration of buying intentions is a key factor in judging whether any of the concepts are worth pursuing further. In the grocery and toiletries industries, for example, companies (and their marketing research agencies) often use *action standards* (e.g. more than 70 per cent of respondents must say they intend to buy) based on past experience to judge new product concepts. Concept testing allows a relatively inexpensive judgement to be made by customers before embarking on a costly product development programme. Although concept testing is not foolproof, obvious non-starters can be eliminated early on in the process.

Business analysis

Based on the results of the concept test and considerable managerial judgement, estimates of sales, costs and profits will be made. This is the business analysis stage. In order to produce sensible figures a marketing analysis will need to be undertaken. This will identify the target market, its size and projected product acceptance over a number of years. Consideration will be given to various prices and the implications for sales revenue (and profits) discussed. By setting a tentative price this analysis will provide sales revenue estimates.

Costs will also need to be estimated. If the new product is similar to existing products (e.g. a brand extension) it should be fairly easy to produce accurate cost estimates. For radical product concepts, costings may be nothing more than informal 'guesstimates'.

Break-even analysis, where the quantity needed to be sold to cover costs is calculated, may be used to establish whether the project is financially feasible. *Sensitivity analysis*, in which variations from given assumptions about price, cost and customer acceptance, for example, are checked to see how they impact on sales revenue and profits, can also prove useful at this stage. Optimistic, most likely and pessimistic scenarios can be drawn up to estimate the degree of risk attached to the project.

If the product concept appears commercially feasible, this process will result in marketing and product development budgets being established based on what appears to be necessary to gain customer awareness and trial, and the work required to turn the concept into a marketable product.

Read Marketing in Action 11.5 to find out how 3D printers can turn ideas into reality.

Product development

At this stage, the new product concept is developed into a physical product. As we have seen, the trend is to move from a situation where this is the sole responsibility of the R&D and/or engineering department. Multi-disciplinary project teams are established with the task of bringing the product to the marketplace. A study by Wheelwright and Clark (1992) lays out six key principles for the effective management of such teams.

1 *Mission*: senior management must agree to a clear mission through a project charter that lays out broad objectives.
2 *Organization*: the appointment of a heavyweight project leader and a core team consisting of one member from each primary function in the company. Core members should not occupy a similar position on another team.
3 *Project plan*: creation by the project leader and core team of a contract book, which includes a work plan, resource requirements and objectives against which it is willing to be evaluated.
4 *Project leadership*: heavyweight leaders not only lead, manage and evaluate other members of the core team, they also act as product champions. They spend time talking to project contributors inside and outside the company, as well as customers and distributors, so that the team keeps in touch with the market.
5 *Responsibilities*: all core members share responsibility for the overall success of the project as well as their own functional responsibilities.
6 *Executive sponsorship*: an executive sponsor in senior management is required to act as a channel for communication with top management and to act as coach and mentor for the project and its leader.

MARKETING IN ACTION 11.5
3D Printers

3D technology is now widely available commercially. 3D printing brings manufacturing to your desktop.
3D printers create physical replicas of images from computer screens. A 3D form can be created layer by layer.

Globally, it is estimated that by 2018 the market for 3D printers will be approaching $20 billion. But this is just the beginning as more and more practical applications for this new technology emerge.
According to Lisa Harouni (2011), we are witnessing 'an industrial revolution in the digital age'. This type of technology is not new; it has been around for about 20 years, but it is only now that the bespoke products built on demand are beginning to find a niche

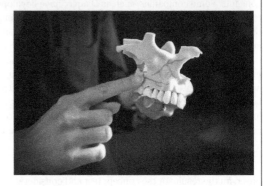

(but growing) market. There are advantages to this form of bespoke manufacturing: it is very localized and significantly reduces carbon footprints, and there is less waste too.

Currently, this technology is being increasingly used to produce body parts and medical devices. 3D printing is improving efficiency and significantly lowering the cost of production in the area of medical health. Additionally, the printers produce high quality products and have even been used to form face replicas and soft tissue used in bone grafts.

The car industry is also using 3D printer technology. Fiat Chrysler has developed models that can be used in engine testing. So, in the future we may be able to download physical goods like car parts, jewellery, phone covers and even chocolates in a similar way to which we download music, software and movies today.

Based on: Rowan (2011); Wheeler (2015)

The aim is to integrate the skills of designers, engineers and production, finance and marketing specialists so that product development is quicker, less costly and results in a high-quality product that delights customers. For example, the practice of **simultaneous engineering** means that designers and production engineers work together rather than passing the project from one stage of development to another once the first department's work is finished. Costs are controlled by a method called *target costing*. Target costs are worked out on the basis of target prices in the marketplace, and given as engineering/design and production targets.

Cutting time to market by reducing the length of the product development stage is a key marketing factor in many industries. This process, known as *virtual engineering*, has been used by Fiat, which, when designing its Bravo and 500, chose to rely solely on computer simulations rather than take the traditional route of making prototypes. This cut design-to-production time from 26 to 18 months (*The Economist*, 2008). In addition, three-dimensional CAD system designs can be shared with suppliers and customers. For example, Boeing engages customers such as British Airways and United Airlines in an online design process that allows them to engage in debates over alternative cabin layouts.

There are two reasons why product development is being accelerated. First, markets such as personal computers, digital cameras, laptops and cars change so fast that to be slow means running the risk of being out of date before the product is launched. Second, cutting time to market can lead to competitive advantage. This may be short-lived but is still valuable while it lasts. For example, Zara being consistently the fastest to market gives the company a competitive advantage in the fashion industry.

Marketing has an important role to play in the product development stage. R&D and engineering may focus on the functional aspects of the product, whereas seemingly trivial factors may have an important bearing on customer choice. For example, the foam that appears when washing-up liquid is added to water has no functional value—a washing-up liquid could be produced that cleans just as effectively but does not produce bubbles. However, the customer sees the foam as a visual cue that indicates the power of the washing-up liquid. Therefore, to market a brand that did not produce bubbles would have a negative outcome. Marketing needs to keep the project team aware of such psychological factors when developing the new product. Marketing staff need to make sure that the project team members understand and communicate the important attributes that customers are looking for in the product.

In the grocery market, marketing will usually brief R&D staff on the product concept, and the latter will be charged with the job of turning the concept into reality. For example, Yoplait, the French dairy cooperative and market leader in fruit yoghurts, found through marketing research that a yoghurt concept based on the following attributes could be a winner.

- Top-of-the-range dessert
- Position on a health–leisure scale at the far end of the pleasure range—the ultimate taste sensation
- A fruit yoghurt that is extremely thick and creamy

This was the brief given to the Yoplait research and development team that had the task of coming up with recipes for the new yoghurt and the best way of manufacturing it. Its job was to experiment with different cream/fruit combinations to produce the right product—one that matched the product concept—and to do it quickly. Time to market was crucial in this fast-moving industry. To help them, Yoplait employed a panel of expert tasters to try out the new recipes and evaluate them in terms of texture, sweetness, acidity, colour, smell, consistency and size of the fruit.

Product testing focuses on the functional aspects of the product and on consumer acceptance. Functional tests are carried out in the laboratory and out in the field to check such aspects as safety, performance and shelf life. For example, a car's braking system must be efficient, a jet engine must be capable of generating a certain level of thrust and a food package must be capable of keeping its contents fresh. Product testing of software products by users is crucially important in removing any 'bugs' that have not been picked up by internal testers. For example, Google releases new products as 'betas' (unfinished versions) so that users can check for problems and suggest improvements (Jarvis, 2009).

Market testing

So far in the development process, potential customers have been asked if they intend to buy the product but have never been placed in the position of having to pay for it. **Market testing** takes measurement of customer acceptance one crucial step further than product testing by forcing consumers to 'put their money where their mouth is'. The basic idea is to launch the new product in a limited way so that consumer response in the marketplace can be assessed. Two major methods are used: the simulated market test and test marketing.

The *simulated market test* can take a number of forms, but the principle is to set up a realistic market situation in which a sample of consumers chooses to buy goods from a range provided by the organizing company, usually a marketing research company. For example, a sample of consumers may be recruited to buy their groceries from a mobile supermarket that visits them once a week. They are provided with a magazine in which advertisements and sales promotions for the new product can appear. This method allows measurement of key success indicators such as *penetration* (the proportion of consumers that buy the new product at least once) and *repeat purchase* (the rate at which purchasers buy again) to be made. If penetration is high but repeat purchase low, buyers can be asked why they rejected the product after trial. Simulated market tests are therefore useful as a preliminary to test marketing by spotting problems, such as in packaging and product formulation, that can be rectified before test market launch. They can also be useful in eliminating new products that perform so badly compared to competition in the marketplace that test marketing is not justified. Indeed, as techniques associated with simulated market tests become more sophisticated and distributors increasingly refuse to cooperate in test marketing, they have become an attractive alternative to a full test market (Chisnall, 2005).

Test marketing involves the launch of the new product in one or a few geographical areas chosen to be representative of its intended market. Towns or television areas are chosen in which the new product is sold into distribution outlets so that performance can be gauged face to face with rival products. Test marketing is the acid test of new product development since the product is being promoted as it would during a national launch, and consumers are being asked to choose it against competitor products as they would if the new product went national. It is a more realistic test than the simulated market test and therefore gives more accurate sales penetration and repeat purchasing estimates. By projecting test marketing results to the full market, an assessment of the new product's likely success can be made.

Test marketing does have a number of potential problems. Test towns and areas may not be representative of the national market, and thus sales projections may be inaccurate. Competitors may invalidate the test market by giving distributors incentives to stock their product, thereby denying the new product shelf space. Also, test marketing needs to run over a long enough period to measure the repeat purchase rate for the product, since this is a crucial indicator of success for many products (e.g. groceries and toiletries). This can mean a delay in national launch stretching to many months or even years. In the meantime, more aggressive competitors can launch a rival product nationally and therefore gain market pioneer advantages. A final practical problem is gaining the cooperation of distributors. In some instances, supermarket chains refuse to take part in test marketing activities or charge a hefty fee for the service.

The advantages of test marketing are that the information it provides facilitates the 'go/no go' national launch decision, and the effectiveness of the marketing mix elements—price, product formulation/packaging, promotion and distribution—can be checked for effectiveness. Sometimes, a number of test areas are used with different marketing mix combinations to predict the most successful launch strategy. Its purpose therefore is to reduce the risk of a costly and embarrassing national launch mistake.

Although test marketing is commonly associated with fast-moving consumer goods, service companies use test marketing to check new service offerings. Indeed, when they control the supply chain, as is the case with banks and restaurants, they are in an ideal situation to do so. Companies selling to organizations can also benefit from test marketing when their products have short repeat purchase periods (e.g. adhesives and abrasives). For very expensive equipment, however, test marketing is usually impractical, although as we have seen product development with lead users is to be recommended.

On a global scale, many international companies roll out products (e.g. cars and consumer electronics) from one country to another. In so doing they are gaining some of the benefits of test marketing in that lessons learned early on can be applied to later launches.

Commercialization

In this section we shall examine four issues: a general approach to developing a commercialization strategy for a new product, specific options for product replacement strategies, success factors when commercializing technology, and reacting to competitors' new product introductions.

Developing a commercialization strategy for a new product

An effective commercialization strategy relies upon marketing management making clear choices regarding the target market (where it wishes to compete), and the development of a marketing strategy that provides a differential advantage (how it wishes to compete). These two factors define the new product positioning strategy, as discussed in Chapter 20.

A useful starting point for choosing a target market is an understanding of the diffusion of innovation process (Rogers, 2003). This explains how a new product spreads throughout a market over time. Particularly important is the notion that not all people or organizations who make up the market will be in the same state of readiness to buy the new product when it is launched. In other words, different actors in the market will have varying degrees of innovativeness— that is, their willingness to try something new. Figure 11.3 shows the *diffusion of innovation* curve which categorizes people or organizations according to how soon they are willing to adopt the innovation.

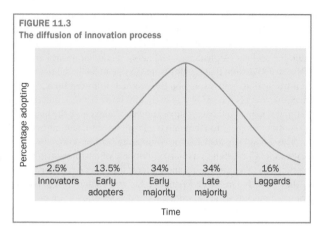

FIGURE 11.3
The diffusion of innovation process

| 2.5% Innovators | 13.5% Early adopters | 34% Early majority | 34% Late majority | 16% Laggards |

Percentage adopting

Time

The curve shows that those actors (*innovators* and *early adopters*) who were willing to buy the new product soon after launch are likely to form a minor part of the total number of actors who will eventually be willing to buy it. As the new product is accepted and approved by these customers, and the decision to buy the new product therefore becomes less risky, so the people that make up the bulk of the market, comprising the *early and late majority*, begin to try the product themselves. Finally, after the product has gained full market acceptance, a group suitably described as the *laggards* adopt the product. By the time the laggards have begun buying the product, the innovators and early adopters have probably moved on to something new.

This diffusion of innovation categories has a crucial role to play in the choice of target market. The key is to understand the characteristics of the innovator and early adopter categories and target them at launch. Simply thinking about the kinds of people or organizations that are more likely to buy a new product early after launch may suffice. If not, marketing research can help. To stimulate the thinking process, Rogers suggests the following broad characteristics for each category (Rogers, 2003).

- *Innovators:* these are often venturesome and like to be different; they are willing to take a chance with an untried product. In consumer markets they tend to be younger, better educated, more confident and more financially affluent, and consequently can afford to take a chance on buying something new. In organizational markets, they tend to be larger and more profitable companies if the innovation is costly, and have more progressive, better-educated management. They may themselves have a good track record in bringing out new products and may have been the first to adopt innovations in the past. As such they may be easy to identify.
- *Early adopters:* these are not quite so venturesome; they need the comfort of knowing someone else has taken the early risk. But they soon follow their lead. They still tend to have similar characteristics to the innovator group, since they need affluence and self-confidence to buy a product that has not yet gained market acceptance. They, together with the innovators, can be seen as opinion leaders who strongly influence other people's views on the product. As such, they have a major bearing on the success of the product. One way of looking at the early adopters is that they filter the products accepted by the innovator group and popularize them, leading to acceptance by the majority of buyers in the market (Zikmund and D'Amico, 1999).
- *Early and late majorities:* these form the bulk of the customers in the market. The early majority are usually deliberate and cautious in their approach to buying products. They like to see products prove themselves on the market before they are willing to part with cash for them. The late majority are even more cautious, and possibly sceptical of new products. They are willing to adopt only after the majority of people or organizations have tried the products. Social pressure may be the driving force moving them to purchase.
- *Laggards:* these are tradition-bound people. The innovation needs to be perceived almost as a traditional product before they will consider buying it. In consumer markets they are often the older and less well-educated members of the population.

 Scan the QR code to see how Samsung's Galaxy S6 smartphone advert targets early adopters.

These categories, then, can provide a basis for segmenting the market for an innovative product (see Chapter 20) and for target market selection (Easingwood and Beard, 1989). For example, Samsung Electronics directs much of its marketing effort towards the innovator/early adopter segments by targeting what it calls 'high-life seekers'—consumers who adopt technology early and are prepared to pay a premium price for it (Pesola, 2005). Note that the diffusion curve can be linked to the product lifecycle, which is discussed in Chapter 20. At introduction, innovators buy the product, followed by early adopters as the product enters the growth phase. Growth is fuelled by the early and late majority, and stable sales during the maturity phase may be due to repurchasing by these groups. Laggards may enter the market during late maturity or even decline. Thus promotion designed to stimulate trial may need to be modified as the nature of new buyers changes over time.

The second key decision for commercialization is the choice of marketing strategy to establish a differential advantage. Understanding the requirements of customers (in particular, the innovator and early adopter groups) is crucial to this process and should have taken place earlier in the new product development process. The design of the marketing mix will depend on this understanding and the rate of adoption will be affected by such decisions. For example, advertising, promotion and sales efforts can generate awareness and reduce the customer's search costs, sales promotional incentives can encourage trial, and educating users in product benefits and applications has been found to speed the adoption process (see Mahajan, Muller and Kerin, 1987; Robertson and Gatignon, 1986; Tzokas and Saren, 1992). The innovative Philips MRI scanner is an example of a company tapping in to the needs of customers in an attempt to create a differential advantage.

As we have seen, the characteristics of customers affect the rate of adoption of an innovation, and marketing's job is to identify and target those with a high willingness to adopt upon launch. The characteristics of the product being launched also affect the diffusion rate and have marketing strategy implications (see Figure 11.4).

First, its differential advantage compared to existing products affects the speed of adoption. The more added customer benefits a product gives to a customer the more customers will be willing to buy. The high differential advantage of a fax machine over sending telegrams (e.g. convenience) or letters (e.g. speed) meant fast adoption. In turn, the convenience of email over fax has meant rapid adoption. The differential advantage can be psychological. More recently, the adoption of the iPad can be explained by high functional (mobile email and Internet access) and psychological (status symbol among business people) benefits.

Second, there is the innovation's *compatibility* with consumers' values, experiences, lifestyles and behaviours. The congruence between mobile phones and the lifestyles of many young people helped their diffusion. The iPhone's rapid diffusion was also aided by such compatibility. The new product also needs to be compatible with consumers' behaviour. If its adoption depends on significant behaviour change, failure or prolonged diffusion may result. For example, the unsuccessful Dvorak typing keyboard was supposed to modestly increase typing speed, but at the behavioural cost of having to 'unlearn' the QWERTY keyboard. Although the telephone is now part of our everyday lives, diffusion was slow because its adoption required significant behaviour change (Gourville,

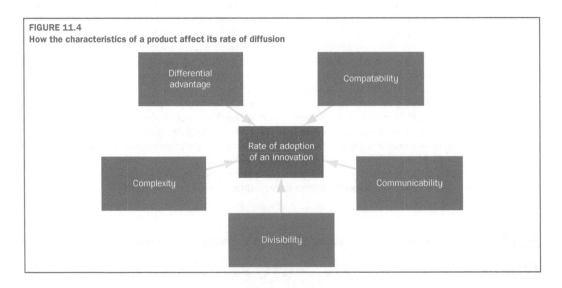

FIGURE 11.4
How the characteristics of a product affect its rate of diffusion

2006). The diffusion of e-books has also been slow, partly because people value the tactility and aesthetics of books rather than reading from an electronic screen.

A third factor affecting diffusion rate is the innovation's *complexity*. Products that are difficult to understand or use may take longer to be adopted. For example, Apple launched its Macintosh computer backed by the proposition that existing computers were too complex to gain widespread adoption. By making its model more user friendly, it gained fast adoption among the large segment of the population that was repelled by the complexity of using computers.

Fourth, an innovation's *divisibility* also affects its speed of diffusion. Divisibility refers to the degree to which the product can be tried on a limited basis. Inexpensive products can be tried without risk of heavy financial loss. The rapid diffusion of Google was aided by the fact that its functionality could be accessed free of charge.

The final product characteristic that affects the rate of diffusion of an innovation is its *communicability*. Adoption is likely to be faster if the benefits and applications of the innovation can be readily observed or described to target customers. If product benefits are long term or difficult to quantify, then diffusion may take longer. For example, Skoda's attempt to produce more reliable cars took time to communicate, as buyers' acceptance of this claim depended on their long-term experience of driving the cars. In service industries, marketing innovations like providing more staff to improve the quality of service are hard to quantify in financial terms (i.e. extra revenue generated) and therefore have a low adoption rate by the management of some companies. The marketing implications are that marketing management must not assume that what is obvious to them will be clear to customers. They need to devise a communications strategy that allows potential customers to become aware of the innovation, and understand and be convinced of its benefits.

Product replacement strategies

As we found at the start of this chapter, product replacement is the most common form of new product introduction. A study of the marketing strategies used to position *product replacements* in the marketplace found eight approaches based on a combination of product change and other marketing modifications (i.e. marketing mix and target market changes) (Saunders and Jobber, 1994a). Figure 11.5 shows the eight replacement strategies used by companies.

1 *Facelift*: minor product change with little or no change to the rest of the marketing mix or target market. Cars are often given facelifts midway through their lifecycle by undergoing minor styling alterations; for example, Chinese and Japanese companies constantly facelift current electronic products such as cameras, LCD screen and smart televisions, tablet and laptop computers and smartphones by changing product features, a process known as **product churning**.

2 *Inconspicuous technological substitution*: a major technological change with little or no alteration of the other elements of the marketing mix. The technological change is not brought to the consumer's attention, a strategy often used by washing powder manufacturers, where the improved performance rather than the technological change is brought to the consumers' attention (e.g. Skip intelligent liquid detergent, which has Fibre Protect technology).

3 *Remerchandising*: a modification of name, promotion, price, packaging and/ or distribution, while maintaining the basic product. For example, Danone's Bio yoghurt changed to Activia; Jif cleaning products were rebranded as Cif; Orange mobile became Everything Everywhere (EE) in the UK when it merged with T-Mobile.

4 *Relaunch*: both the product and other marketing mix elements are changed. Relaunches are common in the car industry where, every four to five years, a model is replaced with an upgraded version. Sky has relaunched Sky 1, 2 and 3 channels as Sky Atlantic, Sky Living and Sky HD.

FIGURE 11.5
Product replacement strategies

		No change	Product modified	Technology change
Marketing	No change	No change	Facelift	Inconspicuous technological substitution
	Remix	Remerchandising	Relaunch	Conspicuous technological substitution
	New market/ segment	Intangible repositioning	Tangible repositioning	Neo-innovation

Source: Saunders and Jobber (1994b)

5   *Conspicuous technological substitution*: a major technological change is accompanied by heavy promotional and other mix changes to stimulate awareness and trial. An example is the replacement of the Rover Mini with the BMW Mini, which, despite remaining faithful to the character of the original, is technologically a fundamentally different car.

6   *Intangible repositioning*: the basic product is retained but other mix elements and target customers change. Diageo has retained the product (Piat D'Or wine) but is targeting a new audience of 45–50-year-old female wine drinkers. New packaging is designed to give clearer branding and shelf appeal (Fox, 2010).

7   *Tangible repositioning*: both the product and target market change. Skoda is an example of the product being significantly improved to appeal to a more upmarket, wealthier target market.

EXHIBIT 11.1
Orange mobile became Everything Everywhere (EE) in the UK when it merged with T-Mobile

8   *Neo-innovation*: a fundamental technology change accompanied by target market and mix changes. For example, Samsung's move into the sustainable energy market has seen the development of new technology for new target customers.

Companies, therefore, face an array of replacement options with varying degrees of risk. Figure 11.5 categorizes these options and provides an aid to strategic thinking when considering how to replace products in the marketplace.

Commercializing technology

Superior commercialization of technology has been, and will continue to be, a key success factor in many industries. Some companies make a significant commitment to developing the capability to bring sophisticated high-tech products to market faster than other companies that treat the commercialization process in a less disciplined manner. For example, Volkswagen spends around $13.5 billion on R&D, which is approximately 5.2 per cent of its revenue. Much of its recent investment has been on highbred vehicles and semi-autonomous features. Samsung spent a similar amount investing in smart televisions and other advanced projection devices. Intel has spent over 20 per cent of is revenue on R&D to keep pace with the demands for ever-increasing computing power. Its latest 14 nm Intel Core M processor is much smaller in size than the previous processor and has 20 per cent longer battery life and 60 per cent less energy consumption (Casey and Hackett, 2014).

Marketing's input in such situations is to provide the insight as to how the technology may provide customer benefits within a prescribed target market. For example, as we have already discussed, traditional marketing research techniques have only a limited role to play when using technology to create new markets; people find it difficult to articulate their views on subjects that are unfamiliar, and acceptance may come only over time (the diffusion of innovation). Indeed, the price the customer will be asked to pay is usually unclear during the early stage of technological development. A combination of these factors may have been responsible for the first-ever forecast for computers, which predicted worldwide sales of 10 units.

The marketing of technological innovations, therefore, calls for a blend of technology and marketing. The basic marketing question, 'What potential benefits over existing products is this product likely to provide?', needs to be asked constantly during product development.

Furthermore, the following lessons from the diffusion of innovation curve need to be remembered.

- The innovator/early adopter segments need to be identified and targeted initially.
- Initial sales are likely to be low; these groups are relatively small.
- Patience is required as the diffusion of an innovation takes time as people/organizations originally resistant to it learn of its benefits and begin to adopt it.
- The target group and message will need to be modified over time as new categories of customer enter the market.

Competitive Reaction to New Product Introductions

New product launches may be in response to new product entries by competitors. Research suggests that when confronted with a new product entry by a competitor, incumbent firms should respond quickly with a limited set of marketing mix elements. Managers should rapidly decide which ones (product, promotion, price and place) are likely to have the most impact, and concentrate their efforts on them (Gatignon, Robertson and Fein, 1997).

Competitors' reaction times to the introduction of a new product have been found to depend on four factors (Bowman and Gatignon, 1995). First, response is faster in high-growth markets. Given the importance of such markets, competitors will feel the need to take action speedily in response to a new entrant. Second, response is dependent on the market shares held by the introducing firm and its competitors. Response time is slower when the introducing firm has higher market share and faster for those competitors who have higher market share. Third, response time is faster in markets characterized by frequent product changes. Finally, it is not surprising to find that response time is related to the time needed to develop the new product.

Scan the QR code to see how Samsung promoted its smart TV and learn about the creative ideas behind the advert.

When you have read this chapter

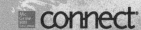

Discover further resources and test your understanding: McGraw-Hill **Connect**™ is a digital teaching and learning environment that improves performance over a variety of critical outcomes; it can be tailored, is easy to use and is proven effective. **LearnSmart**™ is the most widely used and intelligent adaptive learning resource that is proven to strengthen memory recall, improve course retention and boost grades. Fuelled by **LearnSmart**™, **SmartBook**™ is the first and only adaptive reading experience available today.

Review

1 **The different types of new product that can be launched**
   - There are four types of new product that can be launched: product replacements, additions to existing lines, new product lines and new-to-the-world products.

2 **How to create and nurture an innovative culture**
   - Creating and nurturing an innovative culture can be achieved by rewarding success heavily, tolerating a certain degree of failure, senior management sending clear messages about the role and importance of innovation, their words being supported by allowing staff time off to develop their own ideas, making available resources and being accessible when difficult decisions need to be taken, and resisting automatic nay-saying.

3 **The organizational options applying to new product development**
   - The options are project teams, product and brand managers, and new product departments and committees. Whichever method is used, effective cross-functional teamwork is essential for success.

4 **Methods of reducing time to market**
- A key method of reducing time to market is the process of simultaneous engineering. Design and production engineers, together with other staff, work together as a team rather than sequentially.
- Consumer goods companies are bringing together teams of brand and marketing managers, external design, advertising and research agency staff to develop simultaneously the brand and launch strategies.

5 **How marketing and R&D staff can work together effectively**
- A study by Gupta and Wileman suggests that marketing and R&D can better work together when teamwork is encouraged, there is an improvement in the provision of marketing information to R&D, R&D people are encouraged to be more customer aware, informal relationships between marketing and R&D are developed, marketing is encouraged to learn about technology, and a formal process of product development is implemented. Senior management staff have an important role to play by locating marketing and R&D close to each other, showing a personal interest in new product development, providing strategic direction, encouraging teamwork, increasing the resources devoted to new product development and enhancing their understanding of the importance of marketing in new product development.

6 **The stages in the new product development process**
- A formal process with review points, clear new product goals and a strong marketing orientation underlying the process leads to greater success.
- The stages are new product strategy (senior management should set objectives and priorities), idea generation (sources include customers, competitors, distributors, salespeople, engineers and marketers), screening (to evaluate their commercial worth), concept testing (to allow the views of target customers to enter the process early), product development (where the concept is developed into a physical product for testing), market testing (where the new product is tested in the marketplace) and commercialization (where the new product is launched).

7 **How to stimulate the corporate imagination**
- Four ways of stimulating the corporate imagination are: to encourage management to escape the tyranny of served markets by exploring how core competences can be exploited in new markets; to search for innovative product concepts—for example, by creating a new way to deliver an existing function (e.g. the electronic notepad); questioning traditional price–performance assumptions and giving engineers the resources to develop cheaper new products; and gaining insights by observing closely the market's most sophisticated and demanding customers.

8 **The six key principles of managing product teams**
- These are the agreement of the mission, effective organization, development of a project plan, strong leadership, shared responsibilities, and the establishment of an executive sponsor in senior management.

9 **The diffusion of innovation categories and their marketing implications**
- The categories are innovators, early adopters, early and late majorities, and laggards.
- The marketing implications are that the categories can be used as a basis for segmentation and targeting (initially the innovator/early adopters should be targeted). As the product is bought by different categories, so the marketing mix may need to change.
- The speed of adoption can be affected by marketing activities—for example, advertising to create awareness, sales promotion to stimulate trial, and educating users in product benefits and applications.
- The nature of the innovation itself can also affect adoption—that is, the strength of its differential advantage, its compatibility with people's values, experiences, lifestyles and behaviours, its complexity, its divisibility and its communicability.

10 **The key ingredients in commercializing technology quickly and effectively**
- The key ingredients are the ability of technologists and marketing people to work together effectively, simultaneous engineering, constantly asking the question 'What benefits over existing products is this new product likely to provide?', and remembering lessons from the diffusion of innovation curve (i.e. target the innovator/early adopter segments first).

Key Terms

brainstorming the technique where a group of people generate ideas without initial evaluation; only when the list of ideas is complete is each idea then evaluated

business analysis a review of the projected sales, costs and profits for a new product to establish whether these factors satisfy company objectives

concept testing testing new product ideas with potential customers

diffusion of innovation process the process by which a new product spreads throughout a market over time

innovation the commercialization of an invention by bringing it to market

invention the discovery of new methods and ideas

market testing the limited launch of a new product to test sales potential

product churning a continuous and rapid spiral of new product introductions

project teams the bringing together of staff from such areas as R&D, engineering, manufacturing, finance and marketing to work on a project such as new product development

simultaneous engineering the involvement of manufacturing and product development engineers in the same development team in an effort to reduce development time

test marketing the launch of a new product in one or a few geographic areas chosen to be representative of the intended market

Study Questions

1. Try to think of an unsatisfied need that you feel could be solved by the introduction of a new product. How would you set about testing your idea to examine its commercial potential?

2. How would you go about evaluating the idea?

3. What are the advantages and disadvantages of test marketing? In what circumstances should you be reluctant to use test marketing?

4. Your company has developed a new range of Thai curry sauce, intended to compete with the market leader. How would you conduct product tests for your new line?

5. What are the particular problems associated with commercializing technology? What are the key factors for success?

6. Discuss how marketing and R&D can form effective teams to develop new products.

Recommended Reading

Atuahene-Gima, K. (1996) Market orientation and innovation, *Journal of Business Research* 35(2) 93–103.

Fossas-Olalla, M., B. Minguela-Rata, J. López-Sánchez and J. Fernández-Menénde (2015) Product Innovation: when should suppliers begin to collaborate? *Journal of Business Research* 68(7), July, 1404–06.

Holman, R., H. Kaas and D. Keeling (2003) The future of product development, *McKinsey Quarterly* 3, 28–40.

Manu, F. and V. Sriram (1996) Innovation, marketing strategy, environment and performance, *Journal of Business Research* 35(1), January, 79–91.

Rogers, E. M. (2010) *Diffusion of innovations*, Simon and Schuster.

Tellis, G. (2013) *Unrelenting Innovation*, John Wiley & Sons Inc.

References

3M (2012) Who we are, http://solutions.3m.co.uk/wps/portal/3M/en_GB/about-3M/information/about/us.

Adler, P. S., H. E. Riggs and S. C. Wheelwright (1989) Product Development Know-How, *Sloan Management Review* 4, 7–17.

Belton, P. (2015). Game of drones: As prices plummet drones are taking off, BBC.co.uk, 16 January. http://www.bbc.co.uk/news/business-30820399

Bergen, S. A., R. Miyajima and C. P. McLaughlin (1988) The R&D/Production Interface in Four Developed Countries, *R&D Management* 18(3), 201–16.

Booz, Allen and Hamilton (1982) *New Products Management for the 1980s*, New York: Booz, Allen and Hamilton, Inc.

Boston Consulting Group (2012) The Most Innovative Companies 2012, Boston Consulting Group. https://www.bcgperspectives.com/content/articles/growth_innovation_the_most_innovative_companies_2012/?chapter=4 (accessed 20 April 2015).

Bowman, D. and H. Gatignon (1995) Determinants of Competitor Response Time to a New Product Introduction, *Journal of Marketing Research* 33, February, 42–53. Brentani, U. de (1991) Success Factors in Developing New Business Services, *European Journal of Marketing* 15(2), 33–59

Casey, M. and R. Hackett (2014) The 10 biggest R&D spenders worldwide, *Fortune*, 17 November. http://fortune.com/2014/11/17/top-10-research-development (accessed 20 April 2015).

Chisnall, P. (2005) *Marketing Research*, Maidenhead: McGraw-Hill.

Cooper, R. G. (1979) The Dimensions of Industrial New Product Success and Failure, *Journal of Marketing* 43 (Summer), 93–103;

Cooper, R. G. and E. J. Kleinschmidt (1986) An Investigation into the New Product Process: Steps, Deficiencies and Impact, *Journal of Product Innovation Management*, June, 71–85.

Day, P. (2012), http://www.bbc.co.uk/programmes/b01gvtjj.

Doyle, P. (1997) From the Top, *Guardian*, 2 August, 17.

Duggan, M. (2012) Frugal innovation, http://knowinnovation.com/frugal-innovation/

Dwyer, L. M. (1990) Factors Affecting the Proficient Management of Product Innovation, *International Journal of Technological Management* 5(6), 721–30.

Easingwood, C. and C. Beard (1989) High Technology Launch Strategies in the UK, *Industrial Marketing Management* 18, 125–38.

Fox, P. (2010) Piat d'Or launches first Sauvignon Blanc, http://www.talkingretail.com/products/drinks-news/piat-dor-launches-first-sauvignon-blanc, 1 July.

Fred, D. (1991) Learning the Ropes: My Life as a Product Champion, *Harvard Business Review*, Sept.–Oct, 46–56.

Gatignon, H., T. S. Robertson and A. J. Fein (1997) Incumbent Defence Strategies Against New Product Entry, *International Journal of Research in Marketing* 14, 163–76.

Geoghegan, J. (2011) Satnavs and smartphones put traditional maps on the road to nowhere as sales drop massively, The Mail online, http://www.dailymail.co.uk/sciencetech/article-2033227/Satnavs-smart-phones-traditional-maps-road-sales-drop-massively.html#ixzz1rwFKziSX, 3 September.

Gourville, J. (2006) The Curse of Innovation: Why Innovative Products Fail, MSI Report No. 05-117.

Govindarajan, V. and S. Srinivas (2013) The Innovation Mindset in Action: 3M Corporation, *Harvard Business review*, 6 August. https://hbr.org/2013/08/the-innovation-mindset-in-acti-3 (accessed 20 April 2015).

Gupta, A. K. and D. Wileman (1990) Improving R&D/Marketing Relations: R&D Perspective, *R&D Management* 20(4), 277–90.

Gupta, A. K. and D. Wileman (1991) Improving R&D/Marketing Relations in Technology Based Companies: Marketing's Perspective, *Journal of Marketing Management* 7(1), 25–46.

Hamel, G. and C. K. Prahalad (1991) Corporate Imagination and Expeditionary Marketing, *Harvard Business Review*, July–August, 81–92.

Harouni, L. (2011) A Primer on 3d Printing https://www.ted.com/talks/lisa_harouni_a_primer_on_3d_printing?language=en (accessed August 2015).

Hegarty, W. H. and R. C. Hoffman (1990) Product/Market Innovations: A Study of Top Management Involvement among Four Cultures, *Journal of Product Innovation Management* 7, 186–99.

Hise, R. T., L. O'Neal, A. Parasuraman and J. U. McNeal (1990) Marketing/R&D Interaction in New Product Development: Implications for New Product Success Rates, *Journal of Product Innovation Management* 7, 142–55.

Honey Bee (n.d.) http://www.sristi.org/hbnew

Huston, L. and N. Sakkab (2006) Connect and Develop: Inside Procter & Gamble's New Model for Innovation, *Harvard Business Review* 84(3), 58–72.

Jarvis, J. (2009) The Foresight of Google, *Media Guardian*, 9 February, 8.

Jobber, D., J. Saunders, G. Hooley, B. Gilding and J. Hatton-Smooker (1989) Assessing the Value of a Quality Assurance Certificate for Software: An Exploratory Investigation, *MIS Quarterly*, March, 19–31.

Johne, A. (1992) Don't Let Your Customers Lead You Astray in Developing New Products, *European Management Journal* 10(1), 80–4.

Johne, A. and C. Storey (1998) New Source Development: A Review of the Literature and Annotated Bibliography, *European Journal of Marketing* 32(3/4), 184–251.

Johne, A. and P. Snelson (1988) Auditing Product Innovation Activities in Manufacturing Firms, *R&D Management* 18(3), 227–33.

Joshi, A. W. and S. Sharma (2004) Customer Knowledge Development: Antecedents and Impact on New Product Performance, *Journal of Marketing*, 68 (October), 47–9.

Jugaad (2012) http://www.jugaad.org/?page_id=2.

Kadri, M. (2010) Finding innovation in every corner, http://changeobserver.designobserver.com/feature/findinginnovation-in-every-corner/12691/, 2 August.

Kashami, K. and T. Clayton (2000)—study reported in Murphy, D. Innovate or Die, *Marketing Business*, May, 16–18.

Koshler, R. (1991) Produkt—Innovation as management als Erfolgsfaktor, in Mueller-Boehling, D. *et al.* (eds) *Innovations—und Technologiemanagement*, Stuttgart: C. E. Poeschel Verlagi.

Kovacs, J. (2012) 3M and NJATC Join Forces to Develop Online Curriculum for All IBEW/NECA Electrical Workers, press release, 10 April, Market Watch, *Wall Street Journal*.

Levitt, T. (1960) Marketing Myopia, *Harvard Business Review*, July–August.

Mahajan, V., E. Muller and R. Kerin (1987) Introduction Strategy for New Product with Positive and Negative Word-of-Mouth, *Management Science* 30, 1389–404.

Maidique, M. A. and B. J. Zirger (1984) A Study of Success and Failure in Product Innovation: The Case of the US Electronics Industry, *IEEE Transactions in Engineering Management*, EM-31 (November), 192–203.

Matthews, V. (2002) Caution Versus Creativity, *Financial Times*, 17 June, 12.

McGregor, J. (2006) The World's Most Innovative Companies, *Business Week*, 24 April, 63–76.

Mitchell, A. (2005) After Some Innovation? Perhaps You Just Need to Ask Around, *Marketing Week*, 16 June, 28–9.

Moosmayer, D. C. and A. Koehn (2011) The moderating role of managers' uncertainty avoidance values on the performance impact of radical and incremental innovation, *International Journal of Business Research* 11(6), 32–39.

Moules, J. (2013) Tech start-ups: Innovation hubs all over world seek to follow Silicon Valley lead, *The Financial Times*, 11 June. http://www.ft.com/cms/s/2/e357a258-b3d2-11e2-b5a5-00144feabdc0.html#axzz3YdUGITLb (accessed 20 April 2015).

Nadworny, R. (2014) Observe your cusomters to unlock innovation, Burlington Free press, 18 December. http://www.burlingtonfreepress.com/story/money/industries/2014/12/18/nadworny-observe-customers-unlock-innovation/20554685

Parkinson, S. T. (1982) The Role of the User in Successful New Product Development, *R&D Management* 12, 123–31.

Pearson, D. (1993) Invent, Innovate and Improve, *Marketing*, 8 April, 15.

Pesola, M. (2005) Samsung Plays to the Young Generation, *Financial Times*, 29 March, 11.

Prahalad, C. K. and R. A. Mashelkar (2010) Innovation's Holy Grail, *Harvard Business Review*, July–August.

Procter & Gamble (2012) Connect + develop, http://www.pg.com/connect_develop/index.shtml.

Richard, H. (1996) Why Competitiveness is a Dirty Word in Scandinavia, *European*, 6–12 June, 24.

Robertson, T. S. and H. Gatignon (1986) Competitive Effects on Technology Diffusion, *Journal of Marketing* 50 (July), 1–12.

Rogers, E. M. (2003) *Diffusion of Innovations*, New York: Free Press.

Rowan, D. (2011) 3D printing—an industrial revolution in the digital age? *IWired*, 9 May, http://www.wired.com/epicenter/2011/05/3d-printing-an-industrial-revolution-in-the-digital-age.

Saunders, J. and D. Jobber (1994a) Product Replacement Strategies: Occurrence and Concurrence, *Journal of Product Innovation Management* (November).

Saunders, J. and D. Jobber (1994b) Strategies for Product Launch and Deletion, in Saunders, J. (ed.) *The Marketing Initiative*, Hemel Hempstead: Prentice-Hall, 227.

Shah, A. (2012) Causes of poverty, http://www.globalissues.org/issue/2/causes-of-poverty, 8 April.

Shrivastava, P. and W. E. Souder (1987) The Strategic Management of Technological Innovation: A Review and a Model, *Journal of Management Studies* 24(1), 24–41.

Slotegraaf, R. J. and K. Atuahene-Gima (2011) Product Development Team Stability and New Product Advantage: The Role of Decision-Making Processes, *Journal of Marketing* 75(1), 96–108.

Tellis, G., J. C. Prabhu and R. K. Chandy (2009) Radical Innovation Across Nations: The Preeminence of Corporate Culture, *Journal of Marketing* 73(1), 3–23.

The Economist (2008) Rebirth of a Carmaker, 26 April, 91–3.

The Economist (2012) Asian Innovation, http://www.economist.com/node/21551028, 24 March.

The Marketers (2008) Marketing Greats, May, 7.

Tzokas, N. and M. Saren (1992) Innovation Diffusion: The Emerging Role of Suppliers Versus the Traditional Dominance of Buyers, *Journal of Marketing Management* 8(1), 69–80.

Viklund, A. (2015) Brainstorming, http://teamvirtute.wordpress.com/promotingcreativity/brainstorming/.

Walsh, W. J. (1990) Get the Whole Organisation Behind New Product Development, *Research in Technological Management*, Nov.–Dec., 32–6.

Wheeler, A. (2015) 3D Printing Industry, *3D Printing Industry*, 23 April. http://3dprintingindustry.com/3dp-applications

Wheelwright, S. and K. Clark (1992) *Revolutionizing Product Development*, New York: Free Press.

Zikmund, W. G. and M. D'Amico (1999) *Marketing*, St Paul, MN: West.

CHAPTER 20
Product Strategy: Product Lifecycle, Portfolio Planning and Product Growth Strategies

Innovation distinguishes between a leader and a follower.

STEVE JOBS, APPLE INC.

LEARNING OBJECTIVES

After reading this chapter, you should be able to:

1. describe the concept of the product lifecycle
2. discuss the uses and limitations of the product lifecycle
3. describe the concept of product portfolio planning
4. explain the Boston Consulting Group Growth-Share Matrix, its uses and the criticisms of it
5. explain the General Electric Market Attractiveness–Competitive Position Model, its uses and the criticisms of it
6. discuss the contribution of product portfolio management
7. discuss product strategies for growth

T his chapter examines the application of analytical tools used in the area of strategic product planning beginning with the product lifecycle. This section also considers the implication for managing brands over a period of time. The next key topic area is managing brand and product line portfolios. Many companies handle numerous products and serve multiple markets segments. Consequently, managers need to address the question of where to place investment for product growth and where and when to withdraw resources. Such questions are considered in the second part of this chapter. Finally, the topic of product strategies for growth is explored.

Managing Product Lines and Brands over Time: the Product Lifecycle

No matter how wide the product mix, both product lines and individual brands need to be managed over time. A useful tool for conceptualizing the changes that may take place during the time that a product is on the market is called the product lifecycle. It is quite flexible and can be applied to both brands and product lines (Polli and Cook, 1969). For simplicity, in the rest of this chapter, brands and product lines will be referred to as products. We shall now look at the product lifecycle, before discussing its uses and limitations.

The classic product lifecycle has four stages (see Figure 20.1): introduction, growth, maturity and decline.

Introduction

When first introduced on to the market a product's sales growth is typically low, and losses are incurred because of heavy development and promotional costs. Companies will be monitoring the speed of product adoption and, if this is disappointing, may terminate the product at this stage.

All leading companies, such as Samsung, IBM, Mercedes, Toyota and Apple, invest heavily in new product development to create products that confer new features and benefits for consumers. Because of this heavy investment, high promotional expenditures and low sales, losses are often suffered during product introduction. Nokian Tyres has made a long-term investment in product research and innovations. The company's expertise in heavy-tyre manufacturing has made it a world-leading specialist manufacturer. It also invests in communicating the benefits of its products (Nokian, 2015).

 Scan the QR code to see how Nokian Tyres uses its features in its advertising.

Growth

This stage is characterized by a period of faster sales and profit growth. Sales growth is fuelled by rapid market acceptance and, for many products, repeat purchasing. Profits may begin to decline towards the latter stages of

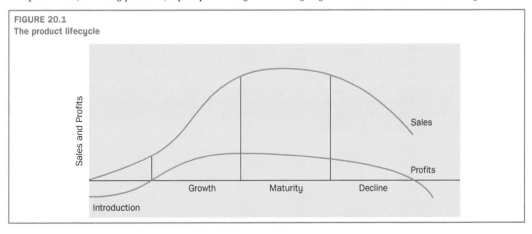

FIGURE 20.1
The product lifecycle

growth as new rivals enter the market, attracted by fast sales growth and high profit potential. The tablet computer market is an example of this. Apple introduced the iPad in 2010 and the rapid sales growth was mirrored by a vast increase in competitors such as Samsung Galaxy Tab and Hewlett-Packard TouchPad (see Exhibit 20.1). The smartphone market developed as technology innovation enabled mobile computing to be integrated into modern handsets. During the growth stage many rival technology companies entered the market with operating systems for the new type of phones, including Apple iOS, Google Android and Microsoft Windows. The end of the growth period is often associated with *competitive shakeout*, when weaker suppliers cease production. Technology markets are particularly susceptible. Read Marketing in Action 20.1 to find out about the winners and losers in the dot-com bubble.

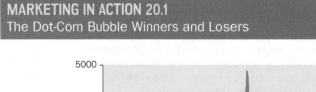

MARKETING IN ACTION 20.1
The Dot-Com Bubble Winners and Losers

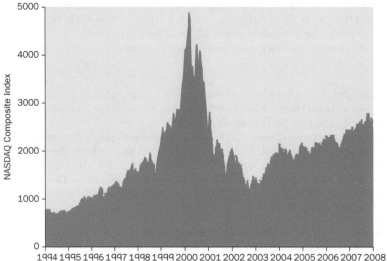

The size of the Internet economy started to grow rapidly from 1996. Between 1999 and 2001 there was a period of intense growth in the value of technology stocks. Forrester Research estimated the total Internet economy was worth US$15 billion, and by 2000 revenues from online consumer spending in the USA alone were estimated at US$45 billion (Boston Consulting Group, 2001). Predictions about the growth of online markets and the rapidly rising share prices got everyone excited. This was a rapid growth market. But there were very few Internet-savvy businesses offering stocks for sale. Investors scrambled to buy Internet stocks. The high demand and low level of supply created a trading frenzy, which stimulated exponential market growth (see image). In the retail sector, predictions suggested that 'by the year 2005 it (the Internet) would capture between 8 and 30 per cent of the UK retail market', leaving high streets looking like ghost towns. Extreme examples of increases in valuations and personal gains for the entrepreneurs (dot-com millionaires) helped to drive the growth even more. For example, Xcelera.com, developed by Norwegian Alexander Vik saw its stock soar from a few pennies to over $200 a share in less than a year, giving the company a market capitalization of $3.8 billion. Indeed, in 2000 there were 63 dot-com millionaires on the *Sunday Times* rich list but by 2001 this was down to just 26. The bubble burst and many innovative companies—which had rushed to move online—collapsed almost overnight. There were some notable winners and losers.

Winners:
- Google
- Amazon
- Lastminute.com
- eBay.

»

Losers:
- Boo.com (spent $180 million in six months trying to create a global fashion store, but went into bankruptcy in 2000)
- America Online (AOL) (merged with Time Warner)
- Geocities.com (bought out by Yahoo!)
- Webvan (filed for bankruptcy in 2001)
- Startups.com (failed in 2002)
- FreeInternet.com (filed for bankruptcy in October 2000)
- Pets.com (pet supplies retailer filed for bankruptcy in 2000).

Based on: Doherty, Ellis-Chadwick and Hart (2003); Ellis-Chadwick, Doherty and Hart (2002); Boston Consulting Group (2001); Pavitt (1997); Wikipedia (n.d.); Virzi (2000); Hudson (2010)

Maturity

Eventually sales peak and flatten as saturation occurs, hastening competitive shakeout. The survivors battle for market share by employing product improvements, advertising and sales promotional offers, dealer discounts and price cutting; the result is a strain on profit margins particularly for follower brands. The need for effective brand building is acutely recognized during maturity as brand leaders are in the strongest position to resist the pressure on profit margins (Doyle, 1989). Heinz has been advertising its brand of beans for over 40 years. The manufacturer differentiated the brand using the slogan 'Beanz Meanz Heinz'. Investment in this iconic advertising campaign enabled Heinz to fend off competitors and stimulate sales in a mature market.

Decline

Sales and profits fall during the decline stage as new technology or changes in consumer tastes work to reduce demand for the product. For example, Sony lost out when the market for cathode-ray TVs went into decline following the development of flat-screen TVs. The technological advance resulted in Samsung and Panasonic overtaking

EXHIBIT 20.1
Samsung reminds its customers there are no limits with new products in its Galaxy range

Sony in sales of televisions (Gapper, 2006). Suppliers may decide to cease production completely or reduce product depth. Promotional and product development budgets may be slashed and marginal distributors dropped as suppliers seek to maintain (or increase) profit margins. Advertising may be used to defend against rivals and prevent the sales of a brand from falling into decline.

Uses of the Product Lifecycle

The product lifecycle (PLC) concept is useful for product management in several ways.

Product termination

First, the PLC emphasizes the fact that nothing lasts for ever. There is a danger that management may fall in love with certain products. Maybe a company was founded on the success of a particular product; perhaps the product champion of a past success is now the chief executive. Under such circumstances there can be emotional ties with the product that can transcend normal commercial considerations. The PLC underlines the fact that companies have to face the fact that products need to be terminated and new products developed to replace them. Without this sequence a company may find itself with a group of products all in the decline stage of their PLC.

Growth projections

The second use of the PLC concept is to warn against the dangers of assuming that growth will continue for ever. Swept along by growing order books, management can fall into the trap of believing that the heady days of rising sales and profits will continue for ever. The PLC reminds managers that growth will end, and suggests a need for caution when planning investment in new production facilities.

Marketing objectives and strategies over the PLC

The PLC emphasizes the need to review marketing objectives and strategies as products pass through the various stages. Changes in market and competitive conditions between the PLC stages suggest that marketing strategies should be adapted to meet them. Table 20.1 shows a set of stylized marketing responses to each stage. Note these are broad generalizations and serve to emphasize the need to review marketing objectives and strategies in the light of environmental change.

TABLE 20.1 Marketing objectives and strategies over the product lifecycle				
	Introduction	**Growth**	**Maturity**	**Decline**
Strategic marketing objective	Build	Build	Hold	Harvest/manage for cash/divest
Strategic focus	Expand market	Penetration	Protect share/innovation	Productivity
Brand objective	Product awareness/trial	Brand preference	Brand loyalty	Brand exploitation
Products	Basic	Differentiated	Differentiated	Rationalized
Promotion	Creating awareness/trial	Creating awareness/ trial/ repeat purchase	Maintaining awareness/ repeat purchase	Cut/eliminated
Price	High	Lower	Lowest	Rising
Distribution	Patchy	Wider	Intensive	Selective

The strategic marketing objective is to build sales by expanding the market for the product. The brand objective will be to create product (as well as brand) awareness so that customers will become familiar with generic product benefits.

The product is likely to be fairly basic, with an emphasis on reliability and functionality rather than special features to appeal to different customer groups. For example, the introduction of the netbook when desktop computers were the de facto machine for all our computing needs. Then the laptop arrived which was a mobile equivalent. Generally, these machines were expensive, heavy and suffered from poor battery life. So there was a gap in the market for target audiences which wanted lighter machines to last longer while on the move. The netbook was able to fill this gap. Fairly basic models were offered, providing mobile computing and Internet access at affordable prices (e.g. Asus, Acer, Samsung). The functionality was basic, and the processor speed and memory fairly limited compared to their desktop and laptop counterparts. This lack of benefits eventually enabled other faster devices with a greater range of benefits to supersede the netbook—for example, tablet computers like the iPad and Microsoft Surface Pro, and smartphones like the Apple iPhone and Samsung Galaxy.

Promotion will support the brand objectives by gaining awareness for the brand and product type, and stimulating trial. Advertising has been found to be more effective in the beginning of the life of a product than in later stages (Vakratsas and Ambler, 1999). Typically price will be high because of the heavy development costs and the low level of competition. Distribution will be patchy as some dealers are wary of stocking the new product until it has proved to be successful in the marketplace.

Growth

The strategic marketing objective during the growth phase is to build sales and market share. The strategic focus will be to penetrate the market by building brand preference. To accomplish this task the product will be redesigned to create differentiation, and promotion will stress the functional and/or psychological benefits that accrue from the differentiation. Awareness and trial to acquire new customers are still important, but promotion will begin to focus on repeat purchasers. As development costs are defrayed and competition increases, prices will fall. Rising consumer demand and increased salesforce effort will widen distribution.

Maturity

As sales peak and stabilize, the strategic marketing objective will be to hold on to profits and sales by protecting market share rather than embarking on costly competitive challenges. Since sales gains can only be at the expense of competition, strong challenges are likely to be resisted and lead to costly promotional or price wars. Brand objectives now focus on maintaining brand loyalty and customer retention, and promotion will defend the brand, stimulating repeat purchase by maintaining brand awareness and values. For all but the brand leader, competition may erode prices and profit margins, while distribution will peak in line with sales.

A key focus will be innovation to extend the maturity stage or, preferably, inject growth. This may take the form of innovative promotional campaigns, product improvements, and extensions and technological innovation. Ways of increasing usage and reducing repeat purchase periods of the product will also be sought.

Decline

The conventional advice to companies managing products in the decline stage of the product lifecycle is to harvest or divest. A harvest strategy would result in the raising of prices while slashing marketing expenditures in an effort to boost profit margins. The strategic focus, therefore, is to improve marketing productivity rather than holding or building sales. The brand loyalty that has been built up over the years is in effect being exploited to create profits that can be used elsewhere in the company (e.g. new products). Product development will cease, the product line will be cut to the bare minimum of brands and promotional expenditure cut, possibly to zero. Distribution costs will be analyzed with a view to selecting only the most profitable outlets. The Internet will be examined to explore its potential as a low-cost promotional and distribution vehicle.

Divestment may take the form of selling products to other companies, or, if there are no willing buyers, product elimination. The strategy is to extract any residual value in the products where possible, and to free up managerial time and resources to be redirected at more attractive products and opportunities. Occasionally, products are harvested and then divested. For example, Nokia sold off its mobile phone business when it lost significant market share to rivals Apple and Samsung, so that it could focus its attention in other areas, for example mobile phone networks and mapping and location devices.

Two other strategies that can be applied at the decline stage are: 1) industry revitalization, and 2) pursuit of a profitable survivor strategy.

Industry revitalization: some products go into decline not because they are inherently unpopular but because of lack of investment. For example, years of under-investment in cinemas meant the facilities were often dilapidated and the programming offered limited choice of films. However, one company saw this scenario as a marketing opportunity. Showcase Cinemas was launched, offering a choice of around 12 films in modern purpose-built premises near large conurbations. This completely changed the experience of going to the cinema, resulting in revitalization of the industry and growth in cinema attendances and profits. Thus, the classic PLC prescription of harvesting in the decline stage was rejected by a company that was willing to invest in order to reposition cinemas as an attractive means of offering evening entertainment.

Profitable survivor strategy: another alternative to harvesting or divestment is called the profitable *survivor strategy* (Aaker, 2007). This involves deciding to become the sole survivor in a declining market. This may involve being willing to incur losses while competitors drop out, or if it is thought that this process is likely to be lengthy and slow, to accelerate it by:

- further reducing the attractiveness of the market by such actions as price cuts or increases in promotional expenditures
- buying competitors (which may be offered at a low price due to the unattractive markets they operate in) or their product lines that compete in the same market
- agreeing to take over competitors' contracts (e.g. supplying spare parts or service contracts) in exchange for their agreement to drop out of the market.

Once in the position of sole supplier, the survivor can reap the rewards of a monopolist by raising prices and resuming profitable operations.

Product planning

The PLC emphasizes the need for *product planning*. We have already discussed the need to replace old products with new. The PLC also stresses the need to analyse the balance of products that a company markets from the point of view of the PLC stages. A company with all of its products in the mature stage may be generating profits today, but as it enters the decline stage, profits may fall and the company become unprofitable. A balanced range of product is better, i.e. some products in the mature stage, some in the growth stage, and prospects of new product launches in the near future. The growth products would replace the mature products as the latter enter decline, and the new product successes would eventually become the growth products of the future. The PLC is, then, a stimulus to thinking about products as an interrelated set of profit-bearing assets that need to be managed as a group. We shall return to this theme when discussing product portfolio analysis later in this chapter.

The dangers of overpowering

The PLC concept highlights the dangers of overpowering. A company that introduces a new-to-the-world product may find itself in a very powerful position early in its PLC. Assuming that the new product confers unique benefits to customers there is an opportunity to charge a very high price during this period of monopoly supply. However, unless the product is patent-protected this strategy can turn sour when competition enters during the growth phase (as predicted by the PLC concept). This situation arose for the small components manufacturer that was the first to solve the technical problems associated with developing a seal in an exhaust recirculation valve used to reduce pollution in car emissions. The company took advantage of its monopoly supply position to charge very high prices to Ford. The strategy rebounded when competition entered and Ford discovered it had been overcharged (Cline and Shapiro, 1979). Had the small manufacturer been aware of the predictions of the PLC concept it may have anticipated competitive entry during the growth phase, and charged a lower price during introduction and early growth. This would have enabled it to begin a relationship-building exercise with Ford, possibly leading to greater returns in the long run.

Limitations of the Product Lifecycle

The product lifecycle is an aid to thinking about marketing decisions, but it needs to be handled with care. Management needs to be aware of the limitations of the PLC so that it is not misled by its prescriptions.

Fads and classics

Not all products follow the classic S-shaped curve. The sales of some products 'rise like a rocket then fall like a stick'. This is normal for *fad* products such as hula hoops (popularized in the 1950s), 'pet rocks' (1970s), Pokemon cards (1990s), and Zumba classes and superfoods such as quinoa (2010s).

Other products (and brands) appear to defy entering the decline stage. For example, classic confectionery products and brands such as Mars bars, Cadbury's Milk Tray and Toblerone have survived for decades in the mature stage of the PLC. Nevertheless, research has shown that the classic S-shaped curve does apply to a wide range of products, including grocery food products, and pharmaceuticals (Polli and Cook, 1969).

Marketing effects

The PLC is the *result* of marketing activities not the cause. One school of thought argues that the PLC is not simply a fact of life—unlike living organisms—but is simply a pattern of sales that reflects marketing activity (Dhalia and Yuspeh, 1976). Clearly, sales of a product may flatten or fall simply because it has not received enough marketing attention, or has had insufficient product redesign or promotional support. Using the PLC, argue the critics, may lead to inappropriate action (e.g. harvesting or dropping the product) when the correct response should be increased marketing support (e.g. product replacement, positioning reinforcement or repositioning).

Unpredictability

The duration of the PLC stages is unpredictable. The PLC outlines the four stages that a product passes through without defining their duration.

EXHIBIT 20.2
Toblerone uses magic and fantasy to maintain its position as a classic chocolate brand

Clearly this limits its use as a forecasting tool since it is not possible to predict when maturity or decline will begin. The exception to this problem is when it is possible to identify a comparator product that serves as a template for predicting the length of each stage. Two sources of comparator products exist: first, countries where the same product has already been on the market for some time; second, where similar products are in the mature or decline stages of their lifecycle but are thought to resemble the new product in terms of consumer acceptance. In practice, the use of comparator products is fraught with problems. For example, the economic and social conditions of countries may be so different that simplistic exploitation of the PLC from one country to another may be invalid; the use of similar products may offer inaccurate predictions in the face of ever-shortening product lifecycles.

Misleading objective and strategy prescriptions

The stylized marketing objectives and strategy prescriptions may be misleading. Even if a product could accurately be classified as being in a PLC stage, and sales are not simply a result of marketing activities, critics argue that the stylized marketing objectives and strategy prescriptions can be misleading. For example, there can be circumstances where the appropriate marketing objective in the growth stage is to harvest (e.g. in the face of intense competition), in the mature stage to build (e.g. when a distinct, defensive differential advantage can be developed), and in the decline stage to build (e.g. when there is an opportunity to dominate).

As was discussed earlier, the classic PLC advice concerning strategy in the decline stage is to harvest or divest, but other strategies—industry revitalization or the profitable survivor strategy—can be employed if the right conditions apply.

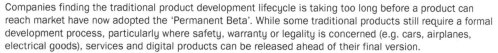

MARKETING IN ACTION 20.2
The Permanent Beta

Companies finding the traditional product development lifecycle is taking too long before a product can reach market have now adopted the 'Permanent Beta'. While some traditional products still require a formal development process, particularly where safety, warranty or legality is concerned (e.g. cars, airplanes, electrical goods), services and digital products can be released ahead of their final version.

There are potential advantages to early product release:

*   *Encourages evangelism*—early adopters can experience early versions of software or services and then provide feedback and reviews on design and performance. Evangelist users often communicate with other potential adopters, and this can spread excitement, which encourages wider adoption.
*   *Allows for errors*—in a freemium economy model (products are provided free of charge—e.g. Google Search, Internet Explorer web browser) mistakes can be made and customers are far more forgiving of a service that does not work—as expected—if they are not paying. Again users are more inclined to provide feedback— passively in the form of usage statistics and data and actively as engaged users who want to contribute to the production of something special. Companies can then experience an early-to-market introduction of a service and respond early to the feedback. Companies such as Dropbox do this regularly for new features in their Cloud storage service to see how they work for a broad range of customers. Because many businesses regard their products as constantly evolving, it makes sense for them to be described as in a state of permanent beta.

However, there are also drawbacks to the permanent beta concept:

*   *Questionable reliability*—in the early days, Google found that it could not convince businesses to take its Gmail and Google Docs services seriously, because businesses did not know how reliable those services were for mission-critical and key operation. In fact, Google's history for ending the lifecycle of products in permanent beta made many suspicious and reluctant to commit to a particular product, and it was only when Google took many products 'out of permanent beta' that there was increased uptake by business users.
*   *Lack of permanence*—while there may be benefits from continual developments, this can also be troublesome as continual investment in training of how to use products might be required.

Arguably, permanent beta is *work in progress*, and this has implications for product management insofar as the whole concept of product development becomes highly fluid and constantly evolving. For the marketing manager this means changing planning horizons between pre-launch activity, launch and eventual divestment.

Based on: Rowan (2012)

A Summary of the Usefulness of the Product Lifecycle Concept

Like many marketing tools, the product lifecycle should not be viewed as a panacea to marketing thinking and decision-making but as an aid to managerial judgement. By emphasizing the changes that are likely to occur as a product is marketed over time, the concept is a valuable stimulus to strategic thinking. Yet as a prescriptive tool it is blunt. Marketing management must monitor the real-life changes that are happening in the marketplace before setting precise objectives and strategies. Marketing in Action 20.2 offers insight into the digital world and the PLC.

Managing Brand and Product Line Portfolios

So far in this chapter we have treated the management of products as distinct and independent entities. However, many companies are multi-product, serving multiple markets and segments. Some of these products will be strong, others weak. Some will require investment to finance their growth, others will generate more cash than they need. Somehow companies must decide how to distribute their limited resources among the competing needs of products so as to achieve the best performance for the company as a whole. Specifically within a product line, management needs to decide which brands to invest in or hold, or from which to withdraw support. Similarly within the product mix, decisions regarding which product lines to build or hold, or from which to withdraw support, need to be taken. Canon, for example, took the strategic decision to focus on its profitable products—mainly copiers, printers and cameras—while divesting personal computers, typewriters and liquid crystal displays (Rowley and Tashiro, 2005). Managers who focus on individual products often miss the bigger picture that helps ensure the company's entire portfolio of products fits together coherently rather than being a loose confederation of offerings that has emerged out of a series of uncoordinated historical decisions (Shah, 2002). Philips found itself in this position, marketing a sprawling set of products, namely semiconductors, consumer electronics, medical equipment, lighting and small electrical appliances (Marsh and Bickerton, 2005). In an attempt to bring coherence to its product lines, Philips has responded by selling its semiconductor business to focus on consumer lifestyle (consumer electronics and domestic appliances), healthcare and lighting. See Exhibit 20.3.

EXHIBIT 20.3
Phillips' innovations in LED lighting products

MARKETING IN ACTION 20.3
Portfolio Planning to the Core

The composition of a company's product portfolio is a vital strategic issue for marketers. Few companies have the luxury of starting with a clean sheet and creating a well-balanced set of products. An assessment of the strengths and weaknesses of the current portfolio is, therefore, necessary before taking the strategic decisions of which ones to build, hold, harvest or divest.

Major multinationals, like Nestlé, Mondelez Foods, Procter & Gamble, GE and Unilever, constantly review their product portfolios to achieve their strategic objectives. The trend has been to focus on core brands and product categories, and to divest minor, peripheral brands.

Nestlé is the world's largest producer of packaged foods and constantly strives to manage its product portfolio. Nestlé sold Crosse & Blackwell and Davigel frozen and chilled foods to focus on key product categories and maintain market leadership. The focus is on the core categories of beverages, confectionery, chilled dairy, milks and nutrition. In line with this strategy, Nestlé has acquired the Ski and Munch Bunch dairy brands from Northern Foods, propelling it into the number-two position behind Müller in the chilled dairy market.

Mondelez Foods has many globally recognized food brands in its product portfolio, for example Oreo, Nabisco, Trident and Tang. It has a mixed portfolio, with 49 per cent of its business in North America, 23 per cent in Europe and 28 per cent in developing markets. Of these businesses, the largest concentration are in the confectionery sector (28 per cent), followed by biscuits (22 per cent), beverages (18 per cent), cheese (14 per cent), convenience meals (10 per cent) and grocery (8 per cent). These holdings in its portfolio make Mondelez Foods the second largest food company in the world and in order to maintain this position, the product portfolio is constantly reviewed, as 80 per cent of its revenues come from products that are market leaders in their categories. In 2008, Mondelez acquired LU, a global biscuit business, but got rid of Post, its cereal food operation. In 2010, Cadbury was added to the portfolio to help build its dominance in the confectionery sector in Europe, while DiGiono, its pizza business, was divested as convenience foods account for only a small part of the portfolio.

This trend is not confined to the grocery business, however. For example, Adidas sold its ski and surf equipment firm Salomon to Amer Sports Corporation so that it could focus on its core strength in the athletic footwear and apparel market as well as the growing golf category. IBM sold its PC division to Lenovo to concentrate on software and services.

Philips rationalized its product portfolio, selling its semiconductor business to focus on consumer lifestyle, healthcare and lighting. Its mission is to centre on health and well-being, and it has invested in healthcare, moving away from its medical imaging business and into patient monitoring and home healthcare. One example is its acquisition of Respironics, a medical equipment maker specialising in sleep therapy. It sees healthcare as a growth market as people live longer.

One advantage of this strategy is to enable maximum firepower to be put behind core brands.

Based on: Costello (2015); Mondelez Foods (n.d.); Mason (2002); Tomlinson (2005); Milner (2006); Steen (2008)

Clearly, these are strategic decisions since they shape where and with what brands/product lines a company competes and how its resources should be deployed. Furthermore these decisions are complex because many factors (e.g. current and future sales and profit potential, cash flow) can affect the outcome. The process of managing groups of brands and product lines is called portfolio planning.

Key decisions regarding portfolio planning involve decisions regarding the choice of which brands/product lines to build, hold, harvest or divest. Marketing in Action 20.3 discusses several companies' approach to portfolio planning.

 Scan the QR code to consider the iWatch, the development of its product features and how the features are used in the iWatch's advertising.

Two methods for managing products are widely discussed in management literature: 1) Boston Consulting Group Growth-Share Matrix, and 2) General Electric Market Attractiveness– Competitive Position portfolio-evaluation models. Like the product lifecycle these are very flexible tools and can be used at both the brand and product line levels. Indeed, corporate planners can also use them when making resource allocation decisions at the strategic business unit level.

The Boston Consulting Group Growth-Share Matrix

A leading management consultancy, the Boston Consulting Group (BCG), developed the well-known BCG Growth-Share Matrix (see Figure 20.2). The matrix allows portfolios of products to be depicted in a 2 × 2 box, the axes of which are based on market growth rate and relative market share. The analysis is based upon cash flow (rather than profits) and its key assumptions are:

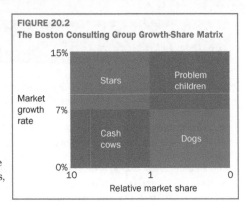

FIGURE 20.2
The Boston Consulting Group Growth-Share Matrix

* market growth has an adverse effect on cash flow because of the investment in such assets as manufacturing facilities, equipment and marketing needed to finance growth
* market share has a positive effect on cash flow as profits are related to market share.

The following discussion will be based on an analysis at the product line level.

Market growth rate forms the vertical axis and indicates the annual growth rate of the market in which each product line operates. In Figure 20.2, it is shown as 0–15 per cent, although a different range could be used, depending on economic conditions, for example. In this example the dividing line between high and low growth rates is considered to be 7 per cent. Market growth rate is used as a proxy for market attractiveness.

Relative market share is shown on the horizontal axis and refers to the market share of each product relative to its largest competitor. It acts as a proxy for competitive strength. The division between high and low market share is 1. Above this figure a product line has a market share greater than its largest competitor. For example, if our product had a market share of 40 per cent and our largest competitor's share was 30 per cent this would be indicated as 1.33 on the horizontal axis. Below 1 we have a share less than the largest competitor. For example, if our share was 20 per cent and the largest competitor had a share of 40 per cent our score would be 0.5.

The Boston Consulting Group argued that cash flow is dependent on the box in which a product falls. Note that cash flow is not the same as profitability. Profits add to cash flow but heavy investment in such assets as manufacturing facilities, equipment and marketing expenditure can mean that a company can make profits and yet have a negative cash flow.

Stars are likely to be profitable because they are market leaders but require substantial investment to finance growth (e.g. new production facilities) and to meet competitive challenges. Overall cash flow is therefore likely to be roughly in balance. *Problem children* are products in high-growth markets, which cause a drain on cash flow, but these are low-share products; consequently they are unlikely to be profitable. Overall, then, they are big cash users. *Cash cows* are market leaders in mature (low-growth) markets. High market share leads to high profitability and low market growth means that investment in new production facilities is minimal. This leads to a large positive cash flow.

Dogs also operate in low-growth markets but have low market share. Except for some products near the dividing line between cash cows and dogs (sometimes called *cash dogs*) most dogs produce low or negative cash flows. Relating to their position in the product lifecycle, they are the also-rans in mature or declining markets.

What are the strategic implications of the BCG analysis? It can be used for setting strategic objectives and for maintaining a balanced product portfolio.

Guidelines for setting strategic objectives

Having plotted the position of each product on the matrix, a company can begin to think about setting the appropriate strategic

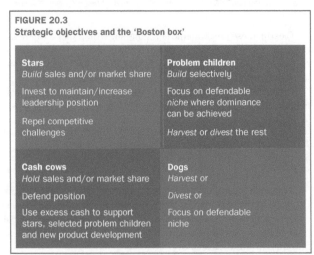

FIGURE 20.3
Strategic objectives and the 'Boston box'

Stars	**Problem children**
Build sales and/or market share	*Build* selectively
Invest to maintain/increase leadership position	Focus on defendable *niche* where dominance can be achieved
Repel competitive challenges	*Harvest* or *divest* the rest
Cash cows	**Dogs**
Hold sales and/or market share	*Harvest* or
Defend position	*Divest* or
Use excess cash to support stars, selected problem children and new product development	Focus on defendable niche

objective for each line. As you may recall from Chapter 18, there are four possible strategic objectives: build, hold, harvest and divest. Figure 20.3 shows how each relates to the star, problem children, cash cow and dog categories. However, it should be emphasized that the BCG Matrix provides guidelines for strategic thinking and should not be seen as a replacement for managerial judgement.

- *Stars*: these are the market leaders in high-growth markets. They are already successful and the prospects for further growth are good. As we have seen when discussing brand building, market leaders tend to have the highest profitability so the appropriate strategic objective is to build sales and/or market share. Resources should be invested to maintain/ increase the leadership position. Competitive challenges should be repelled. These are the cash cows of the future and need to be protected.

- *Problem children*: as we have seen these are cash drains because they have low profitability and need investment to keep up with market growth. They are called problem children because management has to consider whether it is sensible to continue the required investment. The company faces a fundamental choice: to increase investment (*build*) to attempt to turn the problem child into a star, or to withdraw support by either *harvesting* (raising price while lowering marketing expenditure) or *divesting* (dropping or selling it). In a few cases, a third option may be viable: to find a small market segment (*niche*) where dominance can be achieved. Unilever, for example, identified its speciality chemicals business as a problem child. It realized that it had to invest heavily or exit. Its decision was to sell and invest the billions raised in predicted future winners such as personal care, dental products and fragrances (Brierley, 1997).

- *Cash cows*: the high profitability and low investment associated with high market share in low-growth markets mean that cash cows should be defended. Consequently the appropriate strategic objective is to *hold* sales and market share. The excess cash that is generated should be used to fund stars, problem children that are being built, and research and development for new products.

- *Dogs*: dogs are weak products that compete in low-growth markets. They are the also-rans that have failed to achieve market dominance during the growth phase and are floundering in maturity. For those products that achieve second or third position in the marketplace (*cash dogs*) a small positive cash flow may result, and for a few others it may be possible to reposition the product into a defendable *niche*. But for the bulk of dogs the appropriate strategic objective is to *harvest* to generate a positive cash flow for a time, or to *divest*, which allows resources and managerial time to be focused elsewhere.

Maintaining a balanced product portfolio

Once all of the company's products have been plotted, it is easy to see how many stars, problem children, cash cows and dogs are in the portfolio. Figure 20.4 shows a product portfolio that is unbalanced. The company possesses only one star and the small circle indicates that sales revenue generated from the star is small. Similarly the two cash cows are also low revenue earners. In contrast, the company owns four dogs and four problem children. The portfolio is unbalanced because there are too many problem children and dogs, and not enough stars and cash cows. What many companies in this situation do is to spread what little surplus cash is available equally between the products in the growth markets (Hedley, 1977). To do so would leave each with barely enough money to maintain market share, leading to a vicious circle of decline.

The BCG remedy would be to conduct a detailed competitive assessment of the four problem children and select one or two for investment. The rest should be harvested (and the cash channelled to those that are being built) or divested. The aim is to build the existing star (which will be the cash cow of the future) and to build the market share of the chosen problem children so that they attain star status.

The dogs also need to be analyzed. One of them (the large circle) is a large revenue earner, which despite low profits may be making a substantial contribution to overheads. Another product (on the left) appears to be in the cash dog situation. But for the other two, the most sensible strategic objective may be to harvest or divest.

Criticisms of the BCG Growth-Share Matrix

The simplicity, ease of use and importance of the issues tackled by the BCG Matrix saw its adoption by a host of

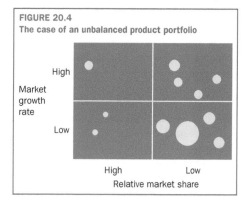

FIGURE 20.4
The case of an unbalanced product portfolio

Market growth rate — High / Low

Relative market share — High / Low

North American and European companies that wanted to get a handle on the complexities of strategic resource allocation. But the tool has also attracted a litany of criticism (see, for example, Day and Wensley, 1983; Haspslagh, 1982; Wensley, 1981). The following list draws together many of the points raised by its critics.

1 The assumption that cash flow will be determined by a product's position in the matrix is weak. For example, some stars will show a healthy positive cash flow (e.g. IBM PCs during the growth phase of the PC market) as will some dogs in markets where competitive activity is low.
2 The preoccupation of focusing on market share and market growth rates distracts managerial attention from the fundamental principle in marketing: attaining a sustainable competitive advantage.
3 Treating the market growth rate as a proxy for market attractiveness, and market share as an indicator of competitive strength is over-simplistic. There are many other factors that have to be taken into account when measuring market attractiveness (e.g. market size, strengths and weaknesses of competitors) and competitive strengths (e.g. exploitable marketing assets, potential cost advantages), besides market growth rates and market share.
4 Since the position of a product in the matrix depends on market share, this can lead to an unhealthy preoccupation with market share gain. In some circumstances this objective makes sense (for example, brand building) but when competitive retaliation is likely the costs of share building may outweigh the gains.
5 The matrix ignores interdependencies between products. For example, a dog may need to be marketed because it complements a star or a cash cow. For example, the dog may be a spare part for a star or a cash cow. Alternatively, customers and distributors may value dealing with a company that supplies a full product line. For these reasons, dropping products because they fall into a particular box may be naive.
6 The classic BCG Matrix prescription is to build stars because they will become the cash cows of the future. However, some products have a very short product lifecycle, in which case the appropriate strategy should be to maximize profits and cash flow while in the star category (e.g. fashion goods).
7 Marketing objectives and strategy are heavily dependent on an assessment of what competitors are likely to do. How will they react if we lower or raise prices when implementing a build or harvest strategy, for example? This is not considered in the matrix.
8 The matrix assumes that products are self-funding. For example, selected problem children are built using cash generated by cash cows. But this ignores capital markets, which may mean that a wider range of projects can be undertaken so long as they have positive net present values of their future cash flows.
9 The matrix is vague regarding the definition of 'market'. Should we take the whole market (e.g. for confectionery) or just the market segment that we operate in (e.g. expensive boxed chocolates)? The matrix is also vague when defining the dividing line between high- and low-growth markets. A chemical company that tends to generate in lower-growth markets might use 3 per cent, whereas a leisure goods company whose markets on average experience much higher rates of growth might use 10 per cent. Also, over what period do we define market growth? These issues question the theoretical soundness of the underlying concepts, and allow managers to manipulate the figures so that their products fall in the right boxes.
10 The matrix was based on cash flow but perhaps profitability (e.g. return on investment) is a better criterion for allocating resources.
11 The matrix lacks precision in identifying which problem children to build, harvest or drop.

General Electric Market Attractiveness–Competitive Position model

As we have already noted, the BCG Matrix enjoyed tremendous success as management grappled with the complex issue of strategic resource allocation. Stimulated by this success and some of the weaknesses of the model (particularly the criticism of its over-simplicity) McKinsey & Co developed a more wide-ranging market attractiveness–competitive position (MA–CP) model in conjunction with General Electric (GE) in the USA.

Market attractiveness criteria

Instead of market growth alone, a range of market attractiveness criteria were used, such as:
- market size
- market growth rate
- beatable rivals
- market entry barriers
- social, political and legal factors.

Competitive strength criteria

Similarly, instead of using only market share as a measure of competitive strength, a number of factors were used, such as:

- market share
- reputation
- distribution capability
- market knowledge
- service quality
- innovation capability
- cost advantages.

Assessing market attractiveness and competitive strength

Management is allowed to decide which criteria are applicable for their products. This gives the MA–CP Model flexibility. Having decided the criteria, management's next task is to agree upon a weighting system for each set of criteria, with those factors that are more important having a higher weighting. Table 20.2 shows a set of weights for market attractiveness. Management has decided that the key factors that should be used to assess market attractiveness are market size, market growth rate, beatable rivals and market entry barriers. Ten points are then shared between these four factors depending on their relative importance in assessing market attractiveness. Market size (weighting = 4.0) is considered the most important factor and market entry barriers (1.5) the least important of the four factors.

TABLE 20.2 An example of market attractiveness assessment			
Market factors	**Relative importance weightings (10 points shared)**	**Factor ratings (scale 1–10)**	**Factor scores (weightings × ratings)**
Market size	4.0	9.0	36
Market growth rate	2.0	7.0	14
Beatable rivals	2.5	8.0	20
Market entry barriers	1.5	6.0	9
			79%

Next, management assesses the particular market for the product under examination on each of the four factors on a scale of 1 to 10. The market is rated very highly on size (rating = 9.0), it possesses beatable rivals (8.0), its growth rate is also rated highly (7.0) and there are some market barriers, although they are not particularly high (6.0). By multiplying each weighting by its corresponding rating, and then summing, a total score indicating the overall attractiveness of the particular market for the product under examination is obtained. In this case, the market attractiveness for the product achieves an overall score of 79 per cent.

Competitive strength assessment begins by selecting the strengths that are needed to compete in the market. Table 20.3 shows that market share, distribution capability, service quality, innovation capability, and cost advantages were the factors considered to be needed for success. Management then assigns a weight by sharing 10 points between each of these strengths according to their relative importance in achieving success. Innovation capability (weighting = 3.0) is regarded as the most important strength required to compete effectively. Distribution capability (1.0) is considered the least important of the five factors. The company's capabilities on each of the required strengths are rated on a scale of 1 to 10. Company capabilities are rated very highly on innovation capability (rating = 9.0), market share (8.0) and cost advantages (8.0), highly on distribution capability (7.0) but service quality (5.0) is mediocre. By multiplying each weighting by its corresponding rating, and then summing, a total score indicating the overall competitive strength of the company is obtained. In this example, the competitive strength of the company achieves an overall score of 76 per cent.

TABLE 20.3 An example of competitive strength assessment

Strengths needed for success	Relative importance weightings (10 points shared)	Factor ratings (scale 1–10)	Factor scores (weightings × ratings)
Market share	2.5	8.0	20
Distribution capability	1.0	7.0	7
Service quality	2.0	5.0	10
Innovation capability	3.0	9.0	27
Cost advantages	1.5	8.0	12
			76%

The market attractiveness and competitive strength scores for the product under appraisal can now be plotted on the MA–CP matrix (see Figure 20.5). The process is repeated for each product under investigation so that their relative positions on the MA–CP Matrix can be established. Each product position is given by a circle, the size of which is in proportion to its sales.

Setting strategic objectives

The model is shown in Figure 20.5. Like the BCG Matrix, the recommendations for setting strategic objectives are dependent on the product's position on the grid. Five zones are shown in Figure 20.5. The strategic objectives associated with each zone are as follows (Hofer and Schendel, 1978).

- *Zone 1*: build—manage for sales and market share growth as the market is attractive and competitive strengths are high (equivalent to star products).
- *Zone 2*: hold—manage for profits consistent with maintaining market share as the market is not particularly attractive but competitive strengths are high (equivalent to cash cows).
- *Zone 3*: build/hold/harvest—this is the question-mark zone. Where competitors are weak or passive, a build strategy will be used. In the face of strong competitors a hold strategy may be appropriate, or harvesting where commitment to the product/market is lower (similar to problem children).
- *Zone 4*: harvest—manage for cash as both market attractiveness and competitive strengths are fairly low.
- *Zone 5*: divest—improve short-term cash yield by dropping or selling the product (equivalent to dog products).

In the example shown in Figure 20.5, the circle labelled A indicates the position of the product, which shows that it falls within zone 1 as it operates in an attractive market and its competitive strengths are high. This would suggest a build strategy that probably involves investing in raising service quality levels, which were found to be relatively weak.

Criticisms of the GE portfolio model

The proponents of the GE portfolio model argue that the analysis is much richer than BCG analysis—thanks to more factors being taken into account—and flexible. These are substantial advantages and the model is widely used, with companies such as BP, IBM, Honda, Nissan, Philips, Centrica, Mitsubishi and GE employing it to aid their strategic thinking. Critics argue, however, that it is harder to use than the BCG Matrix since it requires managerial agreement on which factors to use, their weightings and scoring. Furthermore, its flexibility provides a lot of opportunity for managerial bias to enter the analysis whereby product managers argue for factors and weightings that show their products in a good light (zone 1). This last point suggests that the analysis should be conducted at a managerial level higher than that being assessed. For example, decisions on which product lines to be built, held, and so on, should be taken at the strategic business unit level, and allocations of resources to brands should be decided at the group product manager level.

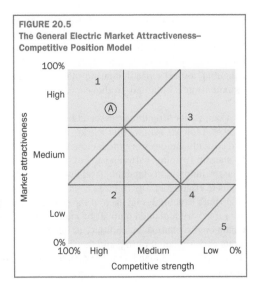

FIGURE 20.5
The General Electric Market Attractiveness–
Competitive Position Model

The contribution of product portfolio planning

Despite the limitations of the BCG and the GE portfolio evaluation models, both have made a contribution to the practice of portfolio planning. We shall now discuss this contribution and suggest how the models can usefully be incorporated into product strategy.

Different products and different roles

The models emphasize the important strategic point that *different products should have different roles* in the product portfolio. Hedley points out that some companies believe that all product lines and brands should be treated equally—that is, set the same profit requirements (Hedley, 1977). The portfolio planning models stress that this should not necessarily be the case, and may be harmful in many situations. For example, to ask for a 20 per cent return on investment (ROI) for a star may result in under-investment in an attempt to meet the profit requirement. On the other hand, 20 per cent ROI for a cash cow or a harvested product may be too low. The implication is that products should be set profitability objectives in line with the strategic objective decisions.

Different reward systems and types of manager

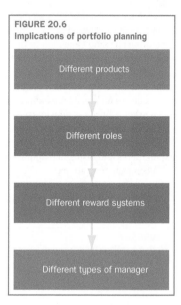

FIGURE 20.6
Implications of portfolio planning

Different products

Different roles

Different reward systems

Different types of manager

By stressing the need to set different strategic objectives for different products, the models, by implication, support the notion that *different reward systems and types of manager* should be linked to them. For example, managers of products being built should be marketing led, and rewarded for improving sales and market share. Conversely, managers of harvested (and to some extent cash cow) products should be more cost orientated, and rewarded by profit and cash flow achievement (see Figure 20.6).

Aid to managerial judgement

Managers may find it useful to plot their products on both the BCG and GE portfolio grids as an initial step in pulling together the complex issues involved in product portfolio planning. This can help them get a handle on the situation and issues to be resolved. The models can then act as an *aid to managerial judgement* without in any way supplanting that judgement. Managers should feel free to bring into the discussion any other factors they feel are not adequately covered by the models. The models can therefore be seen as an aid to strategic thinking in multi-product, multi-market companies.

Product Strategies for Growth

The emphasis in product portfolio analysis is on managing an *existing* set of products in such a way as to maximize their strengths, but companies also need to look to new products and markets for future growth. The Dyson DC08 vacuum cleaner is an example of a new product that is an addition to an existing line.

A useful way of looking at growth opportunities is the Ansoff Matrix, as shown in Figure 20.7 (Ansoff, 1957). By combining present and new products, and present and new markets into a 2 × 2 matrix, four product strategies for growth are revealed. Although the Ansoff Matrix does not prescribe when each strategy should be employed, it is a useful framework for thinking about the ways in which growth can be achieved through product strategy.

Figure 20.8 shows how the Ansoff Matrix can be used to implement a growth strategy. The most basic method of gaining **market penetration** in existing markets with current products is by *winning competitors' customers*. This may be achieved by more effective use of promotion or distribution, or by cutting prices. Increasing

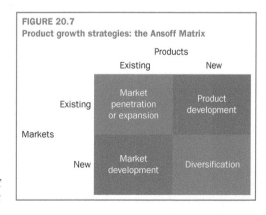

FIGURE 20.7
Product growth strategies: the Ansoff Matrix

		Products	
		Existing	New
Markets	Existing	Market penetration or expansion	Product development
	New	Market development	Diversification

promotional expenditure is a method of winning competitors' customers and market penetration. Greggs, the UK's largest retail food brand, with more shops than McDonald's and Subway, made a significant investment in digital promotion by using Facebook to find out what its 20,000 customers thought about the brand. Eleven thousand replied and the information gathered from this promotional initiative was used to deliver a 7.5 per cent increase in annual turnover (Handley, 2012). Another way of gaining market penetration is to *buy competitors*. An example is the Morrisons supermarket chain, which bought Safeway, a competitor, in order to gain market penetration. This achieves an immediate increase in market share and sales volume. To protect the penetration already gained in a market, a business may consider methods of *discouraging competitive entry*. *Barriers* can be created by cost advantages (lower labour costs, access to raw materials, economies of scale), highly differentiated products, high switching costs (the costs of changing from existing supplier to a new supplier, for example), high marketing expenditures and displaying aggressive tendencies to retaliate.

A company may attempt **market expansion** in a market that it already serves by converting *non-users to users* of its product. This can be an attractive option in new markets when non-users form a sizeable segment and may be willing to try the product given suitable inducements. Lapsed users can also be targeted. Kellogg's has targeted

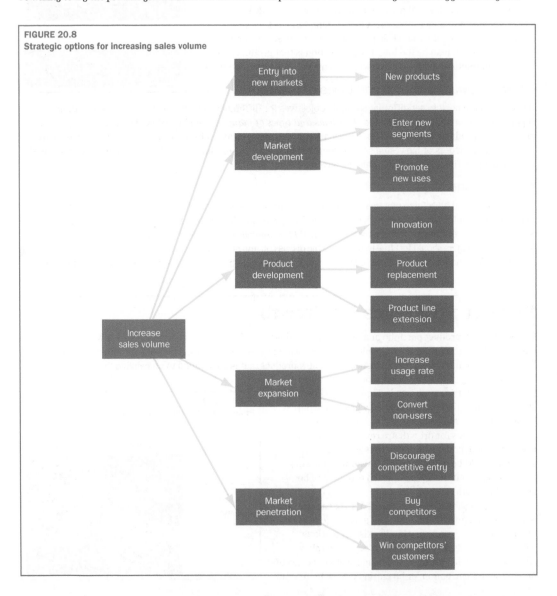

FIGURE 20.8
Strategic options for increasing sales volume

MINI CASE 20.1
Domyos Product Growth Strategies

Created in 1998 by Decathlon, Domyos is the group's brand dedicated to fitness. As the Top 10 global fitness brand in 2014, its intention was to make fitness sports accessible to as many people as possible, with a vision of fitness that places pleasure at the heart of sport. Originally, Domyos designed and sold, in all Decathlon stores, a complete range of products including textiles, materials, accessories, shoes and so on.

Ten years after its creation, however, in order to expand its market, Domyos extended its activity and transformed into a service provider. In November 2008, Domyos created an original concept, unique in the world: a new type of brand experience, with shopping and sports facilities in one location. It set up its international headquarters within a sports complex—the Domyos Centre, an 8-hectare wooded site with:

- a fitness centre, the Domyos Club
- the largest European speciality store dedicated to fitness sports, offering a wide range of Domyos products
- the World Centre for Domyos product design
- a restaurant, *Pause Forme*, in which to relax and enjoy healthy, balanced meals
- a 2-kilometre external track
- a car park with 600 spaces.

Based on its success,[1] a second Domyos Club opened in 2010. At the end of 2014, on average 1,500 athletes were crossing the threshold of Domyos on a daily basis. Domyos's price approach was novel among fitness clubs: users could pay €5 for a one and a half hour class without a subscription.

In 2014, the brand also developed an exclusive free service for its customers: Domyos Live. To give everyone the chance to enjoy their favourite activity, Domyos fitted out two of its rooms in order to broadcast around 50 live fitness classes per week. The same service was rolled out in China, followed by the rest of Europe.

If the fitness industry has gained new members over the last decade, it is thanks to new sports that are more 'fun', like Zumba, which in 2001 revolutionized fitness by providing an activity half way between dance and fitness, with a Latino ambiance. Could Domyos in its turn launch a new sports discipline that would enable the extension of the fitness market while creating new business opportunities for the brand? To penetrate and gain a share of the Chinese market, in July 2013 Domyos came up with the original idea of 'Tai-Chip-Hop', a new discipline that fuses Tai-Chi (the most popular form of exercise in China) with western hip-hop moves. At the end of 2014, 18 months later, the idea had broken through in China and sales of the clothing brand had increased by 10 per cent, a rate faster than that of the Chinese sports market.

[1] In 2009, 245,000 hours of classes were sold.

Questions:
1 What strategies do Domyos brand managers use to increase their sales volume?
2 How does product development nourish market development and market expansion?

Based on: Ruaud, Boulocher and Daly (2015)

lapsed breakfast cereal users (fathers) who rediscover the pleasure of eating cornflakes when feeding their children. Market expansion can also be achieved by *increasing usage rate*. Kellogg's has also tried to increase the usage (eating) rate of its cornflakes by promoting eating in the evening as well as at breakfast. Affordability and improving sustainability market expansion have also been found to aid market expansion (Banga and Joshib, 2010).

The **product development** option involves the development of new products for existing markets (Ansoff, 1957). One variant is to *extend existing product lines* to give current customers greater choice. For example, the original iPod has been followed by the launches of the iPod nano, shuffle and touch, giving its target market

MARKETING IN ACTION 20.4
Sweden is the Land of Innovation

Sweden is a small country with a population of 9.5 million, but it is home to many of the world's most successful innovations, which have had an impact on the lives of individuals. The three-point seat belt, safety matches and Spotify are among the many innovations to have been designed and developed in Sweden. The country ranks very highly on the Innovative Capacity Index (Harvard Business School) and the Global Innovation Index (INSEAD Business School). Sweden's success is attributed to: continual investment in research and design; its focus on specific areas in which to achieve excellence, for example medicine, bioscience, technology and the climate; and encouraging young people to become interested in technology and entrepreneurship at a young age.

In the field of medicine, the very first battery-run heart pacemaker that was small enough to be implanted under a patient's skin was developed by a surgeon and the Karolinska University Hospital in Stockholm. Over half a million patients every year are fitted with a pacemaker to ensure the heart keeps beating regularly, and subsequently benefit from normalized heart rhythms.

The TetraPak is a revolution in paper-based packaging that allows billions of shoppers to take home their milk and other liquids in a carton instead of a glass bottle. Erik Wallenberg came up with the idea and it was then produced by Ruben Raising, who was instrumental in setting up the first specialized packaging company in Sweden. Since then, the company has grown and it now supplies more than 8.5 billion packs a year, which can be recycled. The company has won many awards for being an environmentally responsible manufacturer.

Skype is another globally recognized application to emerge from Scandinavia. Niklas Zennstrom (from Sweden) worked with Janus Friis (from Denmark) with Estonian developers to produce this innovative software application that enables Internet users to make free voice calls via the web.

The Swedish government has a strategy that aims to continue to foster the right conditions for the development of many more innovations. The strategy aims to meet global societal challenges by focusing on sustainability, increasing competitiveness and creating jobs in the knowledge economy, and increasing the efficiency of public services. The innovation strategy focuses on creating the best possible conditions for innovation by enabling people to be innovative, investing in research and higher education, and creating an infrastructure that provides solid foundations for the future.

Based on: Swedish Institute (2015); Tetrapak (2015); Swedish Ministry of Enterprise, Energy and Communications (2015)

of young music lovers greater choice in terms of size, capacity and price. When new features are added (with an accompanying price rise) trading up may occur, with customers buying the enhanced-value product on repurchase. However, when the new products are cheaper than the original (as is the case with the iPod) the danger is cannibalization of sales of the core product. *Product replacement* activities involve the replacement of old brands/models with new ones. This is common in the car market and often involves an upgrading of the old model with a new (more expensive) replacement. For Skoda, the third oldest car manufacturer in the world, product replacement has been essential to its survival, and in recent years the introduction of new models—Fabia, Superb, Citigo and Rapid—has enabled the brand to retain and develop its market share, selling more than a million vehicles in 2014. A final option is the replacement of an old product with a fundamentally different one, often based on technology change. The business thus replaces an old product with an *innovation* (although both may be marketed side by side for a time). Microsoft operating systems are a classic example of replacement products being introduced, but the older products continue to be marketed and supported: for example, Windows Vista (released in 2006) was superseded by Windows 7 in 2009 (Microsoft, 2013), Windows 8 in 2012, and Windows 10 in 2015. See Marketing in Action 20.4 to find out about the innovative products and technology applications that have helped Sweden become Europe's third most innovative nation.

Scan the QR code to take the Skoda attention test to see how alert you are to the brand's advertising messages.

Market development entails the promotion of *new uses of existing products to new customers*, or the marketing of *existing products (and their current uses) to new market segments*. The promotion of new uses accounted for the growth in sales of nylon, which was first marketed as a replacement for silk in parachutes but expanded into shirts, carpets, tyres, etc. Tesco, the UK supermarket chain, practised market development by marketing existing grocery products, which were sold in large out-of-town supermarkets and superstores, to a new market segment—convenience shoppers—by opening smaller grocery shops in town centres and next to petrol stations. Market development through entering new segments could involve the search for overseas opportunities. Andy Thornton Ltd, an interior design business, successfully increased sales by entering Scandinavia and Germany, two geographic segments that provided new expansion opportunities for its services. The growth of overseas markets in China, India, Russia and eastern Europe is providing major market development opportunities for companies such as BP, Vodafone, Walmart and Carrefour (*The Economist*, 2008). When Wagner, the German manufacturer of spray guns for painting, expanded to the USA in search of market development it found that it had to refocus on an entirely different market segment. In Europe it sells its products to professional painters but in the USA its products are bought by people who use spray guns in their own homes to paint interiors and outside surfaces such as fences (Bolfo, 2005).

The entry into new markets (diversification) option concerns the development of *new products for new markets*. This is the most risky option, especially when the entry strategy is not based on the *core competences* of the business. However, it can also be the most rewarding, as exemplified by Honda's move from motorcycles to cars (based on its core competences in engines), and Apple Computer's launch of the iPod mobile music player, which can download music via a computer (based on its core competences in computer electronics). This was followed by its highly successful diversification into smartphones (the iPhone) based on its new-found competences in mobile communication and tablet computers with the iPad. It is the lure of such rewards that has tempted the Internet networking equipment maker Cisco to venture into consumer electronics, and Intel, which manufactures microprocessors that power personal computers, to diversify into platforms combining silicon and software, which has led to new devices and technologies in consumer electronics, wireless communications and healthcare (see Palmer, 2006; Edwards, 2006).

Ethical Issues and Products

The final section in this chapter considers the three major ethical issues relating to products.

1 *Product safety* is a major concern, particularly in relation to consumables. Genetically modified (GM) products have attracted the attention of pressure groups such as Greenpeace, who have spoken out about the dangers of genetic modification. People are sharply divided as to whether GM products are safe. Although plant breeders have for thousands of years been tampering with the genes of plants through traditional cross-pollination of plants of the same species, genetic modification goes one step further as it allows scientists to cross the species barrier.

Concerns about product safety also relate to tobacco (lung cancer), the levels of fat, sugar and salt in foods (obesity and heart problems), and sugar in soft drinks (obesity and tooth decay). Such issues have led to bans on tobacco advertising, the setting up of independent bodies to protect consumers' interests in the food and drinks industries, and reductions in the levels of fat, sugar and salt in many food and drink brands, particularly the level of sugar in food and soft drinks consumed by children. For example, Nestlé has reduced the level of sugar in its cereals targeted at children and reformulated its Rowntree range of children's sweets to make them free from artificial flavours and colours.

2 *Planned obsolescence.* Many products are not designed to last a long time. From the producer's point of view this is sensible, as it creates a repeat purchase situation. Hence cars rust, clothes wear out and fashion items are replaced by the latest styles. Consumers accept that nothing lasts forever, but the issue concerns what is an acceptable length of time before replacement is necessary. One driving force is competition. To quell the Japanese invasion, car manufacturers such as Ford and Volkswagen have made the body shells of their cars

much more rust-resistant than before. Furthermore, it has to be recognized that many consumers welcome the chance to buy new clothes, new appliances with the latest features, and the latest models of car. Critics argue that planned obsolescence reduces consumers' 'right to choose', since some consumers may be quite content to drive an old car so long as its body shell is free from rust and the car functions well. As we have noted, the forces of competition may act to deter the excesses of planned obsolescence.

3   *Deceptive packaging.* This can occur when a product appears in an oversized package to create the impression that the consumer is buying more than is the case. This is known as 'slack' packaging and has the potential to deceive when the packaging is opaque. Products such as soap powder and breakfast cereals have the potential to suffer from 'slack' packaging. A second area where packaging may be deceptive is through misleading labelling, for example the failure of a package to state that the product contains genetically modified soya beans. This relates to the consumer's 'right to be informed', which can include stating ingredients (including flavouring and colourants), nutritional contents and country of origin on labels. Nevertheless, labelling can be misleading. For example, in the UK, 'country of origin' is only the last country where the product was 'significantly changed'. So oil pressed from Greek olives in France can be labelled 'French', and foreign imports that are packed in the UK can be labelled 'produce of the UK'. Consumers should be wary of loose terminology. For example, smoked bacon may well have received its 'smoked' flavour from a synthetic liquid solution, 'farm fresh eggs' are likely to be un-date-marked eggs of indeterminate age laid by battery hens, and 'farmhouse cheese' may not come from farmhouses but from industrial factories.

The use of loose language and meaningless terms in the UK food and drink industry has been criticized by the Food Standards Agency (FSA). A list of offending words has been drawn up, which includes 'fresh', 'natural', 'pure', 'traditional' and 'original'.

Recommendations regarding when it is reasonable to use certain words have been drawn up. For example, 'authentic' should only be used to emphasize the geographic origin of a product, and 'homemade' should be restricted to the preparation of the recipe on the premises, and must involve 'some degree of fundamental culinary preparation'. The FSA has also expressed concern about the use of meaningless phrases such as 'natural goodness' and 'country style', and recommended that they should not be used.

When you have read this chapter

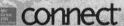

Discover further resources and test your understanding: McGraw-Hill **Connect**™ is a digital teaching and learning environment that improves performance over a variety of critical outcomes; it can be tailored, is easy to use and is proven effective. **LearnSmart**™ is the most widely used and intelligent adaptive learning resource that is proven to strengthen memory recall, improve course retention and boost grades. Fuelled by **LearnSmart**™, **SmartBook**™ is the first and only adaptive reading experience available today.

Review

1   **The concept of the product lifecycle**
   • A four-stage cycle in the life of a product illustrated as sales and profit curves, the four stages being introduction, growth, maturity and decline. It is quite flexible and can be applied to both brands and product lines.

2   **The uses and limitations of the product lifecycle**
   • Its uses are that it emphasizes the need to terminate old and develop new products, warns against the danger of assuming growth will last forever, stresses the need to review marketing objectives and strategies

as products pass through the four stages, emphasizes the need to maintain a balanced set of products across the four stages, and warns against the damages of overpowering (setting too high prices early in the cycle when competition is low).

- The limitations are that it is wrong to assume that all products follow the classic S-shaped curve and it is misleading to believe that the product lifecycle sales curve is a fact of life; it depends on marketing activity. The duration of the stages are unpredictable, limiting its use as a forecasting tool, and the stylized marketing objectives and strategy prescriptions associated with each stage may be misleading in particular cases.
- Overall, it is a valuable stimulus to strategic thinking but as a prescriptive tool it is blunt.

3 **The concept of product portfolio planning**
- This is the process of managing products as groups (portfolios) rather than separate, distinct and independent entities.
- The emphasis is on deciding which products to build, hold, harvest and divest (i.e. resource allocation).

4 **The Boston Consulting Group Growth-Share Matrix, its uses and associated criticisms**
- The matrix allows portfolios of products to be depicted in a 2 × 2 box, the axes of which are based on market growth rate (proxy for market attractiveness) and relative market share (proxy for competitive strength).
- Cash flow from a product is assumed to depend on the box in which a product falls.
- Stars are likely to have cash flow balance; problem children cause a drain on cash flow; cash cows generate large positive cash flow; and dogs usually produce low or negative cash flow.
- Its uses are that the matrix provides guidelines for setting strategic objectives (for example, stars should be built; problem children built selectively, harvested or divested; cash cows held; and dogs harvested or divested), and emphasizes the need to maintain a balanced portfolio with the cash generated by the cash cows being used to fund those being built.
- The criticisms are: the assumption that cash flow is determined by a product's position in the matrix is weak; it distracts management from focusing on sustainable competitive advantage; treating market growth rate and market share as proxies for market attractiveness and competitive strength is over-simplistic; it can lead to an unhealthy preoccupation with market share; it ignores interdependencies between products; building stars may be inappropriate; competitor reactions are ignored; the assumption that products are self-funding ignores capital markets; the theoretical soundness of some of the underlying concepts (e.g. market definition) is questionable; cash flow may not be the best criteria for allocating resources; and the matrix lacks precision in identifying which problem children to build, harvest or divest.

5 **The General Electric market attractiveness–competitive position model, its uses and associated criticisms**
- The model is based on market attractiveness (e.g. market size, market growth rate, strength of competition) and competitive strength (e.g. market share, potential to develop a differential advantage, cost advantages). By weighting the criteria and scoring products, these can be positioned on a matrix.
- Its advantages over the 'Boston Box' are that more criteria than just market growth rate and market share are used to determine the position of products in the matrix, and it is more flexible.
- Its uses are that the matrix provides guidelines for setting strategic objectives based upon a product's position in the matrix, and that the analysis is much richer than that of the Boston Box because more factors are being taken into account, leading to better resource allocation decisions.
- The criticisms are that it is harder to use than the Boston Box, and its flexibility can provide an opportunity for managerial bias.

6 **The contribution of portfolio planning**
- The models emphasize the important strategic point that different products should have different roles in a product portfolio, and different reward systems and managers should be linked to them.
- The models can be useful as an aid to managerial judgement and strategic thinking, but should not supplant that judgement and thinking.

7 **Product strategies for growth**
- A useful way of looking at growth opportunities is offered by the Ansoff Matrix as it is a practical framework for thinking about how growth can be achieved through product strategy.

- It comprises four general approaches to sales growth: market penetration/expansion, product development, market development and diversification.
- Market penetration and expansion are strategies relating to growing existing products in existing markets. Market penetration depends on winning competitors' customers or buying competitors (thereby increasing market share). Defence of increased penetration may be through discouraging competitive entry. Market expansion may be through converting non-users to users or increasing usage rate. Although market share may not increase, sales growth is achieved through increasing market size.
- Product development is a strategy for developing new products for existing markets. It has three variants: extending existing product lines (brand extensions) to give current customers greater choice; product replacement (updates of old products); and innovation (developing fundamentally different products).
- Market development is a strategy for taking existing products and marketing them in new markets. This may be through the promotion of new uses of existing products to new customers, or the marketing of existing products to new market segments (e.g. overseas markets).
- Diversification (entry into new markets) is a strategy for developing new products for new markets. It is the most risky of the four growth strategies but also potentially the most rewarding.

8   **Ethical issues**
- Ethical issues associated with products fall into three main categories: 1) product safety, 2) planned obsolescence, 3) deceptive packaging.

Key Terms

entry into new markets (diversification) the entry into new markets by new products

market development to take current products and market them in new markets

market expansion the attempt to increase the size of a market by converting non-users to users of the product and by increasing usage rates

market penetration to continue to grow sales by marketing an existing product in an existing market

portfolio planning managing groups of brands and product lines

product development increasing sales by improving present products or developing new products for current markets

product lifecycle a four-stage cycle in the life of a product illustrated as sales and profits curves, the four stages being introduction, growth, maturity and decline

Study Questions

1. To what extent can the product lifecycle help to inform marketing management decision-making? Discuss.

2. Evaluate the usefulness of the BCG Matrix. Do you believe that it has a role to play in portfolio planning?

3. What is the difference between product and market development in the Ansoff Matrix? Give examples of each form of product growth strategy.

4. How does the GE Matrix differ from the BCG Matrix? What are the strengths and weaknesses of the GE Matrix?

5. Evaluate the contribution of product portfolio planning models to product strategy.

6. Suggest possible advantages of actively managing a company's product portfolios.

7. Suggest how product portfolio planning might be affected by changing forces in the marketing environment.

Recommended Reading

Aaker, D. (2013) *Strategic Market Management*, New York, Wiley

Hill, S., Ettenson, R. & Tyson, D. (2005) Achieving the ideal brand portfolio, *Sloan Management Review*, 46 (2), 85–91

Moon, Y. (2005) Break free from the product life cycle, *Harvard Business Review*, 83 (5), 86–95

Morgan, N. A., & Rego, L.L. (*2009*) Brand Portfolio Strategy and Firm Performance. *Journal of Marketing*: 73) (1), 59–74

Qiu, T. (*2014*) Product Diversification and Market Value of Large International Firms: A Macroenvironmental Perspective. *Journal of International Marketing*: 22, (4), 86–107

Reeves, M., Love, C., & Tilmans, P. (2012) Your Strategy Needs a Strategy, BCG Perspectives https://www.bcgperspectives.com/content/articles/strategic_planning_vision_mission_your_strategy_needs_a_strategy (accessed July 2015).

References

Aaker, D. (2007) *Strategic Marketing Management*, New York: Wiley.

Ansoff, I. (1957) Strategies for Diversification, *Harvard Business Review*, Sept.–Oct., 113–24.

Banga, V. V. and S. L. Joshib (2010) Market expansion strategy–performance relationship, *Journal of Strategic Marketing* 18(1), 57–75.

Bolfo, B. (2005) The Art of Selling One Product to Two Markets, *Financial Times*, 10 August, 11.

Boston Consulting Group (2001) On-line Retail Market in North America to reach $65 billion in 2001, http://www.beg.com.

Brierley, D. (1997) Spring-Cleaning a Statistical Wonderland, *European*, 20–26 February, 28.

Cline, C. E. and B. P. Shapiro (1979) *Cumberland Metal Industries (A): Case Study*, Cambridge, Mass: Harvard Business School.

Costello, M. (2015) Nestlé to shed frozen and chilled goods brand Davigel, *The Times*, 16 April. http://www.thetimes.co.uk/tto/business/industries/consumer/article4412839.ece

Day, G. S. and R. Wensley (1983) Marketing Theory with a Strategic Orientation, *Journal of Marketing*, Fall, 79–89.

Dhalia, N. K. and S. Yuspeh (1976) Forget the Product Life Cycle Concept, *Harvard Business Review*, Jan.–Feb., 102–12.

Doherty, N. F., F. E. Ellis-Chadwick and C. A. Hart (2003) An analysis of the factors affecting the adoption of the Internet in the UK retail sector, *Journal of Business Research* 56, 887–97.

Doyle, P. (1989) Building Successful Brands: The Strategic Options, *Journal of Marketing Management* 5(1), 77–95.

Edwards, C. (2006) Inside Intel, *Business Week*, 9 January, 43.

Ellis-Chadwick, F., N. Doherty and C. Hart (2002) Signs of change? A longitudinal study of Internet adoption in the UK retail sector, *Journal of Retailing and Consumer Services* 9, 71–80.

Gapper, J. (2006) Sony is Scoring Low at its Close Game, *Financial Times*, 6 November, 17.

Handley, L. (2012) Greggs finds ingredient for growth on Facebook, *Marketing Week*, 1 March, 15–18.

Haspslagh, P. (1982) Portfolio Planning: Uses and Limits, *Harvard Business Review*, Jan.–Feb., 58–73.

Hedley, B. (1977) Boston Consulting Group Approach to the Business Portfolio, *Long Range Planning*, February, 9–15.

Hofer, C. and D. Schendel (1978) *Strategy Formulation: Analytical Concepts*, St Paul, MN: West.

Hudson, A. (2010) Whatever happened to the dotcom millionaires? http://news.bbc.co.uk/1/hi/technology/8505260.stm.

Marsh, P. and I. Bickerton (2005) Stewardship of a Sprawling Empire, *Financial Times*, 18 November, 13.

Mason, T. (2002) Nestlé Sells Big Brands in Core Strategy Focus, *Marketing*, 7 February, 5.

Microsoft (2013) A history of Windows, http://windows.microsoft.com/en-US/windows/history

Milner, M. (2006) £1.2bn Sale of Schweppes' European Drinks Business Agreed, *Guardian*, 22 November, 26.

Mondelez Foods (n.d.) About Us. http://www.Mondelezfoodscompany.com

Nokian (n.d.) http://www.nokianheavytyres.com/en/innovation/tailored-special-expertise

Palmer, M. (2006) Cisco Lays Plans to Expand into Home Electronics, *Financial Times*, 16 January, 21.

Pavitt, D. (1997) Retailing and the super highway: the future of the electronic home shopping industry, *International Journal of Retail & Distribution Management*, 25(1), 38–43.

Polli, R. and V. Cook (1969) Validity of the Product Life Cycle, *Journal of Business*, October, 385–400.

Rowan, D. (2012) Reid Hoffman: The network philosopher, *Wired*, April. http://www.wired.co.uk/magazine/archive/2012/04/features/reid-hoffman-network-philosopher (accessed 20 April 2015).

Rowley, I. and H. Tashiro (2005) Can Canon Keep Printing Money? *Business Week*, 5/12 September, 18–20.

Ruaud, S., V. Boulocher and P. Daly (2015) Domyos or the Fitness Revolution: Service Innovation, case study, Paris: CCMP.

Shah, R. (2002) Managing a Portfolio to Unlock Real Potential, *Financial Times*, 21 August, 13.

Steen, M. (2008) Reinventing the Philips Brand, *Financial Times*, 27 March, 18.

Swedish Institute (2015) Innovation in Sweden, Sweden.Se, https://sweden.se/business/innovation-in-sweden (accessed 20 April 2015).

Swedish Ministry of Enterprise, Energy and Communications (2015) The Swedish Innovation Strategy, Swedish Ministry of Enterprise, Energy and Communications. http://www.government.se/content/1/c6/20/25/58/ace0cef0.pdf (accessed 20 April 2015).

Tetrapak (2015) About Tetrapak, Tetrapak. http://www.tetrapak.com/uk/about-tetra-pak/the-company/history/ourfounder (accessed 20 April 2015).

The Economist (2008) Face Value, 31 May, 86.

Tomlinson, H. (2005) Adidas Sells Ski and Surf Group for £329m, *Guardian*, 3 May, 5.

Vakratsas, D. and T. Ambler (1999) How Advertising Works: What Do We Really Know? *Journal of Marketing* 63, January, 26–43.

Virzi, A. M. (2000) Billionaire builds wealth at Internet speed, *Forbes.com*, http://www.forbes.com/2000/06/30/feat.html.

Wensley, R. (1981) Strategic Marketing: Betas, Boxes and Basics, *Journal of Marketing*, Summer, 173–83.

Wikipedia (n.d.) Dot-com bubble. http://en.wikipedia.org/wiki/Dot-com_bubble

CHAPTER 19
Analysing Competitors and Creating a Competitive Advantage

If you don't have a competitive advantage, don't compete.

JACK WELCH, FORMER CHIEF EXECUTIVE OF GENERAL ELECTRIC

LEARNING OBJECTIVES

After reading this chapter, you should be able to:

1 describe the determinants of industry attractiveness
2 explain how to analyse competitors
3 distinguish between differentiation and cost leader strategies
4 discuss the sources of competitive advantage
5 discuss the value chain
6 explain how to create and maintain a differential advantage
7 explain how to create and maintain a cost leadership position
8 discuss the nature of competitive behaviour
9 explain the key elements of a competitive marketing strategy

S atisfying customers is central to the marketing concept, but it is not enough to guarantee success. The real question is whether a company can satisfy customers better than the competition. For example, many car manufacturers market cars that give customer satisfaction in terms of appearance, reliability and performance. They meet the basic requirements necessary to compete. Customer choice, however, will depend on creating more value than the competition. Extra value is brought about by establishing a competitive advantage—a topic that will be examined later in this chapter.

Since corporate performance depends on both customer satisfaction and creating greater value than the competition, companies need to understand their competitors as well as their customers. By understanding its competitors, a firm can better predict their reactions to any marketing initiative that the firm might make, and exploit any weaknesses. Competitor analysis is thus crucial to the successful implementation of marketing strategy. Our discussion of competitors in this chapter begins by examining competitive industry structure, then explains how to create competitive and differential advantage, then cost leadership. Finally we explore the key elements associated with developing a competitive marketing strategy.

Analysing Competitive Industry Structure

An **industry** is a group of companies that market products that are close substitutes for each other. There is more to understanding an 'industry' and how it works than the core product or service being sold. Commonly we refer to the oil, computer or retail industry. Some industries are more profitable than others. In the past the car, steel, coal and textile industries have been highly profitable, but in more recent years they have had poor profitability records, whereas recently the creative industries, (e.g. television, publishing, web development), pharmaceuticals and soft drinks industries have enjoyed high profits. Not all of this difference can be explained by the fact that one industry provides better customer satisfaction than another. Other determinants of industry attractiveness and long-run profitability shape the rules of competition. These are the threat of entry of new competitors, the threat of substitutes, the bargaining power of buyers and of suppliers, and the rivalry between the existing competitors (Porter, 1980). The intensity of these forces shapes an industry and its levels of performance. Their influence is shown diagrammatically in Figure 19.1, which shows what is known as the Porter model of competitive industry structure. Each of the 'five forces' in turn comprises a number of elements that, together, combine to determine the strength of each force and its effect on the degree of competition. Each force is discussed below.

The threat of new entrants

New entrants can raise the level of competition in an industry, which may ultimately reduce its attractiveness. For example, Starbucks is entering the 'coffee capsules market' to take on market leaders Nespresso. Nestlé owns the Nespresso brand and has made significant investment in building the market for this product in Europe using an extensive advertising campaign fronted by Hollywood actor George Clooney, which led to a 20 per cent rise in sales. Nespresso's high levels of profitability have attracted many new entrants including Green Mountain, Côte D'Or, and Kenco (see Exhibit 19.1) (Simonian and Lucas, 2012). The threat of new entrants depends on the barriers to entry. High entry barriers exist in some industries (e.g. pharmaceuticals), whereas other industries are much easier to enter (e.g. restaurants).

 Scan the QR code to see how Nespresso uses Celebrity endorsement to differentiate the brand from the competition.

Key **entry barriers** include:
- economies of scale
- capital requirements
- switching costs
- access to distribution
- expected retaliation.

For present competitors, industry attractiveness can be increased by raising entry barriers. High promotional and R&D expenditures, and clearly communicated retaliatory actions to entry are some methods of raising

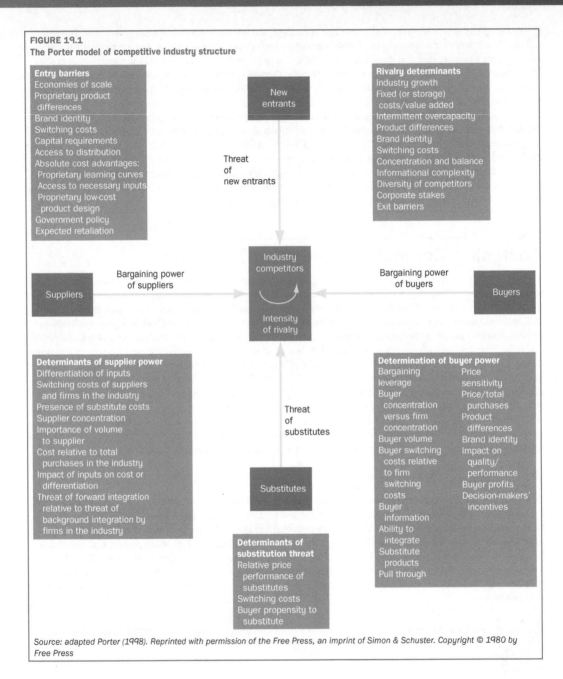

FIGURE 19.1
The Porter model of competitive industry structure

Entry barriers
Economies of scale
Proprietary product
 differences
Brand identity
Switching costs
Capital requirements
Access to distribution
Absolute cost advantages:
 Proprietary learning curves
 Access to necessary inputs
 Proprietary low-cost
 product design
Government policy
Expected retaliation

New
entrants

Rivalry determinants
Industry growth
Fixed (or storage)
 costs/value added
Intermittent overcapacity
Product differences
Brand identity
Switching costs
Concentration and balance
Informational complexity
Diversity of competitors
Corporate stakes
Exit barriers

Threat
of
new entrants

Bargaining power
of suppliers

Suppliers

Industry
competitors

Intensity
of rivalry

Bargaining power
of buyers

Buyers

Determinants of supplier power
Differentiation of inputs
Switching costs of suppliers
 and firms in the industry
Presence of substitute costs
Supplier concentration
Importance of volume
 to supplier
Cost relative to total
 purchases in the industry
Impact of inputs on cost or
 differentiation
Threat of forward integration
 relative to threat of
 background integration by
 firms in the industry

Threat
of
substitutes

Substitutes

**Determinants of
substitution threat**
Relative price
 performance of
 substitutes
Switching costs
Buyer propensity to
 substitute

Determination of buyer power
Bargaining   Price
 leverage   sensitivity
Buyer   Price/total
 concentration   purchases
 versus firm   Product
 concentration   differences
Buyer volume   Brand identity
Buyer switching   Impact on
 costs relative   quality/
 to firm   performance
 switching   Buyer profits
 costs   Decision-makers'
Buyer   incentives
 information
Ability to
 integrate
Substitute
 products
Pull through

*Source: adapted Porter (1998). Reprinted with permission of the Free Press, an imprint of Simon & Schuster. Copyright © 1980 by
Free Press*

barriers as in the situation with the Nespresso coffee pods. Nestlé continues to make a significant investments in these areas. Other ways of raising barriers are by taking out patents and developing strong relationships/ partnerships with suppliers and/or distributors. Some managerial actions can unwittingly lower barriers. For example, new product designs that dramatically lower manufacturing costs can ease entry for newcomers.

The bargaining power of suppliers

The cost of raw materials, components and intellectual skills can have a major bearing on a company's profitability. The higher the bargaining power of suppliers, the higher these costs. For example when Apple decided to adopt Intel processors there were lengthy extensive negotiations. The bargaining power of suppliers will be high when:

- there are many buyers and few dominant suppliers
- there are differentiated highly valued products
- suppliers threaten to integrate forward into the industry
- buyers do not threaten to integrate backward into supply
- the industry is not a key customer group to the suppliers.

A company can reduce the bargaining power of suppliers by seeking new sources of supply, threatening to integrate backward into supply, and designing standardized components so that many suppliers are capable of producing them.

Backwards integration means that a buyer (like Apple) purchases the supplier and a form of vertical integration takes place. Currently, there is speculation that Apple might switch from using Intel chips and replace them with ARM (processor chips made by Apple, through an acquisition of PA Semi), but this move has far-reaching implications that would mean popular Apple apps such as iTunes, TextEdit and Logic Pro would need to be rewritten (Gruman, 2015).

EXHIBIT 19.1
Nespresso aims to retain its competitive advantage in the coffee capsule market by using celebrity endorsement of the brand

The bargaining power of buyers

The concentration of buyers can lower manufacturers' bargaining power. For example, the large retailers in Europe (e.g. Dixons Carphone, Carrefour and Bauhaus GMbH) buy from many suppliers in large volumes and this has increased the bargaining power. The bargaining power of buyers is greater when:

- there are few dominant buyers and many sellers
- products are standardized
- buyers threaten to integrate backwards into the industry
- suppliers do not threaten to integrate forwards into the buyer's industry
- the industry is not a key supplying group for buyers.

Manufacturing companies in the industry can attempt to lower buyer power by increasing the number of buyers they sell to, threatening to integrate forwards into the buyer's industry and producing highly valued, differentiated products. Apple has become a leading retailer around the world with its dedicated, high-tech, Apple product stores, see Exhibit 19.2.

Threat of substitutes

The presence of substitute products can lower industry attractiveness and profitability because these put a constraint on price levels. For example, tea and coffee are fairly close substitutes in many European countries. Raising the price of coffee, therefore, would make tea more attractive. The threat of substitute products depends on:

- buyers' willingness to substitute
- the relative price and performance of substitutes
- the costs of switching to substitutes.

The threat of substitute products can be lowered by building up switching costs, or for example, by creating a strong distinctive brand and maintaining a price differential in line with perceived customer values. If these tactics fail to deter a rival from launching a substitute product, the incumbent is faced with the following options: copy the substitute; copy but build

EXHIBIT 19.2
The design of Apple's Store in Shanghai reflects the innovativeness of its products

in a differential advantage; form a strategic alliance with the rival; buy the rival; or move to a new market. For example, BlackBerry products manufacturer Research in Motion (RIM) saw its market share plummet as adopters switch to faster touchscreen smartphones like iPhone and Samsung Galaxy (Garside, 2012). MySpace was a pioneer in the world of social media: it introduced the concept of friends' social networks on a large scale. But once Facebook was launched and started to grow, it provided people with more reasons to belong to its network than to that of its rival MySpace (Dredge, 2015).

Industry competitors

The intensity of rivalry between competitors in an industry will depend on the following factors.

* *Structure of the competition*: there is more intense rivalry when there are a large number of small competitors or a few equally balanced competitors, and less rivalry when a clear market leader exists with a large cost advantage.
* *Structure of costs*: high fixed costs encourage price-cutting to fill capacity.
* *Degree of differentiation*: basic commodity products encourage rivalry, while highly differentiated products that are hard to copy are associated with less intense rivalry.
* *Switching costs*: rivalry is reduced when switching costs are high because the product is specialized, the customer has invested a lot of resources in learning how to use the product or has made tailor-made investments that are worthless with other products and suppliers. For example, a product might be customized, production, logistical or marketing operations might be geared to using the equipment of a particular supplier (e.g. computer systems), or retraining may be required as a result of a switch to another supplier.
* *Strategic objectives*: when competitors are pursuing build strategies, competition is likely to be more intense than when playing hold or harvesting objectives.
* *Exit barriers*: when barriers to leaving an industry are high due to such factors as lack of opportunities elsewhere, high vertical integration, emotional barriers or the high cost of closing down plant, rivalry will be more intense than when exit barriers are low.

Companies need to be careful not to spoil a situation of competitive stability. They need to balance their own position against the well-being of the industry as a whole. For example, an intense price or promotional war may gain a few percentage points in market share but lead to an overall fall in long-run industry profitability as competitors respond to these moves. It is sometimes better to protect industry structure than follow short-term self-interest.

A major threat to favourable industry structure is the use of a no-frills, low-price strategy by a minor player seeking positional advantage. For example, the launch of generic products in the pharmaceutical and airline industries has lowered overall profitability.

Despite meeting customers' needs with high-quality, good-value products, companies can 'compete away' the rewards. An intensive competitive environment means that the value created by companies in satisfying customer needs is given away to buyers through lower prices, dissipated through costly marketing battles (e.g. advertising wars) or passed on to powerful suppliers through higher prices for raw materials and components.

In Europe, the competitive structure of industries was fundamentally changed with the advent of the single European market. The lifting of barriers to trade between countries has radically altered industry structures by affecting the underlying determinants. For example, the threat of new entrants and the growth in buyer/supplier power through acquisition or merger are fundamentally changing the competitive climate of many industries. See Marketing in Action 19.1 to find out more about the world's most competitive industry.

MARKETING IN ACTION 19.1
Rovio and Supercell Battle for Market Share in the Intensely Competitive Apps Market

There are more mobile devices in the world than there are people, according to the US Census Bureau. So it is perhaps no surprise that the competitive pressure for mobile app developers is intense. What also makes this such a highly competitive industry are the low entry barriers, the large number of competitors with similar capabilities, low switching costs for the customers, and many competitors trying to build market share. As a result there are apps for almost every aspect of modern life, for example games, photo editors, magic pianos, healthy living.

>>

»

The app industry is reliant on downloads and revenues, but the increase in the quality of freely downloadable games has succeeded in getting customers to switch to new products. The industry has been affected by this change in pricing structure, and free downloads have come to dominate. So, companies competing in this market must find different ways to ensure a strong revenue stream and create competitive advantage. Some examples follow.

Rovio, a Finnish developer of *Angry Birds*, a highly successful mobile game app, regularly tops the charts in the app market. In 2014, *Angry Birds* was downloaded by 600 million mobile gamers. Despite the popularity of this game, the company has seen its profits fall. Part of the reason for this was a reduction in sales from associated merchandise, for example soft toys, clothing, gifts. So the company had to find other ways to extend the franchise around this game title, for example the *Angry Birds Movie*. It is also developing new apps for the games market, for example Nibblers.

Supercell is also a Finnish developer and one of the fastest growing technology companies in Europe. The company is known for producing successful game apps, for example *Clash of the Clans*, *Hay Day* and *Boom Beach*. Supercell has managed to take market share from market-leading app developers like Electronic Arts. The key to its success has been its ability to successfully enter Asian markets, something that other developers have failed to achieve.

These are just two examples of successful app companies. Finnish app developers seem to have been able to garner competitive advantage from a number of sources to ensure their success in this highly competitive industry—for example, distinctive graphics that have global appeal, successful targeting of Apple's iPad and smartphone platforms with high-quality apps that have been through extensive product testing prior to launch, and by developing creative pricing strategies.

Based on: Boren (2014); Sinclair (2015); Rovio (2015); Kuittinen (2013, 2014); Reisinger (2015); Cellan-Jones (2015)

Competitor Analysis

The analysis of how industry structure affects long-run profitability has shown the need to understand and monitor competitors. Their actions can spoil an otherwise attractive industry, their weaknesses can be a target for exploitation, and their response to a firm's marketing initiatives can have a major impact on their success. Indeed, companies that focus on competitors' actions have been found to achieve better business performance than those who pay less attention to their competitors (Noble, Sinha and Kumar, 2002). Competitive information can be obtained from marketing research surveys, secondary sources (e.g. the web, trade magazines, newspaper articles), analyzing competitors' products and gathering competitors' sales literature.

Competitor analysis seeks to answer five key questions.

1 Who are our competitors?
2 What are their strengths and weaknesses?
3 What are their strategic objectives and thrust?
4 What are their strategies?
5 What are their response patterns?

These issues are summarized in Figure 19.2. Each question will now be examined.

Who are our competitors?

We need to take a wide view of potential competition. If only those companies that are producing technically similar products are considered to be the competition, (e.g. paint companies) it is possible to miss other sources of competition. For example, by ignoring companies that produce substitute products that perform a similar function (e.g. polyurethane varnish companies) and those that solve a problem or eliminate it in a dissimilar way (e.g. PVC double-glazing companies). The actions of all of these types of competitors can affect the performance of a company and therefore should be monitored. Their responses also need to be assessed as they will determine the outcome of any competitive move that the company may wish to make, which can result in loss of market share or being made irrelevant. Making the competition irrelevant is a strategic option discussed later in the chapter.

The marketing environment needs to be scanned for potential entrants into the industry. These can take two forms: entrants with technically similar products and those invading the market with substitute products. Companies with similar core competences to the present incumbents may pose the threat of entering with technically similar products. For example, Apple's skills in computer electronics provided the springboard for it to become market leader in several key technology markets, for example the portable music player market with its iPod brand, tablet computers with its iPad, and mobile phone with its iPhone. The source of companies entering with substitute products may be more difficult to locate, however. A technological breakthrough may transform an industry by rendering the old product obsolete, for example the computer replacing the typewriter. In such instances it is difficult to locate the source of the substitute product well in advance. Figure 19.3 illustrates this competitive arena.

What are their strengths and weaknesses?

Having identified our competitors the next stage is to complete a competitor audit in order to assess their relative strengths and weaknesses. Understanding competitor strengths and weaknesses is an important prerequisite for developing a competitor strategy and identifying a competitor's vulnerabilities.

The process of assessing competitors' strengths and weaknesses may take place as part of a marketing audit (see Chapter 18). As much internal, market and customer information should be gathered as is needed. For example, financial data concerning profitability, profit margins, sales and investment levels, market data relating to price levels, market share and distribution channels used, and customer data concerning awareness of brand names, and perceptions of brand and company image, product and service quality, and selling ability may be relevant.

Not all of this information will be easily accessible. Management needs to decide the extent to which each element of information is worth pursuing. For example, a decision is required regarding how much expenditure is to be allocated to measuring customer awareness and perceptions through marketing research.

This process of data gathering needs to be managed so that information is available to compare our company with its competitors on the *key factors for success* in the industry. A three-stage process can then be used.

1 Identify key factors for success in the industry
   These should be restricted to about six to eight factors otherwise the analysis becomes too diffuse (Macdonald and Wilson, 2011). Which factors to use is a matter of managerial judgement. They may be functional (such as financial strength or flexible production) or generic (for example, the ability to respond quickly to customer needs, innovativeness, or the capability to provide other sales services). Since these factors are critical for success they should be used to compare our company with its competitors.

2 Rate our company and competitors on each key success factor using a rating scale
   Each company is given a score on each success factor using a rating device. This may be a scale ranging from 1 (very poor) to 5 (very good); this results in a set of company capability profiles (an example is given in Figure 19.4). Our company is rated alongside two competitors on six key success factors. Compared with our company, competitor 1 is relatively strong regarding technical assistance to customers and access to international distribution channels, but relatively weak on product quality. Competitor 2 is relatively strong on international distribution channels but relatively weak on innovativeness, financial strength and having a well-qualified workforce.

3 Consider the implications for competitive strategy
   The competitive profile analysis helps to identify possible competitive strategies. This analysis would suggest that our company should consider taking steps to improve technical assistance to customers to

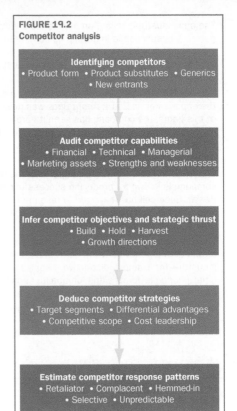

FIGURE 19.2
Competitor analysis

Identifying competitors
• Product form • Product substitutes • Generics
• New entrants

Audit competitor capabilities
• Financial • Technical • Managerial
• Marketing assets • Strengths and weaknesses

Infer competitor objectives and strategic thrust
• Build • Hold • Harvest
• Growth directions

Deduce competitor strategies
• Target segments • Differential advantages
• Competitive scope • Cost leadership

Estimate competitor response patterns
• Retaliator • Complacent • Hemmed-in
• Selective • Unpredictable

match or exceed competitor 1's capability on this factor. At the moment, our company enjoys a differential advantage over competitor 1 on product quality. Our strength in innovativeness should be used to maintain this differential advantage and competitor 1's moves to improve product quality should be monitored carefully.

Competitor 2 is weaker overall than competitor 1 and our company. However, it has considerable strengths in having access to international distribution channels. Given our company's weakness in this area, a strategic alliance with or take-over of competitor 2 might be sensible if our company's objective is to expand internationally. Our company's financial strength and competitor 2's financial weakness suggests that a take-over might be feasible.

What are their strategic objectives and thrust?

The third part of competitor analysis is to infer their *strategic objectives*. In Chapter 18, we discussed how companies might determine their broader strategic aims by deciding which products they need to sell into particular markets. Likewise, knowing the strategic thrust of competitors can help with strategic marketing planning decision-making and also set the overall direction which defines the target market (Varadarajan, 2010). Equally, it is useful to know which strategic objectives are being pursued by competitors, because their response pattern and marketing strategies may depend upon their objectives. Knowing whether a competitor is planning to build, hold, harvest or **divest** particular products and/or strategic business units is also important for planning.

Determining a competitor's objectives can be difficult, as information of a strategic nature can be hard to come by. However, by studying market conditions it is possible to garner insight into what objectives a competitor might be seeking to achieve, and then infer the possible implementation actions it might pursue in order to succeed. Table 19.1 summarizes the market conditions and implementation actions that might occur when a competitor starts to pursue a particular strategic marketing objective.

FIGURE 19.3
Competitor identification

> **The competitive arena**
>
> **Product form competitors**
> • technically similar products
>
> **Product substitutes**
> • technically dissimilar products
>
> **Generic competitors**
> • products that solve the problem or eliminate it in a dissimilar way
>
> **Potential new entrants**
> • with technically similar products
> • with technically dissimilar products

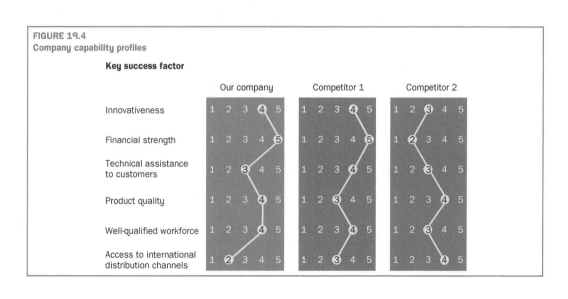

FIGURE 19.4
Company capability profiles

Key success factor

Key success factor	Our company	Competitor 1	Competitor 2
Innovativeness	1 2 3 ④ 5	1 2 3 ④ 5	1 2 ③ 4 5
Financial strength	1 2 3 4 ⑤	1 2 3 4 ⑤	1 ② 3 4 5
Technical assistance to customers	1 2 ③ 4 5	1 2 3 ④ 5	1 2 ③ 4 5
Product quality	1 2 3 ④ 5	1 2 ③ 4 5	1 2 3 ④ 5
Well-qualified workforce	1 2 3 ④ 5	1 2 3 ④ 5	1 2 ③ 4 5
Access to international distribution channels	1 ② 3 4 5	1 2 ③ 4 5	1 2 3 ④ 5

TABLE 19.1 Market conditions and implementation actions related to different marketing objectives

Strategic objectives	Market conditions	Implementation actions
Build	Growth markets Exploitable competitor weaknesses Firm has exploitable strengths, capabilities & resources	**Market expansion** e.g., attracting new customers; finding ways to develop new uses for the goods; increasing the frequency of use **Winning marketing** share through innovative application of the marketing mix e.g., exploiting new channels to market; new products **Mergers and acquisition** **Forming strategic alliances**
Hold	Firm is market leader in a mature or declining state Costs exceed the possible benefits of building market share	**Continually monitoring the competition** e.g., in a market characterized by competitive stability where no one is willing to destabilize the industry structure. Monitoring is necessary to check that there are no significant changes in competitor behaviour **Confronting the competition** e.g., where rivalry is intense and strategic action may be required to defend market share from aggressive challenges
Harvest	Market in decline Core of loyal customers exist Firm has future new products	**Eliminate R&D expenditure** e.g., reduce investment in the products **Reformulation of product** e.g., to reduce costs **Rationalize of product lines** e.g., cutting product variants, keeping best sellers **Reduce marketing spend** e.g., cutting promotional budgets & spend on advertising **Increase prices** as loyal customer will continue to buy
Divest	Low market share in declining markets Too expensive to revive products Removal will not impact on other products	**Exit the market** e.g., get out quickly to minimize costs and potential future losses
Niche	Niche market opportunities Small budget available Opportunities to create competitive advantage	**Market segmentation** e.g. survey market, apply segmentation strategies to identify underserved market opportunities. **Focused R&D** e.g. focus on developing sustainable differential advantage **Differential advantage** e.g. understanding the needs of the customer group & satisfying their needs better than the competition **Thinking small** e.g. emphasis is on high margins not high volume

What are their strategies?

At the product service level, competitor analysis will attempt to deduce positioning strategy. This involves assessing a competitor's target market and differential advantage of its product and/or service. The marketing mix strategies (e.g. price levels, media used for promotion, and distribution channels) may indicate target market, and marketing research into customer perceptions can be used to assess relative differential advantages.

Companies and competitors should be monitored continuously for changes in positioning strategy. For example, Volvo's traditional positioning strategy, based on safety, has been modified to give more emphasis to performance and style enabling the company to compete with other high performance cars.

Strategies can also be defined in terms of competitive scope. For example, are competitors attempting to service the whole market or a few segments of a particular niche? If a niche player, is it likely that they will be content to stay in that segment or will they use it as a beachhead to move into other segments in the future? Japanese companies are renowned for their use of small niche markets as springboards for market segment expansion (e.g. the small car segments in the USA and Europe).

Competitors may use cost-leadership, focusing on cost-reducing measures rather than expensive product development and promotional strategies. (Cost leadership will be discussed in more detail later in this chapter.) If competitors are following this strategy it is more likely that they will be focusing research and development expenditure on process rather than product development in a bid to reduce manufacturing costs.

What are their response patterns?

A key consideration in making a strategic or tactical move is the likely response of competitors. Indeed, it is a major objective of competitor analysis to be able to predict competitor response to market and competitive changes. A competitor's past behaviour is also a guide to what they might do in the future. Market leaders often try to control competitor response by retaliatory action. These are called *retaliatory* competitors because they can be relied on to respond aggressively to competitive challenges. For example, Amazon bought out LoveFilm, which offered streaming video and DVD rentals, in a competitive move against US rival Netflix. Amazon Instant video service provides a service for consumers in the UK and Germany. Amazon planned to challenge Netflix as market leader in the UK with this move (Sweney, 2014).

By punishing competitor moves, market leaders can condition competitors to behave in predicted ways— for example, by not taking advantage of a price rise by the leader. It is not only market leaders that retaliate aggressively. Where management is known to be assertive, and our move is likely to have a major impact on their performance, a strong response is usual.

The history, traditions and managerial personalities of competitors also have an influence on competitive response. Some markets are characterized by years of competitive stability with little serious strategic challenge to any of the incumbents. This can breed complacency, with predictably slow reaction times to new challenges. For example, innovation that offers superior customer value may be dismissed as a fad and unworthy of serious attention.

Another situation where competitors are unlikely to respond is where their previous strategies have restricted their scope for retaliation. An example of such a *hemmed-in competitor* was a major manufacturer of car number plates that were sold to car dealerships. A new company was started by an ex-employee who focused on one geographical area, supplying the same quality product but with extra discount. The national supplier could not respond since to give discount in that particular region would have meant granting the discount nationwide.

A fourth type of competitor may respond *selectively*. Because of tradition or beliefs about the relative effectiveness of marketing instruments, a competitor may respond to some competitive moves but not others. For example, extra sales promotion expenditures may be matched but advertising increases to, say, build brand awareness may be ignored. Another reason for selective response is the varying degree of visibility of marketing actions. For example, giving extra price discounts may be highly visible, but providing distributors with extra support (e.g. training, sales literature, loans) may be less discernible.

A final type of competitor is totally *unpredictable* in its response pattern. Sometimes there is a response and, at other times, there is no response. Some moves are countered aggressively; with others reaction is weak. No factors explain these differences adequately; they appear to be at the whim of management.

Interestingly, research has shown that managers tend to over-react more frequently than they under-react to competitors' marketing activities (Leeflang and Wittink, 1996).

Competitive Advantage

The key to superior performance is to gain and hold a *competitive advantage*. Companies can gain a competitive advantage through *differentiation* of their product offering to provide superior customer value, or by managing for *lowest delivered cost*.

Competitive strategies

These two means of competitive advantage, when combined with the competitive scope of activities (broad vs narrow), result in four generic strategies: differentiation, cost leadership, differentiation focus, and cost focus.

The differentiation and cost leadership strategies seek competitive advantage in a broad range of market or industry segments, whereas differentiation focus and cost focus strategies are confined to a narrow segment (Porter, 1980).

Differentiation

Differentiation strategy involves the selection of one or more choice criteria that are used by many buyers in an industry. The firm then uniquely positions itself to meet these criteria. Differentiation strategies are usually associated with a premium price, and higher than average costs for the industry as the extra value to customers (e.g. higher performance) often raises costs. The aim is to differentiate in a way that leads to a price premium in excess of the cost of differentiating. Differentiation gives customers a reason to prefer one product over another and thus is central to strategic marketing thinking. Here are some examples of brands that have achieved success using a differentiation strategy.

* Nissan produced the Leaf, a battery electric car, which met the needs of customers looking for a *greener* solution. The innovations incorporated into the car enabled it to become the best-selling electronic vehicle in Europe.
* Toyota has built its success and reputation by targeting a broad market with highly reliable, high build quality, stylish and environmentally friendly cars, which differentiate the brand from its competitors, such as GM, Ford and Fiat.
* Dyson differentiated its vacuum cleaners by inventing a bagless version that outperformed its rivals by providing greater suction and convenience, and by eliminating the need to buy and install dust bags. Its vacuum cleaners are also differentiated from other brands by their distinctive design.
* Google created a differential advantage over its search engine rivals by enabling the most relevant websites to be ranked at the top of listings.

Cost leadership

This strategy involves the achievement of the lowest cost position in an industry. Many segments in the industry are served and great importance is attached to minimizing costs throughout the business so long as the price achievable for its products is around the industry average, cost leadership should result in superior performance. Thus, cost leaders often market standard products that are believed to be acceptable to customers. Heinz and United Biscuits are believed to be cost leaders in their industries. They market acceptable products at reasonable prices, which means that their low costs result in above-average profits. Walmart is also a cost leader, which allows the company the option of charging lower prices than its rivals to achieve higher sales and yet achieve comparable profit margins, or to match competitors' prices and attain higher profit margins. Zara, owned by Inditex, has an extremely efficient supply chain that not only enables the brand to produce very low-cost fashion garments, but also to get products to market faster than its competitors.

Differentiation focus

With this strategy, a firm aims to differentiate within one or a small number of target market segments. The special needs of the segment mean that there is an opportunity to differentiate the product offering from that of the competition, which may be targeting a broader group of customers. For example, some small speciality chemical companies thrive on taking orders that are too small or specialized to be of interest to their larger competitors. Differentiation focusers must be clear that the needs of their target group differ from those of the broader market (otherwise there will be no basis for differentiation) and that existing competitors are underperforming. Examples of differentiation focusers are Burberry, Bang & Olufsen, Mercedes and Ferrari; each of these markets differentiated products to one or a small number of target market segments. Not all attempts to differentiate succeed as Marketing in Action 19.2 explains.

Cost focus

With this strategy a firm seeks a cost advantage with one or a small number of target market segments. By dedicating itself to the segment, the cost focuser can seek economies that may be ignored or missed by broadly targeted competitors. In some instances, the competition, by trying to achieve wide market acceptance, may be over-performing (for example, by providing unwanted services) to one segment of customers. By providing a basic product offering, a cost advantage will be gained that may exceed the price discount necessary to sell it. Examples of cost focusers are easyJet and Ryanair, who focus on short-haul flights with a basic product trimmed to reduce costs. Lidl is also a cost focuser, targeting price-sensitive consumers with a narrow product line (around 300 items in stock) but with large buying power. Ibis, the no-frills hotel brand in the Accor Hotels portfolio, is another example with its focus on one market segment: price-conscious consumers.

MARKETING IN ACTION 19.2
Maybach: The Rise, Fall and (Possible) Rise Again of a Luxury Icon

In 2002, Mercedes-Benz announced, with great fanfare, that after a 60-year hiatus it was reviving the storied Maybach brand. The expectation was that the Maybach would successfully compete against both Rolls-Royce and Bentley in the exclusive arena known as the ultra-luxury car market. But sadly for Mercedes-Benz, it was not to be. Less than 10 years after its glorious return, it was announced that the Maybach division would be closing, with final production ceasing by 2013. Analysts believed the main reason for the brand's demise was years of disappointing sales. What happened? How could a company like Mercedes-Benz, so well known for the luxury and high performance of its cars, mess up so badly with the revival and introduction of an 'ultra-luxury' car brand?

The attractiveness of the ultra-luxury car market is its proven resistance to the effects of recession, and Mercedes-Benz believed that the Maybach had what it took to compete head on with the old-world masters of luxury. Each car was a work of art, being built by hand and incorporating only the finest materials. Available options were dizzying. Customers could have a 'movie-theatre-like' experience thanks to high-resolution television screens placed in the rear, as well as leather seats similar to those found in a private business jet. For the paranoid, it was even possible to get steel- and Kevlar-reinforced armour plating.

But with luxury features came a luxury price tag. Prices for the Maybach started at around $343,000 for the 'basic' Maybach 57, but could go up to well over $1 million for the 'luxury' 62S Landaulet model.

Mercedes-Benz is recognized as a world-class leader in luxury. But the problem was that it just wasn't seen in the same class as Rolls-Royce and Bentley. A common complaint was that the power-train and interior were both a bit 'stale.' Some cynics said that Mercedes-Benz tried to get by on the cheap, basing its new ultra-luxury car's chassis on the previously designed W140 platform, which was used in the 1991–99 S-Class. Critics also argued that Maybach suffered from flawed and poorly executed strategic marketing, with the message of the car's 'purpose' or how it was preferentially differentiated from a Rolls-Royce Phantom, for example, never being made clear. In the end, Mercedes-Benz lost an estimated $1 billion on the Maybach.

In November 2014, Mercedes-Benz announced (for a second time) the triumphant return of the Maybach brand, but this time plans appeared to be far less ambitious than previous ones. The revived brand is being targeted at what is called the 'super-premium' market. In Goldilocks fashion, Mercedes-Benz is trying to provide not too much luxury, not too little luxury, but just the right amount of luxury with the new version of the Maybach. The car is not a stand-alone brand this time. Rather, it is called the 'Mercedes-Maybach' and is based on an elongated version of the successful S-series.

Choosing a competitive strategy

The essence of corporate success is to choose a generic strategy and pursue it with gusto. Below-average performance is associated with the failure to achieve any of these generic strategies. The result is no competitive advantage: a *stuck-in-the-middle position* that results in lower performance than that of the cost leaders, differentiators or focusers in any market segment. An example of a company that made the mistake of moving to a stuck-in-the-middle position is Fiat. The Fiat 500 was sold in the US through a stand-alone dealership network. Dealers were required to make a heavy investment in creating an Italian feel in their showrooms. This was in preference to launching the car through the 500-strong Chrysler dealers (Chrysler acquired a stake in Fiat in 2009). The advantages of the first option were an image of exclusivity, but heavy investment was required—for example, $3 million for the showroom makeover. In the second option leveraging (Wunker, 2012) advantage from Chrysler could have meant making use of existing sales and service infrastructures. One of the downsides was that the Fiat 500 had a higher ticket price than similar performing cars like the Nissan Versa or Toyota Yaris and being sold in the same location could have had a negative impact on sales. So, the Fiat 500 was, arguably, stuck in the middle and its strategy did not lead to the coverage needed to establish the brand as rapidly as it would have liked.

Companies need to understand the generic basis for their success and resist the temptation to blur strategy by making inconsistent moves. For example, a no-frills cost leader or focuser should beware the pitfalls of moving to a higher cost base (perhaps by adding expensive services). A focus strategy involves limiting sales volume. Once domination of the target segment has been achieved there may be a temptation to move into other segments in order to achieve growth with the same competitive advantage. This can be a mistake if the new segments do not value the firm's competitive advantage in the same way.

In most situations differentiation and cost leadership strategies are incompatible: differentiation is achieved through higher costs. However, there are circumstances when both can be achieved simultaneously. For example, a differentiation strategy may lead to market share domination, which lowers costs through economies of scale and learning effects; or a highly differentiated firm may pioneer a major process innovation that significantly reduces manufacturing costs leading to a cost-leadership position. When differentiation and cost leadership coincide, performance is exceptional since a premium price can be charged for a low-cost product.

Sources of competitive advantage

In order to create a differentiated or lowest cost position, a firm needs to understand the nature and location of the potential *sources of competitive advantage*. The nature of these sources are the superior skills and resources of a firm. Management benefits by analyzing the superior skills and resources that are contributing, or could contribute, to competitive advantage (i.e. differentiation or lowest cost position). Their location can be aided by value chain analysis. A value chain is the discrete activities a firm carries out in order to perform its business.

Superior skills

Superior skills are the distinctive capabilities of key personnel that set them apart from the personnel of competing companies (Day and Wensley, 1988). The benefit of superior skills is the resulting ability to perform functions more effectively than other companies. For example, Sergey Brin and Larry Page worked together to produce a search engine that outperformed its rivals. Their technical know-how enabled them to use their superior skills not only to create Google, but also to lead the company to become the world's most influential Internet search tool.

Superior resources

Superior resources are the tangible requirements for advantage that enable a firm to exercise its skills. Examples of superior resources include:
- the number of salespeople in a market
- expenditure on advertising and sales promotion
- distribution infrastructure
- expenditure on R&D
- scale of and type of production facilities
- financial resources
- brand equity
- knowledge.

Core competences

The distinctive nature of these skills and resources makes up a company's core competences. For example, Google is able to use its technical skills and vast resources to enable the company to operate a global search engine. Google's operation has grown thanks to its innovative use of technology and its data centres in the USA, Northern Europe and Asia.

Value chain

A useful method for locating superior skills and resources is the value chain (Porter, 1985). All companies consist of a set of activities that are conducted to design, manufacture, market, distribute and service its products. The value chain categorizes these into primary and support activities (see Figure 19.5). This enables the sources of costs and differentiation to be understood and located.

Primary activities include inbound physical distribution (e.g. materials handling, warehousing, inventory control), operations (e.g. manufacturing, packaging, reselling), outbound physical distribution (e.g. delivery, order processing), marketing (e.g. advertising, selling) and service (e.g. installation, repair, customer training). A key skill of Walmart is its inbound logistics, which are based on real-time information systems and lets customers decide what appears in its stores. The Internet is used to inform suppliers what was sold the day before. In this way, it buys only what sells. Zara's competitive advantage relies on its marketing skills, which relate product design to fashion trends, and operational and logistical skills that get new clothing designs in stores faster than competitors.

Support activities are found within all of these primary activities, and consist of purchased inputs, technology, human resource management and the firm's infrastructure. These are not defined within a given primary activity because they can be found in all of them. Purchasing can take place within each primary activity, not just in the purchasing department; technology is relevant to all primary activities, as is human resource management;

FIGURE 19.5
The value chain

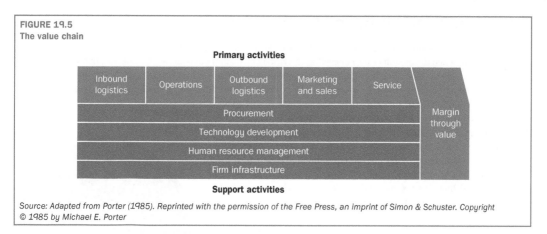

Source: Adapted from Porter (1985). Reprinted with the permission of the Free Press, an imprint of Simon & Schuster. Copyright © 1985 by Michael E. Porter

and the firm's infrastructure, which consists of general management, planning, finance, accounting and quality management, supports the entire value chain.

By examining each value-creating activity, management can look for the skills and resources that may form the basis for low cost or differentiated positions.

To the extent that skills and resources exceed (or could be developed to exceed) those of the competition, they form the key sources of competitive advantage. Not only should the skills and resources within value-creating activities be examined, the *linkages* between them should be examined too. For example, greater coordination between operations and inbound physical distribution may give rise to reduced costs through lower inventory levels.

Value chain analysis can extend to the value chains of suppliers and customers. For example, just-in-time supply could lower inventory costs; providing salesforce support to distributors could foster closer relations. Thus, by looking at the linkages between a firm's value chain and those of suppliers and customers, improvements in performance can result that can lower costs or contribute to the creation of a differentiated position.

Overall, the contribution of the value chain is in providing a framework for understanding the nature and location of the skills and resources that provide the basis for competitive advantage. Furthermore, the value chain provides the framework for cost analysis. Assigning operating costs and assets to value activities is the starting point of cost analysis so that improvement can be made, and cost advantages defended. For example, if a firm discovers that its cost advantage is based on superior production facilities, it should be vigilant in upgrading those facilities to maintain its position against competitors. Similarly, by understanding the sources of differentiation, a company can build on these sources and defend against competitive attack. For example, if differentiation is based on skills in product design, then management knows that sufficient investment in maintaining design superiority is required to maintain the firm's differentiated position. Also, the identification of specific sources of advantage can lead to their exploitation in new markets where customers place a similar high value on the resultant outcome. For example, Marks & Spencer's skills developed in clothing retailing were successfully extended to provide differentiation in food retailing. Finally, analysis of the value chain can lead to its reconfiguration to fundamentally change the way a market is served. Figure 19.6 provides some examples.

FIGURE 19.6
Value chain reconfiguration

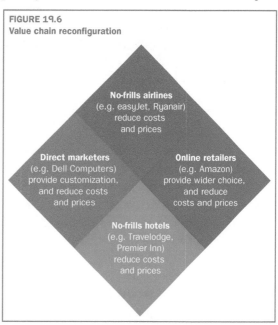

Creating a Differential Advantage

Although skills and resources are the sources of competitive advantage, they are translated into a differential advantage only when the customer perceives that the firm is providing value above that of the competition. (For methods of calculating value in organizational markets, see Anderson and Narus (1998).) The creation of a differential advantage, then, comes from linking skills and resources with the key attributes (choice criteria) that customers are looking for in a product offering. However, it should be recognized that the distinguishing competing attributes in a market are not always the most important ones. For example, if customers were asked to rank safety, punctuality and onboard service in order of importance when flying, safety would undoubtedly be ranked at the top. Nevertheless, when choosing an airline, safety would rank low because most airlines are assumed to be safe. This is why airlines look to less important ways of differentiating their offerings (e.g. by giving superior onboard service).

A differential advantage can be created with any aspect of the marketing mix. Product, distribution, promotion and price are all capable of creating added customer value (see Figure 19.7).

The key to knowing whether improving an aspect of marketing is worthwhile is to know whether the potential benefit provides value to the customer. Table 19.2 lists ways of creating differential advantages and their potential impact on customer value.

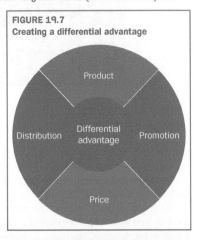

FIGURE 19.7
Creating a differential advantage

TABLE 19.2 Creating a differential advantage using the marketing mix		
Marketing mix	Differential advantage	Value to the customer
Product	Performance	Lower costs; higher revenue; safety; pleasure; status; service; added functions
	Durability	Longer life; lower costs
	Reliability	Lower maintenance and production costs; higher revenue; fewer problems
	Style	Good looks; status
	Upgradability	Lower costs; prestige
	Technical assistance	Better-quality products; closer supplier–buyer relationships
	Installation	Fewer problems
Distribution	Location	Convenience; lower costs
	Quick/reliable delivery	Lower costs; fewer problems
	Distributor support	More effective selling/marketing; close buyer–seller relationships
	Delivery guarantees	Peace of mind
	Computerized reordering	Less work; lower costs
Promotion	Creative/more advertising	Superior brand personality
	Creative/more sales promotion	Direct added value
	Cooperative promotions	Lower costs
	Well-trained salesforce	Superior problem-solving and building close relationships
	Dual selling	Sales assistance; higher sales
	Fast, accurate quotes	Lower costs; fewer problems
	Free demonstrations	Lower risk of purchase
	Free or low-cost trial	Lower risk of purchase
	Fast complaint handling	Fewer problems; lower costs

»

»

Marketing mix	Differential advantage	Value to the customer
Price	Lower price	Lower cost of purchase
	Credit facilities	Lower costs; better cash flow
	Low-interest loans	Lower costs; better cash flow
	Higher price	Price–quality match

Product

Product performance can be enhanced by, say, raising speed, comfort and safety levels, capacity and ease of use, or improving taste or smell. For example, improving comfort levels (e.g. of a car), taste (e.g. of food), or smell (e.g. of cosmetics) can give added pleasure to consumption. There are many ways to enhance performance. For example, Apple has enhanced the performance of its iPhone with the creation of its App Store, which allows users to access software applications from independent developers. This creates additional functions that the iPhone can carry out, such as Foursquare, which allows users to find the location, price range and reviews of restaurants nearby. For further discussion on marketing apps, see Marketing in Action 19.1.

Exclusive designs and style are another way products can be used to differentiate a brand. Bang & Olufsen and Audi are two companies that have used style as a way to compete in highly competitive markets. Bang & Olufsen has long been regarded as the style leader in audio and television equipment, and Audi has become one of the car industry's most successful luxury brands, producing some of the world's most coveted and copied cars.

Apple has become a world-leading brand by continually introducing innovative products, the latest being the iWatch. However, currently, the small battery means the watch has to be charged regularly; so while the iWatch may be a desired high-status product, its performance might create an opportunity for competitors to enter this market. Performance can also be improved by added functions that create extra benefits for customers.

 Scan the QR code to discover how Vodafone differentiates its products from the competition by encouraging its customers to live life to the full.

The *durability* of a product has a bearing on costs since greater durability means a longer operating life. Improving product *reliability* (i.e. lowering malfunctions or defects) can lower maintenance and production costs, raise revenues through lower downtime and reduce the hassle of using the product. Product *styling* can also give customer value through the improved looks that good style brings. This can confer status to the buyer and allow the supplier to charge premium prices, for example Bridgestone (Japanese), Michelin (French) and Pirelli (Italian).

The capacity to *upgrade* a product (to take advantage of technological advances) or to meet changing needs (e.g. extra storage space in a computer) can lower costs, and confer prestige by maintaining state-of-the-art features. The Apple MacBook Pro and MacBook Air computers demonstrate how style can be used to create a differential advantage.

Products can be augmented by the provision of *guarantees* that give customers peace of mind and lower costs should the product need repair, as well as giving *technical assistance* to customers, so that they are provided with better-quality products. Both parties benefit from closer relationships and from the provision of product *installation*, which means that customers do not incur problems in properly installing a complex piece of equipment.

Distribution

Wide distribution coverage and/or careful selection of distributor *locations* can provide convenient purchasing for customers. *Quick and/or reliable delivery* can lower buyer costs by reducing production downtime and lowering inventory levels. Reliable delivery, in particular, reduces the frustration of waiting for late delivery. Providing distributors with *support* in the form of training and financial help can bring about more effective selling and marketing, and offers both parties the advantage of closer relationships. FedEx has continued to prosper by giving *delivery guarantees* of critical documents 'down to the hour' (*Business Week*, 2006). Working with organizational customers to introduce *computerized reordering* systems can lower their costs, reduce their workload and increase the cost for them of switching to other suppliers.

Promotion

A differential advantage can be created by the *creative use of advertising*. For example, *spending more on advertising* can also aid differentiation by creating a stronger brand personality than competitive brands. For example, Twinings tea's 'get back to where you belong' campaign targeted women using new emotive techniques and animations to significantly grow market share (Owen, 2012). Similarly, using *more creative sales promotional methods* or simply *spending more on sales incentives* can give direct added value to customers. By engaging in *cooperative promotions* with distributors, producers can lower their costs and build goodwill.

The salesforce can also offer a means of creating a differential advantage. Particularly when products are similar, a *well-trained salesforce* can provide superior problem-solving skills for their customers.

EXHIBIT 19.3
Bang & Olufsen's stylish audio and television equipment

 Scan the QR code to see how Twinings tea used emotional appeals to differentiate its brand and increase sales.

Price

Using low price as a means of gaining differential advantage can fail unless the firm enjoys a cost advantage and has the resources to fight a price war. For example, Acer has successfully challenged Dell and Hewlett-Packard in the computer market by launching a very low-cost desktop PC. Its strategy is to exploit its lowest cost position, allowing it to become extremely aggressive on price (Einhorn, 2009). Budget airlines such as Ryanair and easyJet have challenged more traditional airlines by charging low prices based on low costs.

A less obvious means of lowering the effective price to the customer is to offer *credit facilities* or *low-interest loans*. Both serve to lower the cost of purchase and improve cash flow for customers. Finally, a *high price* can be used as part of a premium positioning strategy to support brand image. Where a brand has distinct product, promotional or distributional advantages, a premium price provides consistency within the marketing mix.

This analysis of how the marketing mix can be used to develop a differential advantage has focused on how each action can be translated into value to the customer. Remember, however, that for a differential advantage to be realized, a firm needs to provide not only customer value but also value that is superior to that offered by the competition. If all companies provide distributor support in equal measure, for example, distributors may gain value, but no differential advantage will have been achieved.

EXHIBIT 19.4
TK Maxx uses price and quality to differentiate from its competitors with its 'Big labels small prices' campaign

Fast reaction times

In addition to using the marketing mix to create a differential advantage, many companies are recognizing the need to create *fast reaction times* to changes in marketing trends. For example, H&M and Zara have developed fast-reaction systems so that new designs can be delivered to stores within three weeks, and top-selling items are requested and poor sellers withdrawn from shops within a week. This is made possible by sophisticated marketing information systems that feed data from stores to headquarters every day.

Scale of operations

Companies can also create a differential advantage when the scale of their operations creates value for their customers. For example, eBay has built a sustainable differential advantage by building a large participant base. As the customer value of an auction site is directly related to the size of the participant base, once eBay gained a large user base advantage it became extremely difficult for any competitor to duplicate the value that it offers (Nagle and Hogan, 2006).

Sustaining a differential advantage

When searching for ways to achieve a differential advantage, management should pay close attention to factors that cannot easily be copied by the competition. The aim is to achieve a *sustainable differential advantage*. Competing on low price can often be copied by the competition, meaning that any advantage is short-lived. Other attempts at creating a differential advantage may also be copied by the competition. For example, when DHL challenged FedEx and UPS in the US postal delivery market, all its attempts at gaining a competitive edge were copied by its rivals. When DHL hired the US Postal Service to carry out its domestic deliveries, a move that was popular with customers, FedEx and UPS followed suit. The result was that DHL could not find a way of creating a differential advantage and was forced to exit the US market (*The Economist*, 2008). The key to achieving a long-term advantage is to focus on areas that the competition find impossible or, at the very least, very difficult to copy, including:

- patent-protected products
- strong brand personality
- close relationships with customers
- high service levels achieved by well-trained personnel
- innovative product upgrading
- creating high entry barriers (e.g. R&D or promotional expenditures)
- strong and distinctive internal processes that deliver the above and are difficult to copy
- scale (where the scale of operations provides value to the customer, for example eBay) (De Chernatony, Harris and Dall'Olmo Riley, 2000).

Eroding a differential advantage

However, many advantages are contestable. For example, IBM's stronghold on personal computers was undermined by cheaper clones. Three mechanisms are at work that can erode a differential advantage (Day, 1999).

1 technological and environment changes that create opportunities for competitors by eroding the protective barriers (e.g. long-standing television companies are being challenged by satellite television)
2 competitors learn how to imitate the sources of the differential advantage (e.g. competitors engage in a training programme to improve service capabilities)
3 complacency leads to lack of protection of the differential advantage. Read Marketing in Action 19.3 to discover how IBM invented an artificial intelligence computer and in doing so acquired a new source of competitive advantage.

Creating Cost Leadership

Creating a cost-leadership position requires an understanding of the factors that affect costs. Porter has identified 10 major *cost drivers* that determine the behaviour of costs in the value chain (see Figure 19.8) (Porter, 1985).

Economies of scale

Scale economies can arise from the use of more efficient methods of production at higher volumes. For example, United Biscuits benefits from more efficient machinery that can produce biscuits more cheaply than that used by

MARKETING IN ACTION 19.3
Want to Know How to Beat the Competition? Ask Watson

Watson is an artificial intelligence computer system that can answer *spoken* questions, using natural language rather than computer code. The machine, devised by IBM, has won the television quiz show *Jeopardy* in the USA by outperforming human opponents in answering questions. Watson's advantage comes from its vast memory store and the speed at which information can be retrieved.

But IBM is not intending to use Watson for playing games; it is being used in various commercial settings in the health industry as a diagnostic tool for use with cancer patients. Watson has been fed information relating to oncology (lung, prostate and breast cancers) which has provided a knowledge base that the machine can interpret. This information includes more than 2 million pages of information from medical journals and 1.5 million patient records. Wellpoint's Samuel Nessbaum claims that Watson can interrogate the knowledge base and produce a diagnosis that is correct 90 per cent of the time, which once again outperforms humans; doctors found to be correct only 50 per cent of the time.

IBM has now launched Watson Health, which is a cloud-computing-based supercomputer for analyzing healthcare data on a global basis. The company has also entered into partnership with Apple and Johnson & Johnson (leading pharmaceutical product manufacturer) to develop consumer and medical devices. At Apple, Watson Health Cloud services will be linked to the Apple Health Kit, which will enable Apple iWatch wearers to take part in a huge health data study.

At Johnson & Johnson, the focus will be on creating intelligent healthcare coaching systems, including for joint replacement and spinal surgery. It also intends to launch new apps for targeting chronic conditions such as diabetes and obesity.

Based on: IBM (2015); Steadman (2013); Mearian (2015)

Fox's Biscuits, which operates at much lower volume. Scale economies also arise from the less-than-proportional increase in overheads as production volume increases. For example, a factory with twice the floor area of another factory is less than twice the price to build. A third scale economy results from the capacity to spread the cost of R&D and promotion over a greater sales volume. Such scale economies mean that companies such as Coca-Cola, General Electric, Intel, Microsoft and Walmart have a huge advantage over their competitors. However, economies of scale do not proceed indefinitely. At some point, diseconomies of scale are likely to arise as size gives rise to over-complexity and, possibly, personnel difficulties.

Learning

Costs can also fall as a result of the effects of learning. For example, people learn how to assemble more quickly, pack more efficiently, design products that are easier to manufacture, lay out warehouses more effectively, cut driving time and reduce inventories. The combined effect of economies of scale and learning as

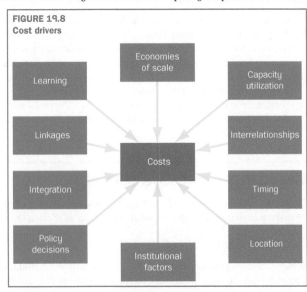

FIGURE 19.8
Cost drivers

cumulative output increases has been termed the **experience curve**. The Boston Consulting Group has estimated that costs are reduced by approximately 15–20 per cent on average each time cumulative output doubles. This suggests that companies with greater market share will have a cost advantage through the experience curve effect, assuming all companies are operating on the same curve. However, a move towards a new manufacturing technology can lower the experience curve for adopting companies, allowing them to leap-frog more traditional companies and thereby gain a cost advantage even though cumulative output may be lower.

Capacity utilization

Since fixed costs must be paid whether a plant is manufacturing at full or zero capacity, underutilization incurs costs. The effect is to push up the cost per unit for production. The impact of capacity utilization on profitability was established by the PIMS (profit impact of marketing strategy) studies, which have shown a positive association between utilization and return on investment (Buzzell and Gale, 1987). Changes in capacity utilization can also raise costs (e.g. through the extra costs of hiring and laying off workers). Careful production planning is required for seasonal products such as ice cream and fireworks, in order to smooth output.

Linkages

These describe how the costs of activities are affected by how other activities are performed. For example, improving quality-assurance activities can reduce after-sales service costs. In the car industry, the reduction in the number of faults on a new car reduces warranty costs. The activities of suppliers and distributors also link to affect the costs of a firm. For example, the introduction of a just-in-time delivery system by a supplier reduces the inventory costs of a firm. Distributors can influence a company's physical distribution costs through their warehouse location decision. To exploit such linkages, though, the firm may need considerable bargaining power. In some instances it can pay a firm to increase distributor margins or pay a fee in order to exploit linkages.

Interrelationships

Sharing costs with other business units is another potential cost driver. Sharing the costs of R&D, transportation, marketing and purchasing means lower costs. Know-how can also be shared to reduce costs by improving the efficiency of an activity. Car manufacturers share engineering platforms and components to reduce costs. For example, Volkswagen does this across its VW, Skoda, Seat and Audi cars. Care has to be taken that the cars appearing under different brand names do not appear too similar, however, or this may detract from the appeal of the more expensive marques (MacKintosh, 2005).

Integration

Both integration and forms of integration can affect costs. For example, owning the means of physical distribution rather than using outside contractors could lower costs. Ownership may allow a producer to avoid suppliers or customers with sizeable bargaining power. De-integration can lower costs and raise flexibility. For example, by using many small clothing suppliers, Benetton is in a powerful position to keep costs low while maintaining a high degree of production flexibility.

Timing

Both first movers and late entrants have potential opportunities for lowering costs. First movers in a market can gain cost advantages: it is usually cheaper to establish a brand name in the minds of customers if there is no competition. Also, they have prime access to cheap or high-quality raw materials and locations. However, late entrants to a market have the opportunity to buy the latest technology and avoid high market development costs.

Policy decisions

Companies have a wide range of discretionary policy decisions that affect costs. Product width, level of service, channel decisions (e.g. small number of large dealers vs large number of small dealers), salesforce decisions (e.g. in-company salesforce vs sales agents) and wage levels are some of the decision areas that have a direct impact on costs. Southwest Airlines, for example, cuts costs by refusing to waste time assigning seats and does not wait for late arrivals. The overriding concern is to get the aeroplane in and out of the gate quickly so that it is in the air earning money. Southwest flies only one kind of aircraft, which also keeps costs down (McNulty, 2001).

Companies can also collaborate to reduce costs. For example, Vodafone has teamed up with O_2's parent company, Telefónica, to share mobile network infrastructure (e.g. masts, equipment and power supply), following a similar deal between T-Mobile and 3 (Kollewe, 2008).

 Scan the QR code to analyse how Quaker Oats supports its parent company's (PepsiCo) corporate strategy.

Ryanair accepts bookings only over the Internet, thus eliminating the need for an inbound telemarketing team and allowing e-ticketing, which cuts postage and paper costs. Other sectors, such as insurance, rail, banking, package holidays and hotels, encourage transactions over the Internet in order to reduce costs. Care must be taken, however, not to reduce costs with regard to activities that have a major bearing on customer value. For example, moving from a company-employed salesforce to sales agents may not only cut costs but at the same time also destroy supplier–customer relationships.

Location

The location of plant and warehouses affects costs through different wage, physical distribution and energy costs. Dyson, for example, manufactures its vacuum cleaners in Malaysia to take advantage of low wage costs (Marsh, 2002). Car manufacturers such as VW, Peugeot, Skoda and Mercedes have moved production to eastern Europe to take advantage of low costs (Milne and Williamson, 2005). Locating near customers can lower outbound distributional costs, while locating near suppliers reduces inbound distributional costs.

Institutional factors

These include government regulations, tariffs and local content rules. For example, regulations regarding the maximum size of lorries affect distribution costs.

Companies employing a cost leadership strategy will be vigilant in pruning costs. This analysis of cost drivers provides a framework for searching out new avenues for cost reduction.

Once a company has identified a strategic direction and developed an understanding of the nature of the competition and how it might compete, it then has to decide on developing a competitive marketing strategy.

Competitive Marketing Strategy

When developing marketing strategy, companies need to be aware of their own strengths and weaknesses, customer needs, and the competition. This three-pronged approach to strategy development has been termed the 'strategic triangle' and is shown in Figure 19.9. This framework recognizes that to be successful it is no longer sufficient to be good at satisfying customers' needs: companies need to be better than the competition. So far, we have considered creating and sustaining competitive advantage; now we explore the development of marketing strategies in the face of competitive activity and challenges, by looking at alternative modes of competitive behaviour and then examining when and how to achieve strategic marketing objectives.

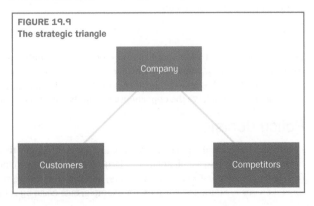

FIGURE 19.9
The strategic triangle

Company

Customers

Competitors

Competitive Behaviour

Rivalry between companies does not always lead to conflict and aggressive marketing battles. Competitive behaviour can take five forms: conflict, competition, co-existence, cooperation and collusion (Easton and Araujo, 1986).

Conflict

Conflict is characterized by aggressive competition, where the objective is to drive competitors out of the marketplace. The retail industry is highly competitive. Compounded by the global economic recession, many businesses have been forced to close as a result of competitive conflict or devise ways of strengthening their market position. Dixons Retail changed the face of its business in the UK by merging with Carphone Warehouse. The move created a very large retailer with over 3,000 physical stores and additional product ranges, strengthened the company's buying power, and created opportunities for growth and costs savings on operational costs (Garside and Farrrell, 2014).

Competition

The objective of competition is not to eliminate competitors from the marketplace, but to perform better than them. This may take the form of trying to achieve faster sales and/or profit growth, larger size or higher market share. Competitive behaviour recognizes the limits of aggression. Competitor reaction will be an important consideration when setting strategy. Players will avoid spoiling the underlying industry structure, which is an important influence on overall profitability. For example, price wars will be avoided if competitors believe that their long-term effect will be to reduce industry profitability.

Co-existence

Three types of co-existence can occur. First, co-existence may arise because companies do not recognize their competitors, owing to difficulties in defining market boundaries. For example, Waterman and Mont Blanc, makers of fine-quality and luxury writing instruments, fountain pens and propelling pencils, may ignore competition from jewellery companies, since their definition may be product-based rather than market-centred (i.e. the gift market). Second, companies may not recognize other companies they believe are operating in a separate market segment. For example, Mont Blanc and Waterman are likely to ignore the actions of Mitsubishi Pencil Company, which manufactures Uniball rollerball pens, as they are operating in different market segments. Third, companies may choose to acknowledge the territories of their competitors (for example, geography, brand personality, market segment or product technology) in order to avoid harmful head-to-head competition.

Cooperation

This involves the pooling of the skills and resources of two or more companies to overcome problems and take advantage of new opportunities. A growing trend is towards strategic alliances, where companies join together through a joint venture, licensing agreement, long-term purchasing and supply arrangements, or joint research and development contract to build a long-term competitive advantage. For example, Shell International Petroleum, Rolls-Royce and Airbus have worked in collaboration to develop alternative fuels for the A380, which has led to the use of cleaner aviation fuels. In today's global marketplace, where size is a key source of advantage, cooperation is a major type of competitive behaviour (Airbus, 2012). See Mini Case 19.1 to find out more about the Diageo way of growing markets.

 Scan the QR code to see how Diageo's 'Keep Walking' creative campaign has maintained the position of its world-beating Johnnie Walker whisky for over a decade.

Collusion

The final form of competitive behaviour is collusion, whereby companies come to some arrangement that inhibits competition in a market. Collusion is more likely where there are a small number of suppliers in each national market, the price of the product is a small proportion of buyer costs, cross-national trade is restricted by tariff barriers or prohibitive transportation costs, and buyers are able to pass on high prices to their customers. For example, Apple joined forces with five major book publishers (Hachette Book Group, HarperCollins, Penguin,

MINI CASE 19.1
Growing Markets the Diageo Way

Diageo is a company that owns over a quarter of the world's leading brands of spirits, for example Smirnoff vodka, Johnnie Walker whisky and Guinness, which is a leading global beer brand. In addition, Diageo also owns local brands, which are used to broaden market penetration in particular parts of the world. For Diageo, growth opportunities are in new markets in Asia Pacific, Latin America and Africa, and the company is making acquisitions of strong local brands that appeal to its target customers.

Diageo's strategies for winning market share make use of the company's marketing knowledge and expertise. Elements of the marketing mix are used innovatively to differentiate its brands—for example the global Johnnie Walker 'Keep Walking' marketing communications campaign, which has increased sales and market share for over a decade. This creative idea has grown and been reinvented for a new generation of digital consumers. Products also undergo regular reinventions, and new flavours, packaging and formats are introduced to ensure the interest of new and existing customers, for example the 'From the bar' premixed drinks range using Gordon's, Pimm's and Smirnoff.

Collaboration with partners is another method used by Diageo to build market share. The company's 'Diageo Way of Selling' programme aims to help retailers and other trade partners achieve high levels of sales through education and sharing best practices, which creates value for all involved in the collaboration. It has made a significant investment in facilitating partnerships. The European Customer Collaboration Centre provides a state-of-the-art facility for Diageo to bring together customers, retailers, trade partners and distributors to aid brand development, integrated planning and research and development for new products and services. This investment not only helps Diageo show support to its business partners and customers, but also to foster constant brand development and innovation, which ultimately increases sales and growth of market share.

Questions:

1 Explain the actions Diageo has used to build market share.
2 Discuss the difference between strategic thrust and strategic objectives, using examples from Diageo.
3 Discuss the importance of setting marketing objectives as part of the marketing planning process.

Based on: BBH (2015); Diageo (2015)

Simon & Schuster and Macmillan) to raise the price of e-books. The US Justice Department and the European Commission decided that Apple's decision to side with the publishers was tantamount to collusion and an example of anti-competitive behaviour. The publishers settled, but Apple went to trial and was found guilty of price fixing and collusion (Hughes, 2014).

Developing Competitive Marketing Strategies

Researchers Ries and Trout (2005), and Kotler and Singh (1981) have drawn attention to the relationship between military and marketing 'warfare'. Their work has stressed the need to develop strategies that are more than customer based. They placed the emphasis on attacking and defending against the competition, and used military analogies to guide strategic thinking. They saw competition as the enemy and thus recognized the relevance to business of the principles of military warfare as put forward by such writers as Sun Tzu (1963) and von Clausewitz (1908). As von Clausewitz wrote:

> 'Military warfare is a clash between major interests that is resolved by bloodshed—that is the only way in which it differs from other conflicts. Rather than comparing it to an art we could more accurately compare it to commerce, which is also a conflict of human interests and activities.'

Earlier in the chapter we discussed analyzing competitors and their marketing objectives, which shape their direction in terms of products and markets and, more specifically, objectives for individual products and services. We now consider the marketing strategies that companies might apply when pursuing particular strategic marketing objectives.

Attack strategies

If a market cannot be expanded, a build strategy implies gaining marketing success at the expense of the competition. Winning market share is an important goal, as market share has been found to be related to profitability in many studies (see Chapter 11). There are several reasons why this should be. Market leaders are often high-price brands (e.g. Coca-Cola, Kellogg's, Heinz, Nestlé, and Nike). They are also in a stronger position to resist distributor demands for trade discounts. Because of economies of scale and experience curve effects, their costs are likely to be lower than those of their smaller-volume rivals. Therefore, their profit margins should be greater than those of their competitors. Since they are market leaders, by definition the unit sales volume is higher and consequently their overall profits (profit margin × sales volume) should be higher than those of their rivals. This is why companies such as GE, Unilever, Procter & Gamble and Heinz are willing to compete only in those markets where they can reach number one or two position.

Companies seek to win market share through product, distribution, promotional innovation and penetration pricing. Kotler and Singh (1981) have identified five competitor confrontation strategies designed to win sales and market share. See Table 19.3.

TABLE 19.3 Competitor confrontation strategies designed to win sales and market share		
Frontal attack		Involves the market challenger taking on the defender head-on. The challenger should have a clear and sustainable competitive advantage. If the advantage is based on cost leadership this will support a low price strategy to fight the market leader. Success is more likely if there is some restriction on the leader's ability to retaliate e.g., patent protection, which can make it difficult for the market leader. However, the challenger needs adequate resorces to withstand any battle that occurs should the leader decide to retaliate.
Flanking		Involves attacking unguarded or weakly guarded ground. In marketing terms it means attacking geographical areas or market segments where the defender is poorly represented. The advantage of a flanking attack is that it does not provoke the same kind of response as head-on confrontation. Since the defender is not challenged in its main market segments, there is more chance that it will ignore the challenger's initial successes. If the defender dallies too long, the flank segment can be used as a beachhead from which to attack the defender in its major markets, as Japanese firms have repeatedly done.
Encirclement		Involves attacking the defender from all sides. Every market segment is hit with every combination of product features to completely encircle the defender. An example is Seiko, which produces over 2,000 different watch designs for the worldwide market. These cover everything the customer might want in terms of fashion and features. A variant on the encirclement attack approach is to cut off supplies to the defender. This could be achieved by the acquisition of major supply firms.
Bypass		Circumvents the defender's position. This type of attack changes the rules of the game, usually through technological leap-frogging. A bypass attack can also be accomplished through diversification. An attacker can bypass a defender by seeking growth in new markets with new products.
Guerrilla		Hurts the defender with pin-pricks rather than blows. Unpredictable price discounts, sales promotions or heavy advertising in a few television regions are some of the tactics attackers can use to cause problems for defenders. Guerrilla tactics may be the only feasible option for a small company facing a larger competitior. Such tactics allow the small company to make its presence felt without the dangers of a full-frontal attack. By being unpredictable, guerrilla activity is difficult to defend against. Nevertheless, the defender may choose to retaliate with a full-frontal attack if sufficiently provoked.

Based on source: Kotler and Singh (1981); Varadarajan, (2010)

Table 19.4 shows examples of companies that are regularly in head-to-head competitive confrontation.

TABLE 19.4 Major marketing head-on battles

Companies	Competitive area
Nike vs. Adidas	Footwear
Coca-Cola vs. Pepsi	Soft drinks
McDonald's vs. Burger King	Fast-food restaurants
Unilever vs. Procter & Gamble	Fast-moving consumer goods
Apple (iPhone) vs. Samsung Galaxy	Smartphones
iPad vs. Samsung Galaxy Tab	Tablet computers
Apple vs. Dell	Computers
Google vs. Yahoo!	Search engines
Intel vs. Advanced Micro Devices	Microchips
Boeing vs. Airbus	Aircraft
Google Plus vs. Facebook	Social networks

Defence strategies

In circumstances where there is rivalry among competitors, strategic action may be required to defend sales and market share from aggressive challenges. The principles of defensive warfare provide a framework for identifying strategic alternatives that can be used in this situation. Table 19.5 illustrates six methods of defence derived from military strategy.

TABLE 19.5 Defence strategies

Position		Involves building a fortification around a firm's existing territory. This reflects the philosophy that the company has good products, and all that is needed is to price them competitively and promote them effectively. This is more likely to work if the products have differential advantages that are not easily copied, for example, through patent protection. Marketing assets like brand names and reputation may also provide a strong defence against aggressors, although it can be a dangerous strategy.
Flanking		Is characterised by the defence of a hitherto unprotected market segment. The danger is that if the segment is left unprotected it will provide a beachhead for new entrants to gain experience in the market and attack the main market later. This means that if it helps to avoid or slow down competitive inroads, it can make sense to a defender to compete in a segment that, in short-term profitability terms, looks unattractive.
Mobile		When a firm's major market is under threat a mobile defence may make strategic sense. The two options are diversification and market broadening. A classic example of a company using diversification as a form of mobile defence is Imperial Tobacco, which responded to the health threat to its cigarette business by diversifying into food and leisure markets.
Counter-offensive		A defender can choose from three options when considering a counter offensive defence. It can embark on a head-on counter-attack, hit the attacker's cash cow or encircle the attacker. With a head-on counter-attack a defender matches or exceeds what the attacker has done. This may involve heavy price cutting or promotion expenditure, for example. This can be a costly operation but may be justified to deter a persistant attacker. Employed by Meublein when its Smirnoff vodka brand was attacked by the cheaper Wolfschmidt brand in the USA.

>>

Pre-emptive		Follows the philosophy that the best form of defence is to attack first. This may involve continuous innovation and new product development e.g., Apple inc. invests heavily in design and innovation. Failure to maintain the ability to lead the market could result in loss of market share and eventual collapse of the brand.
Strategic withdrawal		Market exit strategy requires a company to define its strengths and weaknesses, and then to hold on to its strengths while divesting its weaknesses. This results in the company concentrating on its core business. An example is Diageo, which withdrew from the fast-food business by selling Burger King, and from food by selling Pillsbury to concentrate on premium drinks.

Based on source: Kotler and Singh (1981); Varadarajan (2010)

Working together in competitive markets

When companies are trading in intensely competitive markets, there is a likelihood that they will interact through attacking and defending market territories. However, in increasingly turbulent and changing markets, collaboration and cooperation often occur. Marketing managers can find themselves considering whether to compete or cooperate with companies that operate in similar market territories. Collaborative networks of competing companies can develop based on shared interests, with the aim of solving common problems (Meng and Layton, 2011). For example, Nissan, BMW and Tesla are rivals in the electronic car market, but they have agreed to collaborate and share patents in order to speed up development of electric cars. Growth in this relatively new industry has been slow, so by cooperating there is potential for all partners to benefit. Table 19.6 shows examples of strategic alliances and other collaborative partnerships

TABLE 19.6 Examples of strategic alliances and collaborative partnerships	
Companies	**Competitive area**
Apple/IBM	Health monitoring/smart watches
British Airways/American Airlines	Transatlantic air travel
Accenture/General Electric	Big data
BP/Schlumberger	Oil drilling processes
Nissan/BMW/Tesla	Electric cars
Warner Group/Shazam	Discovering new acts and signing them to new labels
Volvo/Dongfeng Motor Group	Commercial vehicles

When you have read this chapter

Discover further resources and test your understanding: McGraw-Hill **Connect**™ is a digital teaching and learning environment that improves performance over a variety of critical outcomes; it can be tailored, is easy to use and is proven effective **LearnSmart**™ is the most widely used and intelligent adaptive learning resource that is proven to strengthen memory recall, improve course retention and boost grades. Fuelled by **LearnSmart**™, **SmartBook**™ is the first and only adaptive reading experience available today.

Review

1 **The determinants of industry attractiveness**
   - Industry attractiveness is determined by the degree of rivalry between competitors, the threat of new entrants, the bargaining power of suppliers and buyers, and the threat of substitute products.

2 **How to analyze competitors**
   - Competitor analysis should identify competitors (product from competitors, product substitutes, generic competitors and potential new entrants); audit their capabilities; analyze their objectives, strategic thrust and strategies; and estimate competitor response patterns.

3 **The difference between differentiation and cost leadership strategies**
   - Differentiation strategy involves the selection of one or more choice criteria used by buyers to select suppliers/brands and uniquely positioning the supplier/brand to meet those criteria better than the competition.
   - Cost leadership involves the achievement of the lowest cost position in an industry.

4 **The sources of competitive advantage**
   - Competitive advantage can be achieved by creating a differential advantage or achieving the lowest cost position.
   - Its sources are superior skills, superior resources, and core competences. A useful method of locating superior skills and resources is value chain analysis.

5 **The value chain**
   - The value chain categorizes the value-creating activities of a company. The value chain divides these into primary and support activities. Primary activities are in-bound physical distribution, operations, outbound physical distribution, marketing and service. Support activities are found within all of these primary activities, and consist of purchased inputs, technology, human resource management and the company's infrastructure.
   - By examining each value-creating activity, management can search for the skills and resources (and linkages) that may form the basis for low cost or differentiated positions.

6 **How to create and maintain a differential advantage**
   - A differential advantage is created when the customer perceives that the company is providing value above that of the competition.
   - A differential advantage can be created using any element in the marketing mix: superior product, more effective distribution, better promotion and better value for money by lower prices. A differential advantage can also be created by developing fast reaction times to changes in marketing trends.
   - A differential advantage can be maintained (sustained) through the use of patent protection, strong brand personality, close relationships with customers, high service levels based on well-trained staff, innovative product upgrading, the creation of high entry barriers (e.g. R&D or promotional expenditures), and strong and distinctive internal processes that deliver the earlier points and are difficult to copy.

7 **How to create and maintain a cost leadership position**
   - Cost leadership can be created and maintained by managing cost drivers, which are economies of scale, learning effects, capacity utilization, linkages (e.g. improvements in quality assurance can reduce after-sales service costs), interrelationships (e.g. sharing costs), integration (e.g. owning the means of distribution), timing (both first movers and late entrants can have low costs), policy decisions (e.g. controlling labour costs), location, and institutional factors (e.g. government regulations).

8 **The nature of competitive behaviour**
   - Competitive behaviour can take five forms: conflict, competition, co-existence, cooperation and collusion.

9 Competitive marketing strategy can appear as a military initiative

- Military analogies have been used in the past to guide strategic thinking, because of the need to attack and defend against competition. While the underlying thinking remains important, the language of war appears less in modern business-speak.
- Attack strategies are the frontal attack, the flanking attack, encirclement, the bypass attack and the guerrilla attack.
- Defence strategies are the position defence, the flanking defence, the pre-emptive defence, the counter-offensive defence, the mobile defence, and strategic withdrawal.

Key Terms

competitive behaviour the activities of rival companies with respect to each other; this can take five forms—conflict, competition, co-existence, cooperation and collusion

competitive scope the breadth of a company's competitive challenge, for example broad or narrow

competitor audit a precise analysis of competitor strengths and weaknesses, objectives and strategies

core competences the principal distinctive capabilities possessed by a company—what it is really good at

counter-offensive defence a counter-attack that takes the form of a head-on counter-attack, an attack on the attacker's cash cow or an encirclement of the attacker

differential advantage a clear performance differential over the competition on factors that are important to target customers

differentiation strategy the selection of one or more customer choice criteria and positioning the offering accordingly to achieve superior customer value

divest to improve short-term cash yield by dropping or selling off a product

entry barriers that act to prevent new companies from entering a market, for example the high level of investment required

encirclement attack attacking the defender from all sides; i.e. every market segment is hit with every combination of product features

experience curve the combined effect of economies of scale and learning as cumulative output increases

flanking attack attacking geographical areas or market segments where the defender is poorly represented

flanking defence the defence of a hitherto unprotected market segment

frontal attack a competitive strategy where the challenger takes on the defender head on

guerrilla attack making life uncomfortable for stronger rivals through, for example, unpredictable price discounts, sales promotions or heavy advertising in a few selected regions

harvest objective the improvement of profit margins to improve cash flow even if the longer-term result is falling sales

hold objective a strategy of defending a product in order to maintain market share

industry a group of companies that market products that are close substitutes for each other

mobile defence involves diversification or broadening the market by redefining the business

niche a small market segment

position defence building a fortification around existing products, usually through keen pricing and improved promotion

pre-emptive defence usually involves continuous innovation and new product development, recognizing that attack is the best form of defence

strategic alliance collaboration between two or more organizations through, for example, joint ventures, licensing agreements, long-term purchasing and supply arrangement, or a joint R&D contract to build a competitive advantage

strategic focus the strategies that can be employed to achieve an objective

strategic withdrawal holding onto the company's strengths while getting rid of its weaknesses

value chain the set of a company's activities that are conducted to design, manufacture, market, distribute and service its products

Study Questions

1. Using Porter's 'five forces' framework, suggest why there is intense rivalry between leading European supermarket brands.

2. For any product of your choice identify the competition using the four-layer approach discussed in this chapter.

3. Why is competitor analysis essential in today's turbulent environment? How far is it possible to predict competitor response to marketing actions?

4. Distinguish between differentiation and cost-leadership strategies. Is it possible to achieve both positions simultaneously?

5. How might Google use differential advantage to stand out from its rivals?

6. How can value chain analysis lead to superior corporate performance?

7. What are cost drivers? Should marketing management be concerned with them, or is their significance solely the prerogative of the accountant?

8. Discuss the favourable conditions for pursuing build and hold marketing strategic objectives.

9. Explain the attack and defence strategies a company might need to use if they are the market leader.

Recommended Reading

Day, G. S. and R. Wensley (1988) Assessing advantage: A framework for diagnosing competitive superiority, *Journal of Marketing* 52, April, 1–20

Fleisher, C. and B. Bensoussan (2015) *Competitive Analysis: Effective Application of New and classic Methods*, Upper Saddle River, NJ, USA: Pearson Education.

Institute for Strategy & Competitiveness (2015) Creating Shared Value. http://www.isc.hbs.edu/about-michael -porter/Pages/default.aspx (accessed July 2015).

Noble, C.H., R. K. Sinha and A. Kumar, A. (2002) Market orientation and alternative strategic orientations: A longitudinal assessment of performance implications, *Journal of Marketing* 66 (4), 25–40

Porter, M. E. and J. E. Heppelmann, J.E. (2014) How Smart, Connected Products Are Transforming Competition, *Harvard Business Review* 92(11) 64–88.

Porter, M. E. (2008) On Competition. Boston, USA: Harvard Business School Publishing.

References

Airbus (2012) Alternative Fuel Sources http://www.airbus.com/ innovation/eco-efficiency/operations/alternative-fuels

Anderson, J. C. and J. A. Narus (1998) Business Marketing: Understand What Customers Value, *Harvard Business Review*, Nov.–Dec., 53–65.

BBH (2015) Case Study: Johnnie Walker, CreativeBrief.com, April. http://www.creativebrief.com/agency/work/686/12/johnnie-walker -advertising-keep-walking-by-bartle-bogle-hegarty-bbh-london

Boren, Z. (2014) There are officially more mobile devices than people in the world, *The Independent*, 7 October. http://www.independent. co.uk/life-style/gadgets-and-tech/news/there-are-officially-more-mobile-devices-than-people-in-the-world-9780518.html

Business Week (2006) Business Week Top 50 US Firms, 3 April, 82–100.

Buzzell, R. D. and B. T. Gale (1987) *The PIMS Principles*, New York: Free Press.

Cellan-Jones, R. (2015) Supercell: Europe's supercharged games success, BBC.co.uk, 15 October. http://www.bbc.co.uk/news/ technology-24541073

Day, G. S. (1999) *Market Driven Strategy: Processes for Creating Value*, New York: Free Press.

Day, G. S. and R. Wensley (1988) Assessing Advantage: A Framework for Diagnosing Competitive Superiority, *Journal of Marketing* 52, April, 1–20.

De Chernatony, L., F. Harris and F. Dall'Olmo Riley (2000) Added Value: Its Nature, Roles and Sustainability, *European Journal of Marketing* 34(1/2), 39–56.

Diageo (2015) Our Strategy, Diageo, April. http://www.diageo.com/ EN-SC/OURBUSINESS/ABOUTUS/Pages/our-strategy.aspx

Dredge, S. (2015) MySpace—what went wrong: 'The site was a massive spaghetti-ball mess', *The Guardian*, 6 March. http://www.

theguardian.com/technology/2015/mar/06/myspace-what-went
-wrong-sean-percival-spotify (accessed 20 March 2015).

Easton, G. and L. Araujo (1986) Networks, Bonding and Relationships
in Industrial Markets, *Industrial Marketing and Purchasing* 1(1),
8–25.

Einhorn, B. (2009) Acer's Game-Changing PC Offensive, *Business Week*,
20 April, 65.

Garside, J. (2012) BlackBerry creators pay price for failing to keep up
with Apple, *The Guardian*. 23 January, 23.

Garside, J. and S. Farrrell (2014) Carphone Warehouse and Dixons
agree £3.8bn merger, *The Guardian*, 15 May. http://www.
theguardian.com/business/2014/may/15/carphone-warehouse
-dixons-agree-merger (accessed 20 April 2015).

Gruman, G. (2015) InfoWorld, InfoWorld, 20 January: http://www.
infoworld.com/article/2868766/macs/will-the-mac-dump-intel-for
-the-same-chip-as-the-ipad.html

Hughes, N. (2014) Apple agrees to pay $450 million to settle ebook
price fixing lawsuit, appleinsider, 16 July. http://appleinsider.com/
articles/14/07/16/apple-settles-ebook-price-fixing-complaint-with-
states-consumers-could-pay-450m

IBM (2015) What is Watson? http://www.ibm.com/smarterplanet/us/en/
ibmwatson/what-is-watson.html

Kollewe, J. (2008) Vodafone Cuts Costs by Sharing Networks with
Telefónica, *The Guardian*, 24 March, 26.

Kotler, P. and R. Singh (1981) Marketing Warfare in the 1980s, *Journal
of Business Strategy*, Winter, 30–41.

Kuittinen, T. (2013) 5 Reasons Why Finnish Apps Are Beating American
Rivals On US iPad Market, *Forbes*, 22 November. http://www.
forbes.com/sites/terokuittinen/2013/11/22/5-reasons-why-finnish
-apps-are-beating-american-rivals-on-us-ipad-market/ (accessed
20 April 2015).

Kuittinen, T. (2014) Rovio's Revenue Crisis and the App Market
Evolution, *Forbes*, 6 March. http://www.forbes.com/sites/
terokuittinen/2013/03/06/rovios-revenue-crisis-and-the-app-market
-evolution (accessed 20 April 2015).

Leeflang, P. H. S. and D. R. Wittink (1996) Competitive Reaction versus
Consumer Response: Do Managers Over-react? *International
Journal of Research in Marketing* 13, 103–19.

Macdonald, M. H. B. and H. Wilson (2011) *Marketing Plans*, Oxford:
Butterworth Heinemann.

MacKintosh, J. (2005) Car Design in a Generalist Market, *Financial
Times*, 6 December, 20.

Marsh, P. (2002) Dismay at Job Losses as Dyson Shifts Production to
Malaysia, *Financial Times*, 6 February, 3.

McNulty, S. (2001) Short on Frills, Big on Morale, *Financial Times*,
31 October, 14.

Mearian, L. (2015) IBM launches Watson Health global analytics
cloud, *Computerworld*, 14 April. http://www.computerworld.com/
article/2909534/ibm-launches-watson-health-global-analytics-cloud
.html (accessed 20 April 2015).

Meng, J. and R. Layton (2011) Understanding managers' marketing
strategy choice in a collaborative competition industry, *European
Business Review* 23(5), 477–501.

Milne, R. and H. Williamson (2005) BMW Ignores Signals and Puts its
Faith in Germany, *Financial Times*, 13 May, 20.

Nagle, T. T. and J. E. Hogan (2006) *The Strategy and Tactics of Pricing*,
Upper Saddle River, NJ: Pearson.

Noble, C. H., R. K. Sinha and A. Kumar (2002) Market Orientation and
Alternative Strategic Orientations: A Longitudinal Assessment of
Performance Implications, *Journal of Marketing*, 66, October, 25–39.

Owen, E. (2012) Twinings to build on Gets You Back To You campaign,
Campaign, 29 February. http://www.campaignlive.co.uk/
news/1119572 (accessed 20 April 2015).

Porter, M. E. (1980) *Competitive Strategy: Techniques for Analysing
Industries and Competitors*, New York: Free Press.

Porter, M. E. (1985) *Competitive Advantage*, New York: Free Press.

Porter, M. E. (1998) *Competitive Strategy*, New York: Free Press, 4.

Reisinger, D. (2015) Angry Birds maker's earnings fall while
games rise, Cnet, 19 March. http://www.cnet.com/uk/news/
angry-birds-maker-rovio-revenue-earnings-fall-but-games-rise

Ries, A. and J. Trout (2005) *Marketing Warfare*, New York: McGraw-Hill.

Rovio (2015) *RAND NEW GAME OUT - NIBBLERS SOFT LAUNCHES
IN CANADA, FINLAND, NEW ZEALAND AND AUSTRALIA!*
Rovio, 24 April. http://www.rovio.com/en/news/blog/651/brand
-new-game-out-nibblers-soft-launches-in-canada-finland-new
-zealand-and-australia

Simonian, H. and L. Lucas (2012) Starbucks takes coffee wars to
Nespresso, *Financial Times* http://www.ft.com/cms/s/0/d90109a4-
66ec-11e1-9e53-00144feabdc0.html, 5 March.

Sinclair, B. (2015) Apps are the most competitive market ever - Rovio
exec, gamesindustry.biz, 16 April. http://www.gamesindustry.biz/
articles/2015-04-16-apps-are-the-most-competitive-market-ever
-rovio-exec

Steadman, I. (2013) IBM's Watson is better at diagnosing cancer than
human doctors, *Wired*, 11 February. http://www.wired.co.uk/news/
archive/2013-02/11/ibm-watson-medical-doctor (accessed 20 April 2015).

Sun Tzu (1963) *The Art of War*, London: Oxford University Press.

Sweney, M. (2014) Amazon takes on Netflix with rebrand of LoveFilm
video-on-demand service, *The Guardian*, 21 February. http://www.
theguardian.com/technology/2014/feb/21/amazon-lovefilm-revamp
-film-tv-rental (accessed 18 April 2015).

The Economist (2008) Failure to Deliver, 15 November, 80.

Varadarajan, R. (2010) Strategic marketing and marketing strategy:
domain, definition, fundamental issues and foundational premises,
Journal of Academy of Marketing Science 38, 119–40. doi:10.1007/
s11747-009-0176-7

Von Clausewitz, C. (1908) *On War*, London: Routledge & Kegan Paul.

Wunker, S. (2012) Fiat's Smart US launch strategy—really, HBR Blog
Network http://blogs.hbr.org/cs/2012/02/fiats_smart_us_launch_
strategy_really.html, 1 February.

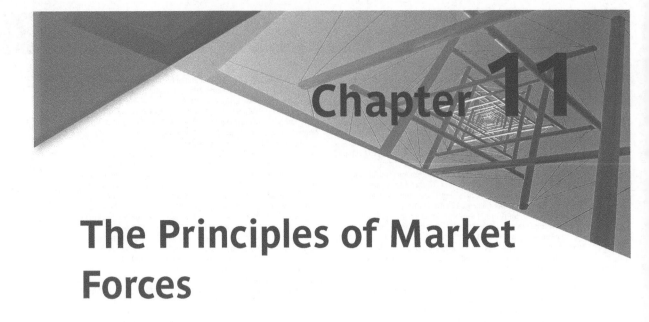

The Principles of Market Forces

Chapter 11

Millions have been captivated by the BBC television series *The Apprentice*, in which millionaire businessman Lord Sugar gives apprentices a series of tasks to prove their potential as a chief executive of the future. Lord Sugar now controls a complex business organization with many subsidiaries and a range of products sold into vastly differing market conditions. But he never forgets the basics of business, which he learned from trading very simple products in the fiercely competitive local markets of east London. So before the apprentices get anywhere near a boardroom position, Lord Sugar gives the hopefuls quite basic tasks that go back to the primitive roots of marketing. Getting tourists to buy T-shirts, caterers to buy a new line of sausages or shops to stock a new ice cream goes to the heart of marketing. The apprentices must survive in a fiercely competitive market in which competitors are just waiting for them to make a mistake, or they simply try to undercut their price by a few pennies. This chapter explores the basics of the fiercely competitive markets in which these TV apprentices had to survive. It describes the basic building blocks of competitive forces – we will look at how the apprentices might try to overcome competitive market forces by trying to create a market niche for themselves.

✓ Learning Objectives

This chapter will explain:

✓ The concept of market structure and the range of structures from atomistic competition to pure monopoly.

✓ The principles of atomistic competition as basic building blocks for understanding a firm's pricing and output decisions.

✓ The interaction of demand and supply leading to price determination.

✓ Elasticity of demand and supply.

11.1   Introduction

'Market forces' is a widely used term that implies some kind of external pressure on an organization, acting as a constraint (and an opportunity) for the goods and services that it buys and sells. A company may have to accept a lower price for the goods it sells because 'market forces' don't allow it to sell its goods at the higher price that it seeks. Similarly, a company may have to pay higher wages to its employees because market forces in the labour market have put upward pressure on wage rates, and if the company is going to be able to employ the staff that it seeks, it will have to pay market rates of pay.

Market forces are a crucial fact of life to most organizations operating in a commercial environment. They occur where companies seek to attract customers from rival companies by offering better products and/or lower prices. Market forces also have an effect in the acquisition of resources, and where these are scarce relative to the demand for them, rival buyers will bid up their price. However, competition in customer and resource markets can be complex and a full understanding of each market is needed if the effects of market forces on an organization are to be fully appreciated. This chapter begins by reviewing the fundamental building blocks on which markets are based. However, all **markets** are not equally aggressive in the way in which 'market forces' operate, and in many cases, an observer would be forgiven for doubting the existence of a market. So before we begin our microeconomic investigation of how markets operate in practice, we will review different types of market structure, to illustrate the very limited circumstances in which market forces are fully effective. In Chapter 12, we will explore the nature of imperfections to markets, which limit the effects of market forces that are described in this chapter.

11.1.1 Market structure

The market conditions facing suppliers of goods and services vary considerably. Customers of water supply companies may feel they are being exploited with high prices and poor service levels by companies that know that their customers have little choice of supplier. On the other hand, customers are constantly wooed by numerous insurance companies that are all trying to sell basically similar products in a market that provides consumers with a lot of choice. Differences in the characteristics and composition of buyers and sellers define the structure of a market.

The term **market structure** is used to describe:

- the number of buyers and sellers operating in a market
- the extent to which the market is concentrated in the hands of a small number of buyers and/or sellers
- the degree of collusion or competition between buyers and/or sellers.

An understanding of market structure is important to businesses, not only to understand the consequences of their own actions but also the behaviour of other firms operating in a market.

Market structures range from the theoretical extremes of perfect competition to pure monopoly. In practice, examples of the extremes are rare and most analysis therefore focuses on levels of market imperfection between the two extremes (Figure 11.1).

It is easy to take a static view of market structure but, in reality, markets are often in transition. This has been most apparent in the economies of the former Soviet bloc countries, which until the late 1980s allocated resources according to their governments' central planning processes. Officially, market forces had little role to play, although they often existed informally, especially in the more liberal Soviet bloc countries such as Hungary. The collapse of communism brought about a major change in the way that resources were allocated in the national economy, with the interaction of supply and demand leading to the price mechanism being used as a means of allocating scarce resources, rather than government bureaucrats. In many countries that have emerged from communism, the transition to market forces has not been an easy one (see 'Thinking around the subject' on p. 366).

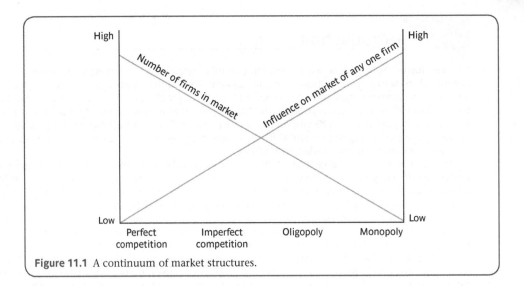

Figure 11.1 A continuum of market structures.

11.2 The characteristics of very competitive markets

Highly competitive market structures are often referred to as atomistic (or 'perfect') competition. This is the simplest type of market structure to understand and corresponds very much with most people's idea of what a very competitive market should be like. Government policy makers often pursue a vision of this as the ideal market structure. Although perfectly competitive markets in their theoretical extreme are rarely found in practice, a sound understanding of the way they work is essential for understanding competitive market pressures in general.

Perfectly competitive markets are attributed with the following key characteristics.

- There are a large number of small producers supplying to the market, each with similar cost structures and each producing an identical product.
- There are also a large number of buyers in the market, each responsible for purchasing only a small percentage of total output.
- Both buyers and sellers are free to enter or leave the market – that is, there are no barriers to entry or exit.
- In a perfectly competitive market, there is a ready supply of information for buyers and sellers about market conditions.

Some markets come close to having these characteristics – for example:

- wholesale fruit and vegetable markets
- the 'spot' market for oil products
- stock markets, where shares are bought and sold (see Figure 11.2).

In reality, very few markets fully meet economists' criteria for **perfect competition** and even those markets described above have imperfections (e.g. wholesale fruit and vegetable markets are increasingly influenced by the practice of large retailers contracting directly with growers or growers' intermediaries).

© mddphoto

Figure 11.2 Stock markets come close to satisfying the requirements of perfect competition, with large numbers of people buying and selling shares, resulting in daily movement in share prices. Regulators of stock markets go to great lengths to preserve the competitiveness of their markets – for example, by requiring full disclosure by firms of information that might affect their share price, and punishing the misuse of 'insider' information, which can give some people an unfair advantage. Where a buyer builds up a significant holding of a company's shares, stock market rules may require this fact to be disclosed.

⟳ Thinking around the subject

From the queues of communism to the high prices of market forces?

By most measures of economic activity, the countries of the former Soviet bloc were lagging well behind most western countries. The level of wealth generated per person, indicated by GDP per head, was typically much less than half that of comparable economies in western Europe. It seemed that central government bureaucrats were no match for market forces in stimulating the economy to produce more goods at lower cost. So long as factories and farms produced their quota of output, everybody seemed happy. The workers had little incentive to produce more output, and at a better quality, because they would not be rewarded for it. Producers simply didn't undertake any market research in order that they might make goods that customers actually wanted, rather than the goods that bureaucrats said should be produced. The result of this centralized planning process was a shortage of goods that people wanted, with 'black markets' often arising in order to satisfy customer demands that could not be met through an open market. Stories abounded of raw materials and agricultural produce left to rot on farms, either because there was little incentive to get them to consumers, or because the farms had simply grown too much of the produce that customers didn't want to buy.

The dismantling of communist government planning processes and the introduction of market forces came as a shock to most people of eastern Europe – both as producers and consumers. Producers were at first slow to learn the principles of marketing and the importance of understanding customers' needs. But, slowly, producers began to pick up signals from the market and started developing new and improved goods and services. In came modern bars and cafes to replace the previous dull outlets. Slowly, goods manufactured by western companies began to appear in East European markets and were highly prized by those consumers who could afford them. The presence of western competitors now gave manufacturers new standards they had to compete against if they were to stay in business.

For consumers, centralized planning had previously meant allocation of resources by queuing. It was not uncommon, for example, to have to wait 20 years from ordering for a new Lada car to be delivered to the buyer. A ten-year wait for a new washing machine was typical for many consumer durables. With the introduction of market forces, prices rather than queuing became the method for allocating scarce resources. So the prices of most goods and services shot up to a level way beyond that most consumers could afford. In any free-market economy, limited supply and strong demand for goods and services can only lead to higher prices. The paradox was that consumers now had much more freedom and choice in the marketplace but, at market-determined prices, the typical consumer did not have anywhere near enough money to pay for the goods and services that were now available. During the transition period, incomes struggled to keep up as factory closures led to rising unemployment. Meanwhile, inflation rates soared, and in many countries prices more than doubled each year.

A market-based economy was further frustrated by the presence in many countries of mafia-style groups that sought to control some aspect of the newly liberated markets. There were stories of gangsters and former Communist Party members using coercion to control the supply of many essential goods and services through the distribution chain. As an example, tomatoes grown in Bulgaria were being sold in shops in the country's capital, Sofia, for a higher price than those same tomatoes sold in export markets such as Britain and France. Retailing and distribution should have become a competitive business, helping to force down prices, but it seemed that the simple transition to a market-based economy was impeded by the presence of mafia-type groups. In the turmoil that accompanied the transition from centralized planning to market-based mechanisms, these groups saw a window of opportunity to re-establish a form of central power that had been lost with the demise of communism.

Competitive market forces may be a fine ideal, but this chapter and the next demonstrate how economies have a tendency to develop anti-competitive practices that undermine the power of markets to produce more output at low price.

Perfect competition implies that firms are price *takers* in that competitive market forces alone determine the price at which they can sell their products. If a firm cannot produce its goods or services as efficiently as its competitors, it will lose profits and eventually go out of business. Customers are protected from exploitative high prices, because as long as selling a product remains profitable, companies will be tempted into the market to satisfy customers' requirements, thereby putting downward pressure on prices. Eventually, competition between firms will result in excessive profits being eliminated so that an equilibrium is achieved where loss-making firms have left the market and the market is not sufficiently attractive to bring new firms into it.

Probably the most important reason for studying perfect competition is that it focuses attention on the basic building blocks of competition: demand, supply and price determination.

11.2.1 Demand

Demand refers to the quantity of a product that consumers are willing and able to buy at a specific price over a given period of time. In economic analysis, demand is measured not simply in terms of what people would like to buy – after all, most people would probably want to buy expensive holidays and cars. Instead, demand refers to how many people are actually *able and willing* to buy a product at a given price, and given a set of assumptions about the product and the environment in which it is being offered. Demand is also expressed in terms of a specified time period – for example, so many units per day.

In general, as the price of a product falls, so the demand (as defined above) can be expected to rise. Likewise, as the price rises, demand could be expected to fall. This relationship can be plotted on a simple graph. In Figure 11.3, a demand curve for medium-fat Cheddar cheese is shown by the line D1. This relates any given price, shown on the vertical axis, to the volume of demand, which is shown on the horizontal axis. Therefore, at a price of £8.00 per kg, demand is 10,000 units per period within a given area, while, at a price of £4.00, the demand rises to 12,000 units.

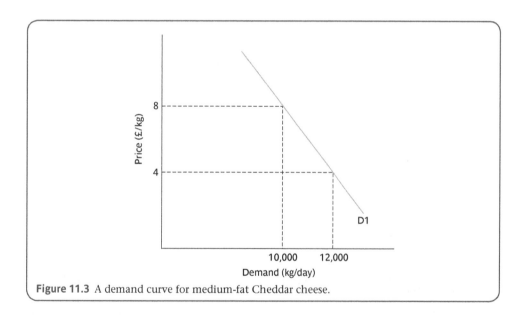

Figure 11.3 A demand curve for medium-fat Cheddar cheese.

It is important to note that the demand curve drawn here refers to total market demand from all consumers and is not simply measuring demand for one producer's output. The importance of this distinction will become clear later, as the implication of this is that firms have to make their price decisions based on overall market conditions.

The demand curve D1 is based on a number of assumptions. These include, for example, assumptions that the price of substitutes for cheese will not change or that consumers will not suddenly take a dislike to Cheddar cheese. Demand curve D1 measures the relationship between price and market demand for one given set of assumptions. When these assumptions change, a new demand curve is needed to explain a new relationship between price and quantity demanded.

In Figure 11.4, two sets of fresh assumptions have been made and new demand curves, D2 and D3, drawn based on these new sets of assumptions. For new demand curve D2, more cheese is demanded for any given price level (or, alternatively, this can be restated in terms of any given number of consumers demanding cheese being prepared to pay a higher price). There are a number of possible causes of the shift of the demand curve from D1 to D2.

- Consumers could have become wealthier, leading them to demand more of all goods, including cheese.
- The price of substitutes for Cheddar cheese (e.g. meat or other types of cheese) could have increased, thereby increasing demand for cheese.
- Demand for complementary goods (such as savoury biscuits) may increase, thereby leading to an increase in demand for Cheddar cheese.
- Consumer preferences may change. This may occur, for example, if Cheddar cheese is found to have health-promoting benefits.
- An advertising campaign for Cheddar cheese may increase demand for cheese at any given price.

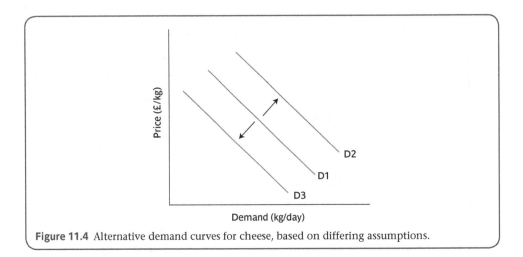

Figure 11.4 Alternative demand curves for cheese, based on differing assumptions.

Similarly, a number of possible reasons can be put forward to explain the shift from demand curve D1 to D3, where, for any given price level, less is demanded.

- Consumers could have become poorer, leading them to demand fewer of all goods, including cheese.
- The price of substitutes for Cheddar cheese (e.g. meat or other types of cheese) could have decreased, thereby making the substitutes appear more attractive and reducing demand for Cheddar cheese.
- Demand for complementary products may fall.
- Cheddar cheese may become associated with health hazards, leading to less demand at any given price.
- An advertising campaign for substitute products may shift demand away from Cheddar cheese.

The demand curves shown in Figures 11.3 and 11.4 have both been straight, but this is a simplification of reality. In fact, demand curves would usually be curved, indicating that the relationship between price and volume is not constant for all price points. There may additionally be significant discontinuities at certain price points, as where buyers in a market have psychological price barriers, above or below which their behaviour changes. In many markets, the difference between £10.00 and £9.99 may be crucial in overcoming buyers' attitudes that predispose them to regard anything over £10 as being unaffordable and anything below it as a bargain.

Actually collecting information with which to plot a demand curve poses theoretical and practical problems. The main problem relates to the cross-sectional nature of a demand curve – that is, it purports to measure the volume of demand across the ranges of price possibilities. However, this kind of information can often only be built up by a longitudinal study of the relationship between prices and volume over time. There is always the possibility that, over time, the assumptions on which demand is based have changed, in which case it is difficult to distinguish between a movement along a demand curve and a shift to a new demand curve. It is, however, sometimes possible for firms to conduct controlled cross-sectional experiments where a different price is charged in different regions and the effects on volume recorded. To be sure that this is accurately measuring the demand curve, there must be no extraneous factors in regions (such as differences in household incomes) that could partly explain differences in price/volume relationships.

The demand curves shown in Figures 11.3 and 11.4 slope downwards, indicating the intuitive fact that, as price rises, demand falls, and vice versa. While this is intuitively plausible, it is not always the case. Sometimes, the demand curve slopes upwards, indicating that, as the price of a product goes up, buyers are able and willing to buy more of the product. Classic examples of this phenomenon occur where a product becomes increasingly desirable as more people consume it. A telephone network that has only one subscriber will be of little use to the first customer, who will be unable to use a telephone to call anyone else. However, as more customers are connected, the value of the telephone network becomes greater to each individual, who is correspondingly willing to pay a higher price. This phenomenon helps to explain why large international airports can charge more than smaller regional airports for aircraft to land. As the number of possible aircraft connections increases, airlines' willingness to pay high prices for landing slots increases.

Upward-sloping demand curves can also be observed for some products sold for their 'snob' value. Examples include some designer-label clothes where high price alone can add to a product's social status. Upward-sloping demand curves can be observed over short time periods where a 'bandwagon' effect can be created by rapidly rising or falling prices. For example, in stock markets, the very fact that share prices are rising may lead many people to invest in shares.

11.2.2 Supply

Supply is defined as the amount of a product that producers are willing and able to make available to the market at a given price over a particular period of time. Like demand, it is important to note that at different prices there will be different levels of supply, reflecting the willingness and/or ability of producers to supply a product as prices change.

A simple supply curve for medium-fat Cheddar cheese is shown in Figure 11.5. The supply curve slopes upwards from left to right, indicating the intuitively plausible fact that, as market prices rise, more suppliers will be attracted to supply to the market. Conversely, as prices fall, marginal producers (such as those who operate relatively inefficiently) will drop out of the market, reducing the daily supply available.

It is again important to distinguish movements along a supply curve from shifts to a new supply curve. The supply curve S1 is based on a number of assumptions about the relationship between price and volume supplied. If these assumptions are broken, a new supply curve based

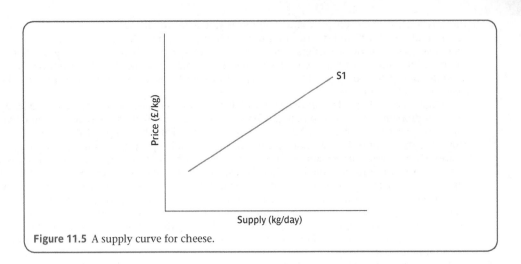

Figure 11.5 A supply curve for cheese.

on the new set of assumptions needs to be drawn. In Figure 11.6, two new supply curves, S2 and S3, are shown. S2 indicates a situation where, for any given price level, total supply to the market is reduced. This could come about for a number of reasons, including the following.

■ Production methods could become more expensive – for example, because of more stringent health and safety regulations. Therefore, for any given price level, fewer firms will be willing to supply to the market as they will no longer be able to cover their costs.
■ Extraneous factors (such as abnormally bad weather) could result in producers having difficulty in getting their produce to market.
■ Governments may impose additional taxes on suppliers (e.g. extending the scope of property taxes to cover agricultural property).

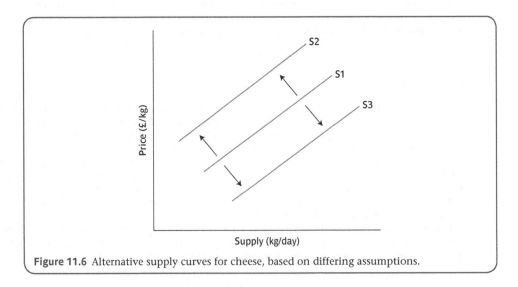

Figure 11.6 Alternative supply curves for cheese, based on differing assumptions.

The new supply curve S3 indicates a situation where, for any given price level, total supply to the market is increased. This could come about for a number of reasons, including the following.

■ Changes in production technology that result in Cheddar cheese being produced more efficiently and therefore suppliers being prepared to supply more cheese at any given price (or, for any given volume supplied, suppliers are prepared to accept a lower price).

■ Extraneous factors (such as favourable weather conditions) could result in a glut of produce that must be sold, and the market is therefore flooded with additional supply.

■ Governments may give a subsidy for each kilogram of cheese produced by suppliers, thereby increasing their willingness to supply to the market.

11.2.3 Price determination

An examination of the demand and supply graphs indicates that they share common axes. In both cases the vertical axis refers to the price at which the product might change hands, while the horizontal axis refers to the quantity changing hands.

It is possible to redraw the original demand and supply lines (D1 and S1) on a single graph (Figure 11.7). The supply curve indicates that, the lower the price, the less cheese will be supplied to the market. Yet at these lower prices, customers are willing and able to buy a lot of cheese – more than the suppliers collectively are willing or able to supply. By following the supply curve upwards, it can be observed that suppliers are happy to supply more cheese, but at these high prices, there are few willing buyers. Therefore, at these high prices supply and demand are again out of balance.

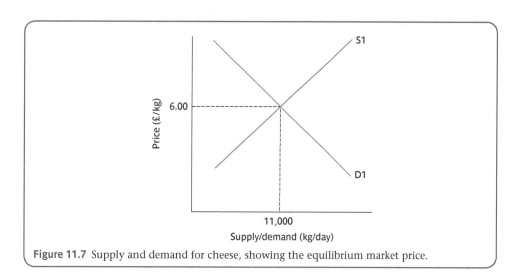

Figure 11.7 Supply and demand for cheese, showing the equilibrium market price.

Between the two extremes there will be a price where the interest of the two groups will coincide. This balancing of supply and demand is the foundation of the theory of market price, which holds that in any free market there is an 'equilibrium price' that matches the quantity that consumers are willing and able to buy (i.e. demand) with the quantity that producers are willing and able to produce (i.e. supply). Working out what this equilibrium price is, is called **price determination**.

In perfectly competitive markets, the process of achieving equilibrium happens automatically without any external regulatory intervention. Perfectly competitive markets do not need any complicated and centralized system for bringing demand and supply into balance, something that is difficult to achieve in a centrally planned economy, such as those that used to predominate in eastern Europe.

In Figure 11.7, supply and demand are brought precisely into balance at a price of £6.00. This is the equilibrium price and, at this price, 11,000 kg of cheese per day will be bought and sold in the market. If a company wants to sell its cheese in the market, it can only do so at this price. In theory, if it charged a penny more, it would get no business because everybody else in the market is cheaper. If it sells at a penny less, it will be swamped with demand, probably selling at a price that is below its production costs.

It is important to remember that in a perfectly competitive market, individual firms are price takers. The market alone determines the 'going rate' for their product. Changes in the equilibrium market price come about for two principal reasons:

1 assumptions about suppliers' ability or willingness to supply change, resulting in a shift to a new supply curve
2 assumptions about buyers' ability or willingness to buy change, resulting in a shift to a new demand curve.

The effects of shifts in supply are illustrated in Figure 11.8. From an equilibrium price of £6.00 and volume of 11,000 kg, the supply curve has shifted to S2 (perhaps in response to the imposition of a new tax on production). Assuming that demand conditions remain unchanged, the new point of intersection between the demand and supply lines occurs at a price of £6.50 and a volume of 10,500 kg. This is the new equilibrium price. A similar analysis can be carried out on the effects of a shift in the demand curve, but where the supply curve remains constant.

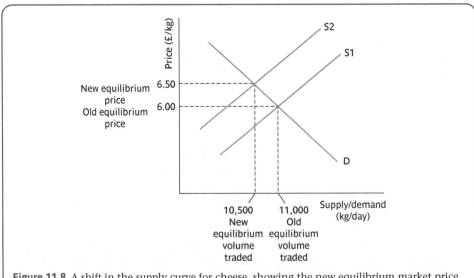

Figure 11.8 A shift in the supply curve for cheese, showing the new equilibrium market price.

New equilibrium prices and trade volumes can be found at the intersection of the supply and demand curves. In practice, both the supply and demand curves may be changing at the same time.

The speed with which a new equilibrium price is established is dependent upon how efficiently a market is working. In pure commodity markets, where products are instantly perishable, rapid adjustments in price are possible. Where speculators are allowed to store goods, or large buyers and sellers are able to unduly influence a market, adjustment may be slower. The extent of

⟳ Thinking around the subject

Effects of increased government regulation

Many industry sectors have complained of the burden of increased government regulation. But how are the effects reflected in demand/supply analysis? Consider the following recent examples.

- *EU Directive on Traditional Herbal Medicinal Products*: the directive requires traditional, over-the-counter herbal remedies to be made to assured standards of safety and quality. Some small-scale producers have not been able to justify the elaborate testing that the directive would require, and have therefore withdrawn from the market – their cost curve had effectively shifted upwards.

- *Financial Services and Markets Act 2000*: required all businesses selling insurance to be registered with the Financial Services Authority and to meet its criteria from January 2005. Some small travel agents, who previously sold travel insurance as an ancillary part of a holiday, decided that the cost of compliance was too great and withdrew from selling insurance.

- *Housing Act 1996*: introduced a discretionary local authority licensing scheme for houses in multiple occupation. To obtain a licence, landlords would need to satisfy a number of standards – for example, in relation to fire exits. Some landlords decided that the cost of improvements to their property could not be justified by the likely returns on their investment.

- *Disability Discrimination Act 1995 Part III – Access to Goods and Services*: from 2004, companies have been required to take 'reasonable measures' to ensure equality of access to a company's goods and services for disabled people. Some organizations are reported to have closed facilities to the public rather than spend money in upgrading them.

The effects of these regulations can be assessed using supply–demand analysis. Each of these regulations may have the effect of increasing producers' costs – some producers more than others. This can be shown as an upward shift in the supply curve. How much of the increase in cost will be passed on to customers? This will depend on the elasticity of demand for the product in question. A highly elastic demand curve may result in customers buying substitute products instead – for example, buying mainstream medicines rather than herbal medicines. If the regulation applies to the whole sector, firms are likely to differ in their ability to absorb additional costs, and the least efficient producers may be forced out of the market because the market price for their product is now below their cost of production.

Try showing the effects of each of the regulations described above on a supply–demand graph, and observe what is likely to happen to the equilibrium price.

changes in price and volume traded is also dependent on the elasticities of demand and supply, which are considered in the following sections.

11.3 Bartering and auctions

Bartering and auctions are traditional methods of determining prices based on interaction between buyer and seller. The practice of bartering is familiar to buyers in Eastern bazaars in which the seller opens with a high offer price and, through a process of negotiation, eventually finds out the maximum price that a buyer is prepared to pay.

The principles of bartering and auctions have attracted renewed interest with the emergence of online auction sites such as eBay. Many more companies have developed auction sites to sell off spare goods or surplus capacity to the highest bidder. If a company is short of cash and desperate to sell its surplus, it might be more willing to accept the best available price that the market is prepared to pay.

As well as consumer sales, internet auctions have found a valuable role for business-to-business procurement (Timmins 2003). A company can put out a tender and invite suppliers to bid, following which it would choose the lowest-price bidder that meets its specifications.

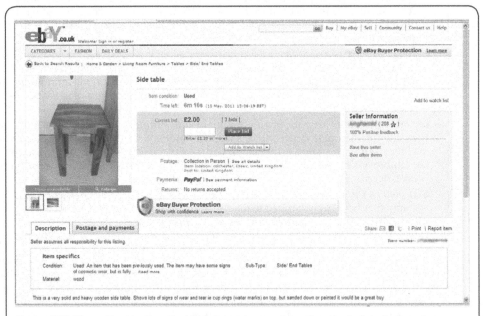

Figure 11.9 The online auction site eBay shows many of the characteristics of a fiercely competitive market. It typically has many small-scale sellers and buyers, with no domination of the market by any individual. There is a good level of information about the organizations in the market, including ratings for sellers' previous performance. Goods and services offered for sale are classified so that a prospective buyer can immediately see what is available for any particular product category and assess whether it meets their requirements. Like any market, eBay requires rules to govern the conduct of buyers and sellers, and the company has taken measures to ensure that the market works efficiently – for example, by reducing the possibilities for fraudulent trading.

11.4 Going rate pricing

The principles of market forces are often seen in markets where competing businesses set their prices according to the 'going rate'. Here, demand may be so sensitive to price that a firm would risk losing most of its business if it charged just a small amount more than its competitors. On the other hand, charging any lower would result in immediate retaliation from competitors. Where cost levels are difficult to establish, charging a going rate can avoid the problems of trying to calculate costs. As an example, it may be difficult to calculate the cost of renting out a video film, as the figure will be very dependent upon assumptions made about the number of uses over which the initial purchase cost can be spread. It is much easier to take price decisions on the basis of the going rate among nearby competitors.

Figure 11.10 In many town centres, clusters of restaurants offer a 'dish of the day' at roughly the same price. The meal is likely to be quite generic (such as fish and chips or chicken tikka masala) and prices for one restaurant will be established by reference to what other restaurants are charging. Restaurants may take a 'going price' from the market and design their meal offering around this price. Just what can they offer for the going rate of £6.00? Although the price of standard set menus may be very strongly determined by competitors' prices, each restaurant may nevertheless offer more specialized meals for which it faces less direct competition and therefore has greater discretion in setting its prices. Differentiation as a means of avoiding direct price competition is discussed later in this chapter.

Thinking around the subject

Penny wise or pound foolish?

One of the assumptions of a competitive market is that buyers have a good awareness of prices within the market. But survey after survey has shown consumers in fact typically have a very distorted knowledge of prices, reflecting individuals' own experiences and background. For example, a survey carried out in 2005 by ICM Research asked young people to estimate the price of a range of goods and services. Two-thirds knew how much a 6GB Apple iPod Mini should cost, within just a few pounds of the actual price charged by most retailers. However, three-quarters of the people interviewed had no idea about the price of a pint of milk. An earlier survey by the telephone company BT had found knowledge of telephone prices to be particularly bad, probably reflecting the plethora of price plans that have emerged in recent years. Respondents gave the average price of a five-minute peak national call as £2.15, whereas in fact it was only 44p. Another sector with confusing price structures is railway travel. Here, respondents estimated the price of a second- class 'saver' ticket from London to Edinburgh at £54, compared to the actual price of £64.

Supermarkets have long known that consumers are typically only able to compare prices on a range of regularly purchased staple items, such as baked beans, potatoes and bread, so price cutting has often been focused on these items. Meanwhile, consumers are likely to be less knowledgeable about infrequently purchased items, and supermarkets may be tempted to let prices of these rise, in the knowledge that consumers would have little idea about whether the price was a good one or not. Of course, there are lots of other ways in which businesses may deliberately or inadvertently make prices difficult for consumers to understand, as witnessed by the complexity of pricing for gas and electricity supply. This reminds us again that it may be fine in theory to talk about competitive markets, but in practice, without consumers' knowledge of the prices available in a market, a market cannot work efficiently.

Many goods and service providers face 'price points' around which customers expect to pay for a service. The UK market for internet service providers (ISPs), for example, has developed a number of price points, and customer evaluation processes may begin with the question 'How much do I want to spend?'; comparison is then based on what level of service (e.g. connection speed, download limits, free telephone calls, helpline availability) they can obtain within this price. The service provider's task then becomes one of designing a profitable service around the price point, rather than designing the service and then fixing a price.

11.5   Elasticity of demand

Elasticity of demand refers to the extent to which demand changes in relation to a change in price or some other variable, such as income. What is important here is to compare the proportionate (or percentage) change in demand with the proportionate (or percentage) change in the other variable, over any given period of time.

The most commonly used measure of elasticity of demand is price elasticity of demand. Information on this is useful to business organizations to allow them to predict what will happen to the volume of sales in response to a change in price. This section is concerned with the responsiveness of a whole market to changes in price. It will be recalled that, in a perfectly competitive market, firms must take their selling price from the market, so the only elasticity that is of interest to them is the elasticity of the market as a whole.

Price elasticity of demand refers to the ratio of the percentage change in demand to the percentage change in price. In other words, it seeks to measure how the sales of a product respond to a change in its price. This can be expressed as a simple formula:

$$\text{Price elasticity of demand} = \frac{\text{change in demand}\,(\%)}{\text{change in price}\,(\%)}$$

Where demand is relatively unresponsive to price changes, it is said to be inelastic with respect to price. Where demand is highly responsive to even a small price charge, demand is described as being elastic with respect to price.

Two demand curves are shown in Figure 11.11. D1 is more elastic than D2, as indicated by the greater effect on volume of a change in price, compared with the effects of a similar price change with D2.

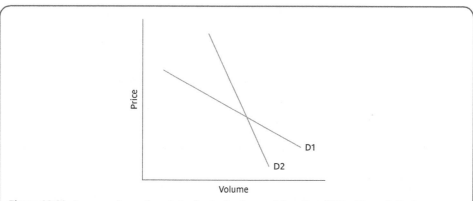

Figure 11.11 A comparison of a relatively elastic demand function (D1) with a relatively inelastic one (D2).

A number of factors influence the price elasticity of demand for a particular product. The most important is the availability of substitutes. Where these are readily available, buyers are likely to switch between alternative products in response to price changes. The absolute value of a product and its importance to a buyer can also influence its elasticity. For example, if infrequently purchased boxes of matches fell in price by 10 per cent from 11p to 10p, buyers would probably not increase their purchases. However, if the price of television sets came down by the same percentage, from £330 to £300, many buyers may enter the market.

For any measure of elasticity, it is important to consider the time period over which it is being measured. In general, products are much more inelastic to changes in price over the short term, when possibilities for substitution may be few. However, over the longer term, new possibilities for substitution may appear. This explains why petrol is very inelastic over the short term but much more so over the long term. Faced with a sudden increase in petrol prices (as happened following the sharp rise in world oil prices during 2008), motorists have little choice other than to pay the increased price. However, over the longer term, they can reduce their purchases of petrol by buying more fuel-efficient cars, rearranging their pattern of life so that they do not need to travel as much, or by sharing cars.

Further measures of elasticity of demand can be made by considering the responsiveness of demand to changes in the assumptions on which the demand curve is based. The most important of these is income elasticity of demand, which measures the responsiveness of demand to changes in buyers' combined incomes, and can be expressed in the following way:

$$\text{Income elasticity of demand} = \frac{\text{change in demand}(\%)}{\text{change in income}(\%)}$$

In general, as a population's income rises, the demand for most products rises, giving rise to a positive income elasticity of demand. Where there is a particularly strong increase in demand in response to an increase in incomes (or vice versa), a product can be said to have a high income elasticity of demand. This is true of luxuries such as long-haul air holidays and fitted kitchens, whose sales have increased during times of general economic prosperity, but declined during recessionary periods. On the other hand, there are some goods and services whose demand goes down as incomes increase. These are referred to as inferior goods; examples in most western countries include local bus services and household coal.

It is useful for business organizations to understand income elasticity of demand in order to plan a response to anticipated changes in aggregate income. If, for example, a general rise in consumer income looks likely to reduce the sales of a product that has a negative income elasticity, a business may seek to shift its resources to making products with a positive income elasticity. In trying to plan for the future, businesses rely on their own historical information about sales/income relationships, and also government and private forecasts about current and future levels and distribution of income.

A third measure of demand elasticity to note is a product's cross-price elasticity of demand. This refers to the percentage change in demand for product A when the price of product B changes. Where products are very close substitutes, this may be a very important measure to understand consumer demand. For example, the price of butter can have a significant effect on demand for margarine.

It is possible to identify numerous other ad hoc measures of elasticity of demand. Firms may be interested in the responsiveness of demand to changes in some measure of the quality of their product. For example, a railway operator may be interested in the effects on demand of improvements in service reliability or a bus operator may be interested in establishing the percentage increase in passenger demand resulting from a given percentage increase in the frequency of a bus route.

11.6   Imperfect competition and elasticity of demand

The analysis of price decisions for firms in a competitive market indicates that, for any one firm, price is given by the market. An individual firm cannot increase profits by stimulating demand through lower prices, nor would it gain any benefit by seeking to raise its prices. This changes in an imperfectly competitive market where a firm acquires a degree of monopoly power over its customers. Each firm now has a demand curve for its own unique product.

Firms face a downward-sloping demand curve for each of their products, indicating that, as prices fall, demand increases, and vice versa. In fact, a number of demand curves describing a firm's market can be described, ranging from the general to the specific brand. For example, in the market for breakfast cereals, the demand curve for cereals in general may be fairly inelastic, on the basis that people will always want to buy breakfast cereals of some description (Figure 11.12). Demand for one particular type of cereal, such as cornflakes, will be slightly more elastic as people may be attracted to cornflakes from other cereals such as porridge oats on the basis of their relative price. Price becomes more elastic still when a particular brand of cereals is considered. To some people, Kellogg's cornflakes can easily be substituted with other brands of cornflakes, so if a price differential between brands developed, switching may occur. By lowering its price, a firm may be able to increase its sales, but what is important to firms is that they increase their total revenue (and, thereby, profits). Whether this happens depends upon the elasticity of demand for the product in question.

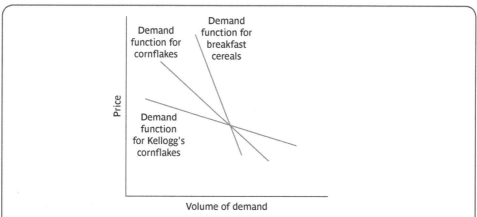

Figure 11.12 A comparison of elasticities of demand for breakfast cereals at different levels of product specificity.

Total revenue is a function of total sales multiplied by the selling price per unit. Table 11.1 summarizes the effects on total revenue of changes in price, given alternative assumptions about elasticity.

Table 11.1   Effects of elasticity of demand and price changes on total revenue.

Price elasticity of demand	Price change	Revenue effect
High (elastic demand)	–	–
	–	+
Low (inelastic demand)	+	+
	–	–

11.7 Elasticity of supply

The concept of elasticity can also be applied to supply, so as to measure the responsiveness of supply to changes in price. **Elasticity of supply** is measured by the formula:

⟳ Thinking around the subject

Where's the veg?

In theory, high market prices act as a signal for companies to enter that market, or to increase the volume they supply to it. But in practice, there can be lengthy delays before firms are able to respond to these market signals, and the market for organic vegetables during the late 1990s illustrates this point. A combination of rising incomes, greater awareness of health issues and a string of food safety scares had led to rapid growth in demand for organic produce throughout Europe. But how can farmers grow organically on land that has been saturated by decades of artificial fertilizer use? The Soil Association, which operates a widely recognized accreditation scheme for organic produce, required that farmland should be free of artificial fertilizer for at least five years before any crops grown on it could be described as organic. So, despite the rapid growth in demand and the price premiums that customers were prepared to pay, retailers found it difficult to satisfy demand. Furthermore, with a difficult and intermittent supply, could retailers risk their brand name by being seen as an unreliable supplier of second-rate produce? Marks & Spencer launched a range of organic vegetables in 1997, only to withdraw them soon afterwards, blaming the difficulty in obtaining regular and reliable supplies. However, by 2004, producers that had earlier taken their signals from the market and prepared themselves for organic production were finally able to increase the volume supplied to the market. But with a sharp increase in supply relative to demand, the price premiums available for organic produce fell.

$$\text{Elasticity of supply} = \frac{\text{change in supply } (\%)}{\text{change in price } (\%)}$$

If suppliers are relatively unresponsive to an increase in the price of a product, the product is described as being inelastic with respect to price. If producers increase production substantially as prices rise, the product is said to be elastic.

As with price elasticity of demand, time is crucial in determining the elasticity of supply. Over the short term, it may be very difficult for firms to increase supply, making it very inelastic with respect to price. In the case of markets for agricultural products, elasticity is determined by the growing cycle, and new supply may be forthcoming only in time for the next season. For many manufacturing processes, supplies can eventually be increased by investing in new productive capacity and taking on additional workers. Over the longer term, supply is more elastic.

11.8   Limitations of the theory of perfect competition

Although government policy makers often view perfectly competitive markets as an ideal to aim towards, the automatic balancing of supply and demand at an equilibrium price, as described above, is seldom achieved in practice. The following are some of the more important reasons why perfect competition is rarely achieved in practice.

- Where economies of scale are achievable in an industry sector, it is always possible for firms to grow larger and become more efficient, and thereby able to exercise undue influence in a market. In general, perfect competition applies only where production techniques are simple and opportunities for economies of scale few.

- Markets are often dominated by large buyers that are able to exercise influence over the market. The domestic market for many specialized defence products may be competitive in terms of a large number of suppliers, but demand for their products is dominated by one government buying agency.

- It can be naive to assume that high prices and profits in a sector will attract new entrants, while losses will cause the least efficient to leave. In practice, there may be a whole range of barriers to entry that could cover the need to obtain licences for production, the availability of trained staff and access to distribution outlets. Also, there are sometimes barriers to exit where firms are locked into long-term supply contracts or where it would be very expensive to lay off resources such as labour.

- A presumption of perfectly competitive markets is that buyers and sellers have complete information about market conditions. In fact, this is often far from the truth. On the simple point of making price comparisons, much research has been undertaken to show that buyers often have little knowledge of the going rate for a particular category of product. For example, the use of bar code scanning equipment by retailers has resulted in many products no longer carrying a price label, weakening customers' retained knowledge of prices. Sometimes, as in the case of telephone call tariffs or credit card interest charges, prices are very difficult to comprehend.

In the following chapter, we will explore market situations that are in some sense 'imperfect', perhaps because a small number of companies dominate the market, or because products are so diverse that each product becomes unique in its own right, and therefore by implication doesn't face any direct competition.

It should be stressed again that, so far in this chapter, we have merely looked at the basic building blocks by which we begin to understand competition within markets. Although perfect competition may be an exception rather than the norm for markets, an understanding of basic market forces should allow us to assess the characteristics of less competitive market structures.

Thinking around the subject

Marketing or markets?

Is marketing a natural ally of free markets, or is it really an enemy? To advocates of marketing, marketing is all about bringing together customers who want to buy with sellers who want to sell. By carefully studying what buyers want to buy, marketers contribute towards the efficient operation of a market. Advocates of marketing would contrast the benefits of having marketers controlled by market disciplines with the inefficiency of having a central bureaucracy making resource allocation decisions.

However, marketers are not always so benign in their thoughts about markets. While most marketers would publicly endorse the power of free markets, many of their activities, consciously or unconsciously, undermine the spirit of free markets. Consider three of the defining characteristics of competitive markets that were discussed above: a homogeneous product; freely available information; and freedom of entry to and exit from the market. Now consider some common marketing strategies.

The idea of all companies selling a homogeneous product is anathema to one of the basic philosophies of marketing, which is to add value to products through differentiation. The following chapter will discuss ways in which companies use branding to try to differentiate their products from those of the competitors. Faced with shelves of slightly differentiated bottled water carrying different brand names, can this be said to be a market in a homogeneous product? Is there any meaningful difference between many of the brands? How can buyers tell?

Information available in a market is often difficult to assimilate, and some people have accused marketers of making their information even more difficult to understand. Try comparing mobile phone calling plans, or the different tariffs offered by gas and electricity companies, and you could come to the conclusion that the companies' information may be freely available to all, but actually understood by very few. Some would accuse marketers of engaging in 'confusion marketing' to try to make informed comparisons more difficult.

Marketers often do their best to reduce the ease of entry to or exit from a market. One consequence of the recent trend towards 'relationship marketing' has been to try to tie customers to the company through a long-term contract. Customers of mobile phone companies cannot easily leave their existing supplier if they are committed to a 12-month contract. Many manufacturers have sought exclusivity contracts with retailers, which makes it difficult for new competitors to enter the market.

Karl Marx once observed that capitalism was essentially all about *reducing* risk rather than *taking* risk. Could marketing be more about trying to undermine the value of markets rather than trying to make them work more efficiently?

Case study:
Can market mechanisms reduce global climate change?

© *Michael Graham*

To anti-capitalism protestors, the cause of global climate change can be attributed to market forces. Market forces imply that individuals focus on buying goods and services for the lowest price, and producers focus on producing those goods and services for the lowest cost. Both buyers and sellers are quite likely to concentrate their evaluation on the costs they directly incur, rather than the 'external' costs – those costs that are incurred by other people. For many shoppers, the price of a pair of shoes is the most important basis for choosing between competing shoes, and market forces have helped to drive down the price of shoes, so that we can now regard shoes almost as a disposable fashion item, regardless of the impact of short-life shoes filling up landfill sites and using scarce natural resources. Similarly, shoe manufacturers have used market forces to cut ruthlessly their production costs, even if this means moving shoes and their component materials long distances round the world, adding to greenhouse gas emissions in the process. So, market forces may indirectly have contributed to current problems of global warming, but can those same market forces also be used to try to redress the problem? Backers of carbon trading hope so.

Greenhouse gases are blamed for causing climate change because they absorb infrared radiation and prevent it from being dispersed into space, thereby having the effect of warming the Earth. This not only increases global average temperatures, but is also claimed to lead to increasingly unpredictable weather. Probable results of climate change include more frequent and fiercer storms, droughts and

floods. If warming causes enough of the world's ice to melt, rises in sea levels could occur, leading to flooding in coastal areas. It is also claimed that melting ice from the Arctic could disrupt the flow and direction of the Gulfstream, having the effect of cooling parts of Europe.

Very few businesses can claim not to be affected by climate change. Bad weather (such as hurricanes, floods and gale-force winds, which have been attributed to climate change) affects companies when they come to renew their insurance policies. The storms that hit the UK in autumn 2000 are estimated to have cost UK insurers more than £1 billion, and these costs were ultimately passed on to businesses and consumers in the form of higher premiums. Damage caused to property by storms can close down a company's factories and disrupt the supply of its raw materials. If the weather becomes more unpredictable, risk will increasingly have to be factored into business planning.

As well as being affected by climate change, companies are increasingly being called upon to take some of the responsibility for slowing the rate of greenhouse gas emissions. An important focus for these efforts was the Kyoto Treaty, drawn up in 1997. This required signatory countries to reduce their dependence on fossil fuels, which produce the greenhouse gases blamed for causing climate change.

One outcome of the Kyoto Treaty was the introduction in 2005 of the EU's Emissions Trading Scheme (ETS), which essentially sought to reduce carbon emissions through a system of quotas traded through market mechanisms. The scheme capped the amount of carbon dioxide that could be emitted from large installations, such as power generation and carbon-intensive factories, and covered almost half the EU's total CO_2 emissions. All businesses in the UK covered by the scheme were allocated a share of the 756 million tonnes of carbon dioxide that the UK was allowed to produce. If they emitted above their individually allocated amount, they would have to buy carbon permits in the specialist carbon trading market that emerged. On the other hand, if they did not need all their quota, they could sell surplus through these same markets. In principle, companies had a strong incentive to reduce their carbon emissions, as market forces would reward them with income from the sale of unused carbon permits.

However, market forces were not as straightforward as first appeared. The ETS commenced with excessive permits for emissions being issued, many would argue in response to political pressure to reduce the immediate effect on high-emissions sectors. There had been many loopholes and incentives for industries to exaggerate their emissions in order to increase the number of permits they were allocated. One consequence of the over-issue of quotas was that most firms had little difficulty in achieving emission levels below their cap, and were therefore able to sell their surplus quota on the open carbon market. Of course, with a generous allocation of quota, there were more sellers of carbon permits than buyers, with the result that the price of carbon permits fell by 60 per cent within the first year of operation of the scheme. The incentive for companies to reduce their emissions was, accordingly, much less than it could have been. Perversely, one estimate claimed that the UK's biggest polluters had earned a 'windfall' profit of nearly £1 billion as a result of over-generous allocation of carbon quotas, which they were able to sell.

The use of market mechanisms to solve the problem of global warming is an innovative way of trying to internalize companies' external costs. Rather than imposing a bureaucratic solution, a market-based system was seen by many as an attractive means by which businesses could overcome an ecological problem by doing what they are good at – trading. However, some argued that markets were inherently incapable of solving the pressing problems of climate change and more drastic action based on strict limits on emissions would bring about more rapid change. There was also the issue that without world agreement on permitted carbon emissions, manufacturers would simply shift production to countries with fewer restrictions on emissions. Another perverse consequence of the ETS could be to shift production from relatively clean and modern European factories to relatively heavy-polluting factories in developing countries. Moreover, additional emissions may have been generated in the process of transporting raw materials and finished goods to take advantage of the favourable emissions regime. It follows therefore that the market-based ETS could actually have led to an increase in total carbon emissions.

A major weakness of the original emissions trading scheme was that the world's biggest economy – the USA – refused to join it, claiming that it would adversely affect the competitive position of its manufacturers. However, with the election of President Obama in 2009, it appeared that the USA was becoming increasingly amenable to taking action. Some in the USA argued that restrictions on fossil fuels could help American industry, and pointed to the strong competitive position and market opportunities for its wind turbine industry.

Meanwhile, some argued that, ultimately, market forces would provide a solution to greenhouse gas emissions because of growing shortages of raw materials and fossil fuels. In 2008, the price of oil and many raw materials rose sharply. At the time, many people blamed this on speculators driving up the market, but price rises continued two years later, even though much of the western world was in the midst of a recession, which would normally have led to reduced demand. It seemed that the insatiable appetite from the increasingly wealthy populations of China, India, Brazil and Russia was pushing up prices. With oil prices reaching new heights during 2010, many companies renewed their efforts to cut down their use of oil and scarce natural resources. Would Adam Smith's 'invisible hand' come to the rescue of the ecological environment by pricing out the use of polluting materials?

QUESTIONS

1 Critically assess the opportunities and challenges for energy-intensive businesses, such as a metal manufacturer, resulting from the introduction of carbon trading.

2 Show, using supply/demand analysis, the effects of the over-issuing of carbon quotas described in the case study.

3 Discuss the extent to which the carbon market represents a perfectly competitive market. What would be the most likely causes of market distortion?

Summary

This chapter has reviewed the variety of market structures that exist, and the effect market structure has on a firm's pricing and product decisions. Perfectly competitive markets are presumed to favour consumers, but can limit the revenues of profit-seeking firms. In its purest extreme, this market structure is unusual; however, the basic building blocks of demand, supply and price determination provide a foundation for understanding more complex market structures. We will return to these market structures in **Chapter 12**. The trend towards globalization of business (**Chapter 14**) is having the effect of making markets more competitive. This chapter has taken a microeconomic perspective on pricing and competition. Pricing is also affected by macroeconomic factors, and these are discussed in **Chapter 13**.

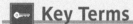 ## Key Terms

Demand (368)	Markets (364)
Elasticity of demand (377)	Perfect competition (365)
Elasticity of supply (381)	Price determination (373)
Market structure (364)	Supply (370)

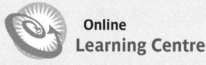 **Online**
Learning Centre

To help you grasp the key concepts of this chapter, explore the extra resources posted on the Online Learning Centre at *www.mcgraw-hill.co.uk/palmer*. Among other helpful resources there are chapter-by-chapter test questions, revision notes and web links.

Chapter review questions

1 In the context of market structure analysis, what are the options available to firms in a highly competitive market to improve profitability? Select one of the options and discuss it, making clear how lasting the profit improvement is likely to be in the long run. (*Based on a CIM Marketing Environment Examination question.*)

2 'Elasticity of demand is a fine theoretical concept of economists, but difficult for marketers to use in practice.' Critically assess this statement.

3 Show, using diagrams, what would happen to the price of whisky if a new technological development suddenly allowed it to be produced at a much lower cost than previously.

Activities

1 Collect information on prices charged for the following products: a top ten DVD film to buy; car insurance quotes; mobile phone charges. What do the prices tell you about the competitiveness of these markets? Identify strategies that companies in these markets have pursued in order to reduce the effects of direct competition.

2 Try to construct a demand curve for an item of consumer technology whose price is falling – for example, a mobile phone with a GPS system. Try to construct a demand curve on the basis of your friends' statements about their likelihood of buying the product at specified price levels. What limitations are there in this approach to determining the demand curve for the product?

3 Identify the impact and discuss the likely marketing response to the following environmental changes affecting a major oil refining and distributing company:

- the introduction of a carbon tax
- a breakthrough in cost-effective solar power stations
- a well-financed new entrant entering its main market
- teleconferencing and telecommunications growing rapidly.

(Based on a CIM Marketing Environment Examination question.)

Further reading

This chapter has provided only a very brief overview of the principles of economics as they affect pricing. For a fuller discussion, one of the following texts would be useful.

Begg, D. (2009) *Foundations of Economics*, 2nd edn, Maidenhead, McGraw-Hill.
Begg, D. and Ward, D. (2009) *Economics for Business*, Maidenhead, McGraw-Hill.
Lipsey, R.G. and Chrystal, K.A. (2011) *Economics*, 12th edn, Oxford, Oxford University Press.

References

Timmins, N. (2003) 'A bid to save money for the government: online auctions', *Financial Times*, 29 January, p. 12.

CHAPTER 5

Costs, supply and perfect competition

Learning outcomes

By the end of this chapter, you should be able to:

- Relate total, average and marginal cost
- Explain the law of diminishing returns
- Assess costs in the short run
- Define technology and production techniques
- Relate returns to scale and average cost curves
- Distinguish long-run and short-run costs
- Analyse a firm's supply decision in the short run and long run
- Understand temporary shutdown and permanent exit

- Show how minimum efficient scale and market size together determine market structure and the number of firms that can survive in the industry
- Explain the concept of perfect competition
- Show why a perfectly competitive firm's output equates price and marginal cost
- Examine incentives for entry and exit
- Derive the supply curve of a perfectly competitive industry
- Analyse the effect of shifts in demand or costs

In this chapter, we explore the costs that a firm faces, and examine how this affects its decision to produce. In the short run, a firm can vary some inputs to production, but is stuck with some things inherited from the past. In the long run, it can eventually change all the inputs to production and the production techniques used to combine these inputs. It has more flexibility in the long run. For a given set of demand conditions, we explore how different costs lead to different output decisions of suppliers.

We then examine how demand and cost structures interact to determine the type of competition that exists in a market. In some cases, individual firms have little or no effect on the price of the products that

CHAPTER 5: Costs, supply and perfect competition

they produce and sell; in other cases, the price received is very sensitive to the output decisions of individual firms. Some firms are tiny, others huge. We analyse why this is the case.

We conclude the chapter by studying one particular form of competition, in which individual firms have no effect at all on the price of their products. The following chapter examines all other forms of competition, which share the feature that each firm recognizes that, by producing more, it will bid down the price that it receives.

 How costs affect supply in the short run

Chapter 3 introduced the bare bones of a theory of supply, which depended on both costs and revenue. Now we need to put more flesh on this theory. Chapters 5–6 deal with two ideas. First, adjusting production methods takes time. Given time, firms may be able to reduce costs by choosing more appropriate methods of production. This leads to a distinction between optimal behaviour in the short run, when some things cannot be changed, and in the long run when everything can be changed.

Second, the revenue obtained from selling any particular output depends on the extent of competition in that market. This means that the general theory of supply is affected by the context of the degree of competition in which firms find themselves. To begin the analysis of the general theory of supply, this chapter deals with the special case of perfect competition. Chapter 6 then examines the theory of supply in other market environments in which competition is more restricted.

New companies, such as Orange and Amazon, lost a lot of money before eventually starting to make profits. Existing companies, such as British Airways and British Telecom, made big losses in the cyclical downturns of 2001–02 and 2008–09, despite previous periods of healthy profits; and banks made huge losses in 2007–08 as a result of over-optimistic lending decisions. But most kept going nevertheless. Firms don't always close down when they are losing money. They may keep going because they expect demand to rise, or costs to fall. We need to distinguish between the *short-run* and the *long-run* supply decisions of firms. In the short run, a firm can't fully adjust to new information. In the long run, full adjustment is possible. In this section, we focus on how costs affect the supply decision. We then turn to the influence of demand and revenue on supply decisions.

> An **input** (sometimes called a **factor of production**) is any good or service used to make output. A **production technique** is a particular way of using inputs to make output. **Technology** is the list of production techniques known today.

Inputs are labour, machinery, buildings, raw materials and energy.

> **Land** is the input supplied by nature; **capital** is the input that exists because of a previous production process, and still exists at the end of the production process. **Raw materials** are the physical inputs used up during the production process.

Thus, machinery and buildings are capital, because they were made previously, but now supply input services to the production processes in which they are now used; and they will still be there again next year. Power stations supply capital input services to making electricity and trains supply capital input services to the production of train journeys. For simplicity, economists often treat land as fixed in supply (even though meticulous application of fertilizer may increase its effective input a little). Capital services are usually fixed in the short run, but variable in the long run. Eventually we can produce more buildings and machinery (thereby increasing their input to future production), or allow them to depreciate (thereby reducing their input to future production).

Raw materials are things such as fertilizer in agriculture or hops in the beer industry, inputs that are entirely used up during the production process. We get some raw materials largely from nature (fresh water, plants, easily collected minerals) but devote considerable amounts of production to making some raw materials for subsequent production processes (high-octane fuel for aircraft, specialist steel for buildings, silicon for computer chips).

Labour is the production input supplied by workers.

With slavery now abolished, firms don't own workers any more, but they do rent or hire the labour services of workers. We usually assume that labour is the most easily variable input in the short run. How productive these workers are depends on the quantities of other inputs with which they can work. In some countries, wheat is produced with few people using lots of machinery: these workers will produce a lot of output per worker. In other countries, the same crop is produced with lots of workers using little machinery: now output per worker will be lower because they have a lower quantity of non-labour inputs with which to co-operate.

Both are possible techniques with which to produce wheat. Which one is adopted will depend on the prices of the different inputs and the chosen scale of production.

Short-run costs and diminishing returns

In the short run, the firm has some fixed inputs.

A **fixed input** can't be varied in the short run. A **variable input** can be adjusted, even in the short run.

The short run varies from industry to industry. It may take ten years to build a new power station, but only days to create a new market stall. Having built a power station, the electricity supplier must treat this input as fixed in the short run – the input of power station services cannot quickly be augmented nor quickly reduced. The existence of fixed inputs in the short run has two implications.

First, in the short run the firm has some fixed costs, which must be paid even if output is zero. It has to pay rent on its premises even if it decides not to produce anything this month. Second, because the firm cannot make all the adjustments it would like, its short-run costs must exceed its long-run costs. If it behaves differently in the long run, this can only be because it prefers to switch to a cheaper production method once this opportunity arises.

Variable costs are the costs of hiring variable factors, typically labour, raw materials and energy. Although firms may have long-term contracts with workers, and with material or energy suppliers, in practice most firms retain some flexibility through overtime and short time, hiring or non-hiring of casual and part-time workers, and purchases of raw material and energy in the open market to supplement contracted supplies.

Fixed costs don't vary with output levels. **Variable costs** change with output.

Chapter 3 introduced the theory of supply. Marginal revenue is the extra revenue obtained from selling another unit of output. Marginal cost is the extra cost of producing another unit of output. A firm will increase its profit if it expands output further whenever marginal revenue exceeds marginal cost, and will also increase its profit if it contracts its output whenever marginal revenue is less than marginal cost. Hence, profits are maximized at the output at which marginal revenue is equal to marginal cost. This was summarized in Figure 3-3, which we show again here as Figure 5-1.

We now wish to understand in more detail what determines the costs of a firm in the short run. For simplicity, we will think about a firm whose only variable input in the short run is labour. To show we are explicitly focusing on the short run, we now draw the short-run marginal

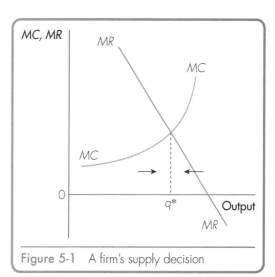

Figure 5-1   A firm's supply decision

CHAPTER 5: Costs, supply and perfect competition

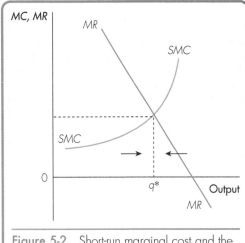

Figure 5-2   Short-run marginal cost and the optimal output level

cost curve *SMC* available to the firm while it has to treat its other inputs as fixed. It can increase output only by using more and more labour to work with fixed amounts of capital and other inputs.

> The **marginal product** of a variable input (labour) is the *extra* output from *adding* 1 unit of the variable input, holding constant the quantity of all other inputs in the short run.

The first worker has a whole factory to work with and has too many jobs to do to produce much. A second worker helps, a lot, and so does a third. Suppose the factory has three machines and the three workers are now specializing in each running one of the factory's machines. The marginal product of a fourth worker is lower. With only three machines, the fourth worker gets a machine only when another worker is resting. A fifth worker only makes tea for the other four. By now there are diminishing returns to labour.

Holding all inputs constant except one, the **law of diminishing returns** says that, beyond some level of the variable input, further rises in the variable input steadily reduce the marginal product of that input.

Output is varied by using more labour input. Changes in the marginal product of labour affect the marginal cost of making output. The more productive a worker, the lower is the cost of making output. Figure 5-2 shows that, as output rises, short-run marginal costs initially fall as we move to the right along *SMC*; however, beyond some output, diminishing returns set in, additional workers add less and less to extra output, and hence marginal cost becomes higher and higher as the firm raises output further by adding to its variable labour input. While the marginal product of labour is rising, each worker adds more to output than the previous workers, and marginal cost is falling.

> **Short-run marginal cost SMC** is the extra cost of making one more unit of output in the short run while some inputs are fixed.

Once diminishing returns to labour set in, the marginal product of labour falls steadily as output is expanded, and marginal costs therefore rise with the level of output. This is the basic insight behind the shape of the marginal cost curve in Figure 5-2. Because other inputs are limited, it takes more and more extra workers to make each extra unit of output.

In Figure 5-2, the output *q** is the most profitable output to produce because it is the point at which *SMC* = *MR*. If *SMC* exceeded *MR* at that output, the firm could make even more profit by contracting output a little (the last unit of production cost more to produce than it added to revenue); if *MR* exceeded *SMC*, the firm could make even more profit by expanding output a little further (thereby making more in revenue than it costs to produce for that extra unit of production).

Sunk costs

If certain costs have *already* been incurred and can't be affected by your decision, ignore them. They shouldn't influence your future decisions. In deciding how much to produce in the short run, the firm ignores its fixed costs which must be incurred anyway.

It may seem a pity to abandon a project in which a lot of money has already been invested. Poker players call this throwing good money after bad. If you don't think it will be worth reading the rest of this book, you should not do it merely because you put a lot of effort into the first four chapters. Your optimal decision of how to spend your time, from now on, is to decide whether the benefits of reading the rest of the book outweigh the costs of reading the rest of the book.

A firm's supply decision in the short run

The firm only has one thing left to check. Should it be producing at all? To answer this question, the firm calculates its total revenue from production and compares this with its total costs in the short run.

Total costs are **total fixed costs** plus **total variable costs**.

In the short run, the firm has to pay the costs of its fixed inputs whether or not it produces any output and earns any revenue. The only decisions it can make are whether to incur variable costs and, if so, how much to produce. (Total revenue *minus* variable costs) is therefore the financial benefit to the firm from deciding to produce, and producing at q^*, at which $SMC = MR$ is guaranteed to maximize this financial benefit.

The firm's short-run supply decision is therefore simple to describe:

(a) If at output q^*, total revenue *exceeds* total variable costs, then produce output q^*.

(b) If, even at output q^*, total revenue is less than total variable costs, then produce zero output: shut down in the short run and hope for better times later.

Two final remarks. First, in the short run, even if the firm decides to produce, it may not be making profits. It is stuck with its fixed costs whatever it does. Ignoring these, it produces if it at least makes a profit on the variable part that it can affect. Either the profit from production is large enough to cover the fixed costs too, in which case the firm is in overall profit, or the profit from production is positive but less than the fixed costs, in which case the decision to produce is partially reducing the losses from the fixed (overhead) costs, even though in total the firm is still losing money.

Second, instead of comparing total revenues and total costs, we can divide both by output to get average revenues and average costs.

Average revenue is total revenue divided by output. But revenue is just output multiplied by price. So average revenue *is* the price the firm receives for its output. **Average cost** is total cost divided by output.

Since total cost = total fixed cost + total variable cost, dividing everything by the same output level we get

Average cost = **average fixed cost** + **average variable cost**

We can therefore restate the firm's supply decision as follows:

(a) If at the best production level q^*, price (hence average revenue) > average variable cost, then choose to produce q^*.

(b) If at output q^*, price < average variable cost, then shut down temporarily and produce 0.

Of course, private firms cannot be compelled to lose money indefinitely – they would rather quit the industry entirely. To examine when temporary shutdown makes sense and when permanent exit makes sense, we need to think about the long run as well as the short run.

CHAPTER 5: Costs, supply and perfect competition

Box 5-1

General Motors survives the slump, but only just

In the good times, well-run companies invest for the future and use the opportunity to think about their strategic direction for the future. Less well-run companies allow cost to creep upwards, get into businesses some way from their core competence and are surprisingly vulnerable when the downturn comes.

For years, General Motors was the pride not just of Detroit but of America. An early convert to global thinking, it had bought Vauxhall in 1925, Germany's Adam Opel in 1928 and Sweden's SAAB in 1989. By 2006 it had 200,000 employees and earned over $200 billion a year, but it had quite expensive labour contracts, had not led the trend towards much smaller cars, had been drawn into ancilliary businesses such as GMAC, its financial services division, and had failed to invest as much as the competition – whereas Ford had turned around Jaguar and Volvo by investing heavily in new model development, SAAB had been left with old models. Despite its $200 billion revenue in 2006, General Motors was barely breaking even.

In 2007 the US housing market fell by around 10 per cent, marking the end of the house price bubble and the beginning of trouble for mortgages secured against housing assets. As households and firms began to perceive the problem, their appetite for costly new vehicles declined abruptly. Loss of confidence also threatened the GM loans business in GMAC.

General Motors declared losses of $38 billion in 2007 and $31 billion in 2008, by which time the company was effectively bust. Significant losses in the financial services business had compounded the losses from car production itself. US presidents were unwilling to allow the pride of Detroit to go under, taking the entire region with it. Even market-oriented George W. Bush provided $14 billion in government support; Barack Obama injected another $39 billion.

If there had been no way in which GM could survive, these injections would merely have been largely a waste of money, and would merely have postponed the inevitable. It was critical, both for GM and the US government, that a successful recovery plan was devised and delivered.

GM managed to implement many of the textbook remedies. It renegotiated its labour contracts, convincing workers and unions that a lower wage in a sustainable company was preferable to a high wage that led to unemployment or bankruptcy. In the global business of auto production, more and more of the world's car supply is being manufactured in countries with lower wage costs. Detroit had to take a big step in this direction or go under.

GM also shrunk its labour force: whether or not it had been inappropriately high in 2006, GM had to prepare for a new slimline operation in which the volume of its car sales would be permanently lower. Having sold 4.5 million vehicles as late as 2006, by 2009 its sales were down to 2 million, a fall of 55 per cent in three years. GM also began to attack more vigorously the small car market with new products such as the new Chevrolet Aveo, more in tune with a world with oil prices at record highs. Leaving aside luxury brands, such as BMW and Mercedes, the brands that have grown during the European recession are Hyundai, Kia and Chevrolet.

What was the combined result of the repositioning of the company and the partial recovery of the US economy after 2009? GM declared a much smaller loss of $4 billion in 2009, but then profits of $4 billion in 2010 and over $7 billion in 2011. Taking a purely short-run view, the company would have been closed in 2007. Since then, it has begun to pay back the investments that were made in it. If the profits continue, the decision may be justified by GM profits alone; taking into account the wider cost to the Michigan economy if GM had folded, the US government probably considers its investment money well spent.

Costs and supply in the long run

A technique is said to be **technically efficient** if no other technique could make the same output with fewer inputs. **Technology** is all the techniques known today. **Technical progress** is the discovery of a new technique that is more efficient than existing ones, making a given output with fewer inputs than before.

Technology relates volumes of inputs to volume of output. But costs are values. To deduce the cheapest way to make a particular output, the firm needs to know input prices as well as what technology is available. At each output level, the firm finds the lowest-cost technique. When labour is cheap, firms choose labour-intensive techniques. If labour is expensive, the firm will switch to more capital-intensive techniques that use less labour.

Faced with higher demand, the firm will want to expand output, but adjustment takes time. In the long run, the firm can adjust all input quantities and the choice of technique. In the short run, the firm can't change all inputs, and may also be unable to change technique. It may be years before a new factory is designed, built and operational.

Long-run total cost LTC is the total cost of making each output level when a firm has plenty of time to adjust fully and produce this output level by the cheapest possible means. **Long-run marginal cost LMC** is the rise in total cost if output permanently rises by one unit. **Long-run average cost LAC** is LTC divided by the level of output Q.

In the long run, most firms face the U-shaped average cost curve shown in Figure 5-3. At higher output levels, the firm achieves efficiency gains and lower average costs. However, beyond some output level Q^*, life gets more difficult for the firm, and its average costs increase if output is higher.

There are **economies of scale** (or increasing returns to scale) if long-run average cost LAC falls as output rises, **constant returns to scale** if LAC is constant as output rises, and **diseconomies of scale** (or decreasing returns to scale) if LAC rises as output rises.

The U-shaped average cost curve in Figure 5-3 has scale economies up to point A, where average cost is lowest. At output levels above Q^*, there are decreasing returns to scale. Since LAC is horizontal at point A, there are constant returns to scale when output is close to Q^*.

Other shapes of cost curve are possible. Later, we shall see that in some industries with large-scale economies, LAC may fall over the entire output range. Conversely, the output Q^* may be so tiny that the LAC curve slopes up over most normal output ranges.

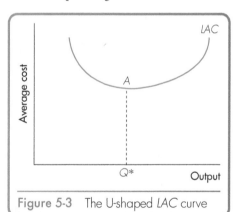

Figure 5-3 The U-shaped LAC curve

Maths 5-1

Average costs and marginal costs

For those of you familiar with calculus, here is a neat example of its elegance. Suppose total costs depend on output through the cost curve $C(q)$. Average cost $A(q)$ is therefore given by $C(q)/q$, which simply divides total cost by the quantity of output produced. The slope of this average cost curve is computed by differentiating with respect to q, which yields $(dC/dq)/q - C/q^2$ and average cost is at a minimum when this slope is zero, which implies $(dC/dq) = C/q$. This says that marginal cost dC/dq = average cost C/q when output q is at the level that attains minimum average cost.

CHAPTER 5: Costs, supply and perfect competition

Scale economies

There are three reasons for economies of scale. Production may entail some *overhead costs* that do not vary with the output level.[1] A firm requires a manager, a telephone, an accountant and a market research survey. It can't have half a manager and half a telephone if output is low. From low initial output, rises in output allow overheads to be spread over more units of output, reducing average cost. Beyond some output level, the firm needs more managers and telephones. Scale economies end. The average cost curve stops falling.

A second reason for economies of scale is *specialization*. At low output levels, each of the few workers has to do many jobs and never becomes very good at any of them. At higher output and a larger workforce, each worker can focus on a single task and handle it more efficiently. The third reason for economies of scale is that large scale is often needed to take advantage of better machinery. Sophisticated but expensive machinery also has an element of indivisibility. A farmer with a small field may as well dig the field by hand. With a larger field, it becomes worth buying a tractor.

Diseconomies of scale

The main reason for diseconomies of scale is that management is hard once the firm is large: there are *managerial diseconomies of scale*. Large firms need many layers of management, which themselves have to be managed. Co-ordination problems arise, and average costs begin to rise. Geography may also explain diseconomies of scale. If the first factory is sited in the best place, a second factory has to be built in a less advantageous location, and the third in a less advantageous location still.

The shape of the average cost curve thus depends on two things: how long the economies of scale persist, and how quickly the diseconomies of scale occur as output rises.

The lowest output at which all scale economies are achieved is called **minimum efficient scale**.

In heavy manufacturing industries economies of scale are substantial. At low outputs, average costs are much higher than at minimum efficient scale. High fixed costs of research and development need to be spread over large output to reduce average costs. Hence, large markets are needed to allow low costs to be attained.

High transport costs used to mean that markets were small. For industries with large fixed costs, this meant that average costs were high. Globalization is partly a response to a dramatic fall in transport costs. By selling in bigger markets, some firms can enjoy large-scale economies and lower average costs.

In other industries, minimum efficient scale occurs at a low output. Any higher output raises average cost again. There is a limit to a hairdresser's daily output. A larger market makes little difference. Globalization has not had a big impact on hairdressing; but the Internet has always been global – admitting another user to Google hardly costs anything at all. Almost all the costs are fixed costs, the costs of setting up the website in the first place. Marginal cost is very low. And average cost falls as more users are admitted and the fixed costs are spread across more and more users.

We begin by discussing the output decision of a firm with a U-shaped average cost curve. Then we show how to amend this analysis when firms face significant economies of scale.

---

[1] Some textbooks refer to these as fixed costs, because they must be paid anyway. We prefer to call them overhead costs, reserving the term 'fixed costs' for those which cannot be varied in the short run but could be altered if there is sufficient time to adjust production methods. In contrast, overhead costs have to be paid by any firm that remains in business, no matter how long it has to adjust.

Box 5-2

Scale economies, sharing platforms and dancing with the devil

The job of competitors is to compete with one another. Yet increasingly we see examples of firms, supposedly in competition, developing co-operative agreements for some of their activities. What lies behind this is often the search for economies of scale.

Car makers have long collaborated on vehicle engines or the car chassis, in order to share expensive costs of R&D and spread them over greater total sales, thereby reducing the cost per car. Recent examples include agreements between Peugeot Citroën and Toyota to share components of a city car – simultaneously sold as the Peugeot 107, the Toyota Aygo and the Citroen C1; between BMW and Fiat to share costs on the platform for the Mini and the Alfa Romeo MiTo; and between Nissan and Renault to share the new platform for the Renault Modus, Renault Clio, Nissan Cube and Nissan Micro.

So prevalent are these agreements in the motor industry, driven by the need for scale economies, especially in the volume car business in which brand and design are a little less important than value for money, that it is increasingly the case that producers either have to forge such links with rivals or else themselves be a massive global producer (such as Ford or VW) where these scale economies can be achieved within the company itself. The days of small, or even medium-sized, independent producers are over, except in niche markets such as sports cars.

A similar example is the proliferation of airline networks, such as *Star Alliance* (including Air Canada, Air China, Lufthansa, Singapore Airlines, United Airlines) and *One World Alliance* (including BA, Cathay Pacific, Iberia, Japan Airlines and Qantas). In part this again entails sharing expensive platforms – new customer reservation systems to handle airline bookings, for example – to enjoy scale economies but it also provides a mechanism for eliminating wasteful duplication and wasteful competition. Instead of all these airlines feeling obliged to operate a route on which they will have half empty planes, a single flight can simultaneously be badged with the flight details of several members within an alliance, allowing that plane to operate much closer to full capacity while leaving each member airline able to claim it offers a wide range of routes on its service.

These examples all entail co-operation between firms at a similar stage in the chain of production, what one might call co-operation between producers making substitute products for one another. They co-operate in some dimensions and then compete like crazy on other dimensions.

Such co-operation has the potential to be in the social interest when it allows society access to services or products at lower cost than could be supplied by an individual company acting alone. However, regulators have to watch out for such alliances merely becoming a vehicle for co-operative price fixing by firms, raising profit margins by negotiating away competition without having any offsetting benefit in cost reduction.

During the last decade, there has been increasing co-operation between logistics giants such as parcel-delivery companies DHL and UPS. For example, UPS, which had some excess capacity in its American air-freight network, carried DHL's packages on its planes inside the US – and between the US, Canada and Mexico – thereby earning from DHL a fee of up to $1 billion a year. This practice then proliferated across companies and regions. In 2012, the EU concluded that some of these arrangements were merely cartels to fix prices at unnecessarily high levels. It concluded that

CHAPTER 5: Costs, supply and perfect competition

there had been a 'gardening club' in which the names of vegetables such asparagus and courgettes were used as code words by the price fixers. The Commission fined 13 firms, including UPS, a total of €169 million. Interestingly, DHL, which blew the whistle, was let off the fine.

Co-operation deals among rivals are tricky because firms need to be very clear about what will and will not be covered by them. For example, newspapers differentiate themselves by their editorial content and the quality of their advertising-sales operations. Editorial and advertising departments of rival papers must be kept separate if they are to retain their distinctive identities. But distribution, printing and back-office operations may be easier to consolidate without blurring brands.

Average cost and marginal cost

As output rises, average cost falls whenever marginal cost is below average cost; average cost rises whenever marginal cost is above average cost. Hence average cost is lowest at the output Q^* at which LAC and LMC cross. Figure 5-4 illustrates.

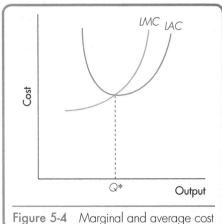

Figure 5-4   Marginal and average cost

This relation between average and marginal is a matter of arithmetic, as relevant to football as to production. Suppose Wayne Rooney scores 3 goals in his first 3 games, thus averaging 1 goal per game. Two goals in the next game, implying 5 goals from 4 games, raises the average to 1.25 goals per game. In the fourth game the marginal score of 2 goals exceeded the average score of 1 goal in previous games, thus raising the average. But if Wayne had not scored in the fourth game (a marginal score of 0), this would have dragged down his average per game from 1 (3 goals in 3 games) to 0.75 (3 goals in 4 games).

Similarly, when the marginal cost of making the next unit of output exceeds the average cost of making the existing units, making another unit *must* raise average cost. Conversely, if the marginal cost of the next unit is below the average cost of existing units, another unit *must* reduce average cost. When marginal and average cost are equal, making another unit leaves average cost unchanged.

Hence, in Figure 5-4, average and marginal cost curves cross at minimum average cost. At outputs below Q^*, LMC is below LAC, so average cost is falling. Above Q^*, LMC is above LAC, so average cost is rising. At output Q^*, average costs are at a minimum. As in Wayne's world, this relation rests purely on arithmetic.

Box 5-3

Scale economies and the Internet

Producing information products such as films, music and news programmes has a high fixed cost, but distributing these products digitally has almost a zero marginal cost and no capacity constraint. Scale economies are vast. Moreover, if marginal cost is close to zero, smart suppliers will price their products so that marginal revenue is also tiny.

EMI, a legend of the music industry, was formed in 1931. Its Abbey Road studios in London hosted giants such as the Beatles, at one time making it the fourth-largest record label and one of the top 100 companies on which the FTSE stock market index was based. Competition from Internet downloads gradually undercut this business completely. In 2011, deep in debt, it was taken over by the US bank Citigroup, which then sought to break up EMI and sell it off in pieces to consortia led by Sony, Vivendi and others.

The viable surviving parts of the business operate largely online, with records and CDs becoming obsolete.

The firm's long-run output decision

We can now describe how a firm chooses its output level in the long run. This is a two-part decision. First, the firm evaluates its marginal cost and marginal revenue, thereby telling the firm the best output at which to produce in the long run. It should produce the output at which $LMC = MR$. If marginal revenue exceeds marginal cost at any particular output, the firm is still making a marginal profit by producing more, and should therefore raise production. If marginal cost exceeds marginal revenue, the firm has made a marginal loss on the last unit of production and should produce less. Only when marginal revenue equals marginal cost is there no scope to increase operating profits by changing the output level. The marginal condition tells us the best positive output level for maximizing profit, namely, where marginal revenue equals marginal cost.

However, the firm also has to check that it should be in business at all. Given that it has chosen the most advantageous output level, is it making profits at this output? Or does it make losses at every output level, in which case the marginal condition has merely identified the least bad output to produce? It might be even better to give up completely and eventually make zero rather than lose money forever.

Suppose Q^{**} is the output at which $LMC = MR$. If, at this output, the price for which this output can be sold (which we deduce from the demand curve) exceeds the average cost LAC of making this output, the firm is making permanent profits and should remain in the industry. However, if at the 'best' output Q^{**} the firm is losing money because LAC exceeds the price for which Q^{**} can be sold, the firm is better off by closing down completely.

Notice the two-stage argument. First we use the *marginal condition* ($LMC = MR$) to find the best output, *then* we use the *average condition* (comparing LAC at this output with the price or average revenue) to determine if the best output is good enough for the firm to stay in business in the long run. If the firm's best output yields losses, it should close down.

It is important to realize that the best output Q^{**} is not, in general, the same as the output Q^* in Figure 5-4 at which long-run average costs are minimized. Figure 5-4 is purely an analysis of costs. What the firm wishes to do depends both on costs and revenues. If demand is strong enough, it is profitable to produce more than the minimum efficient scale Q^* because at this output level there are still further profits to be exploited by producing even more. Conversely, demand may be so weak that the firm chooses to produce less than minimum efficient scale. Any attempt to produce more would drive prices down too much. The

CHAPTER 5: Costs, supply and perfect competition

Table 5-1   A firm's supply decisions

Output decision	Marginal condition: output at which	Produce this output unless
Short run	$MR = SMC$	$P <$ *Short-run average variable cost*; if it is, shut down temporarily
Long run	$MR = LMC$	$P < LAC$; if it is, quit permanently

firm would lose more from lower prices than it would gain from being able to reduce average costs. This completes our analysis of the supply decision, as demonstrated in Table 5-1.

Short-run and long-run costs

Even if losing money in the short run, a firm will stay in business if it at least covers its variable costs. In the long run it must cover all its costs to stay in business. A firm may reduce its costs in the long run, converting a short-run loss into a long-term profit. In the short run, its technique of production is fixed and it has some fixed inputs to production. In the long run, it can vary everything.

The firm will only wish to vary things where, by doing so, costs are reduced and hence profitability is increased.

Case study 5-1   Gone today but steel here tomorrow

Thirty years ago, British Steel was a state-owned monopoly, selling largely in the UK. Then the firm was privatized and its market became global, in which British Steel was a relatively small player. It merged with a Dutch steel maker to form a new company, Corus, which also failed, and was then taken over by an Indian company, Tata Steel.

© Alistair Forrester Shankie

Despite all these changes, the UK plants struggled to break even. Partly, as with the car industry in Detroit, this reflected globalization. UK labour costs in steel manufacture are now six times those in Brazil and ten times those in India. If the UK wishes to be a high-wage producer within the global economy, it needs either to have massive investment to make UK factories ultra-modern and technically sophisticated or else to recognize that more basic production will be undertaken in lower-wage countries than the UK. The industry tried to move into niche hi-tech steel, which entailed shutting down more basic capacity that was being outcompeted by cheaper producers abroad.

As competitive pressures mounted, the UK steel industry faced the classic choice: undertake expensive investment to restore competitiveness, shut down temporarily and hope for better demand conditions in the future, or exit the industry in order to avoid making permanent losses. If you had been a shareholder, would you have thought it worth contributing more money in the hope of saving the business, or concluded that it was more prudent to contract, saving your money for other, more profitable ventures with a greater prospect of international success?

Whoever owned the UK steel industry, they always concluded that it needed to shrink yet further to become commercially viable. Even Tata Steel, a huge global success, concluded that further parts of the UK steel industry needed to be closed. This was not just a cyclical decision reflecting temporary recession, but a longer-run view that UK costs did not justify the major investment needed for ongoing success.

Just when Teesside had almost given up hope of retaining its steel-making economy, SSI Industries of Thailand re-opened the plant in April 2012, having bought the Teesside Cast Products plant from Tata for £400 million in 2010. The plant will produce steel slabs for export to Thailand.

How market structure affects competition

We now explore how market structures differ in the type of competition they exhibit, and how this relates to the underlying determinants of cost and demand. We begin by looking at different types of competition.

> A **perfectly competitive** firm faces a horizontal demand curve at the going market price. It is a price-taker.

A perfectly competitive firm is insignificant relative to the market demand that it faces. Its output decisions have no effect on the price that it faces.

Perfect competition is a useful benchmark, and represents one extreme in the spectrum of possible market structures. What determines the structure of a particular market? Why are there 10 000 florists but only a handful of chemical producers? How does the structure of an industry affect the behaviour of its constituent firms?

In any market structure other than perfect competition, each firm faces a downward-sloping demand curve for its product and is therefore an *imperfectly competitive* firm.

> An **imperfectly competitive** firm recognizes that its demand curve slopes down. To sell more of its own output, it needs to reduce its own price.

Within this general category are three particular examples.

> For a **pure monopoly**, the demand curve for the firm is the industry demand curve itself. There is only one firm in the industry and it has no fear of entry by others.

CHAPTER 5: Costs, supply and perfect competition

Table 5-2   Market structure

Form of competition	Number of firms	Ability to affect price	Entry barrier	Example
Perfect competition	Many	Nil	None	Fruit stall
Imperfect competition				
Monopolistic competition	Many	Small	None	Corner shop
Oligopoly	Few	Medium	Some	Cars
Pure monopoly	One	Large	Huge	Post Office

An industry with **monopolistic competition** has many sellers making products that are close but not perfect substitutes for one another. Each firm then has a limited ability to affect its output price.

Between these two lies **oligopoly**, an industry with only a few, interdependent producers.

Table 5-2 offers an overview of market structure. As with most definitions, the distinctions can get a little blurred. How do we define the relevant market? Was British Gas a monopoly in gas or an oligopolist in energy? Is Network Rail a monopoly in train lines or an oligopolist in transport infrastructure competing, for example, with the British Airports Authority?

We also have to be careful about the relevant definition of the market. When a small country trades in a competitive world market, even the sole domestic producer may have little influence on market price, which may be determined in the world market.

Why market structures differ

We now develop a general theory of how the economic factors of demand and cost interact to determine the likely structure of each industry. The car industry is not an oligopoly one day but perfectly competitive the next. It is long-run influences that induce different market structures. In the long run, one firm can hire another's workers and learn its technical secrets. In the long run, all firms or potential entrants to an industry essentially have similar cost curves.

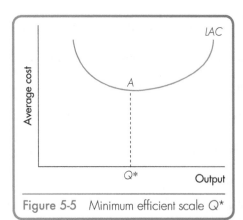

Figure 5-5   Minimum efficient scale Q^*

Earlier in this chapter, we discussed minimum efficient scale, *MES*, the lowest output at which a firm's long-run average cost curve bottoms out. This is shown as the output Q^* in Figure 5-5.

When *MES* is tiny relative to the size of the market, the industry demand curve is drawn a long way to the right in Figure 5-5. There is room for lots of little firms, each producing Q^* but trivial relative to the output of the whole industry – a good approximation to perfect competition. Conversely, when *MES* occurs at an output nearly as large as the entire market – imagine drawing a demand curve only just to the right of point *A* in Figure 5-5 – there is room for only one firm. A second firm trying to squeeze into the remaining space would have room only to produce a small output; but then its *LAC* curve would imply much higher average costs because it enjoys inadequate scale economies. So there is no room for a second firm to enter and make a profit. A natural monopoly enjoys sufficient scale economies to have no fear of entry by others.

When *MES* occurs at, say, a quarter of the market size as reflected by the position of the demand curve, the industry is an oligopoly, with each firm taking a keen interest in the behaviour of its small number of rivals.

Monopolistic competition lies midway between oligopoly and perfect competition. There is room for many small firms but, unlike perfect competition, the firms are not identical to one another. Each corner shop is slightly closer to some customers than others. So each small firm has a little scope to affect the price it charges for its products.

Market structure thus reflects the interaction of two things: the shape and position of long-run average cost curves (and in particular the output corresponding to minimum efficient scale for a single firm) and the size of the market (as determined by the output levels consistent with the industry demand curve as a whole). Together, these determine how many firms are likely to survive in the industry and hence the type of competition that will then take place between them.

Perfect competition is one end of this spectrum, with *MES* so small relative to industry demand that each firm is insignificant. Next we look at the opposite case, in which only a single firm can survive.

Box 5-4

Facing the music

Operating in every major music market, three firms now dominate the global music industry – Sony Bertelsmann, Vivendi SA and AOL Time Warner. Each of the three (a) owns a large collection of labels that were formerly independent companies, and (b) also operates in other aspects of entertainment such as publishing or telecommunications.

Why are there so few companies in the global music business? Because most of it is now digital and the marginal cost of connecting another user is tiny, whereas the fixed costs of developing playlists are large. These costs are independent of the subsequent number of users. This is a classic case in which economies of scale are huge. There is no point being a small producer. Actually, life is not that easy for the giants either: the value of the global recorded music market is falling every year because of price competition and endemic Internet piracy.

Global recorded music sales fell by almost 9 per cent in 2010 and a further 3 per cent in 2011 as digital piracy continued to take its toll on the industry, with the UK overtaken by Germany as the second-largest music market after 'physical' sales of CDs collapsed by almost a fifth. Global recorded music revenues fell by £10 billion in 2011, according to the annual report by the IFPI, which represents the international music industry.

Digital revenues grew by 8 per cent year-on-year to account for 31 per cent of all recorded music revenues. However, the growth of digital is impeded by piracy and winning consumers over to legal download models.

Sources: bbcworldservice.com; www.guardian.co.uk

We conclude this chapter by studying the case of perfect competition in more detail. In the next chapter we explore the various types of imperfect competition.

Perfect competition

The previous two sections have explored how costs vary in the short run and in the long run, and how the firm therefore chooses whether to supply any output and, if so, what quantity of output is best. Throughout this analysis of costs and supply, we treated demand conditions as given.

We now switch our attention from costs to demand and revenue, for which we need to know about the structure of the industry in which the firm operates.

An **industry** is the set of all firms making the same product.

The output of an industry is the sum of the outputs of its firms. Yet different industries have very different numbers of firms. The UK has thousands of florists but only one producer of nuclear energy. We begin with perfect competition, a hypothetical benchmark against which to assess other market structures.

In **perfect competition**, actions of individual buyers and sellers have no effect on the market price.

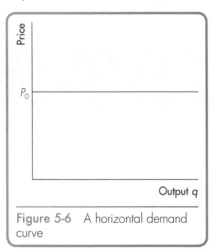

Figure 5-6   A horizontal demand curve

This industry has many buyers and many sellers. Each firm in a perfectly competitive industry faces a horizontal demand curve, shown in Figure 5-6. Whatever output q the firm sells, it gets exactly the market price P_0, and the tiny firm can sell as much as it wants at this price. If it charges more than P_0, the firm loses all its customers. If it charges less than P_0, it attracts all the vast number of customers of other firms. This horizontal demand curve is *the* crucial feature of a perfectly competitive firm. We sometimes say such a firm is a *price-taker*. It has to treat the market price as given, independent of any decisions made by the individual firm. Next time you visit a fruit market, in which there are many stalls selling identical onions, you can think of each stall as a price-taker in the market for onions.

For each firm to face a horizontal demand curve, the industry must have four characteristics. First, there must be many firms, each trivial relative to the industry as a whole. Second, the firms must make a standardized product, so that buyers immediately switch from one firm to another if there is any difference in the prices of different firms. Thus, all firms make essentially the same product, *for which they all charge the same price.*

Why don't all the firms in the industry do what OPEC did, collectively restricting supply to raise the market price of their output? A crucial characteristic of a perfectly competitive industry is *free entry and exit.* Even if existing firms could organize themselves to restrict total supply and drive up the market price, the consequent rise in revenues and profits would attract new firms into the industry, raising total supply and driving the price back down. Conversely, when firms in a perfectly competitive industry are losing money, some firms close down. This reduces total supply and drives the price up, allowing the remaining firms to survive.

The firm's supply decision

We have already developed a general theory of the supply decision of a firm. First, the firm uses the marginal condition ($MC = MR$) to find the best positive level of output; then it uses the average condition to check whether the price for which this output is sold covers average cost. *The special feature of perfect competition is the relationship between marginal revenue and price.* Facing a horizontal demand curve, a competitive firm does *not* bid down the price as it sells more units of output. Since there is no effect on the revenue from existing output, the marginal revenue from an additional unit of output *is* its price: $MR = P$.

The firm's short-run supply curve

Firms in any industry choose the output at which short-run marginal cost *SMC* equals marginal revenue *MR*. In perfect competition, *MR* always equals the price *P*. Hence, a competitive firm produces the output at which price equals marginal cost, then checks whether zero output is better.

Figure 5-7 illustrates the firm's supply decision in the short run. P_1 is the shutdown price below which the firm fails to cover variable costs in the short run. At all prices above P_1, the firm chooses output to make $P = SMC$.

> A competitive firm's **short-run supply curve** is that part of its short-run marginal cost curve above its shutdown price (the price that just covers its short-run average variable costs).

This shows how much the firm wants to make at each price it might be offered. For example, at a price P_4, the firm chooses to supply Q_4.

The firm's long-run supply curve

Similar reasoning applies in the long run. Figure 5-8 shows the firm's average and marginal costs in the long run. Facing a price P_4, equating price and long-run marginal cost, the firm chooses the long-run output Q_4 at point *D*. Here it makes profits, since it is earning a price P_4 in excess of its average cost; equivalently, its total revenue exceeds its total cost.

In the long run, the firm exits from the industry only if, at its best positive output, price fails to cover long-run average cost *LAC*. At price P_2, the marginal condition leads to point *B* in Figure 5-8, but the firm is losing money and leaves the industry in the long run.

A competitive firm's long-run supply curve is that part of its long-run marginal cost *above* minimum average cost. At any price below P_3, the firm leaves the industry. At price P_3, the firm makes Q_3 and just breaks even after paying all its economic costs.

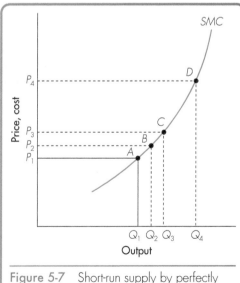

Figure 5-7 Short-run supply by perfectly competitive firm

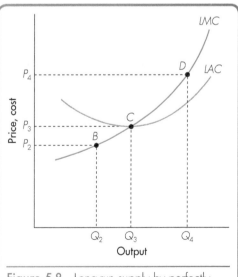

Figure 5-8 Long-run supply by perfectly competitive firm

CHAPTER 5: Costs, supply and perfect competition

Entry and exit

The price P_3 corresponding to the minimum point on the *LAC* curve is called the *entry or exit price*. There is no incentive to enter or leave the industry. The resources tied up in the firm are earning just as much as their opportunity costs – what they could earn elsewhere. Any price less than P_3 will induce the firm to exit from the industry in the long run.

Entry is when new firms join an industry. **Exit** is when existing firms leave.

We can also interpret Figure 5-8 as the decision facing a potential entrant to the industry. At a price P_3, an entrant could just cover its average cost if it produced an output Q_3. Any price above P_3 yields economic profits and induces entry by other firms in the long run.

Industry supply curves

A competitive industry comprises many firms. In the short run, two things are fixed: the quantity of fixed factors used by each firm, and the number of firms in the industry. In the long run, each firm can vary all its factors of production, but the number of firms can also change through entry and exit.

The short-run industry supply curve

Just as we can add individual demand curves by buyers to get the market demand curve, we can add the individual supply curves of firms to get the industry supply curve. In Figure 5-9, at each price we add together the quantities supplied by each firm to get the total quantity supplied at that price. In the short run, the number of firms in the industry is given. Suppose there are two firms, A and B. Each firm's short-run supply curve is the part of its *SMC* curve above its shutdown price. Firm A has a lower shutdown price than firm B, perhaps because it has modern machinery. Each firm's supply curve is horizontal up to its shutdown price. At a lower price, no output is supplied.

The industry supply curve is the horizontal sum of the separate supply curves. Between P_1 and P_2 only the lower-cost firm, A, is producing. At P_2, firm B starts to produce too. When there are many firms, each with a different shutdown price, there are many small discontinuities as we move up the industry supply curve. Since each firm in a competitive industry is trivial relative to the total, the industry supply curve is in effect smooth.

The long-run industry supply curve

As the market price rises, the total industry supply rises in the long run for two distinct reasons: each existing firm moves up its long-run supply curve, and new firms find it profitable to enter the industry.

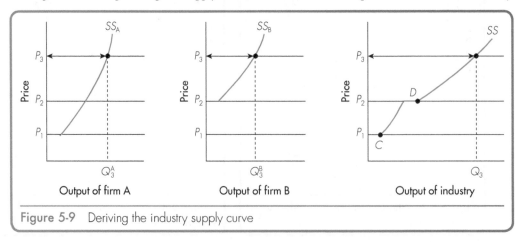

Figure 5-9   Deriving the industry supply curve

Thus, total quantity rises both because each existing firm makes additional output and because new firms enter the industry and produce. Conversely, at lower prices, all firms move down their long-run supply curves, producing less output because prices are lower, and some firms may also leave the industry because they can no longer break even at the lower prices.

At any price, the industry supply is the horizontal sum of the outputs produced by the number of firms in the industry at that price. Hence, the long-run supply curve is flatter than the short-run supply curve for two reasons: each firm can vary its factors more appropriately in the long run; and higher prices attract *extra* firms into the industry. Both raise the output response to a price increase.

For each firm, the height of the minimum point on its *LAC* curve shows the critical price at which it can just survive in the industry. If different firms have *LAC* curves of different heights, they face different exit prices. At any price, there is a marginal firm only just able to survive in the industry, and a marginal potential entrant just waiting to enter if only the price rises a little.

The *long-run* industry supply curve normally slopes up, but in one special case it is horizontal. Suppose all existing firms and potential entrants have *identical cost curves*. In particular, they have the same long-run average cost curves *LAC* and thus the same price, shown as P_3 in Figure 5-8, at which they will enter or exit the industry in the long run. In this special case, if the market price ever exceeds P_3, new firms will enter the industry since they can make profits at any price above P_3. This flood of new entrants creates extra output, reduces scarcity and bids down equilibrium prices until the price reverts to P_3, at which price there is no longer any incentive for firms to enter the industry. Conversely, if the price ever falls below this critical price, firms leave the industry, which makes output scarcer and raises the equilibrium price, until prices rise again to P_3, at which price there is no longer any pressure on firms to leave the industry.

Thus, in the long run, if all firms face identical cost curves, industry supply entails each individual firm producing at the output corresponding to the bottom of its average cost curve, and changes in industry output would be entirely accomplished by changes in the number of firms, via entry and exit. The industry supply curve in the long run is then *horizontal* at price P_3 corresponding to minimum average cost.

But this is a very special case. Normally, firms will have slightly different cost curves from one another for a whole host of reasons – differences in location, in expertise and knowledge, and in materials. Perfect competition does not require that firms are identical, merely that each firm is tiny relative to the market as a whole. Once firms are different, there is no possibility of expanding industry output indefinitely merely by attracting yet more of these identical firms.

On the plausible assumption that the lowest-cost producers are *already* in the market, inducing a rise in the quantity that an industry supplies generally requires higher prices, for two reasons: to induce existing firms to move along upward-sloping *LMC* curves and to attract new firms able at least to break even now that prices are higher than previously. Saying that higher prices are needed to induce the industry to supply more output is just to say that the industry supply curve slopes upwards.

Equilibrium in a competitive industry

Although each individual firm faces a horizontal demand curve for its output, the industry as a whole faces a downward-sloping demand curve for its total output. People will only buy a larger total quantity if the price is lower. To induce people as a whole to buy more flowers from flower stalls, the price of flowers needs to fall. Only then will romantic partners buy fewer boxes of chocolates and instead take home more roses for Valentine's Day.

Industry demand obeys the general laws of demand that we discussed in Chapter 2. Having now also discussed the industry supply curve, we can examine how supply and demand determine equilibrium price in the short run and the long run in a perfectly competitive industry.

In short-run equilibrium, the market price equates the quantity demanded to the total quantity supplied by the given number of firms in the industry when each firm produces on its short-run supply curve. In long-run equilibrium, the market price equates the quantity demanded to the total quantity supplied by the number of firms in the industry when each firm produces on its long-run supply curve. Since firms

CHAPTER 5: Costs, supply and perfect competition

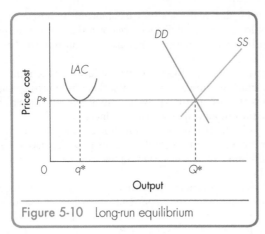

Figure 5-10   Long-run equilibrium

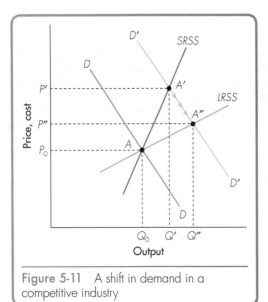

Figure 5-11   A shift in demand in a competitive industry

can freely enter or exit from the industry, the marginal firm must make only normal profits so that there is no further incentive for entry or exit.

Figure 5-10 shows long-run equilibrium for the industry. Demand is *DD* and supply is *SS*. At the equilibrium price P^*, the industry as a whole produces Q^*. This is the sum of the output of each tiny producer. At price P^*, the marginal firm is making q^* at minimum *LAC* and just breaks even. There is no incentive to enter or exit.

A rise in costs

Beginning from this equilibrium, suppose a rise in the price of raw materials raises costs for all firms in the industry. The average cost curve of every firm shifts up. The marginal firm is now losing money at the old price, P^*. Some firms eventually leave the industry. With fewer firms left, the industry supply curve *SS* shifts to the left. With less supply, the equilibrium price rises. When enough firms have left, and industry output falls enough, higher prices allow the new marginal firm to break even, despite an upward shift in *LAC*. Further incentives for entry or exit disappear.

Notice two points about the change in the long-run equilibrium that higher costs induce. First, the rise in average costs is eventually passed on to the consumer in higher prices. Second, since higher prices reduce the total quantity demanded, industry output must fall.

A rise in industry demand

The previous example discussed only long-term effects. We can of course discuss short-run effects as well. And we can examine changes in demand as well as changes in cost and supply. Figure 5-11 illustrates the effect of a shift up in the industry's demand curve from *DD* to *D'D'*.

The industry begins in long-run equilibrium at *A*. Overnight, each firm has some fixed inputs, and the number of firms is fixed. Horizontally adding their short-run supply curves (the portion of their marginal cost curves above the shutdown price), we get the short-run industry supply curve *SRSS*. The new short-run equilibrium is at *A'*. When demand first rises, it needs a big price rise to induce individual firms to move up their steep short-run supply curves, along which some inputs are fixed.

In the long run, firms adjust all factors and move on to their flatter long-run supply curves. In addition, economic profits attract extra firms into the industry. The new long-run equilibrium is at *A''*. Relative to *A'* there is a further expansion of total output, but, with a more appropriate choice of inputs and the entry of new firms, extra supply reduces the market-clearing price.

Case study 5-2 — Globalization and potential competition make firms price takers

The key feature of perfect competition is that each individual producer understands that it cannot affect the price by its production decisions. So what are these industries populated by trivially small firms? Some service industries provide good examples. There are no haircut hypermarkets. Most hairdressers are small because the technology does not yield large-scale producers any cost advantage. Because each operates on a small scale, but the market in the aggregate is large, each is therefore small relative to the market as a whole.

Perfect competitors can be producers of goods as well as services. There are also lots of small sheep farmers, each with a small patch of hillside, and lots of car washes, each having to charge similar prices.

Farms cultivating wheat usually operate on a much larger scale nowadays. If there were only 100 UK wheat farmers, would this mean that they would no longer be price takers? Each is surely large enough to affect the price of UK wheat. Does this mean that wheat should not be viewed as a perfectly competitive industry? This argument would make sense if the UK did not trade with the rest of the world. But, for the national economy, international trade is increasing all the time, as shown in the table below.

Imports as percentage of national output	1967	2012
Belgium	36	79
Netherlands	43	72
UK	18	31
France	14	30

Source: OECD, Economic Outlook

UK firms have to compete not just with other UK firms but also with foreign firms who actually export to the UK or would like to do so. Potential entrants to the UK market are not only UK firms but foreign firms that can sell to UK consumers not merely by building factories in the UK but simply by exporting goods from their factories abroad.

In theory, we could have a situation in which the entire UK market is supplied by a single UK firm but that firm is still a price taker, and has no effect on UK prices at all. Suppose the whole of Norfolk became a giant wheat field supplying wheat to every UK bakery. If this superfarm thinks it faces no competition, it will be tempted to raise prices in order to make larger profits. It will try to do to wheat what OPEC did to oil: harvest a little less, make the good more scarce, force up the price (as with oil, the demand for wheat is inelastic – we all need our daily bread). So the superfarm has a small bonfire of its wheat crop to make the remaining wheat scarce. Imagine its disappointment when it subsequently discovers that high wheat prices then induce a flood of wheat imports as French and German farmers see profitable opportunities to sell their wheat in the UK!

Perhaps in the original situation, the UK superfarm faced only slightly cheaper costs of supplying the UK market than the costs faced by French and German farmers. For example, the only difference arose from the slightly higher transport costs of bringing wheat through the Channel Tunnel. Once UK wheat prices rise by more than the initial cost advantage of UK producers, suddenly there is a flood of new supply from abroad.

CHAPTER 5: Costs, supply and perfect competition

The more globalization takes place – national markets are increasingly integrated into a single world market – the more the relevant definition of the market is that global market itself and the prices that prevail in that market. We may therefore see situations in which even large UK firms have little ability to affect the price of their output because these firms are tiny *relative to the world market that sets the price*.

The fact that a UK firm looks large relative to the size of the UK market may not be an indication that the industry cannot be perfectly competitive. When products are standardized and can be shipped relatively easily (and therefore cheaply) from one country to another, national prices may in fact be set by international market forces.

UK firms drilling for oil in the North Sea do not set the world price of oil, nor do UK coal miners set the world price of coal. Whenever a commodity is easily traded internationally, it is in the world market that the price is set. American and Chinese supply may affect world prices, but in most cases the output from a small country such as the UK has a negligible effect on the price.

Some commodities, such as concrete, are so expensive to transport – relative to their intrinsic value, that the relevant market is much more localized. It is then important to think about the number of *domestic* firms in relation to the size of the domestic market. Similarly, although there are lots of golf courses in the UK, most people do not want to drive 400 miles for a weekend golf game. Again, the market is more localized. Learning to judge the size of the relevant market is one of the skills you will develop as you read this book.

Recap

- The main production inputs are labour, capital, land, raw materials and energy. Land is supplied by nature and often treated as fixed in quantity. Capital is the input previously produced by people, and not used up during the current production process to which it is an input. Raw materials are used up during the production process to which they are an input. Labour is the service provided by use of workers.
- The short run is the period in which some inputs are fixed but some (especially labour, but perhaps also energy and raw materials) are variable. The production technique may also be fixed in the short run. In the long run, all input quantities and the choice of production technique can be varied if the firm wishes.
- The short-run marginal cost curve (*SMC*) rises because of diminishing returns to the variable input as output rises. Diminishing returns arise because more and more of the variable input(s) must be added to given quantities of the fixed input(s).
- Short-run total cost is short-run fixed cost + short-run variable cost. Hence, short-run average cost is short-run average fixed cost + short-run average variable cost, since in each case we simply divide the relevant total cost by the same output level.
- The firm sets output in the short run to equate *SMC* and *MR*, provided price covers short-run average variable cost. In the short run, the firm may produce at a loss if it recoups part of its fixed costs. Otherwise, it shuts down temporarily.

Recap

- In the long run, a firm can adjust all its inputs. In the short run, some inputs are fixed.
- The long-run total cost curve is the cheapest way to make each output level, when all inputs and the production technique are adjusted. It depends on technology and input prices. Technology is the set of all production techniques currently known.
- Average cost is total cost divided by output. The long-run average cost curve *LAC* is typically U-shaped. There are economies of scale on the falling bit of the U. The rising part reflects diseconomies of scale. Where the curve is horizontal, there are constant returns to scale and average cost is neither rising nor falling as output increases.
- When marginal cost is below average cost, average cost is falling. When marginal cost is above average cost, average cost is rising. Average and marginal cost are equal only at the lowest point on the average cost curve.
- In the long run, the firm supplies the output at which long-run marginal cost *LMC* equals *MR* provided price covers *LAC* at that output. If price is lower, the firm goes out of business.
- Market structure refers to the relative size of minimum efficient scale and the total size of the market as reflected by the position of the industry demand curve.
- Market structure is also affected by the shapes of these curves. The steeper the industry demand curve, the more an entrant's extra output will bid down the price, making it harder to enter; and the steeper the *LAC* curve at outputs below minimum efficient scale, the harder it is for an entrant to enter and produce a small output.
- In an imperfectly competitive industry, each firm faces a downward-sloping demand curve. The more output it produces, the lower the price it receives.
- In a perfectly competitive industry, each buyer and seller is a price taker, and cannot affect the market price.
- Perfect competition is most plausible when a large number of firms make a standard product, there is free entry to and exit from the industry, and customers can easily verify that the products of different firms really are the same.
- For a competitive firm, marginal revenue and price coincide. Output is chosen to equate price to marginal cost. The firm's supply curve is its *SMC* curve above its short-run average variable cost. At any lower price, the firm temporarily shuts down. In the long run, the firm's supply curve is that part of its *LMC* curve above its *LAC* curve. At any lower price, the firm exits the industry.
- Adding, at each price, the quantities supplied by each firm, we get the industry supply curve. It is flatter in the long run both because each firm can fully adjust all factors and because the number of firms in the industry can vary.
- A rise in demand leads to a large price increase, but only a small rise in quantity. Existing firms move up their steep *SMC* curves. Price exceeds average costs. Profits attract new entrants. In the long run, output rises further but the price falls back a bit. In the long-run equilibrium, the marginal firm breaks even and there is no further change in the number of firms in the industry.
- A rise in costs for all firms reduces the industry's output and raises the price. In the long run, a higher price is needed to allow the firm that is now the marginal firm to break even. The price rise is achieved by exit from the industry, and a reduction in industry supply.

Review questions

To check your answers to these questions, go to pages 379–81.

1 (a) Is it sufficient for a firm to know the set of available production techniques?
(b) What other information is needed to run a firm?

2 (a) Why might scale economies exist? (b) The table below shows some production techniques. The cost of a worker is £5. A unit of capital costs £2. Complete the table and calculate the least-cost way to make 4, 8 and 12 units of output. (c) Are there increasing, constant or decreasing returns to scale in this output range? Which applies where?

Units of	Method 1	Method 2	Method 3	Method 4	Method 5	Method 6
Labour input	5	6	10	12	15	16
Capital input	4	2	7	4	11	8
Output	4	4	8	8	12	12
Total cost						
Average cost						

3 Suppose the cost of capital rises from 2 to 3 in the question above. (a) Would the firm change its method of production for any levels of output? Say which, if any. (b) How do the firm's total and average costs change when the cost of capital rises?

4 From the total cost curve shown below, calculate marginal and average cost at each output. Are these short-run or long-run cost curves? How can you tell?

Output	0	1	2	3	4	5	6	7	8
Total cost	12	25	40	51	60	70	84	105	128

5 Why does a marginal cost curve always pass through the minimum point on the average cost curve?

6 Why are these statements wrong? (a) Firms making losses should quit at once. (b) Big firms can always produce more cheaply than smaller firms. (c) Small is always beautiful.

7 The domestic economy has only one firm, but faces a flood of imports from abroad if it tries to charge more than the world price. Is this firm perfectly competitive?

8 Suppose an industry of identical competitive firms has a technical breakthrough that cuts costs for all firms. What happens in the short run and the long run? Explain for both the firm and the industry.

9   If every firm is a price taker, who changes the price when a shift in demand causes initial disequilibrium?

10 Which industry has a more elastic long-run supply curve: coal mining or hairdressing? Why?

11 Suppose average cost falls whenever output is increased, no matter how large output becomes. Draw the average and marginal cost curves. Does marginal cost pass through the point of minimum average cost? How many firms do you expect to find in such an industry? Explain your answer.

12 You observe a competitive industry that has been in equilibrium for a long time. (a) What is happening to the price and total quantity produced? (b) You now observe a large fall in the price accompanied by a small reduction in quantity; some time later, the price partially recovers but output falls even more. In terms of supply and demand curves, what happened?

13 Since Ford and Vauxhall are very competitive with one another, should we view them as perfectly competitive firms?

14 Why are these statements wrong? (a) Since competitive firms break even in the long run, there is no incentive to be a competitive firm. (b) Competition prevents firms passing on cost increases.

15 **Essay question** 'Globalization means a larger market, less market power, and hence the increasing relevance of the economist's model of perfect competition.' Do you agree? What might prevent perfect competition being established in all industries?

16 **Essay question** If firms in a competitive industry make only normal profits, why is there any incentive to invest in research and development in such industries?

Online Learning Centre

To help you grasp the key concepts of this chapter check out the extra resources posted on the Online Learning Centre at www.mcgraw-hill.co.uk/textbooks/begg.

There are additional case studies, self-test questions, practice exam questions with answers and a graphing tool.

Imperfect competition

Learning outcomes

By the end of this chapter, you should be able to:

- Define and distinguish forms of imperfect competition
- Analyse pure monopoly
- Discuss how a monopolist chooses output
- Compare this output with that in a competitive industry
- Show how a monopolist's ability to price discriminate affects output and profits
- Define and analyse monopolistic competition

- Explain the tension between collusion and competition within a cartel
- Explain oligopoly and interdependence
- Analyse games between interdependent firms
- Define commitment and credibility
- Show why there is little market power in a contestable market
- Distinguish innocent entry barriers and strategic entry barriers

In the previous chapter, we explored the costs faced by a firm, how these interact with its demand curve to determine the output decision of the firm, and how cost structure and market demand determine the degree of competition in a market. In particular, we then analysed the case of perfect competition in which each firm believes that it has no effect on the price of its output and therefore acts as a price taker.

We now discuss all the other forms of competition, in which firms believe they face a downward-sloping demand curve and therefore have to assess how their marginal revenue differs from the price that they face, because additional output bids down the price received on all previous units of output.

It is helpful to recall the different types of imperfect competition that we introduced in the previous chapter.

For a **pure monopoly**, the demand curve for the firm is the industry demand curve itself. There is only one firm in the industry and it has no fear of entry by others.

An industry with **monopolistic competition** has many sellers making products that are close but not perfect substitutes for one another. Each firm then has a limited ability to affect its output price.

Between these two lies **oligopoly**, an industry with only a few, interdependent producers.

We now analyse each of these in turn. The larger the output of minimum efficient scale (lowest point of long-run average cost curve), relative to the market size (output on the industry demand curve), the smaller will be the number of firms that the industry can support.

 ## Pure monopoly

The perfectly competitive firm is too small to worry about the effect of its own decisions on industry output. In contrast, a pure monopoly *is* the entire industry.

A **monopolist** is the sole supplier or potential supplier of the industry's output.

A sole national supplier need not be a monopoly. If it raises prices, it may face competition from imports or from domestic entrants to the industry. In contrast, a pure monopoly does *not* need to worry about competition from either existing firms or from firms that could enter.

Profit-maximizing output

To maximize profits, a monopolist chooses the output at which marginal revenue *MR* equals marginal cost *MC*, then checks that it is covering average costs. Figure 6-1 shows the average cost curve *AC* with its usual U-shape.

Marginal revenue *MR* lies below the downward-sloping demand curve *DD*. The monopolist recognizes that, to sell extra units, it has to lower the price, even for existing customers. The more units the firm is already making and selling, the more any price reduction to sell a new unit has the effect of depressing revenue earned on existing units produced. Hence, as we move to the right and output increases, the marginal revenue schedule lies increasingly below the demand curve. Indeed, marginal revenue can become negative. In cutting the price to sell an additional output unit, the firm can lose more revenue on existing units than it gains in revenue by being able to sell an extra unit.

It is implicit in this argument that the firm has to charge a single price to all purchasers, and therefore has to reduce the price for which existing units are sold in order to sell an extra unit by inducing buyers to move downwards along their demand curve. Later, we analyse what happens when the monopolist can charge different prices to different customers. Initially, however, we assume that this is impossible.

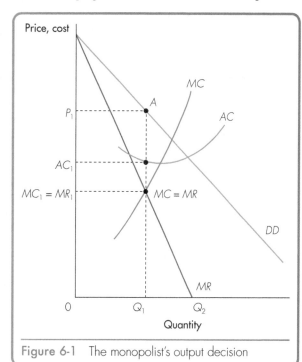

Figure 6-1   The monopolist's output decision

CHAPTER 6: Imperfect competition

Any firm maximizes profits choosing the output at which marginal revenue MR equals marginal cost MC. In Figure 6-1, the monopolist thus chooses the output Q_1. The demand curve DD implies that the monopolist sells Q_1 at a price P_1 per unit. Profit per unit is thus $[P_1 - AC_1]$, price minus average cost at the output Q_1. Total profit is the area $(P_1 - AC_1) \times Q_1$.

Even in the long run, the monopolist *continues* to make these monopoly profits. By ruling out the possibility of entry, we remove the mechanism by which profits are competed away in the long run by additional supply.

Price-setting

A competitive firm is a *price taker*, taking as given the price determined by supply and demand at the industry level. In contrast, the monopolist is a *price setter*. Having decided to make Q_1, the monopolist quotes a price P_1 knowing (from the demand curve) that the output Q_1 will be bought at this price.

When demand is elastic, lower prices increase revenue by raising quantity demanded a lot. When revenue rises, the marginal revenue from the extra output is positive. Conversely, when demand is inelastic, marginal revenue is negative. To raise output demanded, prices must be cut so much that total revenue falls.

To maximize profits, a monopolist sets $MC = MR$. Since MC is always positive, MR must also be positive at the profit-maximizing output. But this means that demand is elastic at this output. Hence, in Figure 6-1, the chosen output must lie to the left of Q_2. *A monopolist will never produce on the inelastic part of the demand curve where* MR *is negative, for then* MR *could not equal* MC, *which can never be negative.*

Monopoly power

At any output, price exceeds a monopolist's marginal revenue since the demand curve slopes down. In setting $MR = MC$, the monopolist sets a price above marginal cost. In contrast, a competitive firm equates price and marginal cost, since its price is also its marginal revenue. A competitive firm cannot raise price above marginal cost. It has no monopoly power.

Monopoly power is measured by price *minus* marginal cost at any output level.

Changes in profit-maximizing output

Figure 6-1 may also be used to analyse the effect of changes in costs or demand. Suppose higher input prices shift the MC and AC curves up. The higher MC curve must cross the MR curve at a lower output. The cost increase must reduce output. Since the demand curve slopes down, lower output induces a higher equilibrium price.

Similarly, with the original cost curves, an upward shift in demand and marginal revenue curves means that MR now crosses MC at a higher output. The monopolist raises output.

Monopoly versus competition

We now compare a perfectly competitive industry with a monopoly. Facing the same demand and cost conditions, how would the *same* industry behave if it organized as a competitive industry or as a monopoly? Cost differences are often the reason why some industries become competitive while others become monopolies. Only in special circumstances could the same industry be either perfectly competitive or a monopolist.

One case in which the comparison makes sense is when an industry has lots of *identical* firms. From Chapter 5 we know that, as a competitive industry, its long-run supply curve $LRSS$ is then horizontal. It can always expand or contract output by changing the number of firms, each producing at the bottom of its long-run average cost curve. If run as a competitive industry, long-run equilibrium occurs where this horizontal supply curve crosses the industry demand curve. In Figure 6-2 this occurs at A, where output is Q_C and the price is P_C.

Now suppose two things happen. The different firms come under a single co-ordinated decision maker, and all future entry is prohibited. Perhaps the industry is nationalized (but told to keep maximizing profits). Long-run costs, both marginal and average, are unaffected, but now the industry supremo recognizes that higher output bids down prices for everyone.

In the special example, *LRSS* is also the marginal cost of output expansion by the multi-plant monopolist. In the long run the cheapest way to raise output is to build more of the identical plants, each operated at minimum average cost. Hence, equating marginal cost and marginal revenue, the multi-plant monopoly produces at *B*. Output Q_M is lower under monopoly than competition, and the price P_M is higher than the competitive price P_C.

The monopolist cuts output in order to create scarcity and raise the equilibrium price. In Figure 6-2 average cost and marginal cost are equal, since each plant is at the bottom of its *LAC* curve, where it crosses *LMC*. Hence, the monopolist's profits are the rectangle $P_M P_C BF$.

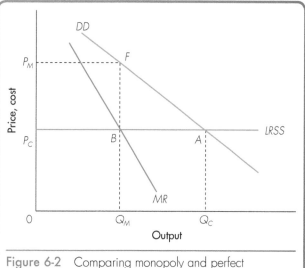

Figure 6-2 Comparing monopoly and perfect competition

Without fear of entry, the consequent profits last forever. Notice the crucial role of blocking competition from entrants. Without this, the attempt to restrict output to raise prices is thwarted by a flood of output from new entrants.

Box 6-1

Barriers at the checkout

When the Morrisons supermarket chain took over its rival Safeway, Morrisons was catapulted from the supermarket minnow, with a 6 per cent market share, to a big league player with 17 per cent of the UK market; only marginally less than Sainsbury's, one-time leader of the supermarket industry. Since the merger, Morrisons has continued to prosper.

The takeover of Safeway was contested, with Tesco, Asda and Sainsbury's all mounting rival bids to Morrisons'. At one stage, Philip Green, the owner of high-street retailer British Home Stores, also registered an interest in Safeway. Safeway was such an attractive target because it provided the last chance to enter the supermarket industry. Without

Market share of UK supermarket revenue, 2011	%
Tesco	31
Asda	17
Sainsbury's	16
Morrisons	12
Big 4	76

Source: 'Supermarkets: changing market share', 16 August 2011, www. guardian.co.uk

access to land sites, and facing difficulty getting planning permission for new supermarkets, the only way in which to become a successful supermarket chain was to enter the industry by taking over a chain that already had all the distribution outlets required. With Safeway in the hands of Morrisons, and the industry consolidated into large players, the next takeover will be that much more difficult. The entry barriers are steadily rising.

CHAPTER 6: Imperfect competition

If the abuse of monopoly power is not to be controlled by having more firms in competition, we need closer scrutiny of the conduct of the small number of powerful firms that remain in the industry. The UK Competition Commission has therefore taken an ongoing interest in monitoring aspects of their behavior to ensure that consumers get a reasonable deal.

Online grocery sales are also booming, and are expected to rise from 3 per cent of the market in 2011 to 6 per cent by 2016. IGD's *ShopperTrack* research found that, while 17 per cent of UK adults now shop online, 44 per cent intend to do so in the next five to ten years. The research also showed that online shopper loyalty was somewhat illusory, with 64 per cent buying from two or more online supermarkets and 47 per cent saying they would like to try another. Smartphone applications were expected to have the greatest impact on future shopping behaviour.

A key issue for competition will be whether the incumbent firms with the largest and best existing stores automatically dominate the online business as well. The table below shows that current web traffic is pretty highly correlated with grocery market share of sales from physical shops. To the extent this continues, there will remain a premium on the best high-street locations.

Grocery and alcohol websites ranked by share of UK visits

Rank	Website	Share of visits (%)
1 Tesco	www.tesco.com/groceries	21.25
2 ASDA	http://groceries.asda.com	11.46
3 Morrisons	www.morrisons.co.uk	9.95
4 Sainsbury's Online Groceries	www.sainsburys.co.uk/groceries	8.86
5 Waitrose	www.waitrose.com	5.94
6 ALDI UK	http://uk.aldi.com	5.69
7 Lidl UK	www.lidl.co.uk	5.01
8 mySupermarket.co.uk	www.mysupermarket.co.uk	4.50
9 Ocado	www.ocado.com	4.24
10 Tesco Wine	www.tesco.com/winestore	1.88
11 Hungry House	www.hungryhouse.co.uk	1.13
12 Milk and More	www.milkandmore.co.uk	0.99
13 Naked Wines	www.nakedwines.com	0.99
14 Waitrose Wine Direct	www.waitrosewine.com	0.94
15 Riverbed Organic Vegetables	www.riverbed.co.uk	0.93

Source: Experian Hitwise

We should also remember the effects of the recession, which are subtly changing the locational advantage of incumbents. First, squeezed households are trading down to budget supermarkets wherever they are located – hence the rise of ASDA, ALDI and Lidl. Second, as more and more shops in other retail sectors go bust and vacate the high street, opportunities to grab useful sites have become a little easier.

Source: www.Internetretailing.net

Discriminating monopoly

Thus far, all consumers were charged the same price. Unlike a competitive industry, where competition prevents any individual firm charging more than its competitors, a monopolist may be able to charge different prices to different customers.

A **discriminating monopoly** charges different prices to different buyers.

Consider an airline monopolizing flights between London and Rome. It has business customers whose demand curve is very inelastic. They have to fly. Their demand and marginal revenue curves are very steep. The airline also carries tourists, whose demand curve is much more elastic. If flights to Rome are too dear, tourists can visit Athens instead. Tourists have much flatter demand and marginal revenue curves.

The airline will charge the two groups *different* prices. Since tourist demand is elastic, the airline wants to charge tourists a low fare to increase tourist revenue. Since business demand is inelastic, the airline wants to charge business travellers a high fare to increase business revenue.

Profit-maximizing output will satisfy two separate conditions. First, business travellers with inelastic demand will pay a fare sufficiently higher than tourists with elastic demand that the marginal revenue from the two separate groups is equated. Then there is no incentive to rearrange the mix by altering the price differential between the two groups. Second, the general level of prices and the total number of passengers are chosen to equate marginal cost to both these marginal revenues. This ensures that the airline operates on the most profitable scale, as well as with the most profitable mix.

When a producer charges different customers different prices, we say it *price discriminates*. There are many examples in the real world. Rail operators charge rush-hour commuters a higher fare than midday shoppers whose demand for trips to the city is much more elastic.

Price discrimination often applies to services, which must be consumed on the spot, rather than to goods, which can be resold. Price discrimination in standardized goods won't work. The group buying at the lower price resells to the group paying the higher price, undercutting the price differences. Effective price discrimination requires that the submarkets can be isolated from one another to prevent resale.

Figure 6-3 illustrates *perfect price discrimination*, where it is possible to charge every customer a different price for the same good. If the monopolist charges every customer the same price, the profit-maximizing output is Q_1, where MR equals MC and the corresponding price is P_1.

If the monopolist can perfectly price discriminate, the very first unit can be sold for a price E. Having sold this unit to the highest bidder, the customer most desperate for the good, the next unit is sold to the next highest bidder, and so on. In reducing the price to sell that extra unit, the monopolist no longer reduces revenue from previously sold units. The demand curve *is* the marginal revenue curve under perfect price discrimination. The marginal revenue of the last unit is simply the price for which it is sold.

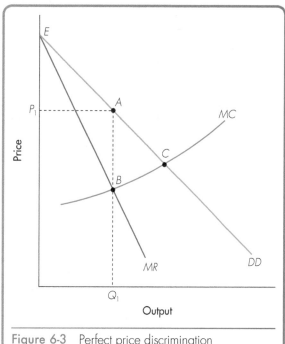

Figure 6-3   Perfect price discrimination

CHAPTER 6: Imperfect competition

A perfectly price discriminating monopolist produces at C, where $MC = DD$, which is now marginal revenue. Price discrimination, if possible, is always profitable. In moving from the uniform pricing point A to the price discriminating point C, the monopolist adds the area ABC to profits. This is the excess of additional revenue over additional cost when output is higher.

The monopolist makes a second gain from price discrimination. Even the output Q_1 now brings in more revenue than under uniform pricing. The monopolist also gains the area EP_1A by charging different prices, rather than the single price P_1, on the first Q_1 units. Economic consultants often earn their fees by teaching firms new ways in which to price discriminate.

Notice, too, that whether or not the firm can price discriminate affects its chosen output by affecting its marginal revenue. In the extreme case, perfect price discrimination leads to the same price and output as under perfect competition, since in both cases the firm then sets $MC = MR = P$.

Maths 6-1

Price discrimination

Consider the linear demand schedule $p = \alpha - \beta q$, which related price to quantity produced, and that α and β are positive constants. Suppose for simplicity that there is a constant average and marginal cost of production γ per unit. Total revenue is $qp = q(\alpha - \beta q)$. If the firm has to charge the same price to all customers, its marginal revenue is $d[q(\alpha - \beta q)]/dq = \alpha - 2\beta q$. Equating marginal cost γ and marginal revenue, the optimal choice of q is given by $q^* = (\alpha - \gamma)/2\beta$, at which point the demand curve shows the corresponding price is $p^* = \alpha - [\beta(\alpha - \gamma)/2\beta] = (\alpha + \gamma)/2$. Hence, maximized revenue p^*q^* is $[(\alpha - \gamma)/2\beta][(\alpha + \gamma)/2] = (\alpha^2 - \gamma^2)/4\beta$. Intuitively, revenue is stronger when demand is stronger (large α) and when costs are lower (small γ).

Suppose now that the firm can sell every unit at a different price. As it increases sales, the demand curve now shows the marginal revenue from each unit sold (since the price of all smaller units of output is no longer bid downwards by the requirement to charge a uniform price). Equating marginal revenue $\alpha - \beta q$ and marginal cost γ now yields $q^* = [\alpha - \gamma]/\beta$, which for this particular demand curve is precisely twice the optimal output compared with the uniform pricing case. The price p^* of the last unit sold is therefore $\{\alpha - \beta[\alpha - \gamma]/\beta\} = \gamma$, which makes sense since the demand curve is the marginal revenue curve here and γ is marginal cost.

In addition to the revenue $p^*q^* = \gamma[\alpha - \gamma]/\beta$, the producer also gets the extra revenue of having sold all units below q^* at a price higher than γ. This extra revenue is given the area of the triangle between the horizontal line at height γ and the portion of the demand curve above this line. The area of this triangle is half its base times its height, which is $(\alpha - \gamma)q^* = (\alpha - \gamma)^2/2\beta$.

Hence, the extra revenue from price discrimination, compared with uniform pricing, is

$$R(PD) - R(UP) = \{[\gamma[\alpha - \gamma]/\beta] + [\alpha - \gamma]^2/2\beta\} - \{(\alpha^2 - \gamma^2)/4\beta\}$$
$$= (\alpha^2 - \gamma^2)/4\beta$$

This is positive provided only that α, the maximum height of the demand curve, exceeds γ, the marginal cost of production. This proves that price discrimination yields higher revenue than uniform pricing. Notice that the gain arises from two sources. First, for the output produced under uniform pricing, the price discriminator gets more revenue by charging higher prices to more desperate customers. Second, the price discriminator produces additional output on which a profit is also made, whereas the uniform pricer does not find this profitable because it drags down the price too much on previous units.

Monopoly and technical change

Joseph Schumpeter (1883–1950) argued that, even with uniform pricing, a monopoly may not produce a lower output and at a higher price than a competitive industry because the monopolist has more incentive than a competitive firm to shift its cost curves down. Technical advances reduce costs, and allow lower prices and higher output. A monopoly has more incentive to undertake research and development (R&D), necessary for cost-saving breakthroughs.

In a competitive industry a firm with a technical advantage has only a temporary opportunity to earn high profits to recoup its research expenses. Imitation by existing firms and new entrants soon compete away its profits. In contrast, by shifting down all its cost curves, a monopoly can enjoy higher profits forever. Schumpeter argued that monopolies are more innovative than competitive industries. Taking a dynamic long-run view, rather than a snapshot static picture, monopolists may enjoy lower cost curves that lead them to charge lower prices, thereby raising the quantity demanded.

This argument has some substance, but may overstate the case. Most Western economies operate a *patent* system. Inventors of new processes acquire a *temporary* legal monopoly for a fixed period. By temporarily excluding entry and imitation, the patent laws increase the incentive to conduct R&D without establishing a monopoly in the long run. Over the patent life the inventor gets a higher price and makes handsome profits. Eventually the patent expires and competition from other firms leads to higher output and lower prices. The real price of copiers and microcomputers fell significantly when the original patents of Xerox and IBM expired.

Case study 6-1   The value of a good patent

Why has Nestlé cleaned up on the espresso coffee business? Not because potential competitors don't know where to find good coffee or how to manufacture home espresso machines. Rather, they have been defeated by the series of patents taken out by Nestlé.

The best cup of coffee requires that all coffee grounds are the same size, are stored in containers that do not allow the coffee to oxidize before it is used, and that it is brewed in hot water of exactly the optimal temperature and pressure. Nestlé's patents for grinding, packaging and delivering coffee through their famous Nespresso system (now licensed and retailed by other brand names) have effectively wiped out the competition. Nestlé's patent lawyers managed to

© Nestlé Nespresso SA

pre-empt the key processes so accurately that Nestlé's competitors gave up trying to challenge the Nestlé monopoly. Now they are simply waiting for the patents to expire. Patents have become a key part of competitive strategy in the knowledge economy. You are probably aware of two other hotly contested patent issues in today's global economy.

The first is the patents of incumbent music companies who argued, successfully eventually, that Napster and other free Internet download music services were infringing the patent (usually called a copyright when it applies to music, writing and the arts) held over the artistes that they had produced. Without such protection, there is no incentive to remain in the industry: expensive investment never has any payback since Internet companies subsequently compete away all the profits. Foreseeing this, recording studios would go bankrupt and there would be no music for the Internet to download. This issue has now been resolved, and the music industry has received sufficient protection that it can now coexist with Napster and iPods, which have to pay a fee for the music to which they have access.

Another contentious issue is the price of drugs that combat HIV/Aids. Global pharmaceutical companies, such as GlaxoSmithKline (GSK), Pfizer and Merck, always argue that drug development is hugely costly, and that many drugs fail to succeed in the testing phase, so that the occasional winner has to earn lots of money to cover the cost of all the ones that fail, just as successful gamblers recognize that their winnings on the occasional horse that they pick has to cover all the losses on the plausible horses that nevertheless failed to win as expected. Yet poor countries, such as those in sub-Saharan Africa where HIV/Aids is a major social and economic problem, argue that they should not be forced to pay drug prices considerably in excess of current production costs merely so that pharmaceutical companies can repay their failed investment in other drugs that did not work out as planned.

Both sides of course are simultaneously correct. If pharmaceutical companies are deprived of profits on their winners, they will have to exit the industry since they will no longer be able to pay for their inevitable losers. Since the latter lose big, it also takes big winnings just to keep pharmaceutical companies in the industry. However, if they charge prices that poor Africans cannot afford, not only do many people find this ethically unattractive, it may even diminish the profits of drug companies themselves. You already know enough economics to appreciate that, if the world price of drugs is substantially above the current production cost, then even a lower price would yield a profit. If Africans could then afford to buy at this lower price, total drug company profits would rise *provided they did not have to reduce the price for which the drugs were sold in rich countries.* Hence, if all countries support this form of price discrimination – and if those allowed to import at lower prices undertake not to attempt to resell to richer countries at higher prices – poor countries will get the cheaper drugs that they need, and drug producers will find that they get the same revenue as before from the rich countries (where prices have not changed), plus some new sales to poor countries that were not taking place before because poor countries could not afford the high prices previously charged to them.

 ## (6-2) Monopolistic competition

The theory of monopolistic competition envisages a large number of quite small firms, each ignoring any impact its own decisions might have on the behaviour of other firms. There is free entry and exit from the industry in the long run. In these respects, the industry resembles *perfect* competition. What distinguishes monopolistic competition is that each firm faces a *downward*-sloping demand curve in its own little niche of the industry.

Different firms' products are only limited substitutes. An example is the location of corner grocers. A lower price attracts some customers from other shops, but each shop has some local customers for whom local convenience matters more than a few pence on the price of a jar of coffee. Monopolistically competitive industries exhibit *product differentiation*. For corner grocers, differentiation is based on location. In other cases, it reflects brand loyalty or personal relationships. A particular restaurant or hairdresser can charge a slightly different price from other producers in the industry without losing all its customers.

Monopolistic competition requires not merely product differentiation, but also few economies of scale. Hence there are many small producers, ignoring their interdependence with their rivals. Many examples of monopolistic competition are service industries.

Each firm produces where its marginal cost equals marginal revenue. If firms make profits, new firms enter the industry. That is the competitive part of monopolistic competition. As a result of entry, the downward-sloping demand curve of each individual firm shifts to the left. For a given market demand curve, the market share of each firm falls. With lower demand but unchanged cost curves, each firm makes lower profits. Entry stops when enough firms have entered to bid profits down to zero for the marginal firm.

Figure 6-4 shows long-run equilibrium once there is no further incentive for entry or exit. Each individual firm's demand curve *DD* has shifted enough to the left to just be tangent to its *LAC* curve at the output q^* the firm is producing. Hence, it makes zero economic profits. Price P^* equals average cost. For a perfectly competitive firm, its horizontal demand curve

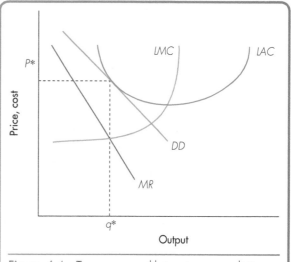

Figure 6-4 Tangency equilibrium in monopolistic competition

would be tangent to *LAC* at the minimum point on the average cost curve. In contrast, the tangency for a monopolistic competitor lies to the left of this, with both demand and *LAC* sloping down. The firm chooses output such that marginal revenue equals long-run marginal cost. That is the monopolistic part of monopolistic competition.

Notice two things about the firm's long-run equilibrium. First, the firm is *not* producing at the lowest point on its average cost curve. It could reduce average costs by further expansion. However, its marginal revenue would be so low as to make this unprofitable.

Second, the firm has some monopoly power because of the special feature of its particular brand or location. Price exceeds marginal cost. Hence, firms are usually eager for new customers prepared to buy more output at the *existing* price. It explains why we are a race of eager sellers and coy buyers. It is purchasing agents who get Christmas presents from sales reps, not the other way round.

Oligopoly and interdependence

Under perfect competition or monopolistic competition, there are so many firms in the industry that no single firm need worry about the effect of its own actions on rival firms. In pure monopoly the firm has no rivals. In contrast, the essence of an oligopoly is the need for each firm to consider how its actions affect the decisions of its relatively few rivals. The output decision of each firm depends on its guess about how its rivals will react. We begin with the basic tension between competition and collusion in such situations.

Collusion is an explicit or implicit agreement between existing firms to avoid competition.

Initially, for simplicity, we ignore entry and exit, studying only the behaviour of existing firms.

The profits from collusion

The existing firms maximize their *joint* profits if they behave like a multi-plant monopolist. A sole decision-maker would organize industry output to maximize total profits. By colluding to behave like a monopolist, oligopolists maximize their *total* profit. There is then a backstage deal to divide up these profits between individual firms.

CHAPTER 6: Imperfect competition

Having cut back industry output to the point at which $MC = MR < P$, each firm then faces a marginal profit $(P - MC)$ if it can expand a little more. Provided its partners continue to restrict output, each individual firm now wants to break the agreement and expand!

Oligopolists are torn between the desire to collude, thus maximizing joint profits, and the desire to compete, in the hope of increasing market share and profits at the expense of rivals. Yet if all firms compete, joint profits are low and no firm does very well.

Cartels

Collusion between firms is easiest when formal agreements are legal. Such *cartels* were common in the late nineteenth century. They agreed market shares and prices in many industries. Such practices are now outlawed in Europe, the US and many other countries. However, secret deals in smoke-filled rooms are not unknown even today.

The kinked demand curve

In the absence of collusion, each firm's demand curve depends on how competitors react. Firms must guess these reactions. Suppose that each firm believes that its own price cut will be matched by all other firms in the industry but that an increase in its own price will induce no price response from competitors.

Figure 6-5 shows the demand curve DD each firm then faces. At price P_0, the firm makes Q_0. Since competitors do not follow suit, a price rise leads to a big loss of market share to other firms. The firm's demand curve is elastic above A at prices above P_0. However, a price cut is matched by its rivals, and market shares are unchanged. Sales rise only because the industry as a whole moves down the market demand curve as prices fall. The demand curve DD is much less elastic for price reductions from the initial price P_0.

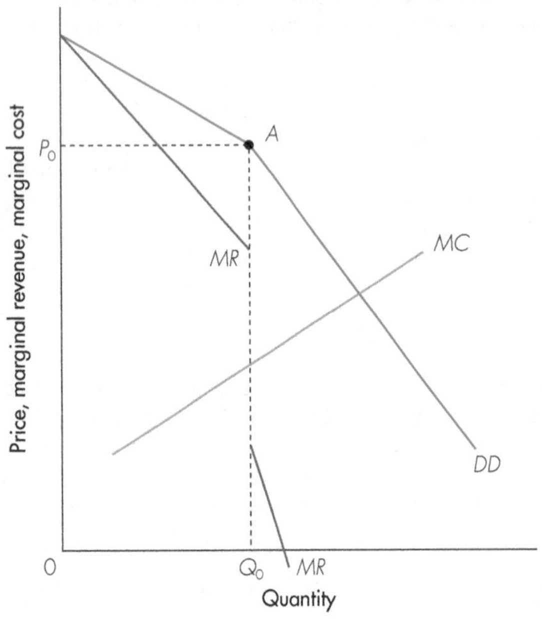

Thus, marginal revenue MR is discontinuous at Q_0. Below Q_0 the elastic part of the demand curve applies, but at Q_0 the firm hits the inelastic portion of its kinked demand curve and marginal revenue suddenly falls. Q_0 is the profit-maximizing output for the firm, given its belief about how competitors will respond.

The model has an important implication. Suppose the MC curve of a single firm shifts up or down by a small amount. Since the MR curve has a discontinuous vertical segment at the output Q_0, it remains optimal to make Q_0 and charge a price P_0. The kinked demand curve model may explain the empirical finding that firms do not always adjust prices when costs change.

It does not explain what determines the initial price P_0. It may be the collusive monopoly price. Each firm believes that an attempt to undercut its rivals induces them to cut prices to defend market share. However, its rivals are happy for it to charge a higher price and lose market share.

Figure 6-5   The kinked demand curve

There is a difference between the effect of a cost change for a single firm and a cost change for all firms together. The latter shifts the marginal cost curve up for the industry as a whole, raising the collusive monopoly price. Each firm's kinked demand curve shifts up since the monopoly price P_0 rises. Thus, we can reconcile the stickiness of a single firm's prices with respect to changes in its own costs alone, and the speed with which the entire industry marks up prices when all firms' costs are increased by higher taxes or wage rises in the whole industry.

Game theory and interdependent decisions

A good poker player sometimes bluffs. Sometimes you make money with a bad hand that your opponents misread as a good hand. Like poker players, oligopolists have to try to second-guess their rivals' moves to determine their own best action. To study how interdependent decisions are made, we use *game theory*.

A **game** is a situation in which intelligent decisions are necessarily interdependent.

The *players* in the game try to maximize their own *pay-offs*. In an oligopoly, the firms are the players and their pay-offs are their profits in the long run. Each player must choose a strategy.

A **strategy** is a game plan describing how the player will act or move in each situation.

Being a pickpocket is a strategy. Lifting a particular wallet is a move. As usual, we are interested in equilibrium. In most games, each player's best strategy depends on the strategies chosen by other players. It is silly to be a pickpocket in a police station.

In **Nash equilibrium**, each player chooses his best strategy, *given* the strategies chosen by other players.

This description of equilibrium was invented by John Nash, who won the Nobel Prize for Economic Science for his work on game theory, and was the subject of the film *A Beautiful Mind*, starring Russell Crowe. Sometimes, but not usually, a player's best strategy is independent of those chosen by others. If so, it is a *dominant strategy*. We begin with an example in which each player has a dominant strategy.

Box 6-2

Michael Porter on competitive advantage

Harvard Business School professor Michael Porter is renowned as a guru on competitive strategy, whose advice is sought by prime ministers and corporate chief executives. Porter advises clients to be clear on what they are trying to accomplish. The diagram helps understand his advice.

First, it is important to understand which part of the market – which customers – are being targeted. A firm can pursue a niche market strategy or chase after most of the entire market. Second, whichever market it is trying to pursue, the firm needs to be clear on whether its competitive advantage will arise because its products (whether goods or

	Uniqueness competency	Low cost competency
Narrow market scope	**Segmentation strategy**	
Broad market scope	**Differentiation strategy**	**Cost leadership**

▶

CHAPTER 6: Imperfect competition

services) will be distinctive in attributes or because the firm has refined its production to the extent that it can undercut its competitors making the same thing.

Where a firm decides to pursue a niche market – examples include BMW in cars, Louis Vuitton in luggage, the *Financial Times* in journalism – the key to success is to limit scope for competition by convincing customers that this market niche really is different. The *Financial Times* is not a differentiated seller of general material – its coverage of the arts may indeed be excellent, but people who buy the *FT* have to be pretty interested in financial affairs in the first place. By convincing more people to take an interest in financial markets, the *FT* can build the niche and its strong position within it. The fewer the substitutes, the less elastic is demand and the more the firm can raise prices without losing too much volume, a sure recipe for enhancing profits.

A second type of product differentiation is not in convincing customers that the market segment is different but in convincing customers that the product has unique attributes even though the market being pursued is broad. Mobile phones and hand-held devices are huge – Apple's success is primarily based on differentiating its product within this generic sector. Apple devices offer brilliant design, are customer friendly and use high quality graphics. Given these attributes, Apple can charge premium prices. Demand is inelastic. Many people simply have to have, and be seen to have, an iPad.

The third source of potential competitive advantage is cost advantage and hence the ability to undercut competitors. For example, the Ford Focus and Ford Mondeo are regularly held up as examples of great value for money packages. The basis for such a cost advantage might be scale, learning through repetition, locational advantage or unique technology.

Collude or cheat?

Figure 6-6 shows a game that we can imagine is between the only two members of a cartel like OPEC. Each firm can select a high-output or low-output strategy. In each box, the first number shows firm A's profits and the second number, firm B's profits for that output combination.

When both have high output, industry output is high, the price is low and each firm makes a small profit of 1. When each has low output, the outcome is more like collusive monopoly. Prices are high and each firm does better, making a profit of 2. Each firm does best (a profit of 3) when it alone has high output; for, then, the other firm's low output helps hold down industry output and keep up the price. In this situation we assume the low-output firm makes a profit of 0.

Now we can see how the game will unfold. Consider firm A's decision. If firm B has a high-output strategy, firm A does better also to have high output. In the two left-hand boxes, firm A gets a profit of 1 by choosing high but a profit of 0 by choosing low. Now suppose firm B chooses a low-output strategy. From the two right-hand boxes, firm A still does better by choosing high, since this yields it a profit of 3, whereas low yields it a profit of only 2. Hence firm A has a dominant strategy. Whichever strategy B adopts, A does better to choose a high-output strategy. Firm B also has a dominant strategy to choose high output. Check for yourself that B does better to go high whichever

		Firm B output	
		High	Low
Firm A output	High	1 1	3 0
	Low	0 3	2 2

Figure 6-6   The Prisoners' Dilemma game

strategy A selects. Since both firms choose high, the equilibrium is the top left-hand box. Each firm gets a profit of 1.

Yet both firms would do better, getting a profit of 2, if they colluded to form a cartel and both produced low – the bottom right-hand box. But neither can afford to take the risk of going low. Suppose firm A goes low. Firm B, comparing the two boxes in the bottom row, will then go high, preferring a profit of 3 to a profit of 2. And firm A will get screwed, earning a profit of 0 in that event. Firm A can figure all this out in advance, which is why its dominant strategy is to go high.

This is a clear illustration of the tension between collusion and competition. In this example, it appears that the output-restricting cartel will never get formed, since each player can already foresee the overwhelming incentive for the other to cheat on such an arrangement. How, then, can cartels ever be sustained? One possibility is that there exist binding commitments.

A **commitment** is an arrangement, entered into voluntarily, that restricts one's future actions.

If both players could simultaneously sign an enforceable contract to produce low output, they could achieve the co-operative outcome in the bottom right-hand box, each earning profits of 2. Clearly, they then do better than in the top left-hand box, which describes the non-cooperative equilibrium of the game. Without any commitment, neither player can go low because then the other player will go high. Binding commitments, by removing this temptation, enable both players to go low, and both players gain. This idea of commitment is important, and we shall meet it many times. Just think of all the human activities that are the subject of legal contracts, a simple kind of commitment simultaneously undertaken by two parties or players.

This insight is powerful, but its application to oligopoly requires some care. Cartels within a country are illegal, and OPEC is not held together by a signed agreement that can be upheld in international law! Is there a less formal way in which oligopolists can commit themselves not to cheat on the collusive low-output solution to the game? If the game is played only once, this is hard. However, in the real world, the game is repeated many times: firms choose output levels day after day. Suppose two players try to collude on low output. Furthermore, each announces a *punishment strategy*. Should firm A ever cheat on the low-output agreement, firm B promises that it will subsequently react by raising its output. Firm A makes a similar promise.

Suppose the agreement has been in force for some time, and both firms have stuck to their low-output deal. Firm A assumes that firm B will go low as usual. Figure 6-6 shows that firm A will make a *temporary* gain today if it cheats and goes high. Instead of staying in the bottom right-hand box with a profit of 2, it can move to the top right-hand box and make 3. However, from tomorrow onwards, firm B will also go high, and firm A can then do no better than continue to go high too, making a profit of 1 for evermore.

However, if A refuses to cheat today it can continue to stay in the bottom right-hand box and make 2 forever. In cheating, A swaps a temporary gain for permanently lower profits. Thus, punishment strategies can sustain an explicit cartel or implicit collusion even if no formal commitment exists.

It is easy to say that you will adopt a punishment strategy in the event that the other player cheats; but this will affect the other player's behaviour only if your threat is credible.

A **credible threat** is one that, after the fact, it is still optimal to carry out.

In the preceding example, once firm A cheats and goes high, it is then in firm B's interest to go high anyway. Hence B's threat to go high if A ever cheats is a credible threat.

Entry and potential competition

So far we have discussed imperfect competition between existing firms. What about potential competition from new entrants? Three cases must be distinguished: where entry is trivially easy, where it is difficult by accident and where it is difficult by design.

CHAPTER 6: Imperfect competition

Contestable markets

Suppose we see an industry with few incumbent firms. Before assuming it is an oligopoly, we must think about entry and exit.

> A **contestable market** has free entry and free exit.

Free exit means that there are no *sunk* or irrecoverable costs. On exit, a firm can fully recoup its previous investment expenditure, including money spent on building up knowledge and goodwill. A contestable market allows *hit-and-run* entry. If the incumbent firms, however few, are pricing above minimum average cost, an entrant can step in, undercut them, make a temporary profit, and exit. If so, even when incumbent firms are few in number, they have to behave as if they were perfectly competitive, setting $P = MC = AC$.

The theory of contestable markets is controversial. There are many industries in which sunk costs are hard to recover, or where expertise takes an entrant time to acquire. Nor is it safe to assume that incumbents will not change their behaviour when threatened by entry. But the theory does vividly illustrate that market structure and incumbent behaviour cannot be deduced by counting the number of firms in the industry. We were careful to stress that a monopolist is a sole producer *who can completely discount fear of entry*.

Innocent entry barriers

Entry barriers may be created by nature or by other rivals.

> An **innocent entry barrier** is one made by nature.

Absolute cost advantages, where incumbent firms have lower cost curves than entrants, may be innocent. If it takes time to learn the business, incumbents have lower costs in the short run.

Scale economies are another innocent entry barrier. If minimum efficient scale is large relative to market size, an entrant cannot get into the industry without considerably depressing the price. It may be impossible to break in at a profit. The greater the innocent entry barriers, the more we can neglect potential competition from entrants. The oligopoly game then reduces to competition between incumbent firms, as we discussed in the previous section.

Where innocent entry barriers are low, incumbent firms may accept this situation, in which case competition from potential entrants prevents incumbent firms from exercising much market power, or else incumbent firms will try to design some entry barrier of their own.

Strategic entry deterrence

The word 'strategic' has a precise meaning in economics.

> Your **strategic move** influences the other player's decision, in a manner helpful to you, by affecting the other person's expectations of how you will behave.

Suppose you are the only incumbent firm. Even if limited scale economies make it feasible for entrants to produce on a small scale, you threaten to flood the market if they come in, causing a price fall and big losses for everyone. Since you have a fat bank balance and they are just getting started, they will go bankrupt. Entry is pointless. You get the monopoly profits. But is your threat credible? Without spare capacity, how can you make extra output to bid down the price a lot.

Seeing this, the potential entrant may call your bluff. Suppose, instead, you build a costly new factory which is unused unless there is no entry. If, at some future date, an entrant appears, the cost of the new factory has largely been paid, and its marginal cost of production is low. The entrant succumbs to your credible threat to flood the market and decides to stay out. Provided the initial cost of the factory (spread suitably over a number of years) is less than the extra profits the incumbent keeps making *as a result of having deterred entry*, this entry deterrence is profitable. It is strategic because it works by influencing the decision of *another* player.

> **Strategic entry deterrence** is behaviour by incumbent firms to make entry less likely.

Is spare capacity the only commitment available to incumbents? Commitments must be irreversible, otherwise they are an empty threat; and they must increase the chances that the incumbent will fight. Anything with the character of fixed and sunk costs may work. Fixed costs artificially increase scale economies, and sunk costs have already been incurred.

Box 6-3

Banking on entry deterrence

Retail banking is a key activity in a modern market economy. As in other countries, British banks have taken a pasting since 2007. Northern Rock had to be nationalized, Royal Bank of Scotland is now 80 per cent owned by the government, and Halifax Bank of Scotland was bailed out by Lloyds TSB (to the fury of Lloyds' shareholders since to date it has proved a lousy investment). By 2010 the UK Office of Fair Trading (OFT) was worrying about how to stimulate renewed competition in the sector, both by enticing in new entrants and in order to find new bidders to buy up assets being sold off by the state or being forcibly removed from private banks in order to leave them less in the position of being 'too big to fail' (and thereby being able to rely on government assistance even when they screw up).

The OFT report of November 2010 assessed four potential sources of entry barrier to new retail banking entrants. First, incumbents might enjoy a considerable advantage in already having regulatory approval for banking licences and customer credit provision. The OFT concluded this was logically possible but in practice nothing much to worry about. Potential new banks could get these approvals without too much trouble.

Next, the OFT worried about banking infrastructure – access to the IT systems needed to run the payment systems, track customers and operate effectively. Here, the OFT concluded that incumbents do have a major advantage – this big investment is a sunk cost that does not need to enter their marginal costing and pricing decisions, whereas an entrant has to finance it and worry about how to get a return on that investment. IT makes up around two-thirds of the start-up cost of entering the retail banking business.

Third, the power of existing brands may prevent customers switching to new banks. This is less likely to be a problem if the incumbent brands have been damaged by the financial crisis. It is also less of a problem if the entrant is itself an established brand. For example, in November 2011 the UK government sold Northern Rock to Virgin Money for £747 million. Virgin may not have been all that well known for its previous activities in financial services, but both its airline and its train business are well established. Similarly, by 2012 RBS had sold 318 branches to Santander, which was already established in the UK banking business after taking over Abbey National in 2004.

Finally, the OFT considered barriers to exit from the industry. The theoretical model of perfect competition requires free exit as well as free entry to the industry. Why? Because if a potential entrant has to worry about costs of exit in the future, this will restrict their willingness to enter today. What are these exit costs in banking? Principally that a bank is likely to want to exit during a financial crisis, which is precisely the time at which other banks are likely to be in trouble too. It will therefore be difficult to sell off the assets – the bank branches, the IT system, the customer network – for a price anywhere near the cost for which these assets had to be built up.

How tough is it to enter the retail banking business? Pretty tough for a complete newcomer. Less tough for a firm already established in banking elsewhere. In the last few decades, the UK has seen entry by Santander from Spain, and from HSBC from East Asia.

CHAPTER 6: Imperfect competition

Summing up

Few industries in the real world closely resemble the textbook extremes of perfect competition or pure monopoly. Most are imperfectly competitive. Game theory in general, and notions such as commitment, credibility and deterrence, let economists analyse many of the practical concerns of big business.

What have we learned? First, market structure and the behaviour of incumbent firms are determined *simultaneously*. At the beginning of the section, we argued that the relation between minimum efficient scale and market size would determine market structure, whether the industry was a monopoly, oligopoly or displayed monopolistic or perfect competition. However, these are not merely questions of the extent of innocent entry barriers. Strategic behaviour can also affect the shape of cost curves and the market structure that emerges.

Second, and related, we have learned the importance of *potential* competition, which may come from domestic firms considering entry, or from imports from abroad. The number of firms observed in the industry today conveys little information about the extent of the market power they truly exercise. The more globalization takes place, the more relevant this argument becomes.

Finally, we have seen how many business practices of the real world – price wars, advertising, brand proliferation, excess capacity, or excessive research and development – can be understood as strategic competition in which, to be effective, threats must be made credible by commitments.

Case study 6-2   Why advertise so much?

Evan Davis is host of the *Dragons' Den*, and co-presenter of BBC Radio 4's flagship *Today* programme. John Kay writes a fortnightly column on corporate strategy for the *Financial Times*. This case study is based on work they did together at the London Business School over 20 years ago, but which is still just as relevant today.

Advertising is not always meant to erect entry barriers to potential entrants. Sometimes, it really does aim to inform consumers by revealing inside information that firms have about the quality of their own goods.

When consumers can tell at a glance the quality of a product, even before buying it, there is little gain from advertising. Black rotten bananas cannot convincingly be portrayed as fresh and delicious. Information is freely available and attempts to deceive consumers are detected rapidly. However, for most goods, consumers cannot detect quality before purchase, and gradually discover quality only after using the good for a while.

The producer then has inside information over first-time buyers. A conspicuous (expensive) advertising campaign *signals* to potential buyers that the firm believes in its product and expects to make enough repeat sales to recoup the cost of the initial investment in advertising. Firms whose lies are quickly discovered by consumers do not invest much in advertising because they never sell enough to recoup their outlay on adverts. Consumers discover the poor quality and refrain from repeat purchasing. Foreseeing this, the firm that knows it will be quickly discovered never wastes money on expensive advertising in the first place.

What about one-off purchases, such as refrigerators, that usually last a decade or more? Consumers would really benefit from truthful advertising but producers of high-quality goods have no incentive to advertise. It would pay producers of low-quality refrigerators to advertise too since it would be ages before gullible consumers needed to return for a repeat purchase. A willingness to advertise no longer signals how much the firm believes in its own product. Since high-quality firms do not

Recap 127

bother advertising, and since low-quality firms mimic the behaviour of high-quality firms, low-quality firms do not advertise either.

The table below shows advertising spending as a fraction of sales revenue for the three types of good identified above. The theory fits the facts well.

Quality detected	Time till buy again	Example	Advertising as percentage of sales revenue
Before buy	Irrelevant	Bananas	0.4
Soon after buy	Soon	Biscuits	3.6
Long after buy	Much later	Refrigerator	1.8

Source: E. Davis, J. Kay and J. Star, 'Is advertising rational?', *Business Strategy Review*, 1991

Recap

- Market structure refers to the relative size of minimum efficient scale and the total size of the market as reflected by the position of the industry demand curve.
- Market structure is also affected by the shapes of these curves. The steeper the industry demand curve, the more an entrant's extra output will bid down the price, making it harder to enter; and the steeper the *LAC* curve at outputs below minimum efficient scale, the harder it is for an entrant to enter and produce a small output.
- A pure monopoly is the only seller or potential seller in an industry. The monopolist has a large minimum efficient scale relative to the size of the industry. Economies of scale are important.
- To maximize profits, a monopolist chooses the output at which $MC = MR$. The relation of price to MR depends on the elasticity of the demand curve.
- A monopolist cuts back output to force up the price. The gap between price and marginal cost is a measure of monopoly power.
- A discriminating monopoly charges higher prices to customers whose demand is more inelastic.
- Monopolies have more ability and incentive to innovate. In the long run, this is a force for cost reduction. Temporary patents achieve some of the same effect even in competitive industries.
- Imperfect competition exists when individual firms face downward-sloping demand curves.
- When minimum efficient scale is very large relative to the industry demand curve, this innocent entry barrier may produce a natural monopoly in which entry can be ignored.
- At the opposite extreme, entry and exit may be costless. The market is contestable, and incumbent firms must mimic perfectly competitive behaviour, or be undercut by a flood of entrants.

▶

CHAPTER 6: Imperfect competition

- Monopolistic competitors face free entry and exit, but are individually small and make similar though not identical products. Each has limited monopoly power in its special brand. In long-run equilibrium, price equals average cost. Each firm's downward-sloping demand curve is tangent to the downward-sloping part of its *LAC* curve.
- Oligopolists face a tension between collusion to maximize joint profits and competition for a larger share of smaller joint profits. Without credible threats of punishment by other collusive partners, each firm is tempted to cheat.
- Game theory describes interdependent decision-making. In the Prisoners' Dilemma game, each firm has a dominant strategy but the outcome is disadvantageous to both players. With binding commitments, both are better off by guaranteeing not to cheat on the collusive solution.
- In Nash equilibrium, each player selects her best strategy, given the strategies selected by rivals.
- Innocent entry barriers are made by nature, and arise from scale economies or absolute cost advantages of incumbent firms. Strategic entry barriers are made in boardrooms and arise from credible commitments to resist entry if challenged.

Review questions

To check your answers to these questions, go to pages 382–3.

1 A monopolist produces at constant marginal cost of £5 and faces the following demand curve:

Price (£)	8	7	6	5	4	3
Quantity	1	2	3	4	5	6

Calculate the *MR* curve. What is the equilibrium output? Equilibrium price? What would be the equilibrium price and output for a competitive industry? Why does the monopolist make less output and charge a higher price.

2 In addition to the data above, the monopolist also has a fixed cost of £2. What difference does this make to the monopolist's output, price and profits? Why?

3 Now suppose the government levies a monopoly tax, taking half the monopolist's profit. (a) What effect does this have on the monopolist's output? (b) What was the marginal profit on the last unit of output before the tax was levied? (c) Does this help you answer (a)?

4 Why do golf clubs have off-peak membership at reduced fees?

5 Why might a monopoly have more incentive to innovate than a competitive firm? Could a monopoly have less incentive to innovate?

6 Why are these statements wrong? (a) By breaking up monopolies we always get more output at a lower price. (b) A single producer in the industry is a sure sign of monopoly.

7 Vehicle repairers sometimes suggest that mechanics should be licensed so that repairs are done only by qualified people. (a) Evaluate the arguments for and against licensing car mechanics. (b) Are the arguments the same for licensing doctors?

8 An industry faces the demand curve:

Q	1	2	3	4	5	6	7	8	9	10
P	10	9	8	7	6	5	4	3	2	1

(a) As a monopoly, with $MC = 3$, what price and output are chosen? (b) Now suppose there are two firms, each with $MC = AC = 3$. What price and output maximize joint profits if they collude? (c) Why do the two firms have to agree on the output each produces? Why might each firm be tempted to cheat?

9 Unilever, makers of Walls ice cream, used helpfully to supply, free of charge, freezer cabinets to small shopkeepers, such as newsagents and corner shops, in exchange for the shop stocking Walls ice cream. What has this to do with entry barriers? If you were in charge of competition policy, would you allow this activity or prohibit it? Why, or why not?

10 Proud parents used to buy their children bound volumes of encyclopaedias to put on their bedroom bookshelves. Then CDs came along offering much the same service at a fraction of the cost. Subsequently, the volunteer-based Wikipedia offered free reference search on the Internet. What do you think happened to the production of encyclopaedias in book form? Would anybody still buy them? How can the readers be sure of the quality of Wikipedia information? Would you believe material offered by Google more?

11 With the industry demand curve in Question 8, two firms, A and Z, begin with half the market each when charging the monopoly price. Z decides to cheat and believes A will stick to its old output level. (a) Show the demand curve Z believes it faces. (b) What price and output would Z then choose?

12 Why are these statements wrong? (a) Competitive firms should collude to restrict output and drive up the price. (b) Firms would not advertise unless it increased their sales.

EASY

INTERMEDIATE

DIFFICULT

CHAPTER 6: Imperfect competition

13 **Essay question** A good-natured parent knows that children sometimes need to be punished, but also knows that, when it comes to the crunch, the child will be let off with a warning. Can the parent undertake any pre-commitment to make the threat of punishment credible?

14 **Essay question** Why do shops offer price discounts, including 2-for-1 offers or coupons that can be redeemed towards the price, rather than simply cut the price of the product?

Online Learning Centre

To help you grasp the key concepts of this chapter check out the extra resources posted on the Online Learning Centre at www.mcgraw-hill.co.uk/textbooks/begg.

There are additional case studies, self-test questions, practice exam questions with answers and a graphing tool.

Chapter 7

Types of Business Organization

Walk through the business district of most towns and you will find small insurance brokers competing with national giants such as AXA and Aviva; privately run banks such as Barclays competing with state-owned banks such as RBS and Lloyds, and with various forms of cooperatively or mutually owned banks such as the Co-operative Bank and the building societies that can be found on most British high streets. Similar diversity can be found in many other sectors — for example, small specialist electronics retailers compete with national chains such as PC World, and in the restaurant sector, countless small family-run restaurants co-exist with national chains. The diversity of business organizations reflects their ability to adapt to their environment, so there is a role in the business environment for both the small specialist retailer and the national chain store. The nature of diversity within business organizations is explored in this chapter.

✓ Learning Objectives

This chapter will explain:

- ✓ The diversity of organizational types.
- ✓ The advantages and disadvantages of sole traders, partnerships and limited companies.
- ✓ The role of public-sector organizations and non-departmental public bodies.
- ✓ The effects of organizational form and size on responsiveness to environmental change.

236   CHAPTER 7 Types of Business Organization

7.1   Introduction: organizations and their environment

Previous chapters have focused on the external environment that affects business organizations. In this chapter we begin to turn our focus inward, to look at the nature of business organizations. We need to understand the factors that facilitate or inhibit an internal response to external environmental change.

But first, we need to ask a basic question: 'Why do organizations exist?' The main reason is that some forms of value creation can be carried out much more efficiently within organizations than by individuals acting alone. Imagine individuals trying to build an aircraft and you can appreciate that they will achieve their objective much more effectively if they come together in some form of organization. However, if a group of individuals want to go into business as household decorators, they might find that the costs of managing the organization put them at a competitive disadvantage compared to individuals acting on their own. Business organizations are extremely diverse in their forms and functions, even within a single business sector. It is therefore difficult to define an 'ideal' organization. Instead, all organizational forms have advantages and disadvantages relative to the environment in which they operate, and successful organizations capitalize on their advantages while recognizing their disadvantages. In a single business sector, there can be a role for both the one-person owner-managed business and the multinational organization. Both can adapt and find a role.

Analogies can be drawn between business organizations and their environment and the animal kingdom. In a natural habitat, the largest and most powerful animals can co-exist with much smaller species. The smaller species can avoid becoming prey for the larger ones by being more agile, or developing defences such as safe habitats that are inaccessible to their larger predators. Sometimes, a symbiotic relationship can develop between the two. In a bid to survive, animals soon learn which sources of food are easily obtainable and abandon those that are either inedible or cause them to face competition from more powerful animals. In Darwinian terms, the 'fittest' survive, and an ecosystem allows for co-existence of living organisms that have adapted in their own way to the challenges of their environment. As in the business environment, macroenvironmental change can affect the relationships between species – as, for example, has occurred with deforestation and the use of intensive farming methods.

Just as any study of the animal world may begin by examining the characteristics of the participants, so an analysis of the business environment could begin by looking at the characteristics of the organizations that make it up. Businesses need to understand the diversity of organizational types for a number of reasons.

- Different types of organization will be able to address their customers, suppliers and employees in different ways. Lack of resources could, for example, inhibit the development of expensive new products by a small business. Sometimes, the objectives of an organization – either formal or informal – will influence what it is able to offer the public.

- As a seller of materials to companies involved in further manufacture, a company should understand how the buying behaviour of different kinds of organization varies. A small business is likely to buy equipment in a different way to a large public-sector organization.

- We should be interested in the structure of business units at the macroeconomic level. Many economists have argued that a thriving small business sector is essential for an expanding economy, and that the effect of domination by large organizations may be to reduce competition and innovation. We should therefore be interested in the rate of new business creation and trends in the composition of business units.

7.1.1 Classification of business organizations

There are many approaches to classifying organizations that would satisfy the interests identified above. Organizations are commonly classified according to their:

- size (e.g. turnover, assets, employees, geographical coverage)
- ownership (e.g. public, private, cooperative)
- legal form (e.g. sole trader, limited company)
- industry sector.

A good starting point for classifying business organizations is to look at their legal form. A business's legal form is often closely related to its size, objectives, and the level of resources it has available for marketing and for new product development (the issues of organizational size and objectives are considered in more detail in the next chapter).

This chapter will first consider private-sector organizations, which range from the small owner-managed sole trader to the very large public limited company. It will then review the diverse range of publicly owned organizations that operate as businesses. A third, and growing, group of organizations cannot be neatly categorized into private or public sector and includes 'quangos' (quasi-autonomous non-governmental organizations) and charities. To put the diversity of organizations into context, Figure 7.1 illustrates the types of organization that will be described in this chapter.

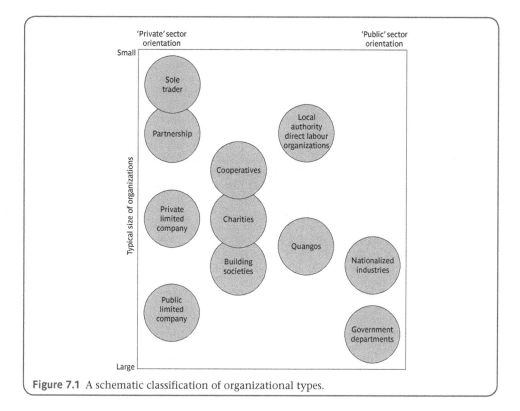

Figure 7.1 A schematic classification of organizational types.

7.2   The sole trader

The most basic level of business organization is provided by the sole trader. In fact, the concept of a separate legal form does not apply to this type of organization, for the business and the individual are considered to be legally indistinguishable. The individual carries on business in his or her own name, with the result that the individual assumes all the rights and duties of the business. It follows that if the business is sued for breach of contract, this amounts to suing the individual. If the business does not have the resources to meet any claim, the claim must be met out of the private resources of the individual.

Becoming a sole trader requires the minimum of formality and for this reason it can be difficult to tell how many are being created or are in existence at any one time. The most commonly used indication is provided by VAT registrations, although this does not give a complete picture as businesses with a turnover of less than £70,000 (2010/11) do not need to register. Maintaining a business as a sole trader also requires a minimum of formality – for example, there is no obligation to file annual accounts, other than for the assessment of the individual's personal tax liability.

It has been estimated that about 80 per cent of all businesses in the UK are sole traders, although they account for only a small proportion of gross domestic product (GDP). In some sectors of the economy they are a very popular business form, and dominate sectors such as newsagents, window cleaners and hairdressers. Sole traders can grow by taking on additional employees. There is no legal limit on the number of employees that a sole trader may have and there are many examples of sole traders employing over 100 people. At the other extreme, it is sometimes difficult to describe just when a sole trader business unit comes into existence, with many sole traders operating on a part-time basis – some 'moonlighting' without the knowledge of the tax authorities. Estimates of the annual value of this so-called 'black economy' are as high as £200 million per annum.

We should recognize a number of important characteristics of sole traders. First, they tend to have limited capital resources. Risk capital is generally provided only by the sole proprietor or close personal backers, and additional loan capital is often made available only against security of the individual's assets. In the field of new product development, this type of business has very often made discoveries, but has been unable to see new products through to production and launch on account of a lack of funds. If a new product does make it into a competitive market, this type of business may face competition in price, promotional effort or product offering from larger and better-resourced firms. The larger firm is likely to have greater resources to mount a campaign to see off a newer competitor.

The small sole trader could find that it is too small to justify having its own expertise in many areas. Many do not have specialists to look after the accounting or advertising functions, for example. Furthermore, the goals and policies of the business can become totally dominated by the owner of the business. Although goals can be pursued determinedly and single-mindedly, the sole trader presents a narrower view than may be offered by a larger board of directors. The goals of a sole trader may appear very irrational to an outsider; for instance, many individuals may be happy to continue uneconomic ventures on emotional grounds alone. Many very small caterers, for example, may be financially better off drawing unemployment benefit, but being a sole trader may satisfy wider goals of status or the pursuit of a leisure interest.

Many sole traders fail after only a short time, often because of the lack of management skills of an individual who may well be an expert in his or her own field of specialization. Others continue until they reach a point where lack of expertise and financial resources impose a constraint on growth. At this point, many sole traders consider going into partnership with another individual, or setting up a company with limited liability.

7.2.1 Sole trader or employee?

It can sometimes be difficult to decide whether a person is a self-employed sole trader or an employee of another organization. The distinction is an important one, because a trend in recent years has been for large organizations to outsource many of their operations, often buying in services from apparently self-employed individuals. There can be many advantages in classifying an individual as self-employed rather than an employee. For the self-employed person, tax advantages could result from being able to claim as legitimate some business expense items that are denied to the employee. The method of assessing income tax liability in arrears can favour an expanding small business. For the employer, designation as self-employed could save on National Insurance payments. It also relieves the employer of many duties that are imposed in respect of employees but not subcontractors, such as entitlement to sick pay, notice periods and maternity leave.

The problem of distinction is particularly great in the construction sector and for service sectors (such as market research), which employ large numbers of part-time workers. The courts would decide the matter, among other things, on the basis of the degree of control that the employer has over the employee and their level of integration within the organization. If the employer is able to specify the manner in which a task is to be carried out, and assumes most of the risk in a transaction, then an employment relationship generally exists. If, however, the required end result is specified but the manner in which it is achieved is left up to the individual, who also bears the cost of any budget overrun, then it is most likely that a contract for services will exist – in other words, self-employment.

⟳ Thinking around the subject

A mountain of paperwork

One of the biggest complaints from sole traders is the amount of paperwork that they are required by government to complete. Most small business owners have a vision of what they want to do: open a hairdressing salon, install kitchens, run a convenience store or exploit a new invention. But the reality is that they are likely to become bogged down in completing paperwork, some of which they may never have envisaged. According to a NatWest survey, conducted on a quarterly basis by the Open University Business School, the average small firm spent 26.7 hours a month in 2006 completing government paperwork. The burden of red tape fell hardest on small sole traders. Businesses with more than 25 staff spend 1.5 hours per employee on forms, whereas those with more than 50 staff spent 0.6 hours per employee. More than half the firms surveyed said the cost of employee regulation and paperwork had meant they employed fewer staff than they would like. More than a third said they would avoid employing more people, while 18 per cent said that growing levels of regulation had led them to reduce their workforce. After employment paperwork, main gripes concerned the paperwork associated with VAT, and the form-filling associated with health and safety assessments. The Small Business Council has been campaigning to keep paperwork simple and to reduce the time it takes to fill out forms. It has pointed out that, for every hour a sole trader spends filling out forms, they are not able to use the time to sell more products or develop new ones. While large companies may be able to employ specialists to cope with paperwork, for the small business, productivity suffers.

Governments continually say that they wish to reduce the paperwork burden on small businesses, but how can this be achieved in practice?

7.3   Partnerships

Two or more persons in partnership can combine their resources and expertise to form what could be a more efficient business unit. The Partnership Act 1890 defines a **partnership** as 'the relation which subsists between persons carrying on a business with a view to profit'. Partnerships can range from two builders joining together to a very large accountancy or solicitors' practice with hundreds of partners.

Partnerships are generally formed by contract between the parties, although, where this is not done, the Partnership Act 1890 governs relationships between the partners. Among the main items in a Partnership Agreement will be terms specifying:

- the amount of capital subscribed by each partner
- the basis on which profits will be determined and allocated between partners, and the management responsibilities of each partner – some partners may join as 'sleeping partners' and take no active part in the management of the business
- the basis for allocating salaries to each partner and for drawing personal advances against entitlement to profits
- procedures for dissolving the partnership and distributing the assets of the business between members.

Despite this internal agreement between partners, partnerships in England and Wales have not had their own legal personality. As a consequence, the partners incur unlimited personal liability for the debts of the business. Furthermore, each partner is jointly liable for the debts incurred by all partners in the course of business. An added complication of a partnership is that the withdrawal of any one partner, either voluntarily or upon death or bankruptcy, causes the automatic termination of the partnership. A new partnership will come into being, as it would if an additional partner were admitted to the partnership.

Because of the lack of protection afforded to partners, this form of organization tends to be relatively uncommon, except for some groups of professional people, where business risks are low and for whom professional codes of practice may prevent the formation of limited companies. To overcome the problem of limited liability, the Limited Liability Partnerships Act 2000 created a new form of partnership with limited liability. The Act extends limited liability to partnerships in specified circumstances, and is most popular with professional partnerships of accountants, solicitors, dentists and opticians.

7.4   Limited companies

It was recognized in the nineteenth century that industrial development would be impeded if investors in business always ran the risk of losing their personal assets to cover the debts of a business over which very often they had no day-to-day control. At the same time, the size of business units had become larger, causing the idea of a partnership to become strained. The need for a trading company to have a separate legal personality from that of its owners was recognized from the Middle Ages, when companies were incorporated by Royal Charter. From the seventeenth century, organizations could additionally be incorporated by Act of Parliament. Both methods of incorporating a company were expensive and cumbersome, and a simpler method was required to cope with the rapid expansion of business enterprises that were fuelling the Industrial Revolution. The response to this need was the Joint Stock Companies Act 1844, which enabled a company to be incorporated as a separate legal identity by the registration of a Memorandum of Association and payment of certain fees. The present law governing the registration of companies is contained in the Companies Act 1985. Today, the vast majority of trading within the UK is undertaken by **limited companies**. The legislation of most countries allows for organizations to be created that have a separate legal personality from their owners. In this way, separate legal identity is signified in the USA by the title 'Incorporated' after a company's name, by 'Société Anonyme' (SA) in France, 'Gmbh' in Germany and 'Sdn. Bhd.' in Malaysia.

When a limited company is created under UK legislation, it is required to produce a Memorandum and Articles of Association. The Memorandum includes a statement as to whether the liability of its members is limited, and if so what the limit of liability will be in the event of the company being wound up with unpaid debts. The majority of companies are limited by shares – members' liability to contribute to the assets of the company is limited to the amount (if any) that is unpaid on their shares. Another important element of the Memorandum is the objects clause, which specifies the scope within which the company can exercise its separate legal personality. Any act that the company performs beyond its powers is deemed to be *ultra vires* and therefore void.

While the Memorandum regulates the relationships of the company with the outside world, the Articles of Association regulate the internal administration of the company, the relations between the company and its members, and between the members themselves. The Articles cover such matters as the issue and transfer of shares, the rights of shareholders, meetings of members, the appointment of directors, and procedures for producing and auditing accounts.

Most limited companies are registered as private limited companies, indicated in company names by the designation 'Limited'. However, a larger company may choose to register as a public limited company (plc) and will thus face tougher regulatory requirements. These are described later in this chapter.

7.4.1 Company administration

A company acts through its directors, who are persons chosen by shareholders to conduct and manage the company's affairs. The number of directors and their powers are detailed in the Articles of Association and, so long as they do not exceed these powers, shareholders cannot normally interfere in their conduct of the company's business. The Articles will normally give one director additional powers to act as managing director, enabling him or her to make decisions without reference to the full board of directors.

Every company must have a secretary on whom Companies Acts have placed a number of duties and responsibilities, such as filing reports and accounts with the Registrar of Companies. The secretary is the chief administrative officer of the company, usually chosen by the directors.

7.4.2 Shareholders

The **shareholders** own the company, and in theory exercise control over it. A number of factors limit the actual control that shareholders exercise over their companies. The Articles of a company might discriminate between groups of shareholders by giving differential voting rights. Even where shareholders have full voting rights, the vast majority of shareholders typically are either unable or insufficiently interested to attend company meetings, and are happy to leave company management to the directors, so long as the dividend paid to them is satisfactory. In the case of pension funds and other institutional holders of shares in a company, their concern may be mainly with the stability of the financial returns from the business. In most large organizations, private investors are in a distinct minority in terms of the value of shares owned. There has been a tendency in recent years for individual shareholders to use their privileged position to raise issues of social concern at companies' annual shareholders' meetings. For example, in 2007, Ben Birnberg, a retired solicitor and small shareholder in Tesco, amassed enough support to force the issue of ethical trading on to the agenda at Tesco's annual shareholders' meeting. Mr Birnberg, who was also the company secretary of the charity War on Want, won the support of more than 100 shareholders – enough to force Tesco to include a resolution to be put to shareholders requiring the supermarket to adopt higher standards in its dealings with suppliers and farmers in low-wage countries.

7.4.3 Company reports and accounts

A company provides information about itself when it is set up, through its Memorandum and Articles of Association. To provide further protection for investors and people with whom the company may deal, companies are required to provide subsequent information.

An important document that must be produced annually is the annual report. Every company having a **share capital** must make a return in the prescribed form to the Registrar of Companies, stating what has happened to its capital during the previous year – for example, by describing the number of shares allotted and the cash received for them. The return must be accompanied by a copy of the audited balance sheet in the prescribed form, supported by a profit and loss account that gives a true and fair representation of the year's transactions. Like the Memorandum and Articles of Association, these documents are available for public inspection, with the exception of unlimited companies, which do not have to file annual accounts. Also, most small companies need only file an abridged balance sheet and do not need to submit a profit and loss account.

As well as providing the annual report and accounts, the directors of a company are under a duty to keep proper books of account and details of assets and liabilities.

7.4.4 Liquidation and receivership

Most limited companies are created with a view to continuous operation into the foreseeable future (although, sometimes, companies are set up with an expectation that they should cease to exist once their principal objective has been achieved). The process of breaking up a business is referred to as **liquidation**. Voluntary liquidation may be initiated by members (for example, where the main shareholder wishes to retire and liquidation is financially more attractive than selling the business as a going concern). Alternatively, a limited company may be liquidated (or wound up) by a court under s.122 of the Insolvency Act 1986. Involuntary liquidation involves the appointment of a receiver, who has authority that overrides the directors of the company. An individual or company that has an unmet claim against a company can apply to a court for it to be placed in **receivership**. Most receivers initially seek to turn round a failing business by consolidating its strengths and cutting out activities that brought about failure in the first place, allowing the company to be sold as a going concern. The proceeds of such a sale are used towards repaying the company's creditors and, if there is a sufficient surplus, the shareholders of the company. However, many directors who have lost their businesses claim that receivers are too eager to liquidate assets, and unwilling to take any risks that may eventually allow both creditors and shareholders to be paid off. The Insolvency Act 1986 allows a period of 'administration' during which a company can seek to put its finances into order with its creditors, without immediate resort to receivership. Section 5.8 of the Act defines the circumstances in which an administration order may be made by a court.

In 2008, the UK retailer Woolworths was placed into administration. Like many administrative orders, this one followed poor trading (in this case, lower than expected levels of Christmas sales), which left the company short of cash. The lack of available credit, exacerbated by the 'credit crunch' fuelled Woolworths' problem. Deloitte was appointed as administrator, and its first task was to control unnecessary expenditure, resulting in redundancies of staff who were not essential to the continued operation of the chain. The administrator then set about selling the chain as a going concern. Despite expressions of interest from several companies, both trade buyers and venture capital firms, no offers for the whole chain were forthcoming. One complicating factor was the requirement for anybody taking over the whole company as a going concern to assume responsibility for Woolworths' pension fund deficit, and for making redundancy payments to any staff they no longer needed after taking over the business. The administrator was mindful that a prolonged search for a buyer would diminish the value of the company, as customers became disillusioned and staff morale sank. No buyer was found and therefore it sold bundles of stores to other retailers, such as Poundland and Sainsbury's, which used them to expand their own branch coverage, usually recruiting their own staff to work in the former Woolworths branches. Some smaller stores attracted no bids, and remained empty for a long while. The brand name Woolworths was sold separately in 2009 to entrepreneurs the Barclay Brothers, who re-established the brand online.

7.4.5 Public limited companies

The Companies Act 1985 recognized that existing company legislation did not sufficiently distinguish between the small owner-managed limited company and the large multinational firm. Thus the concept of the **public limited company** – abbreviated to plc – came about. The basic principles of separate legal personality are similar for both private and public limited companies, but the Companies Act 1985 confers a number of additional duties and benefits on public limited companies.

The difference is partly one of scale – a plc must have a minimum share capital of £50,000 compared to the £100 of the private limited company. It must have at least two directors instead of the minimum of one for the private company. Before a plc can start trading, or borrow money, it must obtain a 'business certificate' from the Registrar of Companies, confirming that it has met all legal requirements in relation to its share capital.

Against these additional obstacles of the plc is the major advantage that it can offer its shares and debentures to the public, something that is illegal for a private company, where shares are more commonly taken up by friends, business associates and family. As a private limited company grows, it may have exhausted all existing sources of equity capital, and 'going public' is one way of attracting capital from a wider audience. During periods of economic prosperity, there has been a trend for many groups of managers to buy out their businesses, initially setting up a private limited company with a private placement of shares. In order to attract new capital, and often to allow existing shareholders to sell their holding more easily, these businesses have often been re-registered as public companies.

There are a number of additional strengths and weaknesses to plc status that can be noted. Many companies highlight plc status in promotional material in order to give potential customers a greater degree of confidence in the company. Another major strength is the greater potential ability to fund major new product developments. Against this, the plc is much more open to public examination, especially from the financial community. Management may develop business plans that will achieve long-term payback, bringing it into conflict with the (possibly short-term) objectives of City financial institutions. Indeed, a number of companies have recognized this problem of plc status and reverted to private status by buying back shares from the public – the Virgin airline business, for example, converted back to a private limited company after a few years as a plc (although the Virgin Mobile business was subsequently floated as a plc in 2004).

Larger limited companies can sometimes be described as **multinational companies**. They have operations in many countries, although subsidiaries would usually be registered locally in each country of operation. A multinational company based overseas may register a subsidiary in the UK as a private limited company in which it holds 100 per cent of the shares. UK-based companies which are holding companies for overseas subsidiaries are most likely to be registered as public limited companies.

Today, although plc are in a numerical minority, they account for a substantial proportion of the equity of the limited company sector and cover a wide range of industries that typically operate on a large scale – for example, banking, car manufacture and property development.

7.4.6 Advantages and disadvantages of limited companies

To summarize, comparisons between sole traders and partnerships, on the one hand, and limited companies, on the other, can be made at a number of levels. First, formation of a limited company is relatively formal and time-consuming – for a sole trader there is the minimum of formality in establishing a business. The added formality continues with the requirement to produce an annual return and set of accounts. On the other hand, limited company status affords much greater protection to the entrepreneur in the event of the business getting into financial difficulty. Raising additional funds would usually be easier for a limited company, although personal guarantees may still be required to cover loans to the company. Additional funding, which limited company status makes possible, especially plc status, allows organizations to embark on more ambitious expansion plans. While a sole trader may concentrate on small, niche markets, a limited company may be in a better position to tackle mainstream mass markets.

7.5 Commercial and quasi-commercial organizations operating in the public sector

Government has traditionally been involved in providing goods and services that cannot realistically be provided by market forces – for example, defence, policing and basic health services. Government involvement has, however, developed beyond providing these basic public services to providing goods and services that could also be provided by private-sector organizations.

Public-sector organizations take a number of forms, embracing government departments and agencies, local government, nationalized industries and all other undertakings in which central or local government has a controlling interest. This chapter will focus on those public-sector organizations that supply goods and services to consumers. Those government organizations that are primarily policy making in nature were considered in more detail in Chapter 2, dealing with the political environment. In between those branches of government responsible for providing goods and services and those responsible for policy are an increasing number that are involved in both. For example, in the UK, many public services, such as National Health Service Trusts, are increasingly being required to compete for contracts to provide services, using the price mechanism to allocate resources, rather than centralized planning.

7.5.1 State-owned enterprises

Goods and services provided on a commercial basis have often been provided through state-owned enterprises, often referred to as **nationalized industries**. Most countries have a state-owned industry sector and the size of the sector generally reflects the political ideology of a nation. The USA has traditionally had very few government-owned business organizations, while in China, state ownership dominates sectors such as banking and manufacturing, which others would consider a prerogative of the private sector. In the UK, a once large state-owned industry sector has shrunk with changes in political ideology. UK state-owned industries accounted for less than 1 per cent of GDP in 2007, having fallen from 9 per cent in 1979, although the banking crisis of 2008 and the effective nationalization of Northern Rock, Lloyds TSB and Royal Bank of Scotland caused this to rise sharply. Throughout the EU, privatization of state-owned enterprises has been occurring, or at least these enterprises are being reorganized to behave more like private-sector organizations. An important item on the agenda of the World Trade Organization (WTO) is to reduce the power of state-owned industries, which can act as a barrier to global competition. This is increasingly the case for the services sector, where many 'utilities', such as gas, water and electricity supply, have traditionally been state controlled, preventing global competition in these services. Sceptics have been quick to point out the dangers of the WTO's agenda for developing countries – for example, privatization of the Indian Post Office might give new opportunities for Federal Express, but could the Indian Post Office realistically be expected to compete for mail business in the USA?

Governments first became involved in industry for largely pragmatic reasons. In 1913, a key shareholding in the Anglo-Iranian Oil Company – the precursor of British Petroleum – was acquired by the British government to ensure oil supplies to the Royal Navy. During the interwar years, the Central Electricity Generating Board, the British Broadcasting Corporation and the London Passenger Transport Board were created to fill gaps that the private sector had not been capable of filling. Whereas the reasons for the creation of these early nationalized industries were largely pragmatic, the early post-Second World War period saw a large number of nationalized industries created for increasingly ideological reasons. During the Labour government of the late 1940s, the state acquired control of the coal, electricity, gas, and iron and steel industries, and most inland transport. Some industries returned to the private sector during the Conservative government of the 1950s, while subsequent Labour governments added others.

The 1980s and 1990s saw a great decline in the role of nationalized industry, not just in the UK but also throughout the world. Post-war Europe may have needed centralized planning and allocation of resources to facilitate the reconstruction effort, but the mood had changed by the relatively affluent, consumer-orientated years of the 1980s. The view went around that governments were bad managers of commercial businesses and that private-sector organizations were much more capable of giving good value to consumers. In the rush to sell off state-owned industries, privatization was often confused with deregulation. Simply transferring a nationalized industry to the private sector could easily create a private monopoly that was unresponsive to consumers' needs. Consequently, most privatization has been accompanied by measures to deregulate sectors of the economy. Where this has been impractical, government intervention has been retained in the form of regulation of prices and service standards. Not all privatizations have been successful and, occasionally, private-sector organizations have been taken back into state control. This happened in the UK in 2001 when the privatized provider of railway infrastructure (Railtrack plc) was seen as failing and its duties subsequently given to the state-owned organization Network Rail. On occasions, governments have taken into state control private-sector organizations that have never been state owned, but are considered important to the national interest. In 1971 the Conservative government nationalized the Rolls-Royce aircraft engine company – which had got into financial difficulties – on the grounds that many high-technology jobs in the UK depended on the continued existence of the company, which no private-sector company had been prepared to rescue. In 2008, the government took a number of banks into state control, including Northern Rock, Lloyds TSB and Royal Bank of Scotland, arguing that a failure of a UK bank would harm the national economy and the country's international reputation in financial services, and a public-sector solution offered better value to taxpayers than the private takeover bids put forward.

Governments have chosen a number of methods to transfer state-owned industries to the private sector (see Table 7.1). The most common are described below.

- *Sale of shares to the public*: before shares in a state-owned organization can be sold to the public, a limited company with a shareholding must be formed. Initially, all of the new company's shares are owned by the government, and privatization subsequently involves selling these shares to the public. For large privatizations, shares may be targeted at international investors in order to secure the substantial amounts of share capital sought.

Sale to the general public has been undertaken where it would be considered politically unacceptable to exclude small investors from the benefits of privatization.

- *Trade sale*: smaller state-owned industries have often been easily sold to other private-sector companies as a complete entity. This happened, for example, in the sale of the then state-owned Rover car company to British Aerospace. Sometimes, parts of nationalized industries have been broken away for sale to private buyers (e.g. the shipping and hotel operations of British Railways were separated from the parent organization for sale to private-sector organizations long before the rail privatization of the 1990s). The administrative costs of this method of disposal are relatively low, but governments are open to allegations that they sold off a private-sector asset too cheaply to favoured buyers (an allegation that was made when British Aerospace subsequently sold Rover to BMW for a much higher price than it had paid for the company).
- *Management/employee buy-out*: this is often a popular option for people-intensive businesses for which financial institutions may have difficulty in deciding on a value, especially in industries with a history of poor industrial relations. It was used as a method of disposing of the National Freight Corporation and parts of the National Bus Company.
- *Public–private partnerships*: sometimes, it may be politically unacceptable, or just impractical, to dispose of government assets into the private sector. Instead, the government may retain ownership of the assets, but pay a contractor to provide services using those assets. Contracts would usually include an incentive for the contractor, so that as their performance improves, the payment that they receive increases. In the UK, much of the management of the motorway network and Royal Navy dockyards is now in the hands

Table 7.1 Methods used in UK privatizations.

Organization	Date of privatization	Method of privatization
British Aerospace	1981	Public sale of shares
National Freight Corporation	1982	Employee/management buy-out
British Telecom	1984	Public sale of shares
Jaguar	1984	Public sale of shares
Sealink	1984	Trade sale
British Gas	1986	Public sale of shares
British Petroleum	1986	Public sale of shares
BA Helicopters	1986	Trade sale
National Bus Company	1986–91	Trade sales/management buy-outs
British Airports Authority	1987	Public sale of shares
British Airways	1987	Public sale of shares
Rolls-Royce	1987	Public sale of shares

(*Continued*)

Table 7.1 (*Continued*)

Leyland Bus Company	1987	Trade sale
British Steel	1988	Public sale of shares
Rover Group	1988	Trade sale
Regional water companies	1989	Public sale of shares
Regional electricity companies	1990	Public sale of shares
Powergen/National Power	1991	Public sale of shares
Scottish electricity companies	1991	Public sale of shares
British Coal	1994	Trade sale
British Rail	1994–97	Public sale of shares/trade sales
National Air Traffic Services	2001	Sale of 51% of shares to airline consortium in public–private partnership
London Underground	2001	Franchise-type agreement with private-sector Metronet and Tube lines to operate and develop infrastructure
Qinetiq	2001	Sale to private equity company

Note: This is not a complete list. In some cases, the sale of shares was phased over a number of periods.

of private-sector consortia, which receive bonus-related payments in return for work undertaken.

Prior to their privatization, many state-owned organizations have been restructured to make them more attractive to potential buyers. This has typically involved writing off large amounts of debt and offering generous redundancy payments to workers who would not therefore become a liability to a new owner. In doing this, Conservative governments have been accused of providing subsidies for private buyers, although, very often, such action has been essential to provide a buyer with a competitive business proposition.

While governments may be ideologically committed to reducing the role of state-owned industries, it has proved difficult to sell many of them, for a variety of practical and ideological reasons. In the case of the Post Office, ideological objections have been raised at the prospect of the Royal Mail letter delivery monopoly being owned by a private-sector company. This has not, however, prevented the Post Office from being reorganized along business lines, with private limited companies being formed for the main business units, one of which – Girobank – was sold off to the Alliance & Leicester Building Society, while another – the parcel delivery service – was restructured to act more like one of the private parcel companies with which it is having to compete in an increasingly competitive market. The letter business was opened to competition in 2005, following EU measures to deregulate postal services.

It is also possible that attitudes towards privatization may be turning, and it is now possible to see the problems as well as the benefits. Very few people would advocate turning back the clock in sectors such as telecommunications, where privatization and deregulation have been associated with rapidly falling prices and improving service standards. However, it is more doubtful whether privatization of the bus or water supply industries has been entirely beneficial. Customers of newly privatized train companies have pointed out that punctuality fell sharply in the years immediately after privatization, while public subsidies more than doubled. The complex relationships between companies in the rail industry have led many people to suggest that gaps in safety coverage exist, and that the centralized 'command and control' approach of the former state-owned British Rail offered a safer railway at a lower cost.

The importance of a customer orientation within public corporations has been influenced by the nature of the market in which they operate. Following the nationalizations of the late 1940s, marketing was seen in many of the nationalized industries as being very secondary to production. The relative unimportance of marketing was often associated with some degree of monopoly power granted to the industry. In these circumstances, public corporations could afford to ignore marketing. However, as production of the basic industries caught up with demand and the economy became more deregulated during the 1980s, consumers increasingly had a choice between the suppliers offered to them. For example, the deregulation of the coach industry in 1981 and the growth in private car ownership placed increasing competitive pressure on British Rail, and hence an increasing importance for the organization to become customer-orientated. British Rail was increasingly set profit objectives rather than poorly specified social objectives.

What could be seen as either a strength or a weakness for the state-owned industries has been finance for investment and new product development. Investment comes from government – either directly or through guarantees on loans from the private sector. Profits earned have not necessarily been ploughed back into the business. The public sector has, since the 1930s, been seen as one instrument for regulating the economy, cutting back or increasing investment to suit the needs of the national economy rather than the needs of the particular market that the corporation is addressing. As well as limiting the amount of investment funds available, government involvement has also been accused of delay caused by the time it has taken to scrutinize and approve a proposal. By the time approval had been granted, the investment could be too late to meet changed market conditions.

State-owned industries are perceived as an instrument of government and although, theoretically, they may have an independent constitution, government is frequently accused of exercising covert pressure in order to achieve political favour. Electricity prices, rail fares and telephone charges have all at some time been subject to these allegations, which makes life more difficult for managers in nationalized industries because of confused objectives.

Britain is widely credited with having taken the lead in privatizing state-owned industries, and many countries have followed. The EU has taken action to reduce the anti-competitive consequences of having large subsidized public-sector organizations distorting markets. This has been particularly true in the case of airlines, where some European countries have continued to support loss-making state-owned carriers. In 2005, the EU Transport Commissioner investigated a proposal by the Italian government to rescue the near-bankrupt state-owned airline Alitalia with public money. By EU rules, such funding had to be justified as part of a restructuring process with the objective of returning the airline to profitable private-sector ownership, and could not be allowed as a straightforward operating subsidy.

7.5.2 Local authority enterprise

In addition to providing basic services such as roads, education, housing and social services, local authorities have a number of roles in providing marketable goods and services in competitive markets. For a long time, local authorities have operated bus services and leisure facilities, among others. Initially they were set up for a variety of reasons – sometimes to provide a valuable public service, at other times to help stimulate economic development or to earn a profit to supplement the local authority's income. Sometimes, where a project was too large for one authority and benefited many neighbouring authorities, a joint board would be formed between the authorities. This sometimes happened with local authority-controlled airports – for example, East Midlands Airport (now privately owned) was originally formed by a joint board comprising Leicester, Derby, Nottingham, Derbyshire and Nottinghamshire authorities.

UK local authorities have been required to turn their trading activities into business-like units, separately accountable from the rest of the local authority's activities. In the case of local authority bus and airport operations, the Local Government Act 1988 required local authorities to create limited companies into which their assets are placed. Like any limited company, local authority-owned companies are required to appoint a board of directors and to produce an annual profit and loss statement. By creating a company structure, it becomes easier to introduce private capital, or indeed to sell off the business in its entirety to the private sector. This has occurred in the case of a large number of local authority bus companies and airports (East Midlands Airport was initially sold to the National Express group and is now owned by Manchester Airport Group).

Even where separate business units have not been created, local authority services are being exposed to increasing levels of competition. Operations in such areas as highway maintenance, refuse collection and street cleaning must now be assessed to ensure that they offer the 'best value' to the local authority. Local authorities have appointed best value units to monitor their activities against competitive benchmarks and, where necessary, have put the provision of services out to competitive tender. Where a private-sector company takes over the provision of services for a local authority and takes on its employees, the new employer will generally take on responsibilities for accrued rights to redundancy payments, among other things. Best value requirements are discussed in Chapter 2.

In other non-commercial local authority services, clients are being offered greater choice. With the development of locally managed foundation schools, the governing bodies of schools are adopting – if somewhat grudgingly – a marketing orientation to ensure that the service they are offering is considered better than neighbouring schools that pupils would have the choice of attending. Only by attracting clients can they ensure funding for their school.

7.5.3 Private-sector and public-sector organizations compared

Although public-sector organizations cover a wide range of services operating in diverse environments, a few generalizations can be made about the ways in which their business activities differ from those practised by the private sector.

- The aim of most private-sector organizations is to earn profits for the owners of the organization. By contrast to these quantifiable objectives, public-sector organizations operate with relatively diverse and unquantified objectives. For example, a museum may have qualitative scholarly objectives in addition to relatively quantifiable objectives, such as maximizing revenue or the number of visitors.

- The private sector is usually able to monitor the results of its marketing activity, as the benefits are usually internal to the organization. By contrast, many of the aims that public-sector organizations seek to achieve are external, and a profit and loss statement sometimes cannot be produced in the way that is possible with a private-sector organization operating to narrow internal financial goals.

- The degree of discretion given to a private-sector manager is usually greater than that given to a counterpart in the public sector. The checks and balances imposed on many of the latter reflect the fact that their organizations are accountable to a wider constituency of interests than the typical private-sector organization.

- Many of the marketing mix elements that private-sector organizations can tailor to meet the needs of specific groups of users are often not open to public-sector organizations. For non-traded public services, price – if it is used at all – is a reflection of centrally determined social values rather than the value placed on a service by consumers.

- Public-sector organizations are frequently involved in supplying publicly beneficial services where it can be difficult to identify just who the customer is. Should the customer of a school be regarded as the student, their parents or society as a whole, which is investing in the trained workforce of tomorrow?

- Just as the users of some public services may have no choice in who supplies their service, so too the suppliers may have no choice to whom they can provide services. Within the public sector, organizations may be constrained by statute from providing services beyond specified groups of users. On the other hand, some public-sector organizations may be required by law to supply services to specific groups, even though a market-led decision may lead them not to supply.

7.6   Quangos

The quangos ('quasi-autonomous non-governmental organization', sometimes referred to as a non-departmental public body (NDPB)) is a type of organization that does not fit neatly into the private or public sector. Quangos have been around in their modern form since before the Second World War, and semi-independent public bodies of one sort or another have been part of British governance for 200 years. They are used to carry out a variety of trading and policy formulation roles. Their policy-formulation roles were discussed in Chapter 2 and so we briefly note here the reasons why they have become an important type of business-orientated organization.

The following are the most important characteristics of quangos.

- They provide services that are considered politically inappropriate for private companies to dominate.

- The assets of the organization are vested in a body whose constitution is determined by government, and cannot be changed without its approval.

- Management of a quango is generally by political appointees rather than directly elected representatives.

- In theory, quangos operate at 'arm's length' from government and are free from day-to-day political interference.

- Quangos have structures and processes that resemble those of private-sector organizations in terms of their speed and flexibility.

- Quangos are generally relatively small organizations compared to the larger bureaucracies from which they were separated. Because of their autonomous nature, quangos may be financially more accountable than a department within a large government departmental structure. However, many would argue that they are generally much less politically accountable where vital public services are concerned.

- Decisions can generally be made much more speedily by a self-governing organization compared to a unit of a large government department where approval must first be obtained from several layers of a hierarchy.

The following are examples of quangos that have recently been created in Britain.

- Housing associations, which now own and maintain much of the housing stock previously owned by local authorities.

- The Meteorological Office, which was previously part of the Ministry of Defence and now supplies meteorological information in a competitive market environment.

- In many areas, organizations with the characteristics of quangos have been created to market the areas as tourism destinations.

In all the above examples, bodies are motivated to satisfy the needs of their users or stakeholders more effectively, as they usually have some element of choice. If a local housing association does not score highly on its performance indicators (such as speed of repairing faults or length of time that houses are unoccupied), it may lose funding for future house investment or maintenance.

In practice, the business activities of quangos are often highly constrained. Many continue to depend on central or local government for a large part of their income, with no realistic short-term threat of competition for resources. Managers cannot act with as much freedom as their equivalents in the private sector, because the public and local media often take a keen interest in vital public services and are ready to voice their opposition to the activities of a non-elected body responsible for essential services. Another issue that has not been significantly put to the test is what happens to a quango if it fails to attract clients and therefore funding. Government would generally not allow such bodies to 'go out of business' in a way that a private-sector organization can go into receivership. Instead, the tendency has been for the assets of a failing quango to be handed over to another quango whose management has proved itself to be more capable of meeting clients' needs efficiently and effectively.

7.7 Public–private partnerships

The concept of a public–private partnership (PPP) – already introduced in Chapter 2 – further blurs the distinction between private and public sector. Public–private partnerships take a number of forms, from a small-scale local tourism marketing initiative, through to major infrastructure projects, such as the construction and maintenance of roads and railway facilities. PPPs are based on the belief that government organizations can get better value for money by bringing in expertise from the private sector to vital public projects. It is also often believed that the private sector is better able to manage the risks associated with major infrastructure projects and, in support of this argument, it has been pointed out that many projects managed by the public sector alone have run massively over budget and been delivered late. The whole subject of PPPs is controversial, and many critics have challenged their claimed benefits. It has been pointed out that, over the longer term, financial savings to government may not exist – the government may end up paying more by way of rental and service charges to the private-sector collaborators compared to the amount it would have paid had it managed the project entirely by itself. The idea of private-sector partners sharing risk has also been challenged. Some critics have claimed that partnership agreements still place the burden of unexpected risk on the public-sector partner, and the private-sector partners may put the collaborative venture into receivership, leaving the risk with the public sector. (This happened in 2007 when the Metronet public–private-sector partnership managing London's deep-level underground railway lines went into receivership.)

7.8 Other types of organization

7.8.1 Cooperative societies

Cooperatives can be divided into two basic types according to who owns them: consumer cooperatives and producer cooperatives.

Consumer cooperative societies date back to the mid-nineteenth century, when their aims were to provide cheap, unadulterated food for their members and to share profits among members rather than hand them over to outside shareholders. The number of retail cooperative societies in the UK grew during the latter half of the nineteenth century but has declined during recent years as a result of mergers, so that there were fewer than 50 in 2005. Nevertheless, cooperative societies collectively remain the fifth largest retailer in the UK. Food retail is by far the largest sector of the Co-op in the UK, accounting for almost half of all turnover, and the Co-operative Group accounts for more than 50 per cent of total cooperative trade. But although food stores are perhaps the most recognizable face of the Co-op, the cooperative societies also comprise travel agencies, funeral homes, the Co-operative Bank, Co-operative Insurance Service and car dealerships.

Each cooperative society is registered under the Industrial and Provident Societies Acts, and not the Companies Acts, and has its own legal personality, very much as a private limited company. The main contrast between the two comes in the form of control of the society – an individual can become a member of a cooperative by buying one share and is entitled to one vote. Further shares can be purchased, but the member still has only one vote, unlike the private limited company, where voting power is generally based on the number of shares held. The appeal of a shop owned by customers has declined of late, as customers have been attracted by competing companies offering lower prices and/or better service. So the cooperative movement has responded by taking on many of the values of the private sector – for example, through the abolition of 'dividend' payments and advertising low prices for all. However, the movement has tried to capitalize on its customer ownership by appealing to customers on the basis of its social responsibility. Promotion of cooperative retail stores has often sought to stress their 'green' credentials, while the Co-operative Bank has stressed that it does not lend for unethical purposes.

Producer cooperatives are formed where suppliers feel they can produce and sell their output more effectively by pooling their resources – for example, by sharing manufacturing equipment and jointly selling output. Producer cooperatives are popular among groups of farmers, allowing individual farmers to market their produce more effectively than they could achieve individually. An example is OMSCo (Organic Milk Supply Company), formed in 1994 when five like-minded organic dairy farmers joined forces to sell their organic milk. Now with around 300 members, OMSCo is the largest and longest-established UK organic milk supplier. For the marketing of a producer cooperative to be successful, members need to share a sense of vision and have clear leadership. Where this is lacking, many producer cooperatives may be successful in buying products for their members at a discount, but less successful at marketing their output. There are currently about 1000 producer cooperative societies within the UK, mainly in the farming and fishing sectors. Farmers' cooperatives are much more important in other EU countries, such as France, where there are many more local, regional and national farmers' cooperatives, the larger of which have diversified into non-farming activities such as banking and transport.

Producer cooperatives may fall foul of legislation to protect the competitiveness of markets where collectively the producers account for a high proportion of sales in the market. However, as most producer cooperatives tend to be quite local in their membership, there is usually the possibility of competition from producers located in other areas.

7.8.2 Charities and voluntary organizations

The aims of this group of organizations can be quite complex. Serving a good cause, such as famine relief or cancer research, is clearly very important. However, these organizations often also set trading objectives, as where charities run shops to raise funds. Often, the way in which such businesses are run is just as important as the funds generated. For example, Barnardo's runs coffee shops where providing training for disadvantaged staff is seen to be as important as providing a fast service for customers or maximizing the profits of the outlet.

In the UK, charities that are registered with the Registrar of Charities are given numerous benefits by the government, such as tax concessions (although recent changes in legislation have introduced stricter controls over their activities in order to reduce abuses of their status – for example, private schools have previously qualified as 'charities', benefiting parents who are arguably among the better-off members of society). Where a charity has substantial trading activities, it is usual for these to be undertaken by a separately registered limited company, which then hands over its profits to the charity.

⟳ Thinking around the subject

People power at John Lewis

Capitalism has always had critics who dislike the idea of private companies exploiting employees and customers in order to provide maximum profits for shareholders. But public-sector ownership is not without its critics, who point to public-sector monopolies that provide poor service and little choice to their captive customers. Problems associated with extreme public- and private-sector-type organizations have led to the development of a variety of hybrid organizations that incorporate the public interest, but not necessarily through government ownership.

Many countries, such as France and Spain, have a long tradition of cooperative-type organizations, which are owned by their employees, often with financial support from banks or government. Some have argued that, today, novel forms of organization provide a solution that neither pure public- nor private-sector organizations can provide.

During the credit crunch of 2008, many private-sector retailers went bankrupt or faced severe financial difficulties because of over-borrowing. But one retailer – John Lewis – stood out from the crowd and appeared to prosper where others were failing. Many attributed its success to its relatively unusual ownership model.

John Lewis is a partnership-based organization, which owns 32 John Lewis shops across the UK, 241 Waitrose supermarkets (www.waitrose.com), an online and catalogue business, johnlewis.com (www.johnlewis.com), a production unit and a farm, with a turnover of nearly £7.4 billion in 2010. All 70,000 permanent staff are 'Partners' and share in the benefits and profits of the business.

When the founder, John Spedan Lewis, set up the partnership in 1928, he was careful to create a governance system, set out in its constitution, that would be both commercial – allowing it to move quickly in a competitive environment – and also democratic, by giving every Partner a voice in the business they co-own. Achieving this involves a careful balancing act.

The Chairman, the Partnership Board, the Divisional Management Boards and the Group Executive form the management of the company. The Partnership Council, which elects five partnership board directors, the divisional and branch-level democracy, make up the democratic bodies that give Partners a voice and hold the management to account. High standards of corporate governance are at the heart of the partnership – the structure is claimed to give managers the freedom to be entrepreneurial and competitive in the way they run the business for long-term success, while giving the company's owners, the Partners, the rights and responsibilities of ownership through active involvement in the business.

Was John Spedan Lewis ahead of his time with his combination of commercial acumen and corporate conscience? Was the ownership structure the main reason for the retailer's continuing success following the credit crunch of 2008, at a time when many of its competitors failed? If the model is such a success, why haven't many other businesses adopted it?

Source: Adapted from www.johnlewis.com.

In some respects, charities have become more like conventional trading organizations – for example, in their increasingly sophisticated use of direct marketing techniques. However, in other respects they can act very differently from private- and public-sector organizations. Customers may show a loyalty to the charity's cause, which goes beyond any rational economic explanation. Employees often work for no monetary reward, providing a dedicated and low-cost workforce, which can help the organization achieve its objectives.

⟳ Thinking around the subject

The National Health Service goes to market

The National Health Service (NHS) is Britain's largest employer and has traditionally operated with a command and control structure. Money was allocated by government and distributed between regions, then between hospitals, and then allocated between wards. There was a sense of security in this centralized planning, and hospitals – even wards – could reasonably expect that their budget in the following year would not be drastically different to that in the current year. Hospitals developed specialisms and tended to take on a steady workload of patients referred through an established network of consultants and primary care trusts. The development of 'Foundation'-status hospital trusts from 2003, and the introduction of a market for hospital services, were intended to improve the effectiveness and efficiency with which trusts operated. From 2004, the government introduced privately operated 'treatment centres' to provide a wide range of elective treatment, such as eye cataract operations and MRI scans. These effectively took 'business' away from NHS hospitals, which would in future have to compete for these patients. In the new NHS market, money followed the patients, and patients were given more choice, while family doctors were increasingly being encouraged to take control of their budgets.

But were managers of the traditionally bureaucratic command-and-control NHS ready for the uncertainty of a market economy? More worryingly, what would happen if a hospital with Foundation Trust status ran out of money? Could it 'go bust'? Foundation Trust hospitals are free-standing businesses that depend on government for their cash flow. Doubts were raised when Bradford Teaching Hospital, one of the first Foundation Trusts, went from a projected surplus of £1 million in 2005 to a potential deficit of £11 million in a matter of months of it coming into existence. At the same time, a number of other Foundation Trusts faced lesser financial difficulties.

The government claimed to have in place procedures for dealing with a failing Foundation Trust hospital. The first resort would be to put in new management. If the failing was more serious, it could be taken over by another Foundation Trust. Ultimately, the Trust could be returned to the Secretary of State's ownership. The government would doubtless be mindful of the political consequences of allowing a hospital trust to close down, or concentrating services in one centralized facility.

In many parts of the country, hospitals provide overlapping services, with very complex sets of relationships with Primary Care Trusts (to be replaced with groups of commissioning GPs), purchasing hospital services. In the new NHS market, the financial skills of boards were called for if a chaotic and unstable environment was to be avoided. It was almost unheard of for a British hospital to go out of business but, as the government pursues a market discipline for the NHS, is going out of business a logical consequence that should be shared with the private sector?

7.8.3 Building societies

Building societies are governed by the Building Societies Acts, which have evolved over time to reflect their changing role. They were for some time seen as almost monopoly providers of money for house purchases, with strict regulations on the powers of societies in terms of their sources of funds and the uses for which loans could be advanced. With the liberalization of the home mortgage market, building societies now have wider powers of lending and borrowing, and face much greater competition. As a result of this, societies have had to embrace marketing activities more fully. The Building Societies Act 1986 further allowed building societies the possibility of converting to plc status, eliminating the remaining controls imposed by the Building Society Acts (Figure 7.2). However, with greater freedom came greater danger, and in 2008 many building societies that had been market led in their lending found themselves unable to raise sufficient capital from the commercial money markets on which they had become dependent. Many smaller building societies, such as the Dunfermline and Cheshire Building Societies, were rescued by larger rivals that had better access to wholesale finance.

Figure 7.2 Public limited companices have grown in number in recent years and added a number of former building societies whose members voted for conversion. Although plc status does give numerous benefits over mutual status, there are also many benefits of remaining mutual. The Coventry Building Society has stressed the benefits of remaining mutual, arguing that it is achieving high levels of customer satisfaction and a financial performance that matches that of plcs and returns the benefits to members. During the 'credit crunch' of 2008, distrust in banks – which many blamed for the financial crisis in world money markets – spread rapidly. Building societies played on this distrust by stressing that they were owned by their members and didn't give big bonuses to greedy bankers. However building societies themselves faced problems and weaker ones, including the Cheshire and Scarborough societies had to be rescued by bigger societies. Coventry Building Society sought greater strength through a merger with the Stroud and Swindon society. However, their fate was not as bad as that which faced those building societies which had chosen to become plcs by replacing their membership structures with shareholders. Of these, Northern Rock and Bradford and Bingley went bankrupt and had to be rescued by government, with members who became shareholders losing the value of their shareholding. (Picture reproduced with permission of Coventry Building Society.)

Case study:
Cooking by yourself or with company?

© Kelly Cline

The restaurant sector in Britain is dominated by thousands of small owner-managed businesses, which compete and co-exist with much larger managed enterprises. Many people dream about setting up their own restaurant, and a BBC television show in 2007 even saw the celebrity chef Raymond Blanc 'rewarding' the winner of a competition with their own restaurant. For somebody who loves food, the prospect of giving up a 9–5 office job and spending all their working life developing new menus may seem irresistible. Sadly, although thousands of people have ventured down the route to becoming a restaurateur, their success rate is low. Estimates vary, but it is generally reckoned that about three-quarters of all new restaurants are not a success and close within three years of opening (see Parsa *et al.* 2005). Large corporate restaurant chains generally do better, but it is the sole trader that is particularly likely to face problems. Instead of experimenting with new recipes for beef bourguignon or duck à l'orange, the small restaurant owner is likely to spend much of their time on more mundane matters: filling out the VAT return, recruiting staff, calculating their income tax and paying their National Insurance contributions, keeping abreast of new legislation concerning minimum wage levels, maternity leave and disability discrimination are all distractions from the kitchen. Then there is the never-ending task of promoting the restaurant. Many restaurateurs think that customers will beat a path to their door, but diners can be fickle and as soon as a new restaurant opens in town, they may be off to try it out. With so much to do in simply running the business, it is not surprising that

many small restaurateurs become disillusioned and move on. Some fail simply because they have not developed a realistic business plan.

There are clearly many advantages to a restaurant that can operate on a larger scale and spread many of these burdensome administrative tasks over a larger volume of business. However, it can be very difficult for a small restaurant owner to establish a chain of outlets. With so much attention to detail needed, a potential chain could be harmed if the standard of service at one restaurant is not the same as the standards elsewhere. For example, a customer eating at a branch of Gordon Ramsay's restaurant may expect the celebrity chef's attention to detail to be present in all places at all times, but ensuring this actually happens demands a high level of management effort and a willingness to delegate.

Nevertheless, large chains of restaurants have prospered, and many have achieved international success. But how can this be done? One approach is a 'command and control' type of management, in which each restaurant is run by a manager who is paid a salary by the company. The successful manager will have earned a bonus and probably promotion within the organization. However, this type of approach can become very bureaucratic and may fail to inspire individuals in an industry where attention to detail can be vital.

One approach adopted by many restaurant chains is to incorporate small businesses within the umbrella of a large franchise organization. We will look in more detail at franchising in the next chapter, but essentially this allows the small entrepreneur to run their own business, while at the same time relying on the franchisor for promotional and administrative support, for which they pay a proportion of their turnover. Within the restaurant sector, franchising has been relatively slow to take hold at the gourmet end of the market, where the owner's individuality and style can add to the appeal of a restaurant. But in the convenience food sector, franchising has really taken hold and allows dedicated individuals to build a secure and profitable business.

The pizza chain Domino's has grown rapidly throughout the world by franchising out its operations to smaller businesses. In some cases, franchisees are sole traders, but can also take the form of large limited companies that operate many outlets. The company has used the energy of talented and hard-working individuals to deliver good financial rewards to its franchisees and quality pizzas to its customers.

In 2004, Domino's reported that ten of its 100-plus UK and Ireland franchisees owned businesses that were worth more than £1,000,000 each. These figures are based on a standard calculation of twice annual turnover. With a typical start-up cost of £250,000 per store this is a significant return on franchisees' initial investment. Only two years previously, one in ten of Domino's stores had a turnover of £10,000 a week; by 2004 this figure was one in three. In 2002, Domino's franchisees earned around £120,000 a year on average (although some considerably more), which was more than three times the average income of a typical business manager (£38,107). Furthermore, no Domino's franchise failed during the year, compared with over 22,000 business failures elsewhere in the UK economy.

Founded in 1960, Domino's makes and delivers nearly 6 million pizzas a week in more than 60 countries around the world. By 2006, it had 8190 stores serving a total of over 1 million pizzas a week. From humble beginnings in 1960, franchising has been a key element of the company's mission to bring pizza to the world. By 2006, 85 per cent of its outlets were owned by franchisees. The UK was an early target for Domino's expansion, and it established a subsidiary company, Domino's Pizza Group Limited, which holds the exclusive master franchise to own, operate and franchise Domino's Pizza stores in the UK and Ireland. In 2010, it operated 665 stores with a total sales turnover of £485 million and a profit before tax of £18.7 million.

Domino's research into the skills set and characteristics of the most successful franchisees, both in the UK and internationally, has uncovered the fact that the majority of franchisees believe the traditional corporate management career path failed to offer either the scope to succeed or the financial rewards within the timescale they want. Typical of the hard-working individuals attracted to a Domino's franchise was James Swift. As a 16-year-old delivery driver for Domino's Pizza, Swift spotted the potential to run his own business at an early age. He soon secured a position as the manager of Domino's branch in

Swindon and learned everything there was to know about running a store. This operational experience was critical for learning everything from how to make a pizza to how to manage a team. It was about three years later that he got the chance to buy a share in the franchise. By the age of 24, he had become co-franchisee of three Domino's outlets in Swindon, Newbury and Bath. He put his success down to sheer hard work and determination, with the backing of a renowned brand and the commitment that only the owner of a business can give.

Maybe one day, James Swift would match the success of Richard P. Mueller Jr, Domino's Pizza's most successful global franchisee. Mueller joined Domino's in 1967 as a delivery driver and became a franchisee in 1970. By 2003 he owned 158 stores in the USA and employed over 3000 team members. His company sold over 10 million pizzas a year, as many as the entire UK Domino's business. That equated to 5 million pounds of dough, 5 million pounds of cheese and enough pizza sauce to fill a large swimming pool. In the process of growing his business, Mueller had become a millionaire.

Given the stressful, tedious conditions of most fast-food operations, it is vital that staff are motivated to succeed. While many part-time staff, such as students and parents of young school children, are happy to just do a few hours of work in return for a bit of extra cash, the business needs to be able to accommodate the ambitions of people who could make good leaders of people. A bureaucratic 'jobsworth' culture will not allow a pizza company to compete effectively with more agile and committed competitors.

Although franchising has figured prominently in Domino's growth, the company retains a proportion of directly managed outlets. As well as providing an internal benchmark against which franchisees can be judged, these outlets are useful for developing new product ideas that may be too risky for individual franchisees to undertake on their own. Recent examples of innovation have included the introduction of an iPhone app for ordering, which accounted for over £1 million of sales in the three months after its UK launch in September 2010. The company has also involved its franchisees in the social media arena. Would such developments be possible without the support of a strong, centrally managed franchise?

Source: based on material provided on the Domino's (www.dominos.com) and British Franchise Association's (www.britishfranchise. org) websites.

QUESTIONS

1 Summarize the relative advantages and disadvantages of the small sole trader, and the large limited company chain within the restaurant sector.

2 What problems does a franchise such as Domino's face in trying to reconcile the individualism of entrepreneurial franchisees with the need for brand consistency?

3 Why do you think that 15 per cent of Domino's outlets are managed directly by the company, rather than by franchisees?

Summary

There are numerous ways of classifying business organizations. Classification based on legal status is useful because this is often related to other factors such as size, the ability to raise fresh capital and the level of constraints imposed on managers. Private-sector organizations range from the informality of the sole trader to the formality of the plc. In between is a diverse range of organizations, each of which has its role in the business environment. Some of these differences will become apparent in **Chapter 11**, which reviews competition within markets. While small sole traders may be associated with perfectly competitive markets, the reality of most markets is domination by a small number of plcs. This chapter has explored the reasons behind the recent resurgence in small business units. The ability to keep in touch with customers and to react to changes in the marketing environment were noted as important advantages. There is also diversity within public-sector organizations, although this group as a whole has tended to diminish in relative importance in most western countries. **Chapter 2** discussed organizational structures within the public sector by focusing on government bodies that are policy making rather than operational. **Chapter 8** will discuss how organizations grow, and this chapter has laid the groundwork by suggesting that there are differences in organizations' inherent ability to grow.

Key Terms

Building society (255)

Charity (252)

Cooperative society (251)

Franchising (256)

Limited company (241)

Liquidation (242)

Multinational company (243)

Nationalized industry (244)

Partnership (240)

Privatization (245)

Public limited company (243)

Receivership (242)

Share capital (242)

Shareholder (241)

Sole trader (238)

**Online
Learning Centre**

To help you grasp the key concepts of this chapter, explore the extra resources posted on the Online Learning Centre at *www.mcgraw-hill.co.uk/palmer*. Among other helpful resources there are chapter-by-chapter test questions, revision notes and web links.

Chapter review questions

1 For what reasons might a manufacturer of fitted kitchens seek plc status? What are the advantages and disadvantages of this course of action?

2 Why have governments found it difficult to privatize state-owned postal services? Suggest methods by which private-sector marketing principles can be applied to state-owned postal services.

3 Critically assess the benefits to the public of turning branches of the National Health Service into self-governing trusts.

Activities

1 Identify three quangos operating in the following areas: education, housing and transport. Critically evaluate the suitability of quango status. Do you think these organizations' service to the public would be improved if they were either purely private-sector or purely public-sector organizations?

2 Choose one of the following business sectors: hotels, fashion retailers, restaurants. Identify a sample of small sole traders and larger limited companies within each sector, and critically examine the ways that their marketing efforts differ.

3 Examine the charges made by a public-sector hospital. These may typically include charges for car parking, telephones and catering. To what extent do you think the organization is business orientated in relation to these? How successfully has it managed to combine its social objectives with its business objectives?

Further reading

A useful starting point for further reading is one of a number of books discussing the nature of different types of organization.

Carnall, C. (2007) *Managing Change in Organizations*, 5th edn, London, FT Prentice Hall.

Clegg, S., Pitsis, T. and Kornverger, M. (2008) *Managing Organizations: An Introduction to Theory and Practice*, 2nd edn, London, Sage.

Down, S. (2010) *Enterprise, Entrepreneurship and Small Business*, London, Sage.

For a review of current statistics on the composition of business units, the following sources are useful.

Department of Trade and Industry, *SME Statistics*, London, The Stationery Office.

Office for National Statistics, *Annual Abstract of Statistics*, London, The Stationery Office.

The nature of public-sector organizations has changed considerably in recent years and the following provides an overview of this change.

Schedler K. Proeller, I. and Siegelm, J.P. (2011) *Strategic Management in the Public Sector*, London, Routledge.

Charities are becoming increasingly involved in business activities and their distinctive characteristics are discussed in the following text.

Sargeant, A. (2009) *Marketing Management for Non-profit Organizations*, 3rd edn, Oxford, Oxford University Press.

Reference

Parsa, H.G., Self, J.T., Njite, D. and King, T. (2005) 'Why restaurants fail', *Cornell Hotel and Restaurant Administration Quarterly*, Vol. 46, No. 3, pp. 304–322.

Chapter 2

The Political Environment

Just think about all the ways in which politicians affect your personal life during a typical day. You may be shocked at the level of tuition fees that you have just paid to your university, when you compare them to the free tuition received by your peers in another country. You get on a train and wonder why the fare is so much more expensive in your country than in many other European countries. You take it for granted that your favourite shops will be open on Sunday, but your friends in other countries tell you how frustrating it can be that their shops remained closed then. You may be feeling very poor, and you wonder why there are high levels of apparent inequality in your society. All of these phenomena that you have observed have some connection to the political environment. Politicians in France, for example, take a different attitude to the Sunday opening of shops than that of politicians in Britain. The political environment has direct and indirect effects on business organizations, and these linkages are explored in this chapter. We rarely see political revolutions in western Europe, but in fact the political environment can be one of the less predictable elements in an organization's business environment. Although politicians issue manifestos and other policy statements, these may change in response to public pressure or an upcoming election. Change in the political environment can result from a variety of internal and external pressures. The fact that democratic governments have to seek re-election every few years has contributed towards a cyclical political environment. This chapter reviews some of the trends in the political environment that have had impacts on the business environment.

✓ Learning Objectives

This chapter will explain:

- ✓ The nature of the political environment.
- ✓ The structure and processes of local, regional, national and supranational government.
- ✓ Political ideologies, and their effects on government policy and implications for business organizations.
- ✓ The two-way influence between business organizations and government.
- ✓ The role of pressure groups in the political process.

2.1 Defining the political environment

All aspects of an organization's business environment are interrelated to some extent, and this is especially true of the political environment. Interlinkages occur in many ways. Here are some examples.

- Political decisions inevitably affect the economic environment – for example, in the proportion of gross domestic product (GDP) accounted for by the state and the distribution of income between different groups in society (Chapter 13).
- Political decisions also influence the social and cultural environment of a country (Chapter 3). For example, governments create legislation, which can have the effect of encouraging families to care for their elderly relatives or allowing shops to open on Sundays. In short, the actions of politicians are both a reflection of the social and cultural environment of a country and also help to shape it.
- Politicians can influence the pace at which new technologies appear and are adopted – for example, through tax concessions on research and development activity or through direct intervention such as the UK government's decision to replace the analogue TV broadcast signal with digital only (Chapter 4).

The political environment is one of the less predictable elements in an organization's business environment. Although politicians issue manifestos and other policy statements, these have to be seen against the pragmatic need of governments to modify their policies during their period in office. Change in the political environment can result from a variety of internal and external pressures. The fact that democratic governments have to seek re-election every few years has contributed towards a cyclical political environment. Turbulence in the political environment can be seen by considering some of the major swings that have occurred in the political environment in the UK since the Second World War.

- During the late 1940s, the political environment stressed heavy government intervention in all aspects of the economy, including ownership of a substantial share of productive capacity.
- During the 1950s, there was a much more restrained, hands-off approach in which many of the previously nationalized industries were deregulated and sold off.
- During the 1960s and 1970s the political environment oscillated in moderation between more and less government involvement in the ways businesses are run.
- The 1980s saw a significant change in the political environment, with the wholesale withdrawal of government from ownership and regulation of large areas of business activity.
- During the 1990s political commentators detected a shift away from the radicalism of the 1980s to more middle-of-the-road policies based on a social market economy.
- During the period of Labour government from 1997 to 2010, many commentators noted a tendency for the role of government to grow in an era of 'big government', including massive expenditure on nationalizing Northern Rock, Lloyds TSB and Royal Bank of Scotland. This was replaced with a new coalition government's aim of replacing many functions of government with community-based involvement, dubbed the 'Big Society' programme.

In its widest sense, the political environment refers not just to those institutions, such as local and national government, that are responsible for developing and implementing policy. It also refers to forces in the environment comprising vested interests that, ultimately, politicians seek to serve. In this chapter we will begin by looking at how political systems work, and introduce lobbyists and pressure groups as part of the political environment.

Political systems

Throughout most of this chapter, we will be describing political systems based on the type of democracy that is prevalent in western countries. However, there is great diversity in political systems. At one extreme is a political system based on an open system of government that is democratically elected by the population of a country. The other extreme may be represented by totalitarian systems of government in which power derives not from popular representation, but is acquired by a select group. This may be in the form of communism, or may be based on the interests of sectional groups, often militarily based, that acquire power through force or tradition.

The link between the dominant political system, economic growth and the nature of the business environment is an interesting and often complex one. There has been a lot of research into the relationship between democracy and economic prosperity. The idea that autocratic regimes have an advantage in economic development was once quite fashionable. The plausibility of such a notion lies in the advantages such regimes were said to have in forcing through development in the long term. There is some evidence for this in the way that countries go about the construction of major transport infrastructure projects. In western countries with open democratic governance, a lengthy process of consultation is likely to take place before a new road is built, and there are likely to be extensive checks and balances to prevent the interests of individuals or groups being threatened or unduly favoured. In countries with less democratic traditions, government is more likely to go ahead regardless of objections. Some commentators have attributed part of the rapid economic development of South-east Asia during the 1980s and 1990s to the absence of democratic government in the western tradition.

An alternative view is that democracy is likely to foster economic development. The political institutions critical to economic development are more likely to exist and function effectively in democratic systems. These institutions include a legal system that protects property rights, individual liberties that encourage creativity and entrepreneurship, the freedom of expression that facilitates the flow of information in an economy, and institutional checks and balances that prevent the theft of public wealth often observed in totalitarian systems. There is a suggestion of a non-linear relationship in which greater democracy enhances growth at low levels of political freedom but depresses growth when a moderate level of freedom has already been attained. Improvements in the standard of living, health services and education may subsequently raise the probability that political freedom will grow.

There are many variations in political systems and their links to economic development. The Chinese system, for example, is one of district, city, regional and state government, which is similar to an electoral college. There are elections at all levels but the system is not democratic on the western model. Also it is interesting to note that there is now a split between political and economic systems. Previously communism was both a political and an economic system, but the modern Chinese system is much more subtle than this. Within a centralized state system are powerful regional governments, and individual free-market systems in many sectors.

Corruption remains a barrier to economic development in many countries. Some companies may survive and prosper by bribing government officials, but the success and growth of such companies is not necessarily based on the value they create for consumers. In many cases, they have simply bought themselves a dominant position in a market that the government is happy to allow them to exploit, in return for a payment that is made. In government systems with poor accountability, such payments may not be made for the public good, but instead just add to the private wealth of government officials.

The link between accountability and ethics is apparent in political systems. Individuals embark on careers in politics for a number of reasons, and it may be quite naive to assume that they all do so for the purpose of implementing policies for the public good that are in accordance with their personal convictions. There is often a grey area of corruption and personal benefit, which political systems have responded to with a need for politicians to be more accountable. During

2010, for example, many UK Members of Parliament were accused of abusing the system of reclaiming personal expenses, resulting in new procedures for making them accountable. Abuse of a privileged political position can also undermine public confidence in the political process. This in turn can lead to lower levels of public engagement in politics, reflected in typically low levels of voting in elections, especially among younger people.

The statistical evidence of a link between democracy and economic growth is mixed. One study of economic growth data for 115 countries from 1960 to 1980 found that countries with high degrees of political openness achieved an average annual real per capita growth rate of 2.53 per cent, compared with 1.41 per cent in more closed political systems. This implies that more democratic countries may grow 80 per cent faster than less democratic countries. However, other studies have given more ambiguous results, including some that reported a weak negative overall effect of democracy on economic growth (Barro 1996).

Table 2.1 reports data for a selection of countries, linking annual GDP per capita with an index of political freedom within the country (for example, the extent of universal voting rights), a ranking of economic freedom (for example, the ease with which new entrants can enter a market), and ranking of corruption. A casual glance at this table will reveal that many of the poorest countries of the world are associated with lower levels of political freedom and a high level of corruption.

Table 2.1   National indices for selected countries linking GDP per capita, political freedom, economic freedom and corruption.

	GDP per capita 2008	Index of political freedom 2009	Ranking of economic freedom 2009	Ranking of corruption 2009
Burundi	144	4.5	160	168
Liberia	222	3.5	163	97
Tanzania	482	3.5	97	126
Haiti	729	4.5	141	168
Pakistan	991	4.5	117	139
India	1,017	2.5	124	84
Zambia	1,134	3.5	100	99
Nigeria	1,370	4.5	106	130
Philippines	1,847	3.5	109	139
China	3,267	6.5	140	79
Hong Kong	30,863	3.5	1	12
Canada	45,070	1	7	8
UK	43,541	1	11	17
Ireland	60,460	1	5	14
Switzerland	64,327	1	6	5
Norway	94,759	1	37	11

Source: based on United Nations (1998); World Bank (2008); Freedom House (2010); Transparency International (2010); World Factbook (2009).

Note: The measure of political freedom comprises a composite of two separate indicators, political rights and civil liberties. The combined score is between 1 and 7, 1 being the freest and 7 being the least free. The organization Freedom House considers countries with scores of between 1.0 to 2.5 'free'; those scoring between 3.0 and 5.0 as 'partly free'; and those scoring between 5.5 and 7.0 as 'not free'. The ranking of Economic Freedom consist of one index, in which the freest economy (Hong Kong) is ranked 1 and the least free economy (North Korea) ranks 179. Ranking of corruption is based on data provided by Transparency International (2010), with the least corrupt country being ranked 1.

A further intriguing issue concerns the role of political systems relative to transnational organizations. It has been suggested that the increasing volume of business transactions that take place across the borders of nation-states is eroding the efficiency of national governing structures, especially democratic ones. Many multinational corporations have a turnover that is much larger than that of small, less developed countries. When one of these countries relies on the multinational company for a lot of its income (a situation common in many economies dependent on natural resources), some would argue that the power of the people to control their government is less than the power of the multinational company (Rodrik 2002).

2.3 The importance of monitoring the political environment

We now move on to explore the reasons why business organizations should constantly monitor their political environment, whether this be a totalitarian or democratic system, or a system that is in the process of changing from one type of system to another. It must not be forgotten that within the past couple of decades businesses have observed and reacted to some dramatic changes in political systems – for example, the transformation of former communist eastern European countries into fledgling democracies. Even here, the ending of communism was only the beginning of a process of political change. In many eastern European countries, the early days of *laissez-faire* capitalism (described by Joseph Stiglitz as 'market bolshevism', in which unregulated free markets were forced on these countries) was replaced over time with calls for more rather than less state involvement. Governments gradually recognized the need to intervene to counteract market failures by creating enforceable laws and collectable taxes, among other things (Stiglitz 2000).

Change in the political environment can impact on business strategy and operations in a number of ways.

- At the most general level, the stability of the political system affects the attractiveness of a particular national market. While radical change rarely results from political upheaval in most western countries, the instability of governments in many less developed countries leads to uncertainty about the economic and legislative framework in which goods and services will be provided.

- At a national level, governments pass legislation that directly affects the relationship between the firm and its customers, and relationships between itself and its suppliers, and between itself and other firms and individuals. Sometimes legislation has a direct effect on the organization – for example, a law giving consumers rights against the seller of faulty goods. At other times, the effect is less direct, as where changes in legislation concerning anti-competitive practices alter an organization's relative competitive advantage in a market.

- Governments see business organizations as an important vehicle for social reform through legislation that affects employment relationships. During the previous 30 years, organizations have been affected by a wide range of employment legislation, affecting, among other things, discrimination against disadvantaged groups, minimum wages, and more stringent health and safety requirements.

- The government is additionally responsible for protecting the public interest at large, imposing further constraints on the activities of firms – for example, where the government lays down design standards for cars to protect the public against pollution or road safety risks.

- The economic environment is influenced by the actions of government. It is responsible for formulating policies that can influence the rate of growth in the economy and hence the total amount of spending power. It is also a political decision as to how this spending power should be distributed between different groups of consumers, and between the public and private sectors.

- Government at both a central and local level is itself a major consumer of goods and services, and accounts for about 40 per cent of the UK's gross domestic product.
- Government policies can influence the dominant social and cultural values of a country, although there can be argument about which is the cause and which the effect. For example, UK government policies of the 1980s emphasized wealth creation as an end in itself; these policies also had the effect of generating a feeling of confidence among consumers. This can be directly linked to an increase in consumer spending at a higher rate than earnings growth, and a renewed enthusiasm for purchasing items of ostentatious consumption.

It should be remembered that organizations not only monitor the political environment – they also contribute to it. This can happen where organizations feel threatened by change and lobby government to intervene to pass legislation that will protect their interests. The role of lobbying and pressure groups will be discussed later in this chapter.

2.4   Political ideologies

It was noted earlier that political ideologies in the UK have changed through a series of cycles during the post-Second World War period. It is important to consider the issue of dominant political ideologies, as they can have such a major impact on the business environment. At one extreme, the ideology of the immediate post-war Labour government placed great importance on the role of the state, and this resulted in many private-sector organizations being taken into state ownership. The political ideology of the incoming Conservative government in 1979 was very different on this and many other issues. As a consequence of this shift in ideology, large parts of state control of business were dismantled and nationalized industries sold off, a process commonly referred to as privatization. This process gave many ordinary people the opportunity to buy shares for the first time. For business organizations, understanding shifts in dominant ideologies can be crucial to understanding the future nature of their business environment. Two important and recurring ideological issues that affect business organizations are the distribution of wealth between different groups in society and the role of the state versus the private sector in delivering goods and services. Political parties represent the gathering of individuals who share a political ideology.

2.4.1 Political parties

Most Members of Parliament (MPs) belong to a **political party.** In general, the views of members of political parties cross a range of policy issues, so political parties can be distinguished from single-interest groups such as the League Against Cruel Sports. The existence of political parties makes the management of parliamentary business more efficient, because party leaders can generally be assured of the support of their members when passing new legislation. Parties also provide a hierarchical organization through which MPs can become junior ministers and eventually take a place in the executive.

From the perspective of the electorate, belonging to a political party identifies an individual candidate with a known set of values. There is a lot of evidence that, when voting for an MP, a substantial proportion of voters are guided primarily by the party affiliation of a candidate, rather than their personal views and characteristics.

Political parties represent an ideological point of view, although it has been noted that in recent years the ideological gap between the main UK parties has been reducing. Some cynics suggested that the incoming Labour government in 1997 shared many ideological values of the previous Conservative government and was far removed from the ideological zeal with which the post-Second World War Labour government took office. In 2010, the Conservative and Liberal Democrat parties, which had been fighting each other in their general election campaigns nevertheless recognized enough common ground to join together in a coalition government. The main parties have tended to converge on a relatively moderate ideology, leaving extreme parties such as the British National Party and Socialist Workers Party to pursue more radical ideologies. Of course, the prevalence of an ideology represents shifts in the value of society as a whole. The radical free market ideology of the incoming Conservative government of 1979 found a ready reception by an electorate that had come to see the shortcomings of the previous Labour government. This was seen by many as being too restrictive and closely aligned with the inflexible attitudes of trades unions. The fact that extreme ideologies have not found great recent support in the UK, and that the difference between the two main parties has been narrowed, is a reflection of relatively moderate political values held by the population as a whole, and possibly contentment with increasing personal wealth and living standards.

Because political parties represent a diverse range of ideological issues, it is not surprising that party leaders often find it difficult to gain the unanimous support of all members on all issues. In the UK, members of the main political parties are divided on issues such as the level of involvement with the EU, defence expenditure and educational policy. Nevertheless, a political party stands for a broad statement of ideological values with which its members can identify. In the UK, the Conservative Party has traditionally been identified with such core values as the self-reliance of individuals, less rather than more government, and the role of law and order. The Labour Party, by contrast, has traditionally stood for state intervention where market failure has occurred, protection of the weak in society from the strong, and efforts to reduce inequalities in wealth. The Liberal Democrat Party has traditionally appealed to people who believe in open democratic government in a market economy, with government intervention where market mechanisms have produced inequalities or inefficiencies.

The Conservative Party has traditionally been seen as the party of business and the Labour Party as the party of organized labour. This is largely true as far as the funding of the parties goes, with the Conservative Party receiving sizeable donations from business organizations while many Labour MPs are sponsored by trades unions (although the number of donations by business to Labour has increased in recent years). In general, the free-market enterprise values of the Conservative Party would appear to favour the interests of businesses, while the socialist values of the Labour Party would appear to be against business interests. Historically, business has been worried at the prospect of a Labour government, as witnessed by the fall in stock market prices that has often followed a Labour Party election victory. However, the UK, like many western countries, has seen increasing levels of convergence between parties, which makes business leaders very uncertain about just what makes a party's policies distinctive. For example, the UK Labour Party has traditionally been opposed to the privatization of public utilities, but the Labour government elected in 1997 had no immediate plans to renationalize previously privatized companies, and indeed subsequently privatized London Underground and the air navigation services. As political parties have targeted the crucial middle-ground 'floating voter', their underlying ideologies have become increasingly indistinguishable.

The UK political environment has traditionally been dominated at a national level by two major parties. By contrast, most other European countries have a long tradition of multiple parties that represent different shades of opinion, and each sends small numbers of members to its legislative body. The result is often that no one party is able to form an executive with an outright majority of members, so executives based on a coalition of parties must be formed. The difference in electoral outcomes between the two systems reflects the method by which the election is conducted. In the UK, the party with the most MPs elected within individual constituencies takes power, and coalition governments (such as the government that came into power in 2010) are quite rare. In most European countries it is the percentage of total votes that determines the number of representatives of each party. Within the Scottish Parliament (see below) proportional representation has resulted in a coalition of Green MSPs (Members of the Scottish Parliament) together with an ideological Scottish Socialist Party.

There is an argument that diversity of parties in the legislature (something that is generally favoured by 'proportional representation' electoral systems) allows for a wide range of political views to be represented in the government, in contrast to two-party systems where minority opinions can easily be lost. Against this, the reality is often that a minority party is able to hold power that is disproportionate to its size, by threatening to withhold its membership of a coalition. Coalition governments (which are common in some European countries, such as Italy and Germany) also have a tendency to be unstable, and withdrawal of one party may bring down an executive. The radical change that occurred with the strong single-party governments of the Conservative Party in the 1980s may be much more difficult where a coalition government has to broker a compromise between all parties.

2.4.2 Social exclusion

Political parties have often based their principal ideology on a desire to see a more equitable distribution of wealth and life chances within society. Some great revolutions in history, such as the French Revolution of 1789, have been brought about by the socially excluded using force to overturn the power of an elite.

Social exclusion is a shorthand term for what can happen when people or areas suffer from a combination of linked problems such as unemployment, poor skills, low incomes, poor housing, high-crime environments, bad health and family breakdown. Often, governments have had policies that tried to deal with each of these problems individually, but it can be a bigger challenge to tackle the complicated links between them. There has also been a tendency for policy to react to events rather than preventing social exclusion arising in the first place.

2.4.3 Redistribution of wealth

Left to market forces, numerous studies have suggested that the wealthier members of a society would continue to get richer, while the poor would find it difficult to escape from their relative poverty. Karl Marx's analysis predicted the end of capitalism on the basis that, without the spending power of the poor, the wealthy owners of resources would have no markets for the products from which they made their profits. In reality, Marx's thesis was weakened by new overseas opportunities to recirculate capital owners' wealth. During the twentieth century, progress towards a more egalitarian distribution of wealth was slow and required intervention by governments.

Governments with socialist leanings have recognized that there is nothing inherently just in the pattern of market rewards that reflects the accidents of heredity and the labour skills that happen to be in demand at the time. A distinguishing feature of the Left in politics is often its belief in a role for government in redistributing wealth. However, redistribution has acquired a bad name because it has been associated with the politics of envy. It has also sometimes been carried out in such a way as to interfere unnecessarily with incentives. This reality was apparent with the Labour government in the UK from 1997 to 2010, with some evidence that inequalities of wealth actually increased during this period of socialist government (Hills *et al.* 2010).

Actually getting benefits to lower-income groups can pose a challenge for policy makers. Minimum wage legislation, introduced in the UK in 1999, may provide guaranteed levels of income for the poorest members of society, but higher-earning individuals invariably seek to maintain differentials, leaving minimum-wage employees in a position of relative poverty, and possibly putting an employer at a competitive disadvantage compared to companies located in low-wage economies. An alternative approach to redistribution has been to increase the benefits paid to individuals who are not in work. But this has often led to a 'poverty trap' whereby it is not financially advantageous for an individual to enter employment, because the benefits that they are giving up are greater than the wages they will earn. There are a number of structural issues that governments have sought to tackle in order to improve the relative economic standing of disadvantaged groups. As an example, many single parents have found it uneconomic to enter the labour market because the loss of benefits and costs of childcare are greater than their earnings

Pursuing full employment may be an admirable goal as a means of reducing poverty. But public perceptions of government programmes to get people off benefits and into employment can very easily change from enlightenment to harassment once pressure is put on people, whether they be the well-meaning unmarried mother or the work-shy who would rather claim benefits than work.

⟳ Thinking around the subject

Will the poor always be with us?

It seems that even a socialist government dedicated to reducing social inequality cannot easily eliminate inequality. According to a report by the Office for National Statistics, the income of the richest and poorest 10 per cent of the population had each grown by around 5 per cent between 1997 (the date when a Labour government was elected) and 2003. But, in absolute terms, the gap between rich and poor had widened. The poorest 10 per cent had seen a £28 a week rise, compared to the richest 10 per cent, which had seen a rise of £119. Furthermore, the wealthiest 1 per cent of the population had prospered. In 1991, they owned 17 per cent of the nation's wealth, but by 2003 the figure had grown to 21 per cent. A large part of this growth was attributed to a rise in house prices (Office for National Statistics 2008).

It has often been argued that the surest way out of inequality is through education, but the report found that children's chances of doing well in exams depended enormously on their parents, qualifications and jobs. In 2002, more than three-quarters of children with parents in higher professional occupations achieved five or more GCSEs at grades A to C. Less than a third of children with parents in manual or clerical jobs achieved this (Office for National Statistics 2004).

Even when the government takes proactive measures to help disadvantaged groups, these may backfire. In 2001, the government abolished entrance fees to national museums, arguing that high charges were deterring poor people from sharing the nation's heritage and learning from it. After the abolition of charges, museum attendance figures rose. However, a subsequent report by the National Audit Office indicated that it was relatively wealthy middle-class parents who were now making more visits to museums, and disadvantaged groups were still underrepresented in the admission figures. Worse still, many of the middle-class parents who were now making more visits to state-subsidized museums now made fewer visits to privately owned museums, many of which were forced to cut back their expenditure and reduce the number of staff they employed.

What policies can in practice be used to overcome social inequality? Given the importance of education as a means of reducing inequality, what can governments do to encourage people from disadvantaged backgrounds to take part in higher education? Even in higher education, is government policy sometimes contradictory, as evidenced by the introduction of tuition fees, which may deter groups in society that have traditionally been afraid of getting into debt?

2.5 The structure of government

To understand the nature of the political environment more fully, and its impact on business organizations, it is necessary to examine the different aspects of government. Government influence on businesses in the UK can be divided into the following categories:

- central government
- regional government
- local government
- European Union (EU) government
- supranational government.

Most countries have hierarchical levels of government that follow a roughly similar pattern. The UK will be used to illustrate the principles of multi-level government influences on businesses, with reference to comparable institutions in other countries.

2.6 Central government

The central government system of most countries can be divided into four separate functions. The UK is quite typical in dividing functions of government between the legislature, the executive, the civil service and the judiciary. These, collectively, provide sovereign government within the UK although, as will be seen later, this sovereignty is increasingly being subjected to the authority of the EU.

2.6.1 Parliament

Parliament provides the supreme legislative authority in the UK and comprises the monarch (the present Queen), the House of Commons and the House of Lords. The House of Commons is the most important part of the **legislature** as previous legislation has curtailed the authority in Parliament of the monarch and the House of Lords. It is useful to be aware of the procedures for enacting new legislation so that the influences on the legislative process can be fully understood (see Figure 2.1).

New legislation starts life as a Bill and passes through parliamentary processes to the point where it becomes an **Act of Parliament**. Most Bills that subsequently become law are government sponsored and often start life following discussion between government departments and interested parties. On some occasions these discussions may lead to the setting up of a Committee of Enquiry or (less frequently) a Royal Commission, which reports to the government. The findings of such a committee can be accepted, rejected or amended by the government, which puts forward ideas for discussion in a Green Paper. Following initial discussion, the government would submit definite proposals for legislation in the form of a White Paper. A Parliamentary Bill would then be drafted, incorporating some of the comments that the government has received in response to the publication of the White Paper. The Bill is then formally introduced to Parliament by a first reading in the House of Commons, at which a date is set for the main debate at a second reading. A vote is taken at each reading and, if it is a government Bill, it will invariably pass at each stage due to the government majority in the House of Commons. If it passes the second reading, the Bill will be sent to a Standing Committee for discussion of the details. The Committee will in due course report back to the full House of Commons and there will be a final debate where amendments are considered, some of which originate from the Committee and some from

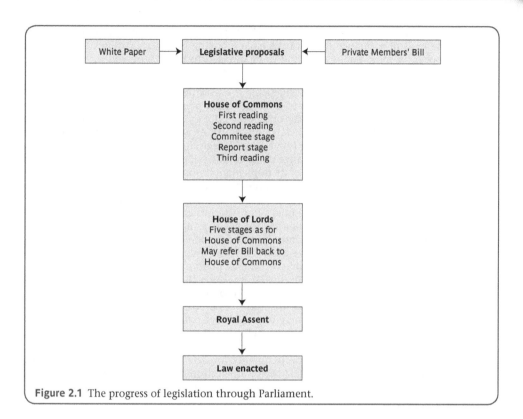

Figure 2.1 The progress of legislation through Parliament.

members of the House of Commons in general. The Bill then passes to the House of Lords and goes through a similar five stages. The Lords may delay or amend a Bill, although the Commons may subsequently use the Parliament Act to force the Bill through. Finally, the Bill goes to the monarch to receive the Royal Assent, upon which it becomes an Act 1911 of Parliament.

This basic model can be changed in a number of ways. First, in response to a newly perceived problem, the government could introduce a Bill with very few clauses and, with the agreement of party managers, could cut short the consultation stages, speed up the passage of the Bill through its various stages and provide Royal Assent within a matter of days, instead of the months that it could typically take. This has occurred, for example, in the case of a one-clause Bill to prohibit trade in human organs, a measure that had received all-party support. A second variation on the basic model is provided by Private Members' Bills. Most Bills start life with government backing. However, backbench Members of parliament can introduce their own Bills, although the opportunities for doing this are limited and if they do not subsequently receive government backing, their chances of passing all stages of the parliamentary process are significantly reduced.

The lobbying of Members of Parliament has become an increasingly important activity, brought about by individuals and pressure groups to try to protect their interests where new legislation is proposed that may affect them. Typical tasks for which professional lobbyists have been employed in recent years are:

- the British Roads Federation regularly lobbies for greater expenditure on roads, and seizes opportunities presented by relevant new Bills to include provisions that are more supportive of increased expenditure on roads

■ each year, prior to the Chancellor of the Exchequer's annual Budget speech (which forms the basis of a Finance Act), considerable lobbying is undertaken by vested interests that appeal for more public spending to be directed to their cause and/or less taxation to be imposed on it.

If organizations are to succeed in influencing their political environment, they need to identify the critical points in the passage of a Bill at which pressure can be applied, and the critical members who should form the focus of lobbying (for example, the members of the Committee to which the Bill is sent for detailed examination). As we will see later, much legislation that passes through the UK Parliament is enacting EU legislation. At this stage it may be too late for lobbyists to achieve significant change in the overall policy underlying the Bill, although it may still be possible to amend details of its implementation. The role of lobbying is considered in more detail later in this chapter in the context of pressure groups as forces within the political system.

Political parties typically make bold promises in their election manifestos. If elected, they may promptly enact legislation that formed the flagship of their campaign. However, after a honeymoon period, governments must set to work addressing structural issues in the economy, which will take some time to make good. This may involve painful economic measures in the short term, but the payoff is improved economic performance in a few years' time. With a five-year election cycle for Parliament in the UK, it is often claimed that voters have short memories and will forget the austere economic conditions of two or three years previously. What matters at election time is the *appearance* that economic conditions are getting better. Therefore, government economic planning may try to achieve falling unemployment, stable prices and a consumer boom just ahead of a general election. This may itself lead to structural problems that must be sorted out after the election, leading to a repeat of this cyclical process (see Figure 2.2). The existence of the political cycle frequently impacts on the economic environment, with periods of increased expenditure just before an election and reduced expenditure shortly after. Organizations may acknowledge this cycle by gearing up for a boom in sales just ahead of a general election.

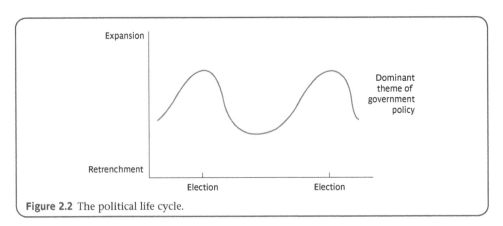

Figure 2.2 The political life cycle.

2.6.2 The executive

Parliament comprises elected representatives whose decisions, in theory, are carried out by the executive arm of government. In practice, the executive plays a very important role in formulating policies, which Parliament then debates and invariably accepts. In the UK, the principal elements of the executive comprise the Cabinet and ministers of state.

The Cabinet

The main executive element of central government is made up of the Prime Minister and Cabinet (comprising approximately 26 members), who determine policy and are responsible for the consequences of their policies. The Cabinet is headed by the Prime Minister, who has many powers, including the appointment and dismissal of ministers and determining the membership of Cabinet committees, chairing the Cabinet and setting its agenda, summarizing the discussions of the Cabinet and sending directives to ministers. The Prime Minister is also responsible for a variety of government and non-government appointments, and can determine the timing of a general election. Many have argued that Britain is moving towards a system of presidential government by the Prime Minister, given the considerable powers at his or her disposal. There are, however, a number of constraints on the power of the Prime Minister, such as the need to keep the loyalty of the Cabinet and the agreement of Parliament, which may be difficult when the governing party has only a small majority in the House of Commons.

In practice, the Prime Minister is particularly dependent upon the support of a small 'inner cabinet' of senior colleagues for advice and assistance in carrying policy through the party. In addition to this small inner cabinet surrounding the Prime Minister, recent years have seen the development of a small group of outside advisers on whose loyalty the Prime Minister can totally rely. Some are likely to be party members sitting in Parliament, while others may be party loyalists who belong to the business or academic community. There have been occasions when it has appeared that the Prime Minister's advisers were having a greater influence on policy than their Cabinet colleagues.

The ideological background of the Prime Minister and the composition of the government may give some indication of the direction of government policy. Organizations should study the composition of the government to try to predict future policy on issues such as government spending and personal taxation.

Ministers of State

The government of the country is divided between a number of different departments of state (see Figure 2.3). Each is headed by a Minister or Secretary of State who is a political appointee, usually a member of the House of Commons. They are assisted in their tasks by junior ministers. The portfolio of responsibilities of a department frequently changes when a new government comes into being. Ministers are often given delegated authority by Parliament, as where an Act may allow charges to be made for certain health services, but the minister has the delegated power to decide the actual level of the charges.

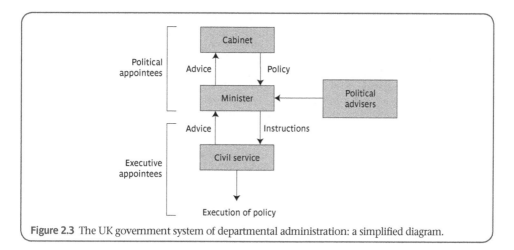

Figure 2.3 The UK government system of departmental administration: a simplified diagram.

2.6.3 The civil service

The civil service is the secretariat responsible for implementing government policy. In the UK, civil servants are paid officials who do not change when the government changes, adding a degree of continuity to government (although in some countries, such as the USA, it is customary for senior officials to be political appointees and therefore replaced following a change of government). Although, legally, civil servants are servants of the Crown, they are technically employed by a separate government department and are responsible to a minister. Each department is generally headed by a Permanent Secretary, responsible to the Public Accounts Committee of Parliament. The Permanent Secretary is a professional administrator who gives advice to his or her minister, a political appointee who generally lacks expertise in the work of the department.

The fact that civil servants are relatively expert in their areas and generally remain in their posts for much longer than their minister gives them great power. A delicate relationship develops between the Permanent Secretary and the minister, based on sometimes conflicting goals. The minister may view an issue in terms of broader political opportunities while the civil servant may be more concerned about his or her status and career prospects resulting from a change affecting his or her department.

The nature of the career civil servant is changing with the emergence of non-departmental public bodies (NDPBs – often referred to as 'quangos') to take over many of the activities of civil service departments (see below). In theory, these new executive agencies should be much freer of ministerial control, meeting longer-term performance standards with less day-to-day ministerial intervention as to how this should be achieved.

Organizations seeking to influence government policy must recognize the power that civil servants have in advising their minister, especially on the details of proposed legislation. Civil servants are usually involved in consultation exercises – for example, on the details of proposed food regulations. In some countries, business may seek to influence the policy-making process at this stage through overt or covert bribery. This is not a feature of most mature democracies such as Britain, and business seeks to exert influence in a more mutually cooperative manner. Civil servants require information on the background to policy and need to understand its possible implications. A close dialogue between the business community and civil servants can increase the chances of civil servants' policy recommendations being based on a sound understanding of business needs, rather than ignorance.

2.6.4 The judiciary

Democratic systems of government provide a number of checks and balances against the abuse of executive power. The judiciary is independent of government, and judges in the UK are answerable to the Crown and not to politicians. Through the court system, citizens can have some redress against a legislature, executive or civil service that acts beyond its authority. If complainants believe that they have suffered because a government minister did not follow statutory consultation procedures, they may apply to the courts for a judicial review of the case. A court may order that ministers reconsider the matter by following statutory procedures.

Business organizations have become increasingly willing to use the courts to challenge allegedly incorrect government procedures that have put them at a disadvantage. The proliferation of industry-sector regulators in the UK has created many opportunities for aggrieved business organizations to challenge the processes of the regulator. As an example, the UK National Lottery regulator Oflot was challenged in the High Court during 2000 by Camelot – the existing Lottery franchise holder – when it alleged that it had been procedurally incorrect in the way that it granted a new franchise to the rival People's Lottery. The Court instructed the regulator to reconsider its decision.

Thinking around the subject

Minister for Spin?

Britain's system of government has often been held out as an example of good governance. Politicians decided policy and if the electorate didn't like their policies, they could be thrown out of office at the next election. Civil servants were the loyal servants of politicians who got on and implemented their masters' policies. Because the electorate could not throw out a civil servant directly, ministers took responsibility for the actions of their civil servants. Carefully honed sets of procedures and codes of conduct were developed, which made the UK civil service an example to the world of professionalism.

What, then, are we to make of recent developments that would appear to blur the distinction between elected politicians and an appointed civil service? Within government, there has been a growing number of policy advisers who report to the Prime Minister or other senior ministers, but who are still technically civil servants. These special advisers are overtly chosen by ministers on the basis of their political views, breaking the tradition of neutrality within the civil service. They have often been given the label of 'spin doctor' for the way in which they represent the views of their minister. Do these advisers debase the whole principle of a politically neutral civil service? Are they one step towards the development of a presidential style of government on the American model? Are 'spin doctors' merely providing a substitute for substantive actions by the politicians? Against this, isn't good government all about strong leadership? Could these special advisers be beneficial in the way that they cut through the delaying tactics of the civil service machinery in their efforts to see the politically accountable executive's wishes implemented?

The blurred distinction between functions doesn't end with special policy advisers. Governments have been increasingly enthusiastic about the use of 'task forces' and so-called policy 'czars' to implement policy in such areas as crime, education, housing and environmental protection. These may draw on individuals' special skills, or draw membership from a wide range of interests, but they are invariably political appointments and not democratically accountable in the way that a civil servant is accountable to their minister. Are the possible benefits for good government worth the possible price of less accountability to the electorate?

2.7   Regional and national government

Although many European countries, such as Germany and France, have historically had some degree of regional government, this has been largely absent in the UK. The end of the 1990s saw a potentially fundamental change in the structure of government in the UK with the emergence of regional elected government. However, this is only a partial system of regional government covering some parts of the UK, and the constitution and powers of each are very different.

2.7.1 Scotland

Scotland was granted devolution by the passing of the Scotland Act in 1998, which means that Scotland has a parliament with 'devolved' powers within the UK. Any powers that remain with the UK Parliament at Westminster are 'reserved', and set out in Schedule 5 of the Scotland Act. Essentially the powers of the Scottish Parliament are defined by what it does not have legislative competence in, rather than by what it can do. Devolved powers include matters such as education, health and prisons. Reserved powers comprise all other areas of decision making, such as defence and foreign policy which have a UK-wide or an international impact.

The Scottish Parliament is made up of 129 members (MSPs), one of whom is elected by the Parliament to serve as the Presiding Officer. Like the UK Parliament, the Scottish Parliament passes laws. It also scrutinizes the work and policies of the Scottish Executive. The Scottish Parliament is staffed by civil servants who serve the Parliament and, like the Presiding Officer, they must remain neutral.

The Scottish Executive is the government in Scotland for all devolved matters. It is formed from the party or parties holding a majority of seats in the Parliament. The Executive is led by the First Minister, who appoints other ministers and is supported by six administrative departments staffed by civil servants.

The Scottish Assembly has powers to vary income tax by plus or minus up to 3p in the pound to spend as it wishes. This, combined with the Scottish Parliament's ability to alter Scots law, increasingly leads to disparities with the rest of the UK, for example with respect to university tuition fees and charges for the care of elderly people.

The UK government continues to appoint a Secretary of State for Scotland, who remains a member of the UK Cabinet and is responsible for reserved items of government within Scotland.

2.7.2 Wales

In Wales, the National Assembly for Wales consists of 60 members elected throughout Wales. The Welsh Assembly is responsible for developing and implementing policies and programmes for all issues that have been devolved to Wales, which include agriculture, ancient monuments and historic buildings, culture, economic development, education and training, the environment, health services, highways, housing, industry, local government, social services, sport and leisure, tourism, town and country planning, transport and roads, and the Welsh language. The First Minister leads the Assembly and chairs a Cabinet of eight other ministers. All ministers are accountable to the Assembly and its committees for their actions. Unlike the Scottish Parliament, the Welsh Assembly has no tax-raising powers, although a referendum held in 2011 voted to seek more powers for the Welsh assembly.

2.7.3 Northern Ireland

In Northern Ireland, an Assembly was established as part of the Belfast (or 'Good Friday') Agreement. Northern Ireland had previously had a high level of devolved administration through the UK government's Northern Ireland Office, and the Good Friday Agreement sought to re-establish a form of Parliament that had previously been suspended during two decades of the 'Troubles'. The newly established Northern Ireland Assembly consists of 108 elected members – six from each of the 18 Westminster constituencies. Its role is primarily to scrutinize and make decisions on the issues dealt with by government departments, and to consider and make legislation. A First Minister and a Deputy First Minister are elected to lead the Executive Committee of Ministers. Due to the history of divisions within Northern Ireland society, there is a complicated system whereby the First Minister and Deputy First Minister must stand for election jointly and, to be elected, they must have cross-community support. Decisions in the Assembly are taken by a 'parallel consent formula', which means that a majority of both the members who have designated themselves Nationalists and those who have designated themselves Unionists, and a majority of the whole Assembly, must vote in favour. After a troubled start, the restored Northern Ireland Assembly has assumed responsibility for government functions previously handled by the UK government's Northern Ireland Office, and is allocated its block allocation of government expenditure.

2.7.4 London

In London, a referendum established the Greater London Authority. This provides for a directly elected Mayor (Ken Livingstone was the first Mayor, elected in 2000, and re-elected until 2008, when he was succeeded by Boris Johnson), who has the role of a policy leader and 'Champion for London'. The Mayor's office is the executive of London's government – managing a budget of over £8 billion and having revenue-raising powers (e.g. the London Congestion Charge is determined by the Mayor). The London Assembly – an elected body – scrutinizes the Mayor's policies, decisions and budget.

The Greater London Authority is made up of the Mayor, the London Assembly and a team of over 600 staff supporting their work to develop and implement London-wide policies in respect of transport, policing, fire and emergency services, economic development, planning, culture and the environment. The Mayor works closely with, and sets budgets for, Transport for London (TfL), the London Development Agency (LDA), the Metropolitan Police Authority (MPA), and the London Fire and Emergency Planning Authority (LFEPA). The Mayor also works closely with London's borough councils, which are responsible for providing many local services. The Mayor works with the boroughs to ensure that local and London-wide policies work together for maximum effect.

2.7.5 Other regional assemblies

Outside of Scotland, Wales, Northern Ireland and London, UK government policy on regional government has been ambivalent. In principle, governments have generally been in favour of more devolution to the regions, but some policies, such as the abolition of Regional Development Agencies in 2010, have appeared to go against this policy.

Advocates of regional government argue that it will allow legislation and economic policy to be developed that is better suited to the needs of their area. Critics would argue that regional government creates more bureaucracy, which will cost businesses time and money. Instead of devolving powers down from central government, a Local Government Association study in 2004 suggested that regional assemblies would actually lead to the transfer of authority upwards from local authorities to the new regional government bodies. Some saw evidence of the effect of this in the Welsh Assembly Government budget for 2008, which critics claimed increased spending by the Assembly but cut the funding allocated to local councils. There has been a muted response to proposals for further regional assemblies. In 2005, a referendum on a proposal to establish a regional assembly in north-east England was overwhelmingly rejected.

Delays in implementing policies may occur where the aims of national and regional governments differ, but cooperation between the two is essential if a regional policy is to be implemented successfully. Legal challenges by the London Assembly against the Department of Transport, Environment and Regions over privatization of the London Underground demonstrated that interdependencies between regional and national governments are likely to remain strong.

The likely effects of regional governments on business organizations are ambiguous. On the one hand, it can be argued that increasing amounts of UK legislation are merely enactments of EU directives, which would need to be enacted regardless of whether it is the UK Parliament or a regional assembly that assumes the responsibility. On the other hand, there are many areas of discretion, which can lead to differences between regions. Where it has tax-raising powers, regional assembly funds can be directed towards what are considered to be regionally important social goals. As an example of the differences that can emerge, the Scottish Parliament has funded long-term care for elderly people, something that was not available in England, and thereby opening up business opportunities in Scotland that were not available in England.

2.8   Local government

Local authorities in the UK are responsible for a wide range of services, from social services and education to refuse collection and street cleaning. The structure of local government that was implemented in 1974 divided the largely rural areas of England into counties ('shire counties'), each with a county council. The chief responsibilities of these county councils included education, social services, emergency services, highways and refuse disposal. Shire counties were further subdivided into district councils (sometimes designated as borough or city councils), which had responsibilities for housing, leisure services and refuse collection. Districts in rural areas were usually further divided into parishes with a parish council (sometimes designated as a town council) responsible for local matters such as the maintenance of playing fields.

In the larger conurbations, metropolitan district councils had greater functions than their shire county counterparts – for example, they were additionally responsible for education and social services. Following the abolition of metropolitan county councils in 1986, responsibility for conurbation-wide services (such as public transport and emergency services) passed to a series of joint boards governed by the district councils. In London, the pattern of government has been broadly similar to that of metropolitan areas, although there is now an assembly for the capital (see above). In Scotland, the structure of local government has been based on a two-tier system of regional and district councils.

From the mid-1990s, the basic structure of local government set up by the Local Goverment Act 1974 has been changed further by the appointment of commissions to study the needs of local government in individual areas. This has led to the emergence of 'unitary' authorities that combine the functions of district and county councils. Many large urban areas, such as Leicester, Nottingham and Bristol, have gained their own unitary authorities, in the hope that previous duplication of facilities provided by district and council councils can be avoided. As an example, the 'unitary' authority for Leicester combines previous city council functions of housing, refuse collection and car parking (among others) with responsibilities transferred from Leicestershire County Council for education, social services and highways.

Arguments for large county councils based on economies of scale and centralized provision have given way to a philosophy based on small, locally responsive units acting as enablers for services provided by subcontracted suppliers. Even a small, re-created county such as Rutland, it is argued, can provide many services previously considered too complex for such a small unit, by buying them in from outside suppliers, or by acting in partnership with other local authorities.

2.8.1 The relationship between central and local government

It has been argued that local government in Britain is losing its independence from central government, despite claims by successive governments that they support a philosophy of less government and a decentralization of powers. There is a great deal of evidence of this erosion of local autonomy.

- Over half of local government income now comes in the form of grants from central government.

- Local authorities have had the ability to set rates on business premises taken away from them altogether and these are now determined by central government.

- Furthermore, central government has the power to set a maximum permitted total expenditure for a local authority and to set a maximum amount for its council tax due from householders.

In addition, legislation setting performance standards in education and social services (among others) has limited the independence of local government to set locally determined standards. Local authorities now have less local discretion in determining what is an acceptable standard for services in their area and in deciding between competing priorities.

Local authorities have had increasing numbers of functions removed from their responsibility and placed with non-departmental public bodies (NDPBs) which are no longer answerable to the local authority (for example, colleges of further education now have their own governing bodies).

2.9 The European Union

The European Union (EU), formerly known as the European Community (EC), was founded by the Treaty of Rome, signed in 1957 by France, West Germany, Italy, Belgium, the Netherlands and Luxembourg. Britain joined the EC in 1972, together with Ireland and Denmark, to be joined by Greece in 1981, Spain and Portugal in 1986, and Austria, Finland and Sweden in 1995. A more significant expansion to the EU occurred in May 2004 when ten countries of central and eastern Europe joined: Cyprus, the Czech Republic, Estonia, Hungary, Latvia, Lithuania, Malta, Poland, Slovakia and Slovenia. Romania and Bulgaria joined the EU in 2007 and these additions brought the EU's population to over 450 million people in 27 countries. Turkey has begun accession talks, but membership still seems far from certain. Further expansion of the EU appears now to be less of a priority, as the EU grapples with the task of integrating countries at different stages of economic and social development. When some of the weaker EU countries (Portugal, Ireland and Greece) needed support from the EU in 2010/11, many politicians in the 'old' and stronger members of the EU, principally Germany and France, questioned the wisdom of further expansion. Norway and Switzerland have always declined to join the EU, but enjoy a similar freedom of movement of capital, goods, people and services, as part of the wider European Economic Area (EEA).

2.9.1 Aims of the EU

An important aim of the Treaty of Rome was the creation of a common market in which trade could take place between member-states as if they were one country. The implication of a common market is the free movement of trade, labour and capital between member-states. Agriculture was the first sector in which a genuinely common market was created, with a system of common pricing and support payments between all countries and free movement of produce between member-states. Further development of a common market has been impeded by a range of non-tariff trade barriers, such as national legislation specifying design standards, the cost and risk of currency exchange and the underlying desire of public authorities to back their own national industries. The creation of the single European market in January 1993 removed many of these barriers, but many practical barriers to trade remain, of which differences in language and cultural traditions are probably the most intractable.

There is considerable debate about the form that future development of the EU should take and, in particular, the extent to which there should be political as well as economic union. Recent debate has focused on the following issues.

- The creation of a common unit of currency has been seen by many as crucial to the development of a single European market, avoiding the cost and uncertainty for business and travellers of having to change currencies for cross-border transactions. A strong single currency would also be able to act as a true international currency comparable to the US dollar, in a way that few individual national currencies could hope to achieve on their own. The launch of the euro (now adopted by 17 of the 27 EU countries) has reduced transaction costs for trade between member-states and has allowed member-states' central banks to reduce their holdings of foreign currency. Within the UK, opposition to monetary union has been based on economic and political arguments. Economically, a common currency would deny to countries the opportunity to revalue or devalue their currency to suit the needs of their domestic economy.

- The lack of political and economic harmonization within the EU Eurozone countries has led to crises within those countries where governments had borrowed heavily in euros, but could not devalue their currency to reduce their indebtedness, something that had been a classic solution to previous financial crises. This lack of flexibility implies a political sacrifice, as control of currency is central to government management of the economy (although it should be noted that the UK government has handed over control of monetary policy to the Bank of England in an attempt to de-politicize financial policy). During 2010, four European countries – Greece, Ireland, Portugal and Spain – faced severe economic problems and many commentators suggested that a common European currency was unsustainable where national economies had not converged. The suggestion has been made that the stronger countries of Europe – notably Germany and France – would benefit from a separate currency to those poorer EU member-states that had weaker economies and poorer management of their governments' budgets.

- Argument continues about the amount of influence the EU should have in nation-states' social and economic policy. For example, previous UK governments have shown reluctance to agree to EU proposals that would harmonize personal taxation and social welfare benefits. The UK government has supported the idea of 'subsidiarity', whereby decisions are taken at the most localized level of government that is compatible with achieving EU objectives. Cynics have, however, pointed out that the UK government has not always been willing to practise this principle at home, as witnessed by the gradual erosion of the powers of local authorities in favour of central government.

- There is concern that enlargement of the EU to include the less developed economies of central and eastern Europe, and possibly Turkey, could put strains on EU budgets. Many have argued that enlargement should allow the EU to become a loose federation of states, rather than a centralizing bureaucracy, which many critics claim it has become.

- The principle of free movement of people across borders remains controversial in view of the possibility of large numbers of refugees or economic migrants being admitted by one state and then being automatically allowed to migrate to other member-states. Following the entry of a number of former communist countries to the EU in 2004, an estimated 600,000 people made their way from these relatively poor countries to find work in the UK during the first year of accession. This sudden influx made planning for public services such as schools and hospitals very difficult.

- Member-states still have difficulty in formulating a coherent foreign policy for the EU as a whole, as was seen in the fragmented approach taken towards the 2004 invasion of Iraq.

- There remains widespread concern about the lack of democratic accountability of EU institutions, not helped by allegations of excessive bureaucracy and corruption.

- In order to meet the challenges posed by growth in the EU, attempts have been made to formalize the rights and responsibilities of member-states through some form of constitution. Inevitably, member-states have widely differing experiences of written constitutions, and there has, not surprisingly, been a lot of debate about what such a constitution should cover (see below).

2.9.2 The structure of the EU

The Treaty of Rome (as modified by subsequent treaties) developed a structure of government whose elements reflect, in part, the structure of the UK government. The executive (or Cabinet) is provided by the **European Council of Ministers**; the secretariat (or civil service) is provided by the **European Commission**; while the legislature is provided by the European Parliament. The judiciary is represented by the **European Court of Justice**.

The Treaty of Rome places constraints upon the policies that the institutions of the EU can adopt. The European Court of Justice is able to rule that an action or decision is not in accordance with the Treaty. In some cases, such as competition policy, the Treaty is quite specific – for example, Articles 85 and 86, which define the basic approach to be adopted in dealing with cartels and monopoly power. On the other hand, the Treaty says little more on transport policy than that there should be a common policy, giving the community institutions considerable power to develop policies.

The activities of the EU are now directly funded from income received from customs duties and other levies on goods entering the EU from non-member countries. In addition, a value added tax collected by member-states on purchases by consumers includes an element of up to 1.45 per cent that is automatically transferred to the EU budget. More recently, a new resource transfer payment between member-states and the EU has been introduced, which is based on the gross domestic product of each member-state. The UK remains a net contributor to the EU budget.

New legislation is increasingly the result of cooperation between the various institutions of the EU. The process of cooperation is illustrated in Figure 2.4 and the role of the principal institutions described below. There have been attempts to simplify this process following expansion of the EU from 15 to 27 members.

2.9.3 The Council of Ministers

The Council of Ministers represents the governments of member-states and can be regarded as the principal lawmaker of the EU, although it can act only on proposals submitted by the Commission. It has powers to:

- adopt legislation
- ratify treaties after consultation with the European Parliament
- ask the Commission to undertake studies and to submit legislation
- delegate executive and legislative powers to the Commission.

Each member-state sends one minister to the European Council of Ministers. Which minister attends will depend on the subject being discussed – for example, agriculture ministers would be sent if the Common Agricultural Policy were being discussed. The ministers of foreign affairs, of agriculture, and those with budgetary responsibilities meet more frequently, making a senior body within the Council, sometimes called the General Council. The chairmanship or presidency of the Council of Ministers rotates between countries in alphabetical order, with each period of presidency lasting for six months (see below for proposed constitutional changes in the method of selecting the President).

The Council of Ministers adopts new legislation either by simple majority, qualified majority or unanimity.

- Simple majority gives each minister one vote and is used for proposals such as procedural rules for the convening of intergovernmental conferences.
- Qualified majority voting is based on a weighted voting system where member-states' votes are roughly proportional to their size and economic strength. Qualified majority voting prevents smaller states being consistently outvoted and eliminates the risk of two of the larger member-states constituting a blocking majority. Examples of applications of this

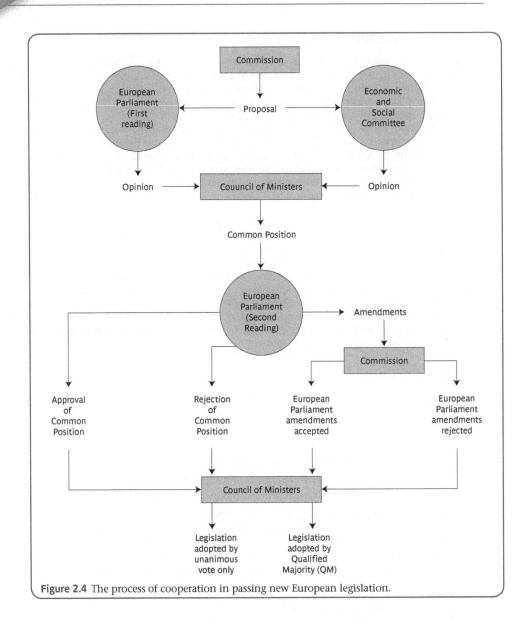

Figure 2.4 The process of cooperation in passing new European legislation.

method of voting include legislation on completion of the internal market; the freedom to provide professional services across national borders; and measures to free up the movement of capital within the EU.

■ Unanimity is required on issues that are fundamental to individual member-states' interests, such as enlargement of the EU, harmonization of taxation and extension of EU powers.

In 2000 an intergovernmental conference of ministers agreed to reduce the number of areas in which unanimity was required, to be further codified by a proposed EU constitution (see below).

With enlargement, achieving unanimity between all member-states has become increasingly difficult.

The Council of Ministers can generally pass laws even if the European Parliament disagrees with them, unlike the practice within the UK and other national parliamentary systems where ministers must obtain the approval of a majority of Members of Parliament. There are two main exceptions to this authority of the Council. First, the European Parliament has power to approve or reject the EU budget (see below). Second, the Single European Act introduced a system of legislative cooperation between the Council and Parliament, obliging the Council and the Commission to take Parliament's amendments to proposals into consideration, although a unanimous vote by the Council of Ministers retains ultimate authority.

The Committee of Permanent Representatives (Coreper) complements the work of the Council of Ministers. Because ministers have responsibilities to their own national governments as well as to the EU, they cannot give a continuing presence. To make up for this, each member-state sends one ambassador to the Committee, which is based in Brussels. Proposals are discussed in Coreper and its subcommittees before they reach ministers. If Coreper reaches full agreement on the matter, it is empowered to pass it through the Council without further debate, but where disagreement occurs it is left for ministers to discuss.

2.9.4 The European Commission

Each member-state sends one commissioner to the Commission (the larger members send two), each appointed by the member government for a renewable term of four years. They are supported in their work by a staff of civil servants, divided between 23 directorates-general and mainly based at the Commission's headquarters in Brussels. Each commissioner is given responsibility for a portfolio, which could be for a policy area, such as transport, or for administrative matters such as the Commission's relations with the Parliament, while others are given a combination of responsibilities in their portfolio. Unlike the Council of Ministers, all members of the Commission are supposed to act primarily for the benefit of the Union as a whole, rather than the country that they represent. This is spelt out in Article 157 of the Treaty of Rome, which states that commissioners 'shall neither seek nor take instruction from any other body'.

The Commission has an initiation, mediation and implementation role. As an initiator, it is the task of the Commission to draft proposals for legislation, which the Council of Ministers has to consider. If the Council does not accept a proposal, it can alter the draft only by a unanimous vote. If unanimity cannot be achieved, the proposal has to go back to the Commission for it to draft a revised proposal that will be acceptable to the Council of Ministers.

As a mediator, the Commission can intervene in disputes between member-states to try to find a solution through negotiation. The Commission has frequently acted as mediator in trade disputes between members, avoiding recourse to the European Court of Justice. As an implementer, the Commission undertakes the day-to-day administration of the EU. This involves monitoring the activities of member-states to ensure that they do not conflict with community policy. In addition, the Commission implements community policies such as the Regional Development Fund and Common Agricultural Policy.

2.9.5 The European Parliament

Unlike the UK Parliament, the European Parliament is primarily consultative and has relatively little power. Its main function is to monitor the activities of other EU institutions. It can give an opinion on Commission proposals but has powers only to amend, adopt or reject legislation, especially the EU budget. It also has the theoretical power to dismiss the entire Commission, for which a censure motion must be passed by a two-thirds majority of members. Although it can dismiss the entire Commission, the Parliament has no control over the selection of new commissioners to replace those who have been dismissed. It does not yet have the power to initiate and enact legislation.

Members of the European Parliament are now directly elected by the constituents of each country, with countries returning members roughly in proportion to their populations. Members of the European Parliament increasingly belong to political rather than national groupings (e.g. the European People's Party represents 74 parties from European countries).

2.9.6 The European Court of Justice

The supreme legislative body of the EU is the Court of Justice. It is the final arbiter in all matters of interpreting community treaties and rules on disputes between member-states, between member-states and the Commission, and between the Commission and business organizations, individuals or EU officials. Although the Court can condemn violations of the Treaty by member governments, it has no sanctions against them except goodwill. The European Court of Justice can investigate complaints that the Commission has acted beyond its powers and, if upheld, can annul the decisions of the Commission.

The European Court of Justice is composed of 15 judges, assisted by nine advocates-general. Each is appointed by common agreement between the member-states on the basis of their qualifications and impartiality, for a renewable six-year term of office. Members of the Court must put European interests before national interests. The Court can be called upon to settle disputes where the persuasion and negotiations of the Commission have failed to yield results. For example, in the area of competition policy, the Commission may by decision forbid an anti-competitive practice or impose a fine. The companies concerned can appeal to the European Court of Justice for the decision to be set aside. In one case, several dye producers appealed to the European Court of Justice against the fines imposed on them for an alleged price cartel.

2.9.7 Towards an EU constitution?

The EU is in a state of flux. Its main institutions – the Commission, the Council of Ministers and the European Parliament – remain widely unloved and vulnerable to charges of inefficiency and lack of transparency. But, paradoxically, the EU is in many respects more active than ever before.

The administration of the EU has changed subtly as the EU has matured. The initiative for many new proposals has come from the European Council – summits of EU leaders held three or four times a year. By contrast, the European Commission has tended to become more of an administrator of programmes rather than the bold innovator that launched the single market in the 1980s. It was badly demoralized in March 1999 when the 20-strong commissioners, headed by Jacques Santer, resigned after a critical report alleging nepotism, fraud and mismanagement.

In 2000, the leaders of member-states identified the urgent task of defining how powers would be divided between Brussels and national governments, and began the process of developing a constitution for the EU. This has become urgently needed because the expansion of the EU to 27 member-states in 2007 had threatened to slow down the process of decision making to the speed of the slowest country.

The treaty to establish a constitution for Europe was agreed by EU heads of government in 2004, but rejected in 2005 by referenda of voters in France and the Netherlands. A revised constitution was proposed following the Lisbon summit in 2007. This has sought to apply the principle of voting by qualified majority, as it was recognized that, otherwise, getting the agreement of all 27 members would stifle progress. However, member-states remain keen to retain a veto, especially in areas of foreign policy, defence and taxation. There is pressure for the European Parliament to have an equal say on decisions requiring majority voting.

There has also been pressure for the appointment of a President of the EU for a term longer than the current rotating six-month presidency. A permanent president would potentially have much greater influence inside and outside the EU.

2.9.8 The relationship between the EU and the UK government

A distinction should be drawn between primary and secondary legislation of the EU. Primary legislation is contained in the Treaty of Rome (and subsequent treaties agreed by an intergovernmental conference) and takes precedence over national legislation, although national legislation may be required to implement it. Primary legislation can be altered only by an intergovernmental conference of all members. Secondary legislation is made by the Council of Ministers and the Commission under authority delegated to them by the treaties. Secondary legislation affects member-states in several forms.

- Regulations automatically form part of the law of member-states and apply directly to every individual in the EU. They give rights and duties to individuals that national courts must recognize.
- Directives are mandatory instructions to member-states, which must take steps to implement them through national legislation. For example, national laws concerning vehicle safety have varied from state to state and, as a result, trade across frontiers may be impeded. One solution has been to harmonize standards between all member-states by means of a directive. The directive will require member-states to amend their national legislation governing the design of cars. Individuals will then have to obey the modified national law.
- Decisions of the EU are directly binding on the specific individuals or organizations to whom they are addressed, as where the Commission intervenes in a proposed merger between organizations.

2.9.9 Effects of EU membership on UK business organizations

The EU is having an increasingly important effect on business organizations in the UK. The relationship between a company and its customers is increasingly being influenced by EU regulations and directives – for example, in the provision of safety features in cars and the labelling of foods. The influence extends to the relationship between the firm and the public at large, as where the EU passes directives affecting advertising standards and pollution controls. Business organizations must monitor proposed EU legislation not only to spot possible changes in legislation that will eventually be implemented through national legislation, but also to lobby to bring about a desired change in EU law. To an increasing extent, lobbying of the UK parliamentary process is becoming less effective as the UK is bound to implement legislation emanating from the EU.

The extent to which the single European market legislation will further affect business organizations is open to debate. The EU has already had the effect of removing tariff barriers within the Community, and great progress has been made on EU legislation specifying common product design standards. Firms are increasingly seeing Europe as one market and designing standardized products that appeal to consumers in a number of EU states. Many would argue that overseas investors, especially American firms, have always regarded Europe as one market, and developed products as varied as soft drinks and cars to satisfy the whole European market. However, no amount of legislation is likely to overcome the hidden barriers to trade provided by language and by ingrained market characteristics such as the UK practice of driving on the left and using electrical plugs that are not used elsewhere in continental Europe.

⟳ Thinking around the subject

EU directives cause a headache for manufacturers of herbal remedies

The importance of understanding the complexities and different levels of political environments was illustrated by the case of a new EU directive affecting food supplements and herbal remedies, which came into force in 2005.

The EU had earlier passed two directives that would place all herbal medicines and vitamin and mineral supplements on the same regulatory basis as medicines. More than 300 widely used 'natural remedies' would be banned altogether and the cost of licensing each product – estimated at up to £2000 per product – would be beyond the means of many of the small producers that dominated the market for natural remedies. The big pharmaceutical companies had been lobbying the EU hard to get such a change, citing 'adverse reactions' from many herbal remedies and vitamin supplements, such as vitamin B6. Of course, they knew that driving thousands of small herbal producers out of business would draw customers to the pharmaceutical companies' mass-produced products. The natural remedy producers were much more fragmented than the large pharmaceutical companies and were slow to get their lobbying together. In November 2002, the sector presented to the UK government a petition protesting about the proposed changes. It contained over 1 million signatures, including those of Sir Paul McCartney and Sir Elton John, but it was too late because the directives had already been passed by the EU and there was now little discretion left for the UK government. The lobbyists of the pharmaceutical industry seemed to have outsmarted the lobbyists of the natural remedy firms, and understood where and when to apply pressure.

In this case, the herbal remedy industry portrayed the EU as a remote and bureaucratic institution that was harming the interests not only of producers, but also the customers who bought its products. However, at other times, businesses have been avid supporters of greater European integration, although sceptics have pointed out that a lot of this may be opportunistic. As an example, brewers have in the past condemned the European Commission's plans for tighter control over the labelling of beer, claiming their national beer is unique, but this has not prevented them also campaigning for a harmonization of taxes where the tax paid in their own country is higher than the EU average.

The EU is accounting for an increasing proportion of the legislation that affects UK businesses. Should the herbal remedy producers have recognized this, and applied their pressure to the EU at an early stage in the drafting of the directives, rather than wait to apply pressure to the UK government?

2.10   Supranational governmental organizations

National governments' freedom of action is further constrained by international agreements and membership of international organizations. In general, although the treaties of the EU impose duties on the UK government that it is obliged to follow, membership of other supranational organizations is voluntary and does not have binding authority on the UK government.

Probably the most important organization that affects UK government policy is the United Nations (UN). Its General and Security Councils are designed as fora in which differences between countries can be resolved through negotiation rather than force. In the field of international trade, the UN has sought to encourage freedom of trade through the United Nations Conference on Trade and Development (UNCTAD). In matters of national security, the UK is a member of the North Atlantic Treaty Organization (NATO), whose role is changing following the end of the 'Cold War'.

Because the importance to the UK of international treaties and organizations lies to such a great extent in their benefits for international trade, they are considered in more detail in Chapter 14.

Thinking around the subject

Can banks be too big for governments?

Throughout the twentieth century, financial markets in most countries became increasingly deregulated. Even in the former communist countries of eastern Europe, state-owned banks, which once controlled investment decisions throughout the whole economy, were gradually sold off to the private sector and decisions about lending left to market forces rather than government diktat.

In the post-Second World War recovery period, government control of banks had been seen as vital to a coordinated and sustained industrial recovery. By the 1980s, many countries had begun to see government control of banks as a hindrance to further economic development. Banks were therefore increasingly able to determine their lending criteria on the basis of their own corporate objectives, rather than the needs of the country as a whole. To free market economists, there should be no contradiction between the needs of banks and the needs of the country, because it was presumed that profit-seeking banks would simply respond to the needs of lenders and borrowers, and if they did not win favour with customers they would not make profits and would not continue in business.

In 2008, politicians' faith in deregulated financial services sectors was rudely shaken with the collapse of many banks around the world, culminating in the collapse of the mighty Lehman Brothers in September 2008. Even in the USA, noted for its favour of free markets, the Federal government bailed out failed banks with billions of dollars of support. The UK government followed suit, and used public funds effectively to nationalize Northern Rock, Royal Bank of Scotland and the Lloyds banking group.

It seemed that the banks had become too big for governments to allow them to fail, in the way that free-market purists would have allowed. The failure of the big banks would have severely limited the amount of liquidity in the economy, with firms unable to borrow money to invest in productive capacity, slowing down the rate of job creation, reducing corporate profits, increasing unemployment and cutting consumer spending. In short, the failure of the banks could have led to an economic 'meltdown'.

From 2008, governments throughout the world became much more involved in the banking sector. As well as bailing out failed banks, regulation of the financial services sector was tightened – for example, by requiring banks to have a higher level of capital relative to their lending. Free-market, deregulated banking had taken national economies to the brink of economic collapse, and governments were determined that the failure of big banks should never again be allowed to destabilize their national economies. It seemed that – as in many aspects of the political environment – the pendulum had swung again from having a lot of government control, to much less, and now it had increased again.

2.11   Improving the standards of government administration

There have been a number of government initiatives to improve the standards of public-sector services that are provided in an environment where there is no market discipline. These generally use a combination of carrot and stick approaches, offering rewards to those public bodies that are performing well, while taking funds away from those that are failing.

In this section, we will consider a number of recent UK government initiatives: performance measures, 'best value indicators' and the sometimes elusive aim of bringing about 'joined-up government'.

2.11.1 Government performance targets

Government organizations have been set increasingly detailed performance targets – for example, the average waiting time for a hospital appointment, the percentage of household waste that is recycled, and the time taken to process a passport application. Managers are often paid a bonus based on their achievement of targets. Of course, such micromanagement by government through targets can lead to dysfunctional outcomes. It was famously noted that when the centralized Russian government set output targets for state-owned nail factories by weight, the factories simply produced very large nails, which few people wanted. To overcome this problem, targets need to be specified in more detail, resulting in a greater data collection burden for managers, and the possibility of further dysfunctional consequences occurring as individual managers seek to maximize their own performance targets, regardless of their effects on other people's targets.

An alternative approach is to encourage public-sector organizations to achieve more general status labels based on their performance. The **Charter Mark** is a UK government award scheme that aims to recognize and encourage excellence in public service. A wide range of government organizations have been successful in applying for a Charter Mark, including branches of the Benefits Agency, NHS Trusts, the Courts Service, and local HGV testing stations. In local government, the **Beacon Council** scheme was set up to facilitate the sharing of excellent practice among local authorities by holding out such authorities as exemplars to be followed by others As an example, Bexley Council was chosen in 2004 as a Beacon Council for its success in cutting anti-social behaviour and crime.

The Local Government Act 1999 introduced the concept of 'best value' in specified local authorities. The Act places on authorities a duty to seek continuous improvement in the way they exercise their functions. At the heart of best value is a statutory performance management framework, which provides for a set of national performance indicators and standards set by central government.

2.11.2 Joined-up government

Central, regional and local government can at times seem an amorphous mass of departments, each not appearing to know what the others are doing. There have been many documented cases where different government departments have taken completely opposing policy directions, thereby cancelling each other out (see 'Thinking around the subject' on p. 69). In recent times, it has been noted, for example, that while the UK's Department for Business, Innovation and Skills has been actively encouraging more overseas students to come to UK universities, the Home Office has been simultaneously made it more difficult by making student visas more expensive and difficult to obtain. In any large organization, the existence of internal 'silos' of people who do not speak to each other is common, so it is probably not surprising that this happens within government. To overcome the problem, central government has conducted a number of reviews that have tried to see service delivery from the perspective of actual users, rather than members of individual departments. The appointment of 'czars' and 'task forces', mentioned above, has been one way of initiating this process. One exercise of integrated-service teams simulated members of the public experiencing one of a number of major life events, such as leaving school, becoming unemployed, changing address, having a baby or retiring. Team members contacted the relevant departments and agencies direct, and this provided insights into the problems resulting from the way services are organized, and what might be done to improve things. Typical points that may be picked up, for example, are the way that people had to give the same information more than once to different – or even the same – organizations – for example, housing benefit and income support forms both ask for very similar information.

Creating 'joined-up' thinking is never easy, even within profit-orientated private-sector organizations. In seeking to achieve integration within government, the administration must balance the need to share responsibilities with the need to hold manageable-sized units accountable for their actions.

⟳ Thinking around the subject

How good is the National Health Service?

One of the recurring problems of public-sector services is monitoring their performance in an environment where market mechanisms alone will not reward the good performers and punish the bad. The UK has prided itself on a centralized National Health Service (NHS), which is free to consumers and paid for largely out of government taxation. But how do you measure the performance of doctors, either individually or in teams? The NHS has focused its efforts on quality-of-service issues. It routinely monitors, for example, the waiting time to see a consultant or to have elective surgery undertaken. But even such apparently simple indicators can mask a lot of problems. What does it mean when one consultant is shown to keep their patients waiting for longer than another consultant? To many people, a long waiting list may be a sign of a top-rated consultant who is very popular with patients, rather than a failing professional who cannot keep up with the demands placed on them. And then, of course, figures for waiting times can often be manipulated, scrupulously or unscrupulously. For example, Accident & Emergency departments use triage nurses to assess new patients upon arrival, thereby keeping within their Patients' Charter target for the time taken to initially see a new patient; however, the hospital may be slower to provide actual treatment. Some ambulance services have been reprimanded for trying to make their response times appear better than they actually are, by measuring the response time from when an ambulance sets out, rather than when a call for help is received.

Attempts to measure doctors' medical performance are much less developed, with debate about the most appropriate methodologies for assessing the efficacy of an operation or clinical diagnosis. Many medical outcomes cannot be assessed simply on the basis of success/failure, but require more subjective quality-of-life assessments to be taken into account. However, even the routine monitoring of patients' recovery rates could have unexpected dysfunctional consequences for patients. Some critics have argued that, in order to keep their performance indicators up, consultants may refuse to treat patients who have complications and a high risk of failure, and instead concentrate on easier cases with more predictable outcomes.

> Some doctors have expressed a concern that merely publishing performance indicators pushes up users' expectations of service delivery, so that in the end they may become more dissatisfied even though actual performance has improved. Is there a case for treating doctors as professionals whose professional ethics leads them to do their very best for their patients? Or is this inward-looking approach to professional standards becoming increasingly untenable in an era of well-informed consumers who know their rights and have high expectations?

2.12 Impacts of government on business operations

We will now return to impacts of the political environment on business organizations and discuss three levels of effect:

1 the transformation of many government departments into 'quangos' (or non-departmental government bodies), so that they act more like a business organization rather than a government department

2 the **outsourcing** of many government functions, and collaboration with the private sector through public–private partnerships (PPPs)

3 the effects of government legislation on business operations.

2.12.1 Quangos (non-departmental public bodies)

It is too simplistic to divide organizations into those belonging to the public sector and those belonging to the private sector. '**Quangos**' (quasi-autonomous non-governmental organizations) or, more correctly, **non-departmental public bodies (NDPBs)**, are a form of organization that shares characteristics of both. In Britain, quasi-governmental bodies exist because direct involvement by a government department in an activity is considered to be inefficient or undesirable, while leaving the activity to the private sector may be inappropriate where issues of public policy are concerned. The quasi-government body therefore represents a compromise between the constitutional needs of government control and the organizational needs of independence and flexibility associated with private-sector organizations.

There is nothing new in arm's length organizations being created by governments – for example, the Arts Council has existed since before the Second World War. As the size of the state increased in the early post-Second World War period, there was concern that government departments were becoming overloaded. Their existence has at times owed a lot to political dogma, with incoming governments often keen to make a statement by handing over some central government activities to arm's length bodies in the interests of 'efficiency', or on the other hand abolishing them, often also using arguments about improving efficiency and effectiveness. Government policies have sometimes appeared ambiguous on the role of quangos – for example, the incoming coalition government of 2010 sought to achieve popularity by announcing the abolition of many apparently unpopular and bureaucratic quangos, but had to reverse this when it realized that their work still had to be carried out by someone and the quango was the most efficient type of organization for doing this.

These are some examples of quangos in the UK:

- Ofcom, which regulates the communications industries
- Ofwat, which regulates private-sector water supply companies
- the Driver and Vehicle Licensing Agency (DVLA).

Quangos enjoy considerable autonomy from their parent department and the sponsoring minister has no direct control over the activities of the body, other than making the appointment of the chairman. The minister therefore ceases to be answerable to Parliament for the day-to-day activities of the body, unlike the responsibility that a minister has in respect of a government department. The responsibilities of quangos vary from being purely advisory to making important policy decisions and allocating large amounts of expenditure. Their income can come from a combination of government grant, precepts from local authorities and charges to users.

The main advantage of delegation to quangos is that action can generally be taken much more quickly than may have been the case with a government department, where it would probably have been necessary to receive ministerial approval before action was taken. Ministers may have less time to devote to the details of policy application with which many quangos are often involved, and may also be constrained to a much greater extent by broader considerations of political policy. Being relatively free of day-to-day political interference, quangos are in a better position to maintain a long-term plan free of short-term diversions, which may be the result of direct control by a minister who is subject to the need for short-term political popularity.

Against the advantages, quangos have a number of potential disadvantages. It is often argued that quangos are not sufficiently accountable to elected representatives for their actions. This can become an important issue where a quangos is responsible for developing policy or is a monopoly provider of an essential service. The actual independence of quangos from government has also been questioned, as many are still dependent on government funding for block grants. Quangos can easily become unpopular with the public, especially where senior managers are seen paying themselves high salaries as they take 'business-like' decisions to cut back on the services that they provide to the public. For this reason, politicians may seek popularity by promising to abolish unpopular quangos, but finding an alternative organizational form may be more difficult.

A major objective of delegation to quangos has been to ensure that services are provided more in line with users' requirements rather than political or operational expediency. High-level appointments to quangos have been made from the private sector with a view to bringing about a cultural change that develops a customer-focused ethos. For the marketing services industry, the development of quangos has resulted in many opportunities as they increasingly use the services of market research firms, advertising agencies and public relations consultants.

Thinking around the subject

Does the left hand know what the right hand is doing?
The government of a large modern economy necessarily involves dividing responsibilities between departments, each of which is given increasingly clear aims and objectives, as well as what are usually vague objectives 'to coordinate their activities with other departments'. But despite talk about 'joined-up government', evidence of disjointed government is often all too clear to see. Consider the following cases.

Farming in Britain and the EU has traditionally relied on high levels of government intervention and farmers have often spotted inconsistencies in government policy. For a period during the 1990s, the Department of Agriculture was paying farmers to drain wetlands to turn into farmland, while at the same time the Department of Environment was paying landowners to create ponds and marshland from farmland in order to foster wildlife.

The Department of Education has promoted the recruitment of students from overseas, which is good for the national economy and the longer-term cultural benefits of having students study in the UK. However, the Home Office has sharply increased its fees for issuing visas to overseas students. Were the government and the country any better off as a result of these apparently conflicting actions?

In 2004, the problem of 'binge drinking' late at night in town centres became a priority area for the Home Office. It was particularly concerned by pubs' practice of offering a 'happy hour' in which drinks were sold at a reduced price, leading to problems of drunkenness. The Home Office urged pubs to drop their happy hours. In one Essex town, pub landlords met under the auspices of their local Licensed Victuallers Association and agreed with the Home Office that the happy hour should be abolished. The pub landlords realized that it would be pointless for just one pub to abolish it, because customers would simply go to those pubs that retained cheap drinks. They therefore agreed collectively to abolish the happy hour for all pubs in the town. But this upset another government agency, the Office of Fair Trading, which claimed that the pub landlords were in danger of prosecution for breaching competition law, which made any agreement between suppliers to fix prices illegal.

Some businesses have exploited gaps in government thinking to their own advantage – for example, in the example above, unscrupulous farmers may have sought government grants for both draining their land and creating wetland out of other land. However, to many businesses, such as the well-meaning pub landlords, the appearance that the left hand of government doesn't know what the right hand is doing can be very frustrating. But how in practice can such a large institution as a national government be made to be entirely consistent in the diverse objectives its departments set?

2.12.2 Public – private partnerships (PPPs)

Throughout Europe, collaborative partnerships between the public and private sectors have become increasingly popular. In the UK, **public–private partnerships (PPPs)** is the umbrella name given to a range of initiatives that involve the private sector in the operation of public services. The **Private Finance Initiative (PFI)** is the most common initiative but PPPs could also extend to other forms of partnership – for example, joint ventures. The key difference between the PFI and conventional ways of providing public services is that the public sector does not own the assets. The authority makes an annual payment to the private company, which provides the building and associated services.

Traditionally, government has procured facilities and services that the private sector has supplied under contract to the public sector. For example, under the traditional route, a private-sector contractor would build a new school to a Local Education Authority's (LEA) specification, with associated maintenance and services then being provided by a range of private companies and the LEA itself. With PPPs, one contractor provides the school and then operates a range of specific services such as maintenance, heating and school meals on behalf of the LEA through a long-term contract. This new way of working allows the private sector to contribute its expertise to the process, so as to find innovative solutions and secure better value for money. A typical PFI project will be owned by a company set up especially to run the scheme. These companies are usually consortia including a building firm, a bank and a facilities management company. While PFI projects can be structured in different ways, there are usually four key elements: design, finance, build and operations. In the case of new hospitals funded by PFI schemes, the clinical, medical and nursing services continue to be provided by the NHS, while the private sector finances the building of the new hospital and runs the non-clinical services in it such as maintenance, cleaning, portering and security.

The most significant benefits to government of PPP come through transferring risk to the private sector. This means that, should a project under the PPP overrun its budget, the government and taxpayers should not be left to pick up the bill. Contrast this with a major project taken forward under direct contract to the public sector, such as Transport for London's Jubilee Line Extension. This overran its planned budget by around £1.4 billion and opened nearly two years late, forcing the government to use taxpayers' money and grant additional funds to get the project completed.

In principle, a PPP should result in a lower level of government borrowing and should also achieve best value. A public-sector comparator is developed in order to establish whether the PPP represents better value than government providing the service by itself. It will show the overall cost of raising the finance and actually doing the work under a wholly public-sector arrangement.

Critics of PPPs argue that the price of involvement by the private sector inevitably includes a high premium to cover the risk of a budget overrun, which could come about for a variety of extraneous reasons. Although the government is saved the initial capital expenditure, over the longer term it has to pay rental charges for the use of facilities, which could work out more expensive than undertaking the whole task itself. The private sector borrows at higher rates of interest than the public sector, and this cost has to be passed on to the purchasing government department. Audit Scotland has calculated these costs as adding £0.2–£0.3 million each year for every £10 million invested. PFI projects can also have high set-up costs due to lengthy negotiations involving lawyers and consultants employed by both sides. It has been reported that the first 15 NHS trust hospital PFIs spent £45 million on advisers, an average of 4 per cent of the capital value (Clark and Simpkins 2006).

There is growing evidence that PFI projects escalate both in scale and cost, reflecting not just inflation but the very nature of PFI itself. In many cases, the PFI agreement places some responsibility for cost overruns with the government rather than the private sector, especially where specifications have changed during the duration of the contract. The higher costs can lead to an affordability gap for the procuring authority that is met by reductions in services and capacity. As with outsourcing contracts in general, there is a need for flexibility to be built in to PPP agreements in order to accommodate the environmental and internal changes that can occur over the lifetime of a contract (Ketter 2008).

There have been casualties among PFI providers. In 2007, Metronet – a company set up to operate some of London's underground railway lines in a PPP with the government body Transport for London – was placed into administration. The companies behind the Metronet consortium – Bombardier, Balfour-Beatty and WS Atkins – came to the conclusion that they could not bear any further cost overruns, which had been disputed with the public-sector partner. They therefore left Transport for London to pick up responsibility for maintaining and renewing the underground lines concerned.

2.12.3 Impacts of government legislation on business operations

Very few governments, whether free market or interventionist, would claim to have made life more difficult for businesses to operate. Yet a frequent complaint of many businesses, especially

⟳ Thinking around the subject

Political vision helps win Olympic Games for London

When London was chosen to host the 2012 Olympic Games, the initial cheers rather overlooked the enormous amount of collaborative work that lay behind London's successful bid, and the even more extensive network of relationships that would be necessary to deliver a successful Olympic Games. It has been claimed that having an elected Mayor and Assembly greatly assisted London in its successful bid to host the Games. At a time when much of the country was ambivalent about bidding for the Games, the Mayor provided a focal point for championing the interests of London. The Games would bring more than 28 days of sporting activities, and provide a lasting legacy in terms of economic growth and social regeneration. Thousands of individual service providers stood to benefit from the Games, ranging from small restaurants catering for construction workers and visitors to the Games through to large infrastructure providers. As well as stimulating the development of world-class sporting facilities, including swimming pools, a velodrome and hockey facilities, it was hoped that the Games would inspire a new generation to greater sporting activity and achievement.

The Mayor agreed with the government a funding package of up to £2.375 billion to help meet the costs of staging the Olympics. The first £2.050 billion would be met, with up to £1.5 billion from the Lottery and up to £550 million from London council tax, which would cost the average London household £20 a year, or 38p a week. At the centre of the collaborative relationships was the Olympic Delivery Authority (ODA). The ODA has statutory backing through the London

© Pete Tripp

Olympic Games and Paralympic Games Act 2006, and has to use a combination of power and persuasion to coordinate the efforts of multiple service providers, who will collectively make up the total Olympic experience for those who visit the Games in person, or who watch on television. The ODA must work closely with key partners such as the London Organising Committee of the Olympic Games, Transport for London (which is responsible for developing transport infrastructure to serve the Games), the London Development Agency and other regional development agencies such as the London Thames Gateway Development Corporation, in order to ensure not only that the Games are successful, but also that the infrastructure achieves long-term planning goals.

The ODA is responsible for making arrangements for building works, which it has done through a series of partnerships and subcontractor arrangements. At the same time as managing relationships with numerous suppliers, the ODA has to work closely with the International Olympic Committee (IOC) to ensure that standards are met. The ODA has responsibilities for protecting the Olympic logo and rights to use it by sponsors and other commercial users, and this requires the ODA to manage a large network of sponsors who contribute to the cost of holding the Games.

small business owners, is that government expects them to do too much administration on behalf of the government. Despite frequent high-profile government campaigns against 'red tape', the volume of **regulation** continues to have a major impact on the costs of business organizations. While large organizations may be able to afford specialists to handle administrative matters and can spread the cost over large volumes of output, government regulation can hit small businesses very hard. Consider some of the following examples of regulations that have added to the costs of business organizations in recent years.

- Value added tax (VAT) effectively makes most business organizations tax collectors on behalf of government, and small business owners must become familiar with complex sets of regulations.

- Legislation to give additional rights to employees bears down particularly heavily on small businesses. The granting of maternity rights to new mothers may easily be absorbed by large organizations, but a small business may experience great difficulties when one person who represents a large and critical part of the workforce decides to exercise their rights.

- The mounting volume of consumer protection and health and safety legislation has a particularly big impact on small businesses, which do not generally have the expertise to readily assimilate the provisions of new regulations.

A number of attempts have been made to quantify the costs to business organizations of government regulation. The British Chamber of Commerce's 'Burdens Barometer' is independently compiled by the London and Manchester Business Schools. Its Barometer for 2008 estimated that the cost of 46 major regulations introduced by the UK government since 1998 resulted in annual costs to business of over £65 billion. Table 2.2 shows a sample of these 46 regulations and the estimated resulting financial burden on business (BCC 2008).

Even the internet, which was supposed to simplify many administrative tasks, has led to new government-imposed burdens on businesses. Worried at the prospect of organized crime using the internet, the government passed the controversial Regulation of Investigatory Powers (RIP) Act 2000. This was bitterly contested by business for its provisions enabling the interception of emails and electronic correspondence.

Incoming governments have a tendency to make high-profile initiatives to simplify life for business – for example, by exempting small businesses from certain obligations. However, further regulation has a tendency to creep back into government policy.

2.13 Influences on government policy formation

Political parties were described earlier as organizations that people belong to in order to influence government policy, generally over a range of issues. Political parties aim to work within the political system – for example, by having members elected as MPs or local councillors. A distinction can be drawn between political parties and pressure groups or interest groups. These latter groups seek to change policy in accordance with members' interests, generally advancing a relatively narrow cause. Unlike members of political parties, members of pressure

Table 2.2   Estimated costs to UK businesses of compliance with selected regulations.

Regulation	Year of first implementation	Estimated annual recurring cost to UK business (£m)	Cumulative cost to UK businesses from date of introduction to July 2008 (£m)
The Working Time Regulations 1999	1999	1,795	16,005
Employment Act 2002	2002	219	1,302
Flexible Working (Procedural Arrangements) 2002	2003	296	1,588
The Maternity and Parental Leave (Amendment) Regulations 2001	2001	5	95
The Money Laundering Regulations 2003	2004	106	472
The Consumer Credit Regulations 2004	2005	102	681
The Tax Credit Acts 1999 and accompanying regulations	2000	100	865
The Part-time Workers (Prevention of Less Favourable Treatment) Regulations 2000	2000	27	218
The Stakeholder Pensions Schemes Regulations 2000 and 2005	2001	78	660
The Disability Discrimination (Providers of Services) (Adjustments to Premises) Regulations 2001	2004	189	1,721
The Animal By-products Regulations 2003	2003	100	540
The Electricity and Gas (Energy Efficiency Obligations) Order 2004	2005	467	1,401
Total for all government regulations on business			65,993

Source: adapted from the British Chambers of Commerce *Burdens Barometer* (BCC 2008).

groups generally work from outside the political system and do not become part of the political establishment.

2.13.1 Pressure groups

Pressure groups can be divided into a number of categories. In the first place there is a division between those that are permanently fighting for a general cause, and those that are set up to achieve a specific objective and are dissolved when this objective is met – or there no longer seems any prospect of changing the situation. Pressure groups set up to fight specific new road-building proposals fit into the latter category.

Pressure groups can also be classified according to their functions. Sectional groups exist to promote the common interests of their members over a wide range of issues. Trades unions and employers' associations fall into this category. They represent their members' views to government on diverse issues such as proposed employment legislation, import controls and vocational training. This type of pressure group frequently offers other benefits to members, such as legal representation for individual members and the dissemination of information to members. Promotional groups, on the other hand, are established to fight for specific causes, such as animal welfare, which is represented by, say, the League Against Cruel Sports.

Businesses themselves also frequently join pressure groups as a means of influencing government legislative proposals that will affect their industry sector. An example of a powerful commercial pressure group is the British Road Federation, which represents companies with interests in road construction and lobbies government to increase expenditure on new road building.

Pressure groups can influence government policy using three main approaches.

1 The first, propaganda, can be used to create awareness of the group and its cause. This can be aimed directly at policy formers, or indirectly by appealing to the constituents of policy formers to apply direct pressure themselves. This is essentially an impersonal form of mass communication.

2 A second option is to try to represent the views of the group directly to policy formers on a one-to-one basis. Policy formers frequently welcome representations that they may see as preventing bigger problems or confrontations arising in the future. Links between pressure groups and government often become institutionalized, such as where the Department for Transport routinely seeks the views of the RAC Foundation on proposals to change road traffic legislation. Where no regular contacts exist, pressure groups can be represented by giving evidence before a government-appointed inquiry, by approaching sympathetic MPs or by hiring the services of a professional lobbyist.

3 A third approach used by pressure groups is to carry out research and to supply information. This has the effect of increasing public awareness of the organization and usually has a valuable propaganda function. The British Road Federation frequently supplies MPs with comparative road statistics purporting to show reasons why the government should be spending more money on road building.

Pressure groups are most effective where they apply pressure in a low-key manner – for example, where they are routinely consulted for their views. The lobbying of MPs – which combines elements of all three methods described above – has become increasingly important in recent years.

Sometimes pressure groups, or sectional interests within them, recognize that they are unlikely to achieve their aims by using the channels described above. Recent years have seen an increase in 'direct action' by pressure groups, or breakaway sections of mainstream groups, against their target. Campaigners for animal rights, or those opposed to the use of genetically modified (GM) crops, have on occasion given up on trying to change the law and have instead sought to disrupt the activities of those organizations giving rise to their concerns. Organizations targeted in this way may initially put a brave face on such activities by dismissing them as inconsequential, but often the result has been to change the organization's behaviour, especially where the prospect of large profits is uncertain. Action by animal rights protestors contributed to the near collapse of Huntingdon Life Sciences (an animal testing laboratory), and many farmers were discouraged from taking part in GM crop trials by the prospect of direct action against their farms.

It is not only national governments to which pressure groups apply their attention – local authorities are frequently the target of pressure groups over issues of planning policy or the provision of welfare services. Increasingly, pressure is also being applied at EU level. Again, the European Commission regularly consults some groups, while other groups apply direct pressure to members of the Commission.

Business organizations have achieved numerous reported triumphs in attempting to influence the political environment in which they operate. The pressure group representing the tobacco industry – the Tobacco Advisory Council – had a significant effect in countering the pressure applied by the anti-tobacco lobby, represented by Action on Smoking Health. Legislation to ban cigarette advertising was delayed, and the pressure group has lobbied against a proposed ban on smoking in public places.

Pressure groups themselves are increasingly crossing national boundaries to reflect the influence of international governmental institutions such as the EU and the increasing influence of multinational business organizations. Both industrial and consumer pressure groups have been formed at a multinational level to counter these influences – a good example of the latter is Greenpeace.

2.13.2 The role of the media

The media – press, radio, television and increasingly the internet – not only spread awareness of political issues but also influence policy and decision making by setting the political agenda and influencing public opinion. The broadcast media in the UK must by law show balance in their coverage of political events, but the press is often more openly partisan. Campaigns undertaken by the press frequently reflect the background of their owners – the *Daily Telegraph* is more likely to support the causes of deregulation in an industry, while the *Guardian* will be more likely to put forward the case for government spending on essential public services. It is often said that *The Times* and the BBC Radio 4 *Today* programme set the political agenda for the day ahead.

⟳ Thinking around the subject

Political apathy becomes militant online

A casual glance at the politics pages in many newspapers in western Europe may lead to the conclusion that most people don't really care about politics. Most countries have seen a succession of broadly moderate political parties, with very few parties proclaiming extreme views that capture the support of large numbers of people. This has been matched by growing levels of apathy about the political process, evidenced in many countries by a declining number of people voting in elections. In the elections for the EU held in the UK in 2004, it was noted that more people voted in television's *Big Brother* contest than voted for European MEPs. But are we right to dismiss such disengagement from politics as evidence of individuals' lack of concern for political issues? While voting in elections may be declining, there is no sign of people staying silent when their cherished views are challenged. Some countries, such as France, have a tradition of popular protest on the streets. In Britain, a more consensual approach has been more traditional. But, even here, there are signs that frustration with the political process can spill over into the streets, witnessed by the nearly half a million people who marched in London in 2002 under the guise of the Countryside Alliance, to protest about government policy on the countryside, and the thousands of students who descended on London in 2010 to protest against proposed increases in university tuition fees.

New technology has opened up new opportunities for people to express their political views without going to the ballot box. One example is the facility for any individual to initiate an online petition to 10 Downing Street. In May 2010, the government announced that those e-petitions that receive 100,000 signatures or more would be eligible for debate in Parliament. One an example of an e-petition is that launched in 2007 by Peter Roberts and a small group who were opposed to the idea of charging for the use of roads; it attracted 1.8 million signatures. Is this the true democratization of politics? For businesses, rather than looking at politicians to try to judge future policy, would it be just as good an idea to look at what really brings people on to the streets, or to an online petition, in order to understand the pressures that politicians will probably eventually respond to?

Case study:
Should government be running the railways?

© Linda Steward

Throughout the world, there have been strong social and economic arguments for state ownership of railways. Railways are often seen as a vital part of the public infrastructure, which allows spatially dispersed economies to function. Some remote areas rely on railways as a vital lifeline, and many of our large conurbations would be unimaginably congested if rail commuters suddenly switched to their cars. The sheer costs and risks involved in building and operating a railway have deterred private investors, mindful of the many bankruptcies that have occurred during earlier 'railway booms'.

To the Conservative government of the 1990s, Britain's railways were suffering from a lack of entrepreneurship, which could be overcome by replacing public-sector employees and finance with new ideas and new capital brought in from the private sector. Britain led the way in privatizing its railways during the 1990s, and many other governments have followed by loosening their countries' railway links with government. the UK government embarked on a radical plan to deliver train services through a franchising system, which in principle copied the approach of a fast-food franchise. But implementing a franchising system was much more difficult and threw up many new problems. Britain's railways have been treated as a political football, and questions have been raised about the relative merits of state ownership and privatization. Along the way, there have been many opportunities, and headaches, for private-sector organizations that have been attracted to the sector.

The principle of rail franchising is simple. The government defined individual routes or groups of routes, and specified a minimum standard of service that it required. It then invited private companies to bid for the right to run the franchise for a specified number of years. For highly profitable routes, the successful bidder would pay the government an annual fee in return for rights to run the service. As with a fast-food franchise, the franchisee could increase its profits by generating more revenue from customers and/or by operating its service more efficiently. In the case of highly profitable routes such as the East Coast Main Line, a bidding war resulted in high payments being made by the franchisee to the government, but in other cases, such as the Valleys Lines of South Wales, it was recognized that these services would never be profitable, and the successful franchisee was the company that could provide the required level of service for the minimum level of government subsidy. In 2009, the UK government paid £3.9 billion in subsidies to rail operators.

So far, the comparison with a fast-food franchise may be fairly sound, but the implementation then raises some very tricky additional issues. First, railways serve a vital function in life, and many people, such as commuters into central London, are effectively captive, something that cannot really be said of McDonald's customers. As a result, franchise agreements include a long list of requirements set by the government to safeguard the interests of passengers and society generally – for example, a requirement for inter-availability of tickets on the services of competing rail operators. In recent years, there has been a tendency for the government to 'micro-manage' franchisees with ever increasing detail, leading many to question the purpose of having private-sector entrepreneurs involved when they are so constrained in using their entrepreneurial skills.

A further problem has occurred where franchise rail operators have made inaccurate assumptions about future costs and revenues, and have been forced to renegotiate or hand back their franchise, leaving the government to take over operations. In 2009, the operator of the East Coast Main Line franchise, National Express, found the £1.4 billion franchise fee that it was committed to paying the government over the life of the franchise unsustainable, because it had over-bid for the franchise and assumed an over-optimistic level of passenger growth, which was sharply undermined by the economic recession.

Many critics of rail franchising have suggested that franchisees would invest very little of their own capital and take all the benefits when the going was good, but when times got hard they would simply abandon the franchise by handing it back to the government - was this a fair allocation of risk between government and franchisee?

There has been debate about the ideal length of a rail franchise: too short, and the franchisee would have little incentive to invest in improvements, knowing that they may lose the franchise in a couple of years to a competitor; too long, and the operator may become complacent, in which case extensive use of key performance indicators needs to be written into the franchise agreement to allow the government to take action if the terms of a franchise agreement are broken.

A further paradox of the rail franchise system is that it was originally designed to bring private-sector skills to the previous state-run bureaucracy of British Rail, but, in practice, Europe's state-owned railways have bought in to British rail operators, either through consortiums or through outright ownership – for example, Germany's state-owned railway DB acquired the Chiltern Railways service between London and Birmingham, Arriva Trains Wales, the Cross Country network, and the largest rail freight operator DB Schencker. French and Dutch state-owned railways also have interests in other franchise operators.

Has franchising been beneficial for the UK rail sector? A report published in October 2008 by the National Audit Office was generally positive, noting that 'rail franchising produces generally well thought through service specifications and generates keen bidding competition. This approach has resulted in better value for money for the taxpayer ...' (NAO 2008).

Maybe some of the early problems with rail franchising resulted from policy makers drawing too much of an analogy with the proverbial fast-food restaurant. As franchising has matured, new models of management have developed, but to critics, if further control is needed by government, why not go the whole way, re-nationalize the sector and cut out the middle man? The state-owned British Rail had been the subject of many bad jokes when it ran the country's railways, so were sceptics wearing rose-tinted spectacles as they applauded the effective re-nationalization of the East Coast Main Line in 2009 when the franchise was taken from National Express?

QUESTIONS

1 Summarize the effects of political ideology on the management and ownership of railways in Britain.

2 What public interest is served by government involvement in the management and ownership of railways?

3 What are likely to be the key differences between the objectives of a railway in private ownership and a railway in state ownership?

Summary

The political environment impinges on many other aspects of an organization's environment – for example, change in the dominant political ideology can result in significant changes in the economic environment. Businesses dislike uncertainty in the political environment, and monitoring and understanding it is useful to pick up early signs of change. This chapter has explored the basis of government in the UK, and the respective roles of national, regional, local and European government. Although examples have been taken from the UK, the elements of the political environment described here are similar in most western democratic countries. A two-way interaction occurs between government and business, in which business organizations monitor changes in the political environment, but also seek to influence the environment through lobbying. Pressure groups represent an increasingly important element of the political environment, working from outside the formal political system.

The overlaps between the political environment and other aspects of a firm's marketing environment are covered in following chapters. Politicians have a significant impact on the national economic environment (**Chapter 13**) and indeed respond to changes in it. The level of competition within any market can be influenced by government policies on anti-competitive practices (**Chapter 12**). Government policy is translated into legislation (**Chapter 6**) and influences the standards of behaviour expected from business (**Chapter 5**).

Key Terms

Act of Parliament (48)

Beacon Council (66)

Best value (66)

Cabinet (51)

Charter Mark (66)

Civil service (52)

Directive (63)

European Commission (59)

European Council of Ministers (59)

European Court of Justice (59)

European Economic Area (EEA) (57)

European Union (EU) (57)

Executive (50)

Ideology (44)

Judicial review (52)

Judiciary (52)

Legislature (48)

Lobbying (49)

Local government (56)

Non-departmental public body (NDPB) (68)

Outsourcing (68)

Political party (44)

Pressure group (75)

Private Finance Initiative (PFI) (70)

Public–private partnership (PPP) (70)

Quango (68)

Regional government (53)

Regulation (73)

Social exclusion (46)

Task force (53)

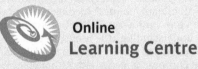

Online Learning Centre

To help you grasp the key concepts of this chapter, explore the extra resources posted on the Online Learning Centre at *www.mcgraw-hill.co.uk/palmer*. Among other helpful resources there are chapter-by-chapter test questions, revision notes and web links.

Chapter review questions

1 For a newspaper lobbying against government proposals to impose value added tax on newspaper sales, identify the key points within the government system to which lobbying could be applied.

2 For a British manufacturing company, briefly summarize the principal problems and opportunities presented by the development of closer economic and political union within the EU.

3 What measures can a large multinational business take to monitor the political environment in its various operating areas?

Activities

1 Take three of the recent regulatory burdens on business that are listed in Table 2.2. Discuss whether these are unfair burdens on business, or a real and worthwhile net benefit for customers, employees and society as a whole.

2 Go to the website of the main political parties in your country, and assess the extent to which you consider their policies to be beneficial for small or medium-sized businesses. Try to distinguish between specific policies that affect business, and more general policies that shape the nature of the country, and may indirectly have an effect on businesses.

3 Try to identify a list of non-departmental public bodies (or 'quangos') that you may have had dealings with (for example, health services, the driver licensing agency, educational establishment). Critically assess the nature of control of these organizations. Is bureaucratic control preferable to control by customers exercising their choice of service provider? Is such choice feasible for your selected quango?

Further reading

For an overview of how government is managed in the UK, the following texts provide a useful insight.

Heywood, A. (2008) *The Essentials of UK Politics*, Basingstoke, Palgrave Macmillan.
Jones, B. and Norton, P. (2010) *Politics UK* (7th edn), Harlow, Pearson.
Moran, M. (2010) *Politics and Governance in the UK*, Basingstoke, Palgrave.

The following provides a more specific focus on local government.

Wilson, D. and Game, C. (2011) *Local Government in the UK* (5th edn), Basingstoke, Palgrave Macmillan.

For a discussion of devolved government in the UK, consult the following.

Mitchell, J. (2009) *Devolution in the United Kingdom*, Manchester, Manchester University Press.
Trench, A. (2007) *Devolution and Power in the United Kingdom*, Manchester, Manchester University Press.

To many, the workings of the EU are extremely complex and the following texts provide a general overview.

Leonard, D. (2010) *Guide to the EU (Economist Guide to the European Union)*, London, Profile Books.
Nugent, N. (2010) *The Government and Politics of the European Union*, Basingstoke, Palgrave.

The following official publications of the EU are also useful for monitoring current developments.

Basic Statistics of the Community.
Bulletin of the European Commission of the European Communities.

Finally, there is extensive coverage of the functions of pressure groups. The following texts are useful for highlighting their relationship to business organizations.

Watts, D. (2007) *Pressure Groups*, Edinburgh, Edinburgh University Press.
Zetter, L. (2008) *Lobbying: The Art of Political Persuasion*, Petersfield, Harriman House.

References

Barro, R.J. (1996) 'Democracy and growth', *Journal of Economic Growth,* Kluwer Academic Publishers, Vol. 1, No. 1, pp. 1–27.
BCC (2008) *Burdens Barometer*, London, British Chamber of Commerce.
Clark, R. and Simpkins, E. (2006) 'Buy now pay later (a lot more, a lot later)', *Daily Telegraph,* 7 May.
Freedom House (2010) *Freedom in the Word*, 2010 Survey Release, Washington DC, Freedom House, Inc.
Hills, J. et al. (2010) *An Anatomy of Economic Inequality in the UK: Report of the National Equality Paneli.* CASE report 60, Centre for Analysis of Social Exclusion, London, London School of Economics and Political Science.
Ketter, P. (2008) 'Companies need to manage outsourcing risks', *T&D Alexandria*, 62 (3), 14.
NAO (2008) *Letting Rail Franchises 2005–2007*, London, National Audit Office.
Office for National Statistics (2004) *Focus on Social Inequalities,* London, ONS.
Office for National Statistics (2008) *Social Trends*, No. 38, London, ONS.
Rodrik, D. (2002) *Feasible Globalization*, Working Paper, Boston, MA, Harvard University, May.
Stiglitz, J. (2000) 'Whither reform? Ten years of the transition', in B. Pleskovic and J. Stiglitz (eds) *Annual World Bank Conference on Development Economics 1999*, Washington DC, World Bank, pp. 27–56.
Transparency International (2010) *Corruption Perceptions Index 2009*, Article first published online: 18 Dec 2009, DOI: 10.1111/j.1467-6346.2009.02664.x.
United Nations (1998) *Human Development Report 1998*, New York, Oxford University Press.
Work Bank (2008) *World Development Report 2008*: *Agriculture for Development*, Washington DC, World Bank.
World Factbook 2009, Central Intelligence Agency, available at https://www.cia.gov/.

The Legal Environment

Some 30 or 40 years ago, a shopkeeper in Britain could afford to be fairly laid back in his attitude to the law. He might have restricted customers' rights to complain if goods were faulty, and might have been 'economical with the truth' in the claims that he made for his goods. He might have enjoyed a cigarette with his workers at the back of a shop that had lots of steps, which made access for disabled people difficult. He might have had a quiet word with other local shopkeepers about agreeing not to undercut one anothers' prices. And he might have had a preference for employing people based on their gender, ethnicity and age. Today, that same shop owner might need a lawyer to make sure he didn't fall foul of the minefield of legislation that faces even small businesses. False claims about goods can result in criminal prosecution and civil claims from consumers. Health and safety regulations have become more onerous, and a raft of employment legislation now affects how he recruits, manages and fires staff. Even a friendly chat with other local shopkeepers could bring action from the regulatory authority if it suspects collusion. The legal environment is one aspect of most organizations' environments that has become increasingly complex in recent years; it and is explored in this chapter.

✓ Learning Objectives

This chapter will explain:

☑ The key legal challenges and opportunities facing business organizations, in respect of their relationships with customers, suppliers, employees and intermediaries.

☑ Sources of law – common law and statute law.

☑ The basic principles of law – contract and tort.

☑ Legal proccesses.

☑ Quasi-law based on voluntary codes of conduct.

☑ Legal protection of intellectual property.

6.1 Introduction

It was noted in the first chapter that all societies need some form of rules that govern the relationship between individuals, organizations and government bodies. In the absence of rules, chaos is likely to ensue, in which the strongest people will survive at the expense of the weakest. Businesses do not like to operate in environments in which there are no accepted rules of behaviour, because there is no guarantee that their investments will be protected from unauthorized seizure. This may partly explain why some countries of central Africa, which have been regarded as lawless areas without proper government, have failed to attract significant inward investment by businesses.

However, a system of rules does not necessarily imply a formal legal system. Many less developed economies manage with moral codes of governance that exert pressure on individuals and organizations to conform to an agreed code of conduct. In such countries, the shame inflicted on the family of a trader who defrauds a customer may be sufficient to ensure that traders abide by a moral code of governance.

In complex, pluralistic societies, moral governance alone may be insufficient to ensure compliance from business organizations. The tendency therefore has been for legal frameworks to expand as economies develop. One observer has pointed out that the Ten Commandments – a biblical code for governing society – ran to about 300 words. The American Bill of Rights of 1791 ran to about 700 words. Today, as an example of the detailed legislation that affects our conduct, the Eggs (Marketing Standards) Regulations 1995 run to several pages. The law essentially represents a codification of the rules and governance values of a society, expressed in a way that allows aggrieved parties to use an essentially bureaucratic system to gain what the society regards as justice. The legal environment of western developed economies is very much influenced by the political environment, which in turn is influenced by the social environment. In this sense, the law does not exist in a vacuum. Developments in the business environment have led to changes in the law affecting businesses, and the law in turn has affected the activities of business organizations.

In previous chapters we have considered the relationship between elements of an organization's micro- and macroenvironments at a fairly abstract level. In reality, these relationships are governed by a legal framework that presents opportunities and constraints for the manner in which these relationships can be developed.

We can identify a number of important areas in which the legal environment impinges on the activities of business organizations.

- The nature of the relationship between the organization and its customers, suppliers and intermediaries is influenced by the prevailing law. Over time, there has been a tendency for the law to give additional rights to buyers of goods and additional duties to the seller, especially in the case of transactions between businesses and private individuals. Whereas the nineteenth-century entrepreneur in Britain would have had almost complete freedom to dictate the terms of the relationship with its customers, developments in statute law now require, for example, the supplier to ensure that the goods are of satisfactory quality and that no misleading description of them is made. Furthermore, the expectations of an organization's customers have changed over time. Previous generations may have resigned themselves to suffering injustice in their dealings with a business, but today the expectation is increasingly for perfection every time. Greater awareness of the law on the part of consumers has produced an increasingly litigious society.

- In addition to the direct relationship that a company has with its customers, the law also influences the relationship that it has with other members of the general public. The law may, for example, prevent a firm having business relationships with certain sectors of the market, as where children are prohibited by law from buying cigarettes or drinking in public houses. Also, the messages that a company sends out in its advertising are likely to be picked up by members of the general public, and the law has intervened to protect the public interest where these messages could cause offence (adverts that are racially prejudicial, for example).

- Employment relationships are covered by increasingly complex legislation, which recognizes that employees have a proprietary interest in their job. Legislation seeks to make up for inequalities in the power between employers and employee.

- The legal environment influences the relationship between business enterprises themselves, not only in terms of contracts for transactions between them, but also in the way they relate to one another in a competitive environment. The law has increasingly prevented companies from joining together in anti-competitive practices, whether covertly or overtly.

- Companies need to develop new products, yet the rewards of undertaking new product development are influenced by the law. The laws of copyright and patent protect a firm's investment in fruitful research.

- The legal environment influences the production possibilities of an enterprise and hence the products that can be offered to consumers. These can have a direct effect – as in the case of regulations stipulating car safety design requirements – or a more indirect effect – as where legislation to reduce pollution increases the manufacturing costs of a product, or prevents its manufacture completely.

The legal environment is very closely related to the political environment. In the UK, law derives from two sources: common law and statute law.

1 The **common law** develops on the basis of judgments in the courts – a case may set a precedent for all subsequent cases to follow. The judiciary is independent of government and the general direction of precedents tends gradually to reflect changing attitudes in society.

2 **Statute law**, on the other hand, is passed by Parliament and can reflect the prevailing political ideology of the government.

We can draw a distinction between *civil* law and *criminal* law. Civil law provides a means by which one party can bring an action for a loss it has suffered as the direct result of actions by another party. A party who is injured by a defective vehicle, or has suffered loss because a promised order for goods has not been delivered, can use the civil law to claim some kind of recompense against the other party. By contrast, criminal law is invoked when a party causes harm to society more generally. In this case, it is the government that brings a claim against a wrongdoer and punishment generally takes the form of a fine or a prison sentence. Most of the subjects covered in this chapter are concerned with the civil law – that is, relationships between an organization and other individuals and organizations in their business environment. However, business organizations are increasingly being prosecuted for breaches of criminal law. Cases discussed in this chapter include breaches of food safety law, breaches of health and safety law, and providing misleading price information.

The law is a very complex area of the business environment. Most businesses would call upon expert members of the legal profession to interpret and act upon some of the more complex elements of the law. The purpose of this chapter is not to give definitive answers on aspects of the law as it affects business organizations – this would be impossible and dangerous in such a short space. Instead, the aim is to raise awareness of legal issues in order to recognize in general terms the opportunities and restrictions that the law poses, and the areas in which business organizations may need to seek the specialized advice of a legal professional.

This chapter will begin by looking at some general principles of law: the law of contract, the law relating to negligence and the processes of the legal system in England. Although the detail will describe the legal system of England, many of the principles apply in other judicial systems. The chapter will then consider the following specific areas of applications of the law, which are of particular relevance to businesses:

- dealings between organizations and their customers for the supply of goods and services
- contracts of employment
- protection of intellectual property rights
- legislation relating to production processes
- legislation to prevent anti-competitive practices.

6.2 The law of contract

A contract is an agreement between two parties where one party agrees to do something (e.g. supply goods, provide a service, offer employment) in return for which the other party provides some form of payment (in money or some other form of value). A typical organization would have contracts with a wide range of other parties, including customers, suppliers, employees and intermediaries.

There can be no direct legal relationship between a company and any of these groups unless it can be proved that a contract exists. An advertisement on its own only very rarely creates a legal relationship. The elements of a contract comprise offer, acceptance, intention to create legal relations, consideration, capacity, and terms and representations. We will consider these in turn.

- *Offer:* an 'offeror' indicates that they intend to be legally bound on the terms stated in the offer, if it is accepted by the person to whom the offer is made (the 'offeree'). An offer must be distinguished from an invitation to treat, which can be defined as an invitation to make offers. Normally, advertisements are regarded as invitations to treat, rather than an offer. Similarly, priced goods on display in shops are invitations to treat. Therefore, if a leather jacket is priced at £20 (through error) in the shop widow, it is not possible to demand the garment at that price. As the display is an invitation to treat, it is the consumer who is making the offer, which the shopkeeper may accept or reject as he wishes.

- *Acceptance:* this may be made only by the person(s) to whom the offer was made, and it must be absolute and unqualified (i.e. it must not add any new terms or conditions, for to do so would have the effect of revoking the original offer). Acceptance must be communicated to the offeror unless it can be implied by conduct. An offer may be revoked at any time prior to acceptance

- *Intention to create legal relations:* generally, in all commercial agreements it is accepted that both parties intend to make a legally binding contract and therefore it is unnecessary to include terms to this effect. In some circumstances, however, there may be no intention on the part of one or both parties to create legal relations, as occurs where a donor casually gives money to a charity organization. In the absence of such intention, a contract cannot exist.

- *Consideration:* consideration is generally essential in any contract and has been defined as some right, interest, profit or benefit accruing to one party, or some forbearance, detriment, loss or responsibility given, suffered or undertaken by the other (i.e. some benefit accruing to one party or a detriment suffered by the other). In commercial contracts generally, the consideration takes the form of a cash payment. However, in contracts of barter, which are common in some countries, goods are often exchanged for goods.

- *Capacity:* capacity refers to the ability of a company or individual to enter into a contract. Generally, any person or organization may enter into an agreement, which may be enforced against them. Exceptions include minors, drunks and mental patients; for this reason, companies usually exclude people under 18 from offers of goods to be supplied on credit. Limited companies must have the capacity to make a contract identified in their Objects clause within their Articles and Memorandum of Association (see Chapter 7).

- *Terms and representations:* a distinction can be made between the terms of a contract and representations, which were made prior to forming the contract. Generally, it is assumed that statements that are made at the formation of a contract are terms of that contract, but many statements made during the course of negotiations are mere representations. If the statement is a term, the injured party may sue for breach of contract and will normally obtain damages that are deemed to put him or her in the position they would have been in had the statement been true. If the statement is a mere representation, it may be possible to avoid the contract by obtaining an order – known as rescission – which puts the parties back in the position they were in prior to the formation of the contract.

⟳ Thinking around the subject

Is a business relationship a contract?

One of the trends in the business environment that we discussed in Chapter 1 is towards closer relationships between companies in a supply chain. So, instead of buying 'job lots' of components and raw materials from the cheapest buyer whenever they are needed, a buyer and seller will come to an arrangement for their supply over the longer term. The parties may not be able to specify the precise products or volumes that they will need to buy, but just by understanding each other's processes and likely future requirements, the supply chain can be made more efficient and effective.

Many of these business relationships are based on 'gentlemen's agreements' with little formal specification in writing. So is this a contract? Can either party unilaterally end a gentleman's agreement?

The question was tested in 2002 in the case of *Baird Textile Holdings Ltd v Marks & Spencer plc* (M&S). Baird had been making lingerie, women's coats and men's clothes for M&S for over 30 years, and had largely built its business round the retail chain's requirements. However, the parties had resisted formalizing the arrangement in order to maintain maximum flexibility in their relationship. But increased competition in the high street led M&S to look for cheaper sources of manufacturing overseas, and Baird was told that with immediate effect its goods were no longer required by M&S.

Baird argued that although there was no written contract governing their relationship, there was an implied term that either party would give reasonable notice of any change to the relationship. The supplier claimed for damages of £53.6 million, which included a £33 million charge to cover redundancy payments, and further amounts in respect of asset write-downs, including IT equipment it used to help fulfil its M&S clothing orders. The claim was intended to put Baird back into the position it would have been in had M&S given it three years' notice, rather than suddenly terminating its agreement. But did the agreement between the two constitute a contract?

The Court of Appeal held that the long-term arrangements between Baird and M&S did not constitute a contract. It stated that there was a clear mutual intent not to enter into a legal agreement and this view was supported by the absence of any precise terms. Both parties clearly wished to preserve flexibility in their dealings with each other. A contract existed only in respect of individual orders when they were placed, but there was no contract governing the continuity of orders.

Non-contractual liability

6.3   Non-contractual liability

Consider now the situation where a consumer discovers that goods are defective in some way but is unable to sue the retailer from which they were supplied because the consumer is not a party to the contract (which may occur where the goods were bought as a gift by a friend). The product may also injure a completely unconnected third party. The only possible course of action here has been to sue the manufacturer. This situation was illustrated in 1932 in the case of *Donaghue v Stevenson,* where a man bought a bottle of ginger beer manufactured by the defendant. The man gave the bottle to his female companion, who became ill from drinking the contents, as the bottle (which was opaque) contained the decomposing remains of a snail. The consumer sued the manufacturer and won. The House of Lords held that on the facts outlined there was remedy in the **tort** of negligence.

To prove **negligence**, there are three elements that must be shown:

1 that the defendant was under a duty of care to the plaintiff
2 that there had been a breach of that duty
3 that there is damage to the plaintiff as a result of the breach, which is not too remote a consequence.

In the case, Lord Atkin defined a **duty of care** by stating that:

You must take reasonable care to avoid acts or omissions which you can reasonably foresee would be likely to injure your neighbour. Who then is my neighbour? The answer seems to be persons who are so closely and directly affected by my act that I ought reasonably to have them in contemplation as being so affected when I am directing my mind to the acts or omissions which are called in question.

The law of negligence is founded almost entirely on decided cases, and the approach adopted by the courts is one that affords flexibility in response to the changing patterns of practical problems. Unfortunately, it is unavoidable that with flexibility comes an element of uncertainty. Whether or not liability will arise in a particular set of circumstances appears to be heavily governed by public policy, and it is not clear exactly when a duty of care will arise. At present, the principles, or alternatively the questions to be asked in attempting to determine whether a duty exists, are:

■ is there foreseeability of harm and, if so ...
■ is there proximity – a close and direct relationship – and, if so ...
■ is it fair and reasonable for there to be a duty in these circumstances?

Having established that a duty of care exists, defendants will be in breach of that duty if they have not acted reasonably. The question is 'What standard of care does the law require?' The standard of care required is that of an ordinary prudent man in the circumstances pertaining to the case. For example, in one case it was held that an employee owed a higher standard of care to a one-eyed motor mechanic and was therefore obliged to provide protective goggles – not because the likelihood of damage was greater, but because the consequences of an eye injury were more serious (*Paris v Stepney BC,* 1951). Similarly, a higher standard of care would be expected from a drug manufacturer than from a greetings cards manufacturer because the consequences of defective products would be far more serious in the former case.

Where a person is regarded as a professional (i.e. where people set themselves up as possessing a particular skill, such as a plumber, solicitor or surgeon) then they must display the type of skill required in carrying out that particular profession or trade.

With a liability based on fault, the defendant can be liable only for damages caused by him or her. The test adopted is whether the damage is of a type or kind that ought reasonably to have been foreseen even though the extent need not have been envisaged. The main duty is that of manufacturers, but cases have shown that almost any party that is responsible for the supply of goods may be held liable. The onus of proving negligence is on the plaintiff. Of importance in this area is s. 2(1) of the Unfair Contract Terms Act 1977, which states: 'a person cannot by reference to any contract term or notice exclude or restrict his liability for death or personal injury resulting from negligence'. Also s. 2(2): 'in the case of other loss or damage, a person cannot so exclude or restrict his liability for negligence except in so far as the contract term or notice satisfies the test of reasonableness'. Thus, all clauses that purport to exclude liability in respect of negligence resulting in death or personal injuries are void, and other clauses (e.g. 'goods accepted at owner's risk') must satisfy the test of reasonableness.

6.4 Legal processes

It is not only changes in the law itself that should be of concern to businesses, but also the ease of access to legal processes. If legal processes are excessively expensive or time-consuming, the law may come to be seen as irrelevant if parties have no realistic means of enforcing the law. In general, developed economies have seen access to the law widened, so that it is not exclusively at the service of rich individuals or companies. As well as individuals and companies having the right to protect their own legal interests, a number of government agencies facilitate enforcement of the law.

In England, a number of courts of law operate with distinct functional and hierarchical roles.

- The Magistrates' Court deals primarily with criminal matters, where it handles approximately 97 per cent of the workload. It is responsible for handling prosecutions of companies for breaches of legislation under the Trade Descriptions and the Consumer Protection Acts. More serious criminal matters are 'committed' up to the Crown Court for trial.
- The Crown Court handles the more serious cases that have been committed to it for trial on 'indictment'. In addition, it also hears defendants' appeals as to sentence or conviction from the Magistrates' Court.
- The High Court is responsible for hearing appeals by way of 'case stated' from the Magistrates' Court or occasionally the Crown Court. The lower court, whose decision is being challenged, prepares papers (the case) and seeks the opinion of the High Court.
- The Court of Appeal deals primarily with appeals from trials on indictment in the Crown Court. It may review either sentence or conviction.
- County Courts are for almost all purposes the courts of first instance in civil matters (contract and tort). Generally, where the amount claimed is less than £25,000, this court will have jurisdiction in the first instance, but between £25,000 and £50,000, the case may be heard here, or be directed to the High Court, depending on its complexity.
- When larger amounts are being litigated, the High Court will have jurisdiction in the first instance. There is a commercial court within the structure that is designed to be a quicker and generally more suitable court for commercial matters; bankruptcy appeals from the County Court are heard here.
- Cases worth less than £5000 are referred by the County Court to its 'Small Claims' division, where the case will be heard informally under arbitration, and costs normally limited to the value of the issue of the summons.
- The Court of Appeals' Civil Division hears civil appeals from the County Court and the High Court.
- The Supreme Court is the ultimate appeal court for both criminal and domestic matters, having been created in 2009 to take over the role previously carried out by the House of Lords.

■ However, where there is a European issue, the European Court of Justice will give a ruling on the point at issue, after which the case is referred back to the UK court.

In addition to the court structure (see Figure 6.1), there are numerous quasi-judicial tribunals that exist to reconcile disagreeing parties. Examples include Rent Tribunals (for agreeing property rents), Valuation Tribunals (for agreeing property values) and Employment Tribunals (for bringing claims covered by employment legislation).

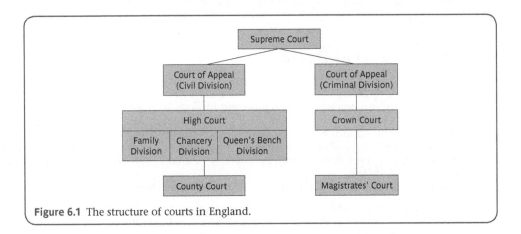

Figure 6.1 The structure of courts in England.

Despite the existence of legal rights, the cost to an individual or a firm of enforcing its rights can be prohibitive, especially where there is no certainty that a party taking action will be able to recover its legal costs. For a typical inter-company dispute over a debt of £50,000, the party suing the debtor can easily incur legal expenses of several thousand pounds, not counting the cost of its employees' time. Where a case goes to the Court of Appeal, a company could be involved in inestimable costs. The legal process can also be very slow. In the case of an intercompany debt claim, a case may take up to ten years between the first issue of a writ and compensation finally being received.

Numerous attempts have been made to make the legal system more widely accessible, such as the small claims section of the County Court, which handles claims of up to £5000 in a less formal and costly manner than a normal County Court claim. There have also been attempts to reduce the risks to individuals by allowing, in certain circumstances, solicitors to charge their clients depending upon results obtained in court (often referred to as a 'no win, no fee' system). Many people feel that the costs of running the courts system could be cut by reducing many bureaucratic and restrictive practices within the legal profession.

Despite moves to make legal remedies more widely available, access to the law remains unequal. Among commercial organizations, a small under-resourced firm may be unable to put the money upfront to pursue a case against a larger company that could defend itself with an army of retained lawyers. Similarly, private consumers are unequal in their access to the law. It has often been suggested that easy access to the law is afforded to the very rich (who can afford it) and the very poor (who may be eligible to receive legal aid). An apparent paradox of attempts to make the law more accessible is that these attempts may themselves overwhelm courts with cases with which they are unable to cope. As an example, the Small Claims Court is reported to have been overwhelmed in 2007 by thousands of bank customers suing their banks for a refund of 'unreasonable' charges levied by the banks. The flood of litigants was assisted by the availability online of template letters promoted by consumer group sites and the ability of aggrieved customers to submit small claims online (www.moneyclaim.gov.uk).

Central and local government is increasingly being given power to act as a consumer champion and to bring cases before the courts that are in the interest of consumers in general. Bodies that pursue actions in this way include the following.

- Trading Standards Departments, which are operated by local authorities, have powers to investigate complaints about false or misleading descriptions of prices, inaccurate weights and measures, consumer credit and the safety of consumer legislation. Consumers' knowledge of their rights has often stretched the resources of Trading Standards Departments so that, at best, they can take action against bad practice only selectively.

- The Environmental Health Departments of local authorities deal with health matters such as unfit food and dirty shops and restaurants. A consumer who suspects that they have suffered food poisoning as a result of eating unfit food at a restaurant may lodge a complaint with the local Environmental Health Department, which may collate similar complaints and use this evidence to prosecute the offending restaurant or take steps to have it closed down.

- Utility regulators have powers to bring action against companies that are in breach of their licence conditions.

6.5 Legislation affecting the supply of goods and services

Prior to 1968, there was very little statutory intervention in the contractual relationship between business organizations and their customers, with a few exceptions such as those that came within the scope of the Food and Drugs Act 1955. Since the 1960s there has been an increasing amount of legislation designed to protect the interests of private consumers, who legislators have seen as unequal parties to a contract. In recent years EU directives have been incorporated into UK legislation to provide additional duties for suppliers of goods and services. It should be noted that much of the legislation applies only to business-to-consumer contracts and not business-to-business contracts. In the latter case, legislation has often presumed that parties have equal bargaining power and therefore do not need additional legislative protection.

 Thinking around the subject

Who benefits from a 'compensation culture'?

Are we becoming a litigious society, dominated by a 'compensation culture'? Newspapers are continually reporting claims made by individuals that at first may seem quite trivial and not warranting legal intervention. Recent reported claims, which some would argue typify a compensation culture, include a teacher who won £55,000 after slipping on a chip, and the parents of a Girl Guide who sued after she was burned by fat spitting from a sausage. Aggrieved parties may have been spurred on by the rise of 'personal injury advisers' who offer to take on a claim at no risk to the claimant. They have sometimes been referred to as 'ambulance chasers' for the way they pursue injured parties, making them aware of the possibility of claiming for a loss or injury, which they may otherwise have written off in their minds as just bad luck. If their claim is rejected by the court, the claimant will pay nothing. If it succeeds, they pay the company handling the claim a percentage of the damages awarded. Such companies have been accused of unrealistically raising clients' expectations of damages, and looking for confrontation where alternative methods of reconciliation may be more effective. The business practices of some companies have been criticized, and one company, the Accident Group, went out of business in 2004 after accumulating large debts and failing to deliver promised benefits to many of its customers.

Is the compensation culture necessarily a bad thing for society? Defending cases costs companies time and money, which will inevitably be passed on in the form of higher prices charged to consumers. Claims against companies sometimes even lead to goods or services no longer being made available to consumers because of an open-ended risk of being sued if there is a problem with the product.

But shouldn't consumers expect businesses to deliver their promises in a responsible manner? Is a compensation culture essentially about redressing the balance between relatively weak consumers and more powerful organizations? If those organizations did their job properly, would there be no case for even talking about a compensation culture? If the cost of obtaining justice made it difficult for aggrieved customers to bring a claim against a company, would the company simply carry on acting irresponsibly because it realized it was beyond reproach? In the case of very dubious claims, such as a customer who sued a restaurant because their cup of coffee was 'too hot', could the company attract sympathy from the majority of its customers, who might regard such a claim as frivolous?

In this section, we consider the following important pieces of statute law that have an impact on the relationship between an organization and its customers:

- the Trade Descriptions Act 1968
- the Sale of Goods Act 1979
- the Misrepresentation Act 1967
- the Consumer Protection Act 1987
- the Consumer Credit Act 1974.

This chapter can provide only a brief summary of a small number of laws that affect business – consumer relationships. Businesses frequently complain about the vast number of regulations that cover their particular sector.

In addition, this section reviews a number of quasi-legal codes of conduct operated by industry bodies.

6.5.1 Trade Descriptions Act 1968

The Trade Descriptions Act 1968 makes it an offence for a person to make a false or misleading trade description and creates three principal offences, as described below.

A false trade description to goods

Under s. 1, this states that 'a person who, in the course of business, applies false trade descriptions to goods or suppliers or offers to supply goods to which a false description has been applied is guilty of an offence'. Section 2 defines a false trade description as including 'any indication of any physical characteristics such as quantity, size, method of manufacture, composition and fitness for purpose'. A description is regarded as false when it is false or, by s. 3(2), misleading to a material degree. In some cases consumers are misled by advertisements that are economical with the truth. A car was advertised as having one previous 'owner'. Strictly this was true, but it had been owned by a leasing company, which had leased it to five different users. The divisional court held this was misleading by s. 3(2) (*R. v London Borough of Wandsworth, The Times*, 20 January 1983).

A false statement of price

Section 11 makes a false statement as to the price an offence. If a trader claims that its prices are reduced, it is guilty of an offence unless it can show that the goods have been on sale at the higher price during the preceding six months for a consecutive period of 28 days (more specific requirements concerning pricing are contained in the Price Marking Order 2004).

A false trade description of services

Section 14 states that it is an offence to make false or misleading statements about services. An example of this is illustrated in the case of a store that advertised 'folding doors and folding door gear – carriage free'. This statement was intended to convey to the consumer that only the folding door gear would be sent carriage-free on purchase of the folding doors. It was held that the advert was misleading and that it was irrelevant that it was not intended to be misleading (*MFI Warehouses Ltd v Nattrass* [1973] 1 All ER 762).

Traders can use a number of defences under the Act, set out in s. 24(i):

(a) that the commission of the offence was due to a mistake or to reliance on information supplied to the company or to the act or default of another person, an accident or some other cause beyond its control, and

(b) that the company took all reasonable precautions and exercised all due diligence to avoid the commission of such an offence by itself or any person under its control.

For the defence to succeed, it is necessary to show that both sub-sections apply. In a case concerning a leading supermarket, washing powder was incorrectly advertised as being 5p less than the price actually charged in the store. The defendants said that it was the fault of the store manager who had failed to go through the system laid down for checking shelves. The court held that the defence applied; the store manager was 'another person' (s. 24(i)(a)) and the store had taken reasonable precautions to prevent commission of the offence (*Tesco Supermarkets Ltd v Nattrass* [1971] 2 All ER 127).

6.5.2 Sale of Goods Act 1979

What rights has the consumer if he or she discovers that the goods purchased are faulty or different from those ordered? The Sale of Goods Act (SOGA) 1979 contains terms specifically to protect the consumer. The term 'consumer' is defined by s. 20(6) of the Consumer Protection Act 1987, and essentially covers situations where a purchase is made for private consumption, rather than for use in the course of a business.

Section 13 of the Sale of Goods Act 1979 states that, 'Where there is a contract for the sale of goods by description there is an implied condition that the goods will correspond with the description.' Goods must be as described on the package. If a customer purchases a blue long-sleeved shirt and on opening the box discovers that it is a red short-sleeved shirt, then he is entitled to a return of the price for breach of an implied condition of the contract.

Section 14(2), as amended by the Sale and Supply of Goods Act 1994, states that where a seller sells goods in the course of a business, there is an implied term that the goods supplied under the contract are of satisfactory quality. For the purposes of this Act goods are of satisfactory quality if they meet the standard that a reasonable person would regard as satisfactory, taking account of any description of the goods, fitness for all the purposes for which goods of the kind in question are commonly supplied, appearance and finish, safety, durability, freedom from minor defects, the price (if relevant) and all other relevant circumstances.

However, s.14(2C) states and which the standard of satisfactory quality need not apply in respect of faults which should be reasonably apparent to a buyer before purchase and which are specifically drawn to the buyer's attention before the contract is made.

The implied term of satisfactory quality applies to sale goods and second-hand goods, but clearly the consumer would not have such high expectations of second-hand goods. For example, a clutch fault in a new car would make it unsatisfactory, but not so if the car were second-hand. In a second-hand car – again, depending on all the circumstances – a fault would have to be major to render the car unsatisfactory. Thus, the question to be asked is, 'Are the goods satisfactory in the light of the contract description and all the circumstances of the case?'

It is often asked for how long the goods should remain satisfactory. It is implicit that the goods remain satisfactory for a length of time reasonable in the circumstances of the case and the nature of the goods. If a good becomes defective within a very short time, this is evidence that there was possibly a latent defect at the time of the sale.

Under s. 14(3), there is an implied condition that goods are fit for a particular purpose where the seller sells goods in the course of a business and the buyer, expressly or by implication, makes known to the seller any particular purpose for which the goods are being bought. Thus, if a seller, on request, confirms suitability for a particular purpose and the product proves unsuitable, there would be a breach of s. 14(3); if the product is also unsuitable for its normal purposes, then s. 14(2) would be breached too. If the seller disclaims any knowledge of the product's suitability for the particular purpose and the consumer takes a chance and purchases it, then if it proves unsuitable for its particular purpose there is no breach of s. 14(3). The only circumstance in which a breach may occur is, again, if it were unsuitable for its normal purposes under s. 14(2).

In business contracts, implied terms in ss. 13–15 of the Sale of Goods Act 1979 can be excluded. Such exclusion clauses, purporting, for example, to exclude a term for reasonable fitness for goods (s. 14), are valid subject to the test of reasonableness provided that the term is incorporated into the contract. However, for consumer contracts, such clauses that purport to limit or exclude liability are void under s. 6(2) of the Unfair Contract Terms Act 1977.

The Supply of Goods and Services Act 1982 (SGSA) offers almost identical protection where goods and services are provided. Section 3 corresponds to s. 13 of SOGA and s. 4 corresponds to s. 14 of SOGA. Section 13 of SGSA provides that, where the supplier of a service under a contract is acting in the course of a business, there is an implied term that the supplier will carry out the service with reasonable care and skill. Reasonable care and skill may be defined as 'the ordinary skill of an ordinary competent man exercising that particular act'. Much will depend on the circumstances of the case and the nature of the trade or profession.

6.5.3 Misrepresentation Act 1967

The Misrepresentation Act 1967 provides remedies for victims of **misrepresentation**. For the purpose of the Act, an actionable misrepresentation may be defined as 'a false statement of existing or past fact made by one party to the other before or at the time of making the contract, which is intended to, and does, induce the other party to enter into the contract'.

Since the 1967 Act, it has been necessary to maintain a clear distinction between fraudulent misrepresentation, negligent misrepresentation and wholly innocent misrepresentation (s. 2(1)). Rescission of a contract is a remedy for all three types of misrepresentation. In addition to rescission for fraudulent misrepresentation, damages may be awarded under the tort of fraud, and in respect of negligent misrepresentation damages may be awarded under s. 2(1) of the

1967 Act. Under s. 2(2) damages may also be awarded at the discretion of the court, but, if so, these are in lieu of rescission.

6.5.4 The Consumer Protection Act 1987

The Consumer Protection Act 1987 implements an EU directive, and provides a remedy in damages for anyone who suffers personal injury or damage to property as a result of a defective product. The effect is to impose a strict (i.e. whereby it is unnecessary to prove negligence) tortious liability on producers of defective goods. The Act supplements the existing law; thus, a consumer may well have a remedy in contract, in the tort of negligence or under the Act if he or she has suffered loss caused by a defective product.

The producer will be liable if the consumer can establish that the product is defective and that it caused a loss. There is a defect if the safety of the goods does not conform to general expectations with reference to the risk of damage to property or risk of death or personal injury. The general expectations will differ depending on the particular circumstances, but points to be taken into account include the product's instructions, warnings and the time elapsed since supply, the latter point to determine the possibility of the defect being due to wear and tear.

The onus is on the plaintiff to prove that loss was caused by the defect. A claim may be made by anyone, whether death, personal injury or damage to property has occurred. However, where damage to property is concerned, the damage is confined to property ordinarily intended for private use, thus excluding commercial goods and property. It is not possible to exclude liability under the Consumer Protection Act.

The Act is intended to place liability on the producer of defective goods. In some cases the company may not manufacture the goods, but may still be liable, as outlined below.

- Anyone carrying out 'industrial or other process' to goods that have been manufactured by someone else will be treated as the producer where 'essential characteristics' (e.g. modifications to a product) are attributable to that process.

- If a company puts its own brand name on goods that have been manufactured on its behalf, thus holding itself out to be the producer, that company will be liable for any defects in the goods.

- Any importer who imports goods from outside EU countries will be liable for defects in the imported goods.

The Act is also instrumental in providing a remedy against suppliers who are unable to identify the importee or the previous supplier to them. If the supplier fails or cannot identify the manufacturer's importee or previous supplier, then the supplier is liable.

6.5.5 Consumer Credit Act 1974

This is a consumer protection measure to protect the public from, among other things, extortionate credit agreements and high-pressure selling off trade premises. The Act became fully operational in 1985, and much of the protection afforded to hire purchase transactions is extended to those obtaining goods and services through consumer credit transactions. It is important to note that contract law governs the formation of agreements coming within the scope of the Consumer Credit Act. Section 8(2) defines a consumer credit agreement as personal credit providing the debtor with credit not exceeding £25,000. Section 9 defines credit as a cash loan and any form of financial accommodation.

There are two types of credit. The first is a running account credit (s. 10(a)), whereby the debtor is enabled to receive from time to time, from the creditor or a third party, cash, goods and services to an amount or value such that, taking into account payments made by or to the credit of the debtor, the credit limit (if any) is not at any time exceeded. An example of this is a credit card facility, e.g. Visa or MasterCard. The second type is fixed-sum credit, defined in s. 10(b) as any other facility under a personal credit agreement whereby the debtor is enabled to receive credit. An example here would be a bank loan.

The Act covers hire purchase agreements (s. 189), which are agreements under which goods are hired in return for periodical payments by the person to whom they are hired and where the property in the goods will pass to that person if the terms of the agreement are complied with – for example, the exercise of an option to purchase by that person. In addition to hire purchase agreements, also within the scope of the Act are conditional sale agreements for the sale of goods or land, in respect of which the price is payable by instalments and the property (i.e. ownership) remains with the seller until any conditions set out in the contract are fulfilled, and credit sale agreements, where the property (ownership) passes to the buyer when the sale is effected.

Debtor–creditor supplier agreements relate to the situation where there is a business connection between creditor and supplier (i.e. a pre-existing arrangement) or where the creditor and the supplier are the same person. Section 55 and ss. 60–65 deal with formalities of the contract between debtor and creditor, their aim being that the debtor be made fully aware of the nature and the cost of the transaction, and his or her rights and liabilities under it. The Act requires that certain information must be disclosed to the debtor before the contract is made. This includes total charge for credit, and the annual rate of the total charge for credit that the debtor will have to pay expressed in an approved format. All regulated agreements must comply with the formality procedures and must contain, among other things, the debtor's right to cancel and to pay off the debt early.

If a consumer credit agreement is drawn up off business premises, the agreement is cancellable, and debtor is entitled to a 'cooling-off' period during which the contract can be set aside without penalty. This is designed to counteract high-pressure doorstep selling.

6.5.6 Codes of practice

Codes of practice do not in themselves have the force of law. They can, however, be of great importance to businesses. In the first place, they can help to raise the standards of an industry by imposing a discipline on signatories to a code not to indulge in dubious marketing practices, which – although legal – act against the long-term interests of the industry and its customers. Second, voluntary codes of practice can offer a cheaper and quicker means of resolving grievances between the two parties compared with more formal legal channels. For example, the holiday industry has its own arbitration facilities, which avoid the cost of taking many cases through to the courts. Third, business organizations are often happy to accept restrictions imposed by codes of practice as these are seen as preferable to restrictions being imposed by laws. The tobacco industry in the UK for a long time avoided statutory controls on cigarette advertising because of the existence of its voluntary code, which imposed restrictions on tobacco advertising.

The Director General of the Office of Fair Trading is instrumental in encouraging trade associations to adopt codes of practice. An example of a voluntary code is provided by the Vehicle Builders and Repair Association, which, among other items, requires members to: give clear estimates of prices; inform customers as soon as possible if additional costs are likely to be incurred; complete work in a timely manner. In the event of a dispute between a customer and a member of the Association, a conciliation service is available that reduces the need to resort to legal remedies. However, in April 2005, the National Consumer Council accused the motor industry of failing to regulate itself adequately, by providing 'shoddy services and rip-off charges'. The Council pledged to submit a 'super complaint' to the Office of Fair Trading (OFT), which would force the OFT to investigate its allegations, unless the industry took prompt remedial action. This raised the possibility of a licensing system for car repairers, something the industry had resisted so far and realized would be more onerous than a voluntary code of conduct.

Useful leaflets published by the OFT giving information regarding codes of practice can be obtained from local Consumer Advice Bureaux.

6.5.7 Controls on advertising

There are a number of laws that influence the content of advertisements in Britain. For example, the Trade Descriptions Act 1968 makes false statements in an advertisement an offence, while the Consumer Credit Act 1974 lays down quite precise rules about the way in which credit can be advertised. However, the content of advertisements is also influenced by voluntary codes. In the UK, the codes for advertising are the responsibility of the advertising industry through two Committees of Advertising Practice: CAP (Broadcast) and CAP (Non-broadcast). CAP (Broadcast) is responsible for the TV and radio advertising codes, and CAP (Non-broadcast) is responsible for non-broadcast advertisements, sales promotions and direct marketing. Both are administered by the Advertising Standards Authority (ASA). The Office of Communications (Ofcom) is the statutory regulator for broadcast advertising in the UK and has delegated its powers to the ASA, which deals with all complaints about such advertising.

The ASA codes are subscribed to by most organizations involved in advertising, including the Advertising Association, the Institute of Practitioners in Advertising, and the associations representing publishers of newspapers and magazines, the outdoor advertising industry and direct marketing.

The Code of Advertising Practice (Non-broadcast) requires that all advertisements appearing in members' publications should be legal, decent, honest and truthful. Two adjudications illustrate how the ASA interprets this. In one case, a national press advert for the retailer Lidl featured a Landmann Lava Rock Gas Barbecue and the message '£10 cheaper compared to B&Q'. It was held that the comparison was misleading, because the precise model sold by B&Q was not accurately specified, therefore the fact of '£10 cheaper' could not be established. In another case from 2008, an advert in the *Daily Mail* for Ryanair under the headline 'Hottest back to school fares . . . one-way fares £10' featured a picture of a teenage girl or woman standing in a classroom and wearing a version of a school uniform consisting of a short tartan skirt, a cropped short sleeved shirt and tie, and long white socks. The ASA considered the model's clothing, together with the setting of the ad in a classroom strongly suggested she was a schoolgirl and considered that her appearance and pose, in conjunction with the heading 'Hottest', appeared to link teenage girls with sexually provocative behaviour. It considered the advert was likely to cause serious or widespread offence, and was in breach of the Code's sections governing social responsibility and decency.

Although the main role of the ASA is advisory, it does have a number of sanctions available against individual advertisers that break the code, ultimately leading to the ASA requesting its media members to refuse to publish the advertisements of an offending company. More often, the ASA relies on publicizing its rulings to shame advertisers into responding (although some critics would say that press coverage of companies breaching the code simply provides free awareness-grabbing publicity for the company).

The advertising codes are continually evolving to meet the changing attitudes and expectations of the public. Thus, restrictions on alcohol advertising have been tightened up – for example, by insisting that young actors are not portrayed in advertisements and by not showing them on television when children are likely to be watching. On the other hand, advertising restrictions for some products have been relaxed in response to changing public attitudes. Television adverts for condoms have moved from being completely banned to being allowed, but only in very abstract form, to the present situation where the product itself can be mentioned using actors in life-like situations.

Numerous other forms of voluntary control exist. As mentioned previously, many trade associations have codes that impose restrictions on how they can advertise. Solicitors, for example, were previously not allowed to advertise at all, but now can do so within limits defined by the Law Society.

The Control of Misleading Advertisements Regulations 1988 (as amended) provides the legislative back-up to the self-regulatory system in respect of advertisements that mislead. The Regulations require the OFT to investigate complaints, and empower the OFT to seek, if necessary, an injunction from the courts against publication of an advertisement. More usually it would initially seek assurances from an advertiser to modify or not repeat an offending advertisement. Before investigating, the OFT can require that other means of dealing with a complaint, such as the ASA system mentioned above, have been fully explored. Action by the OFT therefore usually results only from a referral from the Advertising Standards Authority where the self-regulatory system has not had the required impact.

In general, the system of voluntary regulation of advertising has worked well in the UK. For advertisers, voluntary codes can allow more flexibility and opportunities to have an input to the code. For the public, a code can be updated in a less bureaucratic manner than may be necessary with new legislation or statutory regulations. However, the question remains as to how much responsibility for the social and cultural content of advertising should be given to industry-led voluntary bodies rather than being decided by government. Do voluntary codes unduly reflect the narrow financial interests of advertisers rather than the broader interests of the public at large? Doubtless, advertisers realize that if they do not develop a code that is socially acceptable, the task will be taken away from them and carried out by government in a process where they will have less influence.

6.6 Statutory legislation on employment

Employment law is essentially based on the principles of law previously discussed. The relationship between an employer and its employees is governed by the law of contract, while the employer owes a duty of care to its employees and can be sued for negligence where this duty of care is broken. Employers are vicariously liable for the actions of their employees, so if an employee is negligent and harms a member of the public during the course of their employment, the injured party has a claim against the employer as well as the employee who was the immediate cause of the injury.

The common law principles of contract and negligence have for a long time been supplemented with statutory intervention. Society has recognized that a contract of employment is quite different from a contract to buy consumer goods, because the personal investment of the employee in their job can be very considerable. Losing a job without good cause can have a much more profound effect than suffering loss as a result of losing money on the purchase of goods. Governments have recognized that individuals should have a proprietary interest in their jobs and have therefore passed legislation to protect employees against the actions of unscrupulous employers who abuse their dominant power over employees. Legislation has also recognized that employment practices can have a much wider effect on society through organizations' recruitment policies.

In this section we consider some of the areas in which statutory intervention has affected the environment in which organizations recruit, reward and dismiss employees. The information here cannot hope to go into any depth on particular legislative requirements, as legislation is complex, detailed and continually changing. There is also considerable difference between countries in terms of legislation that affects employment. The following brief summary can only aim to identify the main issues of concern covered by legislation, in England specifically. This chapter should also be read in conjunction with Chapter 10, on the internal environment. In that chapter we look in general terms at issues such as the need for flexibility in the workforce. This chapter identifies particular legal opportunities and constraints, which help to define an organization's internal environment.

6.6.1 When does an employment contract occur?

It is not always obvious whether a contract of employment exists between an organization and individuals providing services for it. Many individuals working for organizations in fact provide their services as self-employed subcontractors, rather than as employees. The distinction between the two is important, because a self-employed contractor does not benefit from the legislation, which only protects employees. There can be many advantages in classifying an individual as self-employed rather than as an employee. For the self-employed, tax advantages result from being able to claim as legitimate business expense items that in many circumstances are denied to the employee. The method of assessing National Insurance and income tax liability in arrears can favour a self-employed subcontractor. For the employer, designation as self-employed could relieve the employer of some duties that are imposed in respect of employees but not subcontractors, such as entitlement to sick pay, notice periods and maternity leave.

There was a great move towards self-employment during the 1990s, encouraged by the trend towards outsourcing of many non-core functions by businesses (see Chapter 8). Not surprisingly, the UK government has sought to recoup potentially lost tax revenue and to protect unwitting self-employed individuals, by examining closely the terms on which an individual is engaged. The courts have decided the matter on the basis of, among other things, the degree of control that the organization buying a person's services has over the person providing them, the level of integration between the individual and the organization, and who bears the business risk. If the organization is able to specify the manner in which a task is to be carried out, then an employment relationship generally exists. If, however, the required end result is specified but the manner in which it is achieved is left up to the individual, then a contract for services will exist – in other words, self-employment. There is still ambiguity in the distinction between employment and self-employment, which has, for example, resulted in numerous appeals by individuals against classification decisions made by HMRC.

6.6.2 Flexibility of contract

Organizations are increasingly seeking a more flexible workforce to help them respond more rapidly to changes in their external environment. In Chapter 10 we see some of the benefits to an organization of developing flexible employment practices.

Short-term employment contracts are becoming increasingly significant in a number of European countries, partly due to the existence of labour market regulations that make it difficult for employers to recruit and dismiss permanent staff. Within Europe, there has been a tendency for national legislation to reflect EU directives by imposing additional burdens on employers of full-time, permanent employees. This can affect the ease with which staff can be laid off or dismissed should demand fall – for example, in Germany, the Dismissals Protection Law (*Kundigungsschutzgesetz*) has given considerable protection to salaried staff who have been in their job for more than six months, allowing dismissal only for a 'socially justified' reason.

The move towards short-term contracts is a Europe-wide phenomenon. In 2005, about 34 per cent of the Spanish workforce was employed with contracts of limited duration compared to less than 16 per cent 20 years previously, while in France the proportion of employees with contracts of limited duration climbed from 6.7 per cent in 1985 to about 13 per cent by 2005 (Eurostat 2006–07). The spread of short-term contracts is most apparent among young workers employed in insecure and highly mobile areas of the labour market, such as the retail, distribution, communication and information technology sectors.

The EU and most member-state governments have been keen to ensure that workers on short-term contracts enjoy similar legal rights as those in full-time, permanent employment. In the UK, the Employment Relations Act 1999 requires the appropriate secretary of state to make regulations to ensure that part-time workers are treated no less favourably than full-time workers. These regulations include provisions to implement the EU-level social partners' agreement and subsequent Council Directive on part-time work (97/81/EC).

Despite imposing additional burdens, many European governments have encouraged the greater use of short-term contracts as a way of improving the flexibility of their national economies – for example, through changes in welfare benefits that do not penalize short-term working.

6.6.3 Terms of the contract of employment

Under the Employment Rights Act 1996 it is required that an employer must issue its employees within 13 weeks of the date they start work the written terms and conditions of their employment in detail. The details can, however, be placed on a staff noticeboard at a point where every member of the workforce concerned can read them. In the statement there should be references to the following:

1 the job title
2 which individuals or groups the document is addressed to
3 the starting date of the employment
4 the scale of wages and the calculations used to work this out
5 the periods in which wages are paid
6 hours of work and the terms and conditions
7 holidays and holiday pay
8 sickness and sickness pay
9 pensions and pension schemes
10 how much notice the employee must give upon leaving and how much notice the company has to give the employee when terminating employment
11 rules for discipline procedures
12 to whom any grievances are to be made, and procedures.

The terms of contract cannot be altered until both parties have discussed and agreed the new conditions.

6.6.4 Minimum acceptable contract terms

Legislators have recognized that employee and employer often possess unequal bargaining power in the process of forming a contract of employment. Legislation therefore protects the interests of the weaker party – generally the employee – against the use of their power by unscrupulous employers. The following are examples of statutory intervention that protect employees' rights. Some would argue that intervention of this type has the effect of increasing the costs of businesses, thereby reducing their competitive advantage. However, as can be seen in Chapter 10, a lot of statutory intervention is merely spreading current best practice to all employees.

Health and safety legislation

There is a wide range of regulations governing employers' duty to provide a safe working environment. Most health and safety legislation is based on the Health and Safety at Work Act 1974, which provides a general duty to provide a safe working environment. The Act makes provision for specific regulations to be issued by government ministers and these detailed regulations can have significant impacts on businesses. The following are some recent examples of regulations:

- the Control of Major Accident Hazards Regulations 1999
- the Control of Substances Hazardous to Health Regulations 1999
- the Lifts Regulations 1997
- the Railway Safety (Miscellaneous Provisions) Regulations 1997.

The Health & Safety Executive oversees enforcement of these regulations.

Figure 6.2 Visitors to Bavaria's beer festivals come away with memories of the beer and barmaids. The event is made memorable by the distinctive dress worn by barmaids, which combines tradition with visual appeal (especially to men, who make up a large part of the festivals' market). The barmaids' garb, known as a 'dirndl', comprises a figure-hugging dress and apron with a tight, low-cut top. The sight of a barmaid dressed in a dirndl and carrying several glasses of beer helps to transform a drink into an experience. Customers love the dress, brewers love it, and apparently the barmaids do too. But this apparently happy service environment was threatened in 2006 by the EU's Optical Radiation Directive, by which employers of staff who work outdoors, such as those in Bavaria's beer gardens, must ensure that staff are protected against the risk of sunburn. The serious point underlying the EU legislation is that in the UK alone about 70,000 new cases of skin cancer are diagnosed each year. Faced with this directive, how should the provider of an outdoor service encounter react? If they leave scantily dressed employees exposed to the sun, they could face fines, and possible legal action by employees who subsequently develop skin cancer. But, contrary to many newspaper reports, the EU directive does not specifically require Bavarian barmaids (or outdoor workers elsewhere) to cover up their low-cut dresses. Management must

undertake a risk assessment and consider what is appropriate to a specific service encounter. Perhaps the unique character of the Munich Oktoberfest could be preserved with the help of sun cream and by reducing each barmaid's hours of exposure to the sun.

⟳ Thinking around the subject

Take risks and go to jail?

One of the defining characteristics of a limited liability company (discussed in Chapter 7) is the separation of the company from its owners. So, in general, if the company breaks the law, whether civil law or criminal, the directors of the company can protect themselves behind a 'veil of incorporation'. Furthermore, many of the punishments available under the criminal law would at first sight seem to be inappropriate to business organizations. How, for example, can an organization be sent to prison for a serious breach of the criminal law? The question has arisen following a number of high-profile cases where a business has caused harm to the general public, but the directors of the company responsible for the wrongdoing have escaped relatively lightly. The *Herald of Free Enterprise* tragedy in 1987, and the Ladbroke Grove train accident of 1999, raised issues about senior management's culpability in these two serious transport accidents. In the first case, questions were raised about unreasonable pressures that management had put on staff loading vehicles on to ferries, one of which subsequently capsized. In the second case, questions were raised about the suitability of staff training programmes, for which management, and ultimately the board of directors, was responsible. Relatives of victims who died in both of these incidents claimed that they were not accidents at all, but the culmination of negligent actions by senior management. In both cases, initial blame was focused on relatively low-paid junior staff who made a mistake. But was senior management responsible for expecting too much of its junior staff? In both cases, attempts were made to bring charges of manslaughter against the directors of the companies involved, but due to the complexity of the cases, and the diffuse lines of responsibility within their organizations, there was insufficient evidence to successfully bring a case. According to the Centre for Corporate Accountability, only 11 directors were successfully prosecuted for manslaughter in the 30 years to 2005. Most of these have been small company directors; for example, in January 2005, the managing director of a building contractor was sentenced to 16 months in jail after a roofing worker died falling through a poorly protected roof light. Campaigners for a law on corporate manslaughter have argued that it is much more difficult to pin down responsibility in a large organization, but this is no reason to not try to make senior staff personally accountable for their actions. Would directors of a company be so keen to pursue potentially dangerous efficiency-gaining strategies if they thought there was a risk that they might personally end up in prison? Or would a corporate manslaughter law stifle initiatives by directors, fearful that, if anything went wrong, there could be very serious consequences for them personally?

Minimum wage legislation

The national minimum wage came into force in the UK in 1999, implementing an earlier EU directive. In October 2010, this rate was set at £5.93 per hour for workers aged 21 and over, £4.92 for 18- to 21-year-olds, and £3.64 for 16- to 17-year-olds. There is provision for annual revision. Most adult workers in the UK must be paid at least the national minimum wage. This includes part-time workers, temporary or short-term workers, home workers, agency workers and casual labourers. An employee cannot be forced by an employer to accept a wage that is below the minimum wage, and can claim compensation if they are sacked or victimized because they sought to enforce their right to the national minimum wage.

Working hours

The EU's Working Time Directive of 1993 was implemented in the UK by the Working Time Regulations of 2000. According to these regulations, workers cannot be forced to work for more than 48 hours a week on average. However, there are various exclusions to this time and workers can cancel any opt-out agreement whenever they want, although they must give their employer at least seven days' notice, or longer (up to three months) if this has been agreed.

6.6.5 Discrimination at work

Companies sometimes find themselves being required to recruit their second choice of staff in order to comply with legislation against racial and sexual discrimination. For example, one UK airline found through its research that the majority of its customers preferred its cabin crew to be female and subsequently recruited predominantly female staff for this role. The airline was fined for unlawful discrimination against men, even though it had been innovative in appointing women to the traditionally male job of pilot. Legislation seeks to protect disadvantaged groups that may be discriminated against simply out of employers' ignorance.

The Sex Discrimination Act 1975 (SDA) prohibits discrimination against women, and men, on the grounds of sex or of being married. The SDA makes the distinction between the concepts of direct and indirect discrimination. Direct sex discrimination occurs when an employee is treated less favourably because of her, or his, sex. Indirect discrimination occurs when a requirement or condition – which may seem 'neutral' in terms of how it impacts upon men and women – in fact has an adverse effect on women, or men, in general (for example, specifying a dress code that is more onerous on women than men). The Equal Pay Act 1970 requires that a woman is entitled to the same pay (and other contractual conditions) as a man working for the same employer, provided they are doing similar work or work of equal value.

The legislation dealing with race discrimination derives from the Race Relations Act 1976 (RRA). By this Act, a person is guilty of race discrimination if 'on racial grounds he treats [a] person less favourably than he treats or would treat other persons'. Like the SDA, the RRA makes it illegal to discriminate directly or indirectly against a person on racial grounds. Research and official statistics demonstrate that people from ethnic minorities continue to experience severe discrimination in the field of employment. A report by the Joseph Rowntree Foundation found particularly high levels of unemployment among Africans, Pakistanis and Bangladeshis (Berthoud 2005).

6.6.6 Termination of contract

The proprietary interest of employees in their jobs is recognized by legislation that restricts the ability of an employer to terminate an employee's contract of employment.

Termination may come about because an individual's position is no longer required and the individual is declared redundant. The Employment Rights Act 1996 defines the circumstances in which redundancy takes effect and a sliding scale of payments that an employee is entitled to if they are made redundant by their employer.

In circumstances other than redundancy, employers may not terminate a contract in a way that constitutes unfair **dismissal**. Under the Employment Relations Act 1999, employees are not entitled to claim unfair dismissal until they have accumulated one year's service. Dismissal may be considered fair where an employee has not acted in good faith and/or has failed to observe previous warnings about poor conduct. Employment Tribunals judge whether a dismissal is fair or not, and judgment frequently centres on procedural issues. A finding of unfair dismissal may lead to an order for compensation and a request for reinstatement.

6.6.7 Rights to workers' representation

The political environment and the dominant political ideology have had a very close bearing on legislation regulating the activities of trades unions. Traditionally, Labour governments have sought to advance the cause of organized labour, while Conservative governments have taken a more individualist approach to relationships between employers and employees. The incoming Conservative government of 1979 dismantled much of the legislation that had been passed by the previous Labour government to give greater rights for trades unions and greater duties for employers. The incoming Labour government of 1997 went some way to restoring trades union rights. Current UK legislation governing employees' rights to representation derive largely from the Employment Relations Act 1999, which makes, among other things, the following provisions:

- individuals affected by industrial action are able to seek an injunction to prevent unlawful industrial action taking place
- seven days' notice must be given by trades unions of ballots and of industrial action
- individuals have a right to challenge collective agreements
- employers may refuse to recognize a trades union in specified circumstances
- all industrial action ballots must be postal and subject to independent scrutiny

- provides a statutory procedure through which independent unions are able to seek recognition for collective bargaining from employers with more than 20 employees
- employees dismissed for taking part in lawfully organized official industrial action can take cases of unfair dismissal to an Employment Tribunal where the dismissal occurs within eight weeks of the start of the action.

The Transnational Information and Consultation of Employees Regulations 1999 came into force in the UK in 2000, implementing the EU Directive on European Works Councils. The Directive covers undertakings that have more than 1000 employees in member-states and more than 150 employees in each of two member-states, and sets out procedures for giving employees a statutory right to be consulted about a range of activities affecting the organization. From 2005, the legislation has given employees a legal right to know about, and be consulted on, an organization's plans that affect them. This can cover anything from the economic health of the business to decisions likely to cause redundancies or changes in how work is organized. This requirement applied initially only to larger organizations – those with 50 or more employees However, from 2007, the threshold was lowered to 100 employees and, in 2008, lowered again to 50 or more employees.

6.7   The Human Rights Act 1998

The Human Rights Act 1998 came into force in the UK in 2000 and has presented a number of new legal challenges for business organizations. The Act incorporates the European Convention on Human Rights into domestic law. The Convention is a 50-year-old code of basic rights drawn up in the aftermath of the Second World War, and covers such rights as that to a family life, to privacy and a fair trial. Prior to 2000, although UK courts could take note of the rights identified by the Convention, they could not be directly enforced, so aggrieved parties often had to take cases to the European Court of Human Rights for a remedy – a lengthy and costly process.

The Act incorporates only part of the European Convention and does not incorporate any of the procedural rights of the Convention. However, it does include all the following substantive rights:

- to life
- to freedom from torture or inhuman or degrading punishment
- to freedom from slavery, servitude, enforced or compulsory labour
- to liberty and security of the person
- to a fair trial
- to respect for private and family life
- to freedom of thought, conscience and religion
- to freedom of expression
- to freedom of assembly and association
- to marry and found a family
- to education in conformity with parents' religious and philosophical convictions
- to freedom from unfair discrimination in the enjoyment of these rights.

Many of the wider rights enshrined in the Human Rights Act are already protected by the UK's domestic legislation (e.g. the Sex Discrimination Act 1975). From 2000, courts in the UK have been able to issue injunctions to prevent violations of rights, award damages and quash unlawful decisions. Individuals are now able to use the Act to defend themselves in criminal proceedings. The Act does not make Convention rights directly enforceable in proceedings against a private litigant, nor against a 'quasi-public' body, unless that body is acting in a public capacity. However, private individuals and companies have to take the Convention into account because the courts will be obliged to interpret the law so as to conform to it wherever possible.

In the early days of the Act a number of examples illustrated its possible impact on business organizations, including challenges about the legitimacy of local authority planning procedures and privacy of personal information. Despite early fears that the Human Rights Act would add significantly to business organizations' costs, it would appear that more recent cases have taken a balanced view on what is reasonable and in the public interest.

6.8 Protection of a company's intangible property rights

The value of a business enterprise can be measured not only by the value of its physical assets, such as land and buildings: increasingly, the value of a business reflects its investment in new product development and strong brand images. To protect a company from imitators benefiting from this investment, but bearing none of its cost, a number of legal protections are available. The most commonly used methods are patents and trademarks, which are described below. Intellectual property can also be protected through copyright (for example, the unauthorized copying and sale of DVD films is a breach of copyright).

6.8.1 Patents

We saw in Chapter 4 that a **patent** is a right given to an inventor that allows him or her exclusively to reap the benefits from the invention over a specified period. To obtain a patent, application must be made to the Patent Office in accordance with the procedure set out in the Patents Act 1977. To qualify for a patent, the invention must have certain characteristics laid down: it must be covered by the Act, it must be novel and it must include an inventive step. Some inventions would not qualify for a patent – for example, anything that has at any time before filing for the patent been made available to the public anywhere in the world by written or oral description, by use, or in any other way (s. 2(2)).

The effect of the Patents Act 1977 has been to bring UK patent law more into line with that of the EU in accordance with the provisions of the European Patent Convention. As a result of the implementation of the Convention, there are almost uniform criteria in the establishment of a patent in Austria, Belgium, Switzerland, Germany, France, the UK, Italy, Liechtenstein, Luxembourg, the Netherlands and Sweden. A European Patent Office has been set up in Munich, which provides a cheaper method to obtain a patent in three or more countries, but it should be noted that, if the patent fails as a result of an application to the European Patent Office, the rejection applies to all member-states unless there is contrary domestic legislation that covers this aspect.

6.8.2 Trademarks

The Trade Marks Act 1994, which replaced the 1938 Act, implemented the Trade Marks Harmonization Directive No. 89/104/EEC, which provides protection for trademarks (they are also protected under the common law of passing off). A **trademark** is defined as any sign capable of being represented graphically that is capable of distinguishing goods or services of one undertaking from those of other undertakings (s. 1(1)).

Any trademark satisfying these criteria is registerable unless prohibited by s. 3; for example, an application may be refused if a trademark is devoid of any distinctive character, or is contrary to accepted principles of morality, or is of such a nature as to deceive the public.

If a trademark is infringed in any way, a successful plaintiff will be entitled to an injunction and to damages.

6.8.3 Law and the internet

The development of the internet does not change the basic principles of law, but the law has on occasions become ambiguous in the light of technological developments.

Unlawful copying of material downloaded from the internet (images, documents and particularly music) has focused attention on issues of ownership of intellectual property. Section 17 of the Copyright, Designs and Patents Act 1988 provides that: 'Copying in relation to a literary, dramatic, musical or artistic work means reproducing the work in any material form. This includes storing the work in any medium by electronic means.' Copying, therefore, includes downloading files from the internet or copying text into or attaching it to an email. Given the ability to copy material virtually instantaneously to potentially huge numbers, the internet presents a serious risk of copyright infringement liability. Just what constitutes 'public domain' information, and can therefore lawfully be copied, has been raised in a number of cases.

In addition to copyright issues, the international nature of communications on the internet makes it essential not to overlook questions such as where the contract is concluded, when it is concluded, what law governs it and where any subsequent dispute will be decided. Unexpected additional obligations may arise as a result of statements made during contract negotiations – for example, in an email from a salesperson to a customer. Even where the final written contract expressly excludes such representations, courts may be prepared to find that a collateral contract came into existence through the exchange of email messages.

EU countries have introduced into national legislation a 1999 EU directive on electronic signatures. The directive comprises two major advances: the legal recognition of electronic signatures, which provide reliable identification of the parties engaged in an online transaction; and encryption, which enables companies to electronically protect documents liable to be intercepted during transmission, by wire or over the air. These measures will help companies doing business over the internet to verify with accuracy the identity of their contracting partners and to improve online security standards for international business.

The internet has also intensified concerns about data privacy. The misuse of personal data has always been an issue with traditional paper-based systems of recording information, but the internet increases the possibility for large amounts of data to be accidentally or deliberately misused. Chapter 4 reviewed some of the principal concerns, and you will recall that, in the UK, the Data Protection Commissioner is responsible for overseeing the provisions of the Data Protection Act 1988, which itself was based on an EU directive. The Act requires companies to keep accurate records that are not unnecessarily excessive in detail, and shall not be kept for longer than is necessary for the purpose of collecting them. Appropriate technical and organizational measures must be taken against unauthorized or unlawful processing of personal data, and against its accidental loss or destruction. Companies have been helped in their efforts to secure their data by the Computer Misuse Act 1990, which makes hacking and the introduction of viruses criminal offences.

Although the emphasis of the Data Protection Act has been on limiting the dissemination of data, the Act also provides individuals and companies with certain rights of access to data about them that are held by companies. There is also a more general provision under the Freedom of Information Act 2002, which allows individuals to request information.

⟳ Thinking around the subject

Taking a punt online

The internet has brought new challenges to the legal environment. Usually, it is quite easy to determine the jurisdiction of a transaction – for example, a British tourist eating in a Spanish restaurant would be covered by the laws of Spain. For exports, the parties can agree between themselves which legal jurisdiction should apply to their transaction – for example, a British exporter and a Spanish buyer may between them agree that British law will govern their contract. But many internet dealings may involve numerous nationalities – for example, a British buyer on holiday in Australia may use an American-based travel agent to buy tickets from an airline based in Hong Kong, using an internet service provider based in Belgium. Regulatory authorities have been keen to control some types of internet activity that are considered to be against the public interest, but have repeatedly come across the problem of defining legal jurisdiction. For service-based transactions, governments face difficulty in stopping such services coming into their country, as they could in the case of goods that need to pass through some kind of customs check. Service-based companies have sometimes moved their operations to jurisdictions that are friendly towards their activities, then 'export' their services to countries where they would otherwise be illegal.

One type of activity that has exercised the minds of lawyers is gambling. In many countries, gambling has been associated with a range of social problems, therefore countries have strict controls on individuals' access to gambling services. Betting shops have been strictly regulated in the UK and many other countries, and it has been made illegal for young people to enter them. But the internet can avoid many of these controls by slipping under regulators' radar and going direct from an offshore service provider to the punter's own home. This has annoyed regulators in the USA, where gambling laws tend to be quite strict. The USA by itself cannot legislate to stop online gambling companies selling their services from other countries in the world. In a free market economy where freedom of speech is valued, the US government is not predisposed to censoring the internet, in the way that the Chinese government has done in respect of political websites. So how can a government use the law to defend the interests of its citizens, when the borderless world of the internet allows many services to reach consumers unchallenged by national borders?

For online gambling companies, such as Partypoker.com and 888.com, the USA is a very attractive market, with a high disposable income and latent demand that has been suppressed by strict anti-gambling legislation. The online gambling companies could not operate legally if they were based in the USA, so most are based in countries with more lax regimes, including the Cayman Islands and the UK. Indeed, in 2007, the UK government expressed an aim to become the world's leading centre for the online gaming industry.

The US government, frustrated by the inability of its anti-gambling laws to control offshore internet operations, has resorted to a number of more indirect approaches to control these companies. Making it illegal for US-based companies to operate online gambling sites simply handed the business opportunity to overseas companies that had no such restriction. But, in 2007, the government sought to implement its laws through American-based banks, making it illegal for them to carry out transactions with online gambling companies. American customers of Partypoker.com suddenly found that their bank wouldn't allow them to pay for gambling using their credit card (although, not to be

⟳

outdone, the gambling companies have attempted to facilitate payment through third-party mechanisms such as PayPal). The US government has also sought to extend its jurisdiction and prosecute the directors of offshore gambling companies. In 2006, the sector was shaken by the arrest of David Carruthers, a UK citizen and Chief Executive Officer of London Stock Exchange listed BetonSports, while in transit in Dallas from the UK to Costa Rica. He and ten other individuals and four corporations faced a 22-count indictment on various charges of racketeering, conspiracy and fraud.

Are the actions of the USA to control the internet intrusive, and beyond what should be its legal jurisdiction? Should there be a higher level of international law to govern an internet world that knows no political boundaries? Would it have any chance of succeeding? How would it reconcile the USA's aims for tighter legislation on gambling with the UK's aim of becoming the centre for the online gambling sector?

6.9 The law and production processes

As economies develop, there is a tendency for societies to raise their expectations about firms' behaviour, particularly where they are responsible for significant external costs (see Chapter 5). The result has been increasing levels of legislation that constrain the activities of firms in meeting buyers' needs. Some of the more important constraints that affect business decisions are described below.

- Pollution of the natural environment is an external cost that governments seek to limit through legislation such as the Environmental Protection Act 1995, the Environment Act 1990 and the Water Resources Act 1991. Examples of impacts on firms include requirements for additional noise insulation, and investment in equipment to purify discharges into water courses and the atmosphere. These have often added to a firm's total production costs, thereby putting it at a competitive disadvantage, or made plans to increase production capacity uneconomic when faced with competition from companies in countries that have less demanding requirements for environmental protection.

- The rights of employees to enjoy safe working conditions have become increasingly enshrined in law as a country develops. In the UK, it was noted earlier in this chapter that the Health & Safety at Work Act 1974 provides for large fines and, in extreme cases, imprisonment of company directors for failing to provide a safe working environment. Definitions of what constitutes an acceptable level of risk for employees to face change over time. As well as obvious serious physical injury, the courts in England now recognize the responsibility of firms to protect their employees against more subtle dangers such as repetitive strain injury. There has also been debate in cases brought before courts as to whether a firm should be responsible for mental illness caused by excessive stress in a job, and the courts have held that companies should be liable if the employee has suffered stress in the past of which the company was aware.

- In many cases it is not sufficient to rely on law to protect customers from the faulty outcomes of a firm's production. It is also necessary to legislate in respect of the quality of the *processes* of production. This is important where buyers are unable to fully evaluate a product without a guarantee that the method of producing it has been in accordance with acceptable criteria. An example of this is the Food Safety Act 1990, which imposes requirements on all firms that manufacture or handle food products to ensure that they cannot become contaminated (e.g. by being kept at too high a temperature during transport). Many small to medium-sized food manufacturers have closed down, claiming that they cannot justify the cost of upgrading premises. Laws governing production processes are also important in the case of intangible services, where customers may have little opportunity for evaluating the credentials of one service against another. For example, to protect the public against unethical behaviour by unscrupulous sales personnel, the Financial Services Act 1986 lays down procedures for regulating business practices within the sector.

The traditional view of legislation on production is that the mounting weight of legislation puts domestic firms at a cost disadvantage to those operating in relatively unregulated environments overseas. Critics of over-regulation point to Britain and the USA as two economies that have priced themselves out of many international markets.

Against this, it is argued that as the economy of a country develops, economic gains should be enjoyed by all stakeholders of business, including employees and the local communities in which a business operates. There are also many persuasive arguments why increasing regulation of production processes may not be incompatible with greater business prosperity.

- Attempts to deregulate conditions of employment may allow firms to be more flexible in their production methods and thereby reduce their costs. However, there is a suggestion that a casualized workforce becomes increasingly reluctant to make major purchases, thereby reducing the level of activity in the domestic economy. In the UK, moves during the 1990s to free employers of many of their responsibilities to employees resulted in a large number of casual workers who were reluctant or unable to buy houses, resulting in a knock-on effect on supplies of home-related goods and services.

- There is similarly much evidence that a healthy and safe working environment is likely to be associated with high levels of commitment by employees and a high standard of output quality. The law should represent no more than a codification of good practice by firms.

- Environmental protection and cost reduction may not be mutually incompatible, as Chapter 5 demonstrates.

6.10 Legislation to protect the competitiveness of markets

Finally, there are presumed benefits of having markets that are competitive and free of harmful monopolistic or collusive tendencies. Because of this, the law of most developed countries has been used to try to remove market imperfections where these are deemed to be against the public interest. We will discuss in Chapter 12 how the common law of England has developed the principle of restraint of trade, through which anti-competitive practices have been curbed.

As the economy has become more complex, common law has proved inadequate on its own to preserve the competitiveness of markets. Common law has therefore been supplemented by statutory legislation. One outcome of statutory intervention has been the creation of a regulatory infrastructure, which in the UK includes the Office of Fair Trading, the Competition Commission and regulatory bodies to control specific industries. However, much of the current regulatory framework in the UK is based on the requirements of Articles 85 and 86 of the Treaty of Rome.

In the UK, the Competition Act 1998 and the Enterprise Act 2002 reformed and strengthened competition law by prohibiting anti-competitive behaviour. The 1998 Act introduced two basic prohibitions: a prohibition of anti-competitive agreements, based closely on Article 85 of the EC Treaty; and a prohibition of abuse of a dominant position in a market, based closely on Article 86 of the EC Treaty. The Act prohibits agreements that have the aim or effect of preventing, restricting or distorting competition in the UK. Since anti-competitive behaviour between companies may occur without a clearly defined agreement, the prohibition covers not only agreements by associations of companies, but also covert practices.

Further discussion of the application of legislation concerning anti-competitive practices, and the task of defining the public interest, may be found in Chapter 12.

Case study:
Legislation strengthened in a bid to end 'nightmare' holidays

© Michał Krakowiak

Tour operators have probably felt more keenly than most businesses the effects of new legislation to protect consumers. Because holidays are essentially intangible, it is very difficult for a prospective customer to check out claims made by tour operators' advertising until their holiday is under way, when it may be too late to do anything to prevent a ruined holiday. Traditional attitudes of 'let the buyer beware' can be of little use to holidaymakers who have little tangible evidence on which to base their decision when they book a holiday.

Consumers have traditionally had very little comeback against tour operators that fail to provide a holiday that is in line with the expectations held out in their brochure. Their brochures have frequently been accused of misleading customers – for example, by showing pictures of hotels that conveniently omit the adjacent airport runway or sewerage works. The freedom of tour operators to produce fanciful brochures was limited by the Consumer Protection Act 1987. Part III of the Act holds that any person, who, in the course of a business of his, gives (by any means whatsoever) to any consumers an indication that is misleading as to the price at which any goods, services, accommodation or facilities are available shall be guilty of an offence. These provisions of the Act forced tour operators to end such practices as promoting very low-priced holidays, which in reality were never available when customers enquired about them – only higher-priced holidays were offered. Supplements for additional items such as regional airport departures could no longer be hidden away in the small print.

When a customer buys a package holiday through a travel agent, she or he is entering into a contract with the tour operator, and the travel agent is essentially a mediator that brings together the customer and tour operator. The tour operator itself enters into a series of contracts with service providers, including hotels, airlines and bus companies, among others. Although these suppliers are contracted to provide services, the tour operator in practice has no effective day-to-day control of its suppliers' operations. It has therefore been quite usual for tour operators to include in their booking conditions an exclusion clause absolving themselves of any liability arising from the faults of their subcontractors. If a customer was injured by a faulty lift in a Spanish hotel, a tour operator would deny any responsibility for the injury and could only advise the holidaymaker to sue the Spanish hotel themselves. For some time, the courts in England recognized that it would be unreasonable to expect UK tour operators to be liable for actions that were effectively beyond their management control. Anyone who had felt unfairly treated by a tour operator had to take the offending company to court personally, often at great expense and inconvenience to themselves.

EU legislation has strengthened the position of consumers. EU Directive 90/314/EEC is designed to protect consumers who contract package travel in the EU, and was implemented in the

UK through the Package Travel Regulations 1992. It covers the sale of a pre-arranged combination of transport, accommodation and other tourist services ancillary to transport or accommodation and accounting for a significant proportion of the package. Consumers are covered only where at least two of these elements are sold or offered for sale at an inclusive price, and the service covers a period of more than 24 hours or includes overnight accommodation.

The Directive contains rules concerning the liability of package organizers and retailers, which must accept responsibility for the performance of the services offered. There are some exceptions – for example, cases of 'force majeure' or similar circumstances, which could be neither foreseen nor overcome. However, even in these cases the organizer must use its best endeavours to help consumers.

The Directive also prescribes rules on the information that must be given to consumers. It contains specific requirements with regard to the content of brochures, where these are issued. For example, any brochure made available to consumers must indicate clearly and accurately the price, destination, itinerary and the means of transport used, type of accommodation, meal plan, passport and visa requirements, health formalities, timetable for payment and the deadline for informing consumers in the event of cancellation.

The Regulations have sought to redress the balance by providing greater protection for customers of tour operators and making all tour operators liable for the actions of their subcontractors. In cases that have been brought before courts in England, tour operators have been held liable for illness caused by food poisoning at a hotel, injury caused by uneven tiles at a swimming pool, and loss of enjoyment caused by noisy building work. To emphasize the effects of the directive, one British tour operator was ordered to compensate a holidaymaker in respect of claims that she had been harassed by a waiter at a hotel that had been contracted by the tour operator.

In the space of less than a decade, the UK tour operating industry has been transformed from relying on exclusion clauses and seeking to govern its dealings with customers through voluntary codes of conduct (especially the code of the Association of British Travel Agents (ABTA)). Many would argue that voluntary regulation had failed to protect consumers in accordance with their rising expectations. Legislation, while it was initially resisted by tour operators, has undoubtedly increased consumers' confidence in buying package holidays, and lessened the chances of them buying a holiday from a rogue company, and thereby harming the reputation of the industry as a whole.

The effects of this and other legislation have borne down heavily on tour operators. Having grown rapidly during the 1970s and 1980s, their pace of growth has slowed considerably. This may be partly explained by consumers' greater confidence and willingness to make up their own packages independently, encouraged by cut-price hotel and flight deals offered by companies who are not bound by the packaged travel regulations. The internet has allowed consumers to easily 'pick and mix' the different parts of the package holiday, so that they can buy the cheapest airline ticket from one source, and the cheapest hotel room from another source, for example. However, if anything goes wrong with such a self-created package, the consumer has fewer statutory rights to rely on. So if a flight is delayed or rescheduled, causing a hotel booking to be wasted, or tickets to a sporting event to be rendered useless, the customer cannot rely on one single company to put things right. In fact, if the airline was at fault and caused them to waste a hotel booking and sports tickets, they may have only a limited claim for compensation against the airline, and almost certainly no claim for consequential loss of the hotel booking or sports tickets (although EU Regulation 261/2004 does require airline passengers to be compensated for delays and compensation in specified circumstances).

Increased legislation can undoubtedly be expensive for companies to comply with. But the legislation itself can add value to a product. In the case of package holidays, consumers could avoid the burden of costs imposed on tour operators by booking independently, but they would also lose many of the benefits provided by legislation.

QUESTIONS

1 What factors could explain the increasing amount of legislation that now faces tour operators?

2 Summarize the main consequences of the EU Directive referred to above on the marketing of package holidays in the UK.

3 Is there still a role for voluntary codes of conduct in preference to legislation as a means of regulating the relationship between a tour operator and its customers?

Summary

This chapter has noted the increasing effects that legislation is having on businesses. The principal sources of law have been identified. Statute law is becoming increasingly important, with more influence being felt from the EU. Legal processes and the remedies available to a firm's customers have been discussed.

Voluntary codes of conduct are often seen as an alternative to law, and offer firms lower cost and greater flexibility.

The discussion of business ethics in **Chapter 5** relates closely to the legal environment. To many people, law is essentially a formalization of ethics, with statute law enacted by government **(Chapter 2)**. The competition environment **(Chapter 11)** is increasingly influenced by legislation governing anti-competitive practices. We saw in **Chapter 4** that legal protection for innovative new technologies is vital if expenditure on research and development is to be sustained. In addition to the aspects of law discussed in this chapter, legislation affects the status of organizations **(Chapter 7)** – for example, in the protection that is given to limited liability companies.

Key Terms

Code of practice (213)	Misrepresentation (211)
Common law (202)	Negligence (205)
Contract (203)	Patent (222)
Discrimination (219)	Statute law (202)
Dismissal (220)	Tort (205)
Duty of care (205)	Trademark (222)
Intellectual property rights (203)	

Online Learning Centre

To help you grasp the key concepts of this chapter, explore the extra resources posted on the Online Learning Centre at *www.mcgraw-hill.co.uk/palmer*. Among other helpful resources there are chapter-by-chapter test questions, revision notes and web links.

Chapter review questions

1 Discuss the main ways in which the legal environment impacts on the activities of the sales and marketing functions of business organizations.

2 Giving examples, evaluate the criticism that government legislation impacts primarily on those firms that can least afford to pay for it, mainly the small and the competitively vulnerable.

3 Using an appropriate example, evaluate the virtues and drawbacks of using voluntary codes of practice to regulate business activity.

Activities

1 Think back to a time when you had a problem with a good or service that didn't meet the agreed specification (e.g. a DVD you ordered didn't have as many tracks as advertised; the seats you ended up with at a rock concert were not as good as the ones you had ordered). Identify the methods of conflict resolution available to you, short of taking legal action. Did the supplier make it easy to resolve the problem? What more could it have done? Is there a voluntary code of conduct or arbitration service that you could have used? Is it easy to use? What factors would encourage or discourage you from taking legal action?

2 Philip, shopping at a large department store, sees a colourful spinning top, which he buys for his grandson Harry. While purchasing the toy, he sees a prominent notice in the store, which states: 'This store will not be held responsible for any defects in the toys sold.' The box containing the spinning top carries the description 'Ideal for children over 12 months, safe and non-toxic' (Harry is 15 months old). Within four weeks the spinning top has split into two parts, each with a jagged edge, and Harry has suffered an illness as a result of sucking the paint. Philip has complained vociferously to the store, which merely pointed to the prominent notice disclaiming liability. Philip has now informed the store that he intends to take legal action against it.

Draft a report to the managing director setting out the legal liability of the store.

3 Zak runs his own painting and decorating business, and has been engaged to decorate Rebecca's lounge. While burning off layers of paint from the door with his blowtorch, Zak's attention is diverted by the barking of neighbour Camilla's Yorkshire terrier and, as he turns round, the flame catches a cushion on the sofa. Within seconds the room is filled with acrid smoke. Both the carpet and sofa are damaged beyond repair, and the dog, terrified, rushes into the road, where it is run over by a car. Consider Zak's legal liability.

Further reading

The following texts provide a general overview of law as it affects commercial organizations.

Adams, A. (2010) *Law for Business Students*, 6th edn, London, Longman.
Clayton, P. (2009) *Essential Law for Your Business: A Practical Guide to all Legal and Financial Requirements*, 13th edn, London, Kogan Page.
Riches, S. and Allen, V. (2009) *Business Law*, 5th edn, Harlow, Pearson.

This chapter has discussed the basics of the law of contract and the following texts provide useful further reading.

Elliott, C. and Quinn, F. (2010) *Contract Law*, 7th edn, London, Longman.

Poole, J. (2010) *Textbook on Contract Law*, 10th edn, Oxford, Oxford University Press.
Trademarks and patent laws are discussed in the following text.

Hart, T., Fazzani, L. and Clark, S. (2009) *Intellectual Property Law*, 5th edn, Basingstoke, Palgrave Macmillan.

A valuable overview of employment law is provided in the following.

Lewis, D. and Sargeant, M. (2009) *Essentials of Employment Law*, 10th edn, London, Chartered Institute of Personnel and Development.

References

Berthoud, R. (2005) *Incomes of Ethnic Minorities*, York, Joseph Rowntree Foundation.
Eurostat (2006–07) *Eurostat Yearbook 2006–07*, Luxembourg, Statistical Office of the European Communities.

Chapter 13

The National Economic and Financial Environment

The workers at the local car components company have been put on reduced-hours working, so their income goes down. Because they work for only three days and not five days a week, they have less money in their pockets, so they don't go as often to the local corner shop to buy their cigarettes, bottles of Coke and bars of chocolate. The corner shop owner sees his income go down, so he postpones his order for replacement windows. Lots of businesses are doing the same, so the window supplier cuts its staff, so households in the area have even less money to spend in the shops. So they lay off more people, or even go out of business completely. All the time, the economy is shrinking and governments suffer as taxation revenue drops. But in order to try to get the economy moving again, governments may feel compelled to borrow money to pump in to the system so that consumers now have money to spend, which results in new jobs being created by firms whose employees spend more money in the shops, and helps to increase the government's tax revenues. These are the basic ideas underlying linkages within national economies that are explored in this chapter. And, with an increasingly globalized business environment, these economic and financial linkages cross national boundaries.

✓ Learning Objectives

This chapter will explain:

☑ The structure of national economies, distinguishing between consumer, producer and government sectors.

☑ Methods of measuring activity within the economy.

☑ Financial linkages and interdependencies between sectors.

☑ The business cycle – causes and consequences for business organizations.

☑ Government economic policy objectives.

☑ Methods used by governments and central banks to manage the national economy.

13.1 Macroeconomic analysis

In the previous chapter, microeconomic analysis of a firm's competitive environment made a number of assumptions about the broader economic environment in which the firm operates. In the analysis of supply and demand in any given market, changes in household incomes or government taxation were treated as an uncontrollable external factor to which a market responded. For most businesses, a sound understanding of this broader economic environment is just as important as understanding short-term and narrow relationships between the price of a firm's products and demand for them.

An analysis of companies' financial results has often indicated that business people attribute their current success or failure to the state of the economy. For example, a retail store that has just reported record profit levels may put this down to a very high level of consumer confidence, while a factory that has just laid off workers may blame a continuing economic recession for its low level of activity. Few business people can afford to ignore the state of the economy because it affects the willingness and ability of customers to buy their products. It can also affect the price and availability of its inputs. The shop that reported record profits may have read economic indicators correctly and prepared for an upturn in consumer spending by buying in more stocks or taking on more sales assistants.

This chapter is concerned with what is often described as macroeconomic analysis. Although the workings of the economy at a national level are the focus of this chapter, it must be remembered that even national economies form part of a larger international economic environment.

The chapter begins by analysing the structure of the national economy and the interdependence of the elements within this structure. The national economy is a complex system whose functioning is influenced by a range of planned and unplanned forces. While unplanned forces (such as turbulence in the world economic system) can have significant impacts on the national economic system, organizations are particularly keen to understand the planned interventions of governments that seek to influence the economy for a variety of social and political reasons. Money is a factor that brings together the different elements of the macroenvironment, with money linking buyers and sellers, firms and households; individuals who have surplus savings with individuals who want to borrow; and flows of money link public and private sectors. In the increasingly globalized business environment, flows of money link strong countries that generate cash with those weaker and growing economies that need to borrow it.

13.2 The structure of national economies

Analyses of national economies have traditionally divided the productive sectors into three categories.

1 The *primary sector*, which is concerned with the extraction and production of basic raw materials from agriculture, mining, oil exploration, etc.

2 The *secondary sector*, which transforms the output of the primary sector into products that consumers can use (e.g. manufacturing, construction, raw material processing).

3 The *services sector*, which comprises intangible products such as hairdressing, and business services such as accounting.

Comparisons can be drawn between the three sectors described above and value chains (described in Chapter 1). In general, these three sectors add progressively higher levels of value to a product. In practice, most organizations are involved in two or more of these production categories; for example, the Ford car company manufactures cars, but it also produces a wide range of services, including financial services, extended warranties and insurance.

A further division in the economy occurs between the production sector and the consumption sector. The production sector creates wealth (e.g. making cars, providing meals in a restaurant), while the consumption sector essentially destroys wealth (using the car until it is worn out, eating the restaurant meal so that there is nothing left to show for it). Distinction is often made between government and private sectors of the economy. Government becomes involved in the economy as both a producer (e.g. educational services) and as a consumer on behalf of the public (e.g. through the purchase of equipment for schools).

The relationship between producers and consumers is the basis for models of the circular flow of income, discussed later in this chapter.

13.2.1 Measures of economic structure

The relative importance of the three productive sectors described above has been changing. Evidence of this change is usually recorded by reference to three key statistics:

1 the share of gross domestic product (GDP) that each sector accounts for
2 the proportion of the labour force employed in the sector
3 the contribution of the sector to a nation's balance of payments.

A key trend in Britain, as in most developed economies, has been the gradual decline in importance of the primary and manufacturing sectors and the growth in the services sector. The extent of the change in the UK **economic structure**, when measured by shifts in GDP and employment, is indicated in Table 13.1.

While the statistics in Table 13.1 appear to show a number of clear trends, the figures need to be treated with a little caution for a number of reasons.

- Fluctuations in the value of GDP for the primary sector often have little to do with changes in activity levels, but instead reflect changes in world commodity levels. Oil represents a major part of the UK's primary sector output, but the value of oil produced has fluctuated

Table 13.1 Composition of the UK productive sector.

	1969	1979	1989	1995	2000	2007
Primary						
GDP (%)	4.3	6.7	4.2	4.4	4.1	3.7
Workforce (%)	3.6	3.0	2.1	1.4	1.5	1.3
Secondary						
GDP (%)	42.0	36.7	34.5	29.4	25.5	24.5
Workforce (%)	46.8	38.5	28.9	18.3	20.8	19.2
Services						
GDP (%)	53.0	56.5	61.3	66.2	70.4	75.0
Workforce (%)	49.3	58.5	69.0	76.5	77.7	79.5

Source: compiled from 'Economic trends', *Employment Gazette*.

from the very high levels of the early 1980s to the very low levels of the 1990s, largely reflecting changes in oil prices.

■ The level of accuracy with which statistics have been recorded has been questioned, especially for the services sector. The system of Standard Industrial Classifications (SICs) for a long while did not disaggregate the service sector in the same level of detail as the other two sectors.

■ Part of the apparent growth in the services sector may reflect the method by which statistics are collected, rather than indicating an increase in overall service level activity. Output and employment is recorded according to the dominant business of an organization. Within many primary- and secondary-sector organizations, many people are employed in service-type activities, such as cleaning, catering, transport and distribution. Where a cook is employed by a manufacturing company, output and employment is attributed to the manufacturing sector. However, during recent years, many manufacturing firms have contracted out some of these service activities to external contractors. Where such contracts are performed by contract catering, office cleaning or transport companies, the output becomes attributable to the service sector, making the service sector look larger, even though no additional services have actually been produced – they have merely been switched from internally produced to externally produced.

Nevertheless, the figures clearly indicate a number of significant trends in the economy.

■ The primary sector in the UK, as in most developed economies, has been contracting in relative importance. There are supply- and demand-side explanations for this trend. On the supply side, many basic agricultural and extractive processes have been mechanized, resulting in them using fewer employees and thereby consuming a lower proportion of GDP. Many primary industries have declined as suppliers have been unable to compete with low-cost producers in countries that are able to exploit poor working conditions. On the demand side, rising levels of affluence have led consumers to demand increasingly refined products. In this way, consumers have moved from buying raw potatoes (essentially a product of the primary sector) to buying processed potatoes (e.g. prepared ready meals), which involve greater inputs from the secondary sector. With further affluence, potatoes have been sold with the added involvement of the service sector (e.g. eating cooked potatoes in a restaurant).

■ The output of the secondary sector in the UK fell from 42 per cent of GDP in 1969 to 25.5 per cent in 2008, reflecting the poor performance of the manufacturing industry (the comparable figure for the 25 EU countries was 25.8 per cent). This can again partly be explained by efficiency gains by the sector, requiring fewer resources to be used, but more worryingly by competition from overseas. The emergence of newly industrialized nations with a good manufacturing infrastructure and low employment costs, rigidities in the UK labour market, declining research and development budgets relative to overseas competitors, and the effects of exchange rate policy have all contributed to this decline.

■ In respect of its share of GDP, the services sector saw almost continuous growth during the period 1969–99, with banking, finance, insurance, business services, leasing and communications being particularly prominent. In 2006, the services sector accounted for 75 per cent of UK GDP, up from 53 per cent in 1969.

13.2.2 Towards a service economy?

There is little doubt that the services sector has become a dominant force in many national economies. According to Eurostat, services accounted for 71.6 per cent of GDP in the 25 EU countries in 2005 (Eurostat 2006). Between 1970 and 1997, it is reported that about 1.5 million new jobs per year were created in the services sectors within the EU – twice the average for the rest of the economy (Eurostat 1998).

The UK, like many developed economies, has traditionally run a balance of trade deficit in manufactured goods (i.e. imports exceed exports), but has made up for this with a surplus in 'invisible' service 'exports'. In 2009, there was a trade surplus in services of £49.9 billion (or £55.4 billion in 2008), but this was more than offset by a deficit of £81.9 billion in manufactured goods (or £93.1 billion in 2008) (ONS 2010).

During periods of recession in the manufacturing sector, the service sector has been seen by many as the saviour of the economy. Many politicians have been keen to promote the service sector as a source of new employment to make up for the diminishing level of employment within the primary and secondary sectors. A common argument has been that the UK no longer has a competitive cost advantage in the production of many types of goods, and therefore these sectors of the economy should be allowed to decline and greater attention paid to those service sectors that showed greater competitive advantage. The logic of this argument can be pushed too far, as outlined below.

- A large part of the growth in the service sector during the 1980s and 1990s reflected the buoyancy of the primary and secondary sectors during that period. As manufacturing industry increases its level of activity, the demand for many business-to-business services, such as accountancy, legal services and business travel, increases. During periods of recession in the manufacturing sectors, the decline in manufacturing output has had an impact on the services sector, as evidenced, for example, through lower demand for business loans and export credits.

- The assumption that the UK has a competitive cost advantage in the production of services needs to be examined closely. In the same way that many sectors of UK manufacturing industry lost their competitive advantage to developing nations during the 1960s and 1970s, there is some evidence that the once unquestioned supremacy in certain service sectors is being challenged. High levels of training in some of Britain's competitor nations have allowed those countries to, first, develop their own indigenous services and then to develop them for export. Banking services that were once a net import of Japan are now exported throughout the world.

- Over-reliance on the service sector could pose strategic problems for the UK. A diverse economic base allows a national economy to be more resilient to changes in world trading conditions.

13.2.3 International comparisons

There appears to be a high level of correlation between the level of economic development in an economy (as expressed by its GDP per capita) and the strength of its services sector. Within the EU there is variation around the mean share of value added from services of 71.6 per cent, with more developed member-states being above this figure (e.g. UK 75 per cent, France 76 per cent), and less developed member-states below (e.g. Lithuania 55 per cent, Slovakia 63 per cent) (Eurostat 2006). According to the International Labour Organization, 71.5 per cent of the total workers from developed economies are employed in the services sector. Lower figures are found in many of the developing economies of Asia – for example, East Asia (34.7 per cent), Southeast Asia and the Pacific (37 per cent), South Asia (30.3 per cent). The lowest level of services employment is found in the least developed countries for example, those in Sub-Saharan Africa (25.7 per cent) (ILO 2008).

It is debatable whether a strong services sector leads to economic growth or is a result of that economic growth. The debate can partly be resolved by dividing services into those 'consumer services' that are used up in final consumption and 'business to business' services that provide inputs to further business processes (see below).

13.2.4 Consumer, producer and government sectors

Consumer goods and services are provided for individuals who use up those goods and services for their own enjoyment or benefit. No further economic benefit results from the consumption of the product. In this way, the services of a hairdresser can be defined as consumer services. On the other hand, producer goods and services are those that are provided to other businesses in order that those businesses can produce something else of economic benefit. In this way, a road haulage company sells services to its industrial customers in order that they can add value to the goods that they produce, by allowing their goods to be made available at the point of demand.

The essential difference between production and final consumption sectors is that the former creates wealth while the latter consumes it. Traditionally, economic analysis has labelled these as 'firms' and 'households' respectively. The discussion later in this chapter will indicate the problems that may arise where an apparently prosperous household sector is not backed by an equally active production sector.

There has been continuing debate about the role of government in the national economy, which has led to shifts in the proportion of GDP accounted for by the public sector. During the 1980s, the UK government regarded the public sector as a burden on the country and set about dismantling much of the state's involvement in the economy. Privatization of public corporations and the encouragement of private pensions were just two manifestations of this. By the mid-1990s, the proportion of UK government expenditure as a proportion of total GDP appeared to have stabilized in the range 38–42 per cent, with increasing social security spending offsetting much of the reduction in expenditure accounted for by state-owned industries. Figure 13.1 illustrates the cyclical nature of public spending and taxation as a proportion of UK GDP.

Governments do not always take such a 'hands-off' approach. The economies of eastern Europe have in the past been dominated by central planning in which the government determined the bulk of income and expenditure in the economy. Even in Britain shortly after the Second World

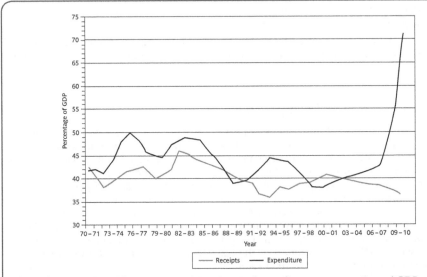

Figure 13.1 Trends in UK government taxation and spending as a proportion of GDP, 1970–2010.

Source: based on HM Treasury Financial Statement and Budget Report, March 2010.

War, the government assumed a very major role in the economy, with the nationalization of many essential industries. Even today, there are variations within western Europe in the proportion of GDP accounted for by the government sector. Many Scandinavian countries, for example, have higher proportions than the UK, reflecting, among other things, a general acceptance by their populations that taxation revenues will be wisely spent on socially necessary expenditure.

Organizations need to keep their eyes on political developments that shift the balance of resources between public and private sectors. A company that is involved in the marketing of health service products, for example, will be very interested in the government's view about the respective roles to be played by the private sector and the National Health Service.

⟳ Thinking around the subject

Service dominant logic?

To some people, the services sector may be seen as economically quite inferior to the manufacturing sector, conjuring up images of fast food, restaurants and hairdressers. But services have in recent years been seen by many as the driving force of the economy rather than simply an 'add on' to traditional manufacturing sectors. The emerging theory of 'service dominant logic' holds that raw materials and manufactured goods have no value without services that create 'value in use' (Vargo and Lusch 2008). Think about trees that have just been felled in the forest to provide timber. Without transport services to move them to customers, intermediaries to handle and process them, and possibly banks to finance stock, the timber would have no value. In many markets, suppliers begin with designing the service level, then developing the physical product offer comes second. Within the manufacturing sector, many companies now compete on service – for example, office equipment is often sold with the benefit of financing schemes, delivery, installation, maintenance contracts and warranties. These may be an important point of differentiation in markets where product design features are fairly standard. Inevitably, when a new idea such as 'service dominant logic' comes along, there are critics who argue about the validity of the new idea. Services can certainly be seen to be driving many sales of manufactured goods, but if the product itself is not well designed, would the service offer make up for this? The photocopying machine may come with a very good maintenance and breakdown repair service, but wouldn't it be better to design a machine that didn't break down in the first place?

13.3   The circular flow of income

Households, firms and government are highly interdependent and the level of wealth created in an economy is influenced by the interaction between these elements. Money is a mediating device which flows between the different elopements. To understand the workings of a national economy, it is useful to begin by developing a simple model of a closed economy comprising just two sectors – firms and households – which circulate money between each other.

The simplest model of a **circular flow of income** involves a number of assumptions.

- Households earn all their income from supplying their labour to firms.
- Firms earn all their income from supplying goods and services to households.
- There is no external trade.
- All income earned is spent (i.e. households and firms do not retain savings).

In this simple model, the income of households is exactly equal to the expenditure of firms, and vice versa. It follows that any change in income from employment is directly related to changes in expenditure by consumers. Similarly, any change in sales of goods and services by firms is dependent upon employment. In this simplified economy, income, output, spending and employment are all interrelated (Figure 13.2). Of course, this simplified model of the economy is almost impossible to achieve in practice, because most economies are affected by factors that upset this stable equilibrium pattern of income and expenditure.

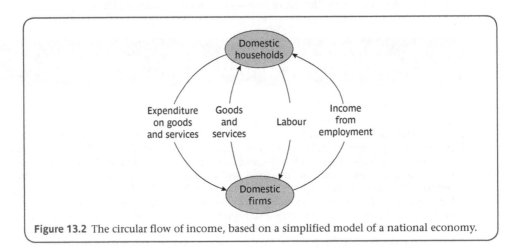

Figure 13.2 The circular flow of income, based on a simplified model of a national economy.

Instability in this static model can come about for two principal reasons: additional money can be injected into the circular flow, while money currently circulating can be withdrawn. Injections have the effect of increasing the volume and speed of circulation of money within this flow, while withdrawals have the opposite effects.

Withdrawals can take a number of forms:

- savings by households that occur when income is received by them, but not returned to firms
- government taxation, which removes income received by households and prevents them from returning it to firms in the form of expenditure on goods and services; taxation of businesses diverts part of their expenditure from being returned to households
- spending on imported goods and services by households means that this money is not received by firms, which cannot subsequently return it to households in the form of wages.

The opposite of withdrawals are **injections** and these go some way to counterbalancing the effects described above, in the following ways.

- Firms may earn income by selling goods to overseas buyers. This represents an additional source of income that is passed on to households.
- Purchases by firms of capital equipment, which represents investment as opposed to current expenditure.
- Instead of reducing the flow of income in an economy through taxation, governments can add to it by spending on goods and services.

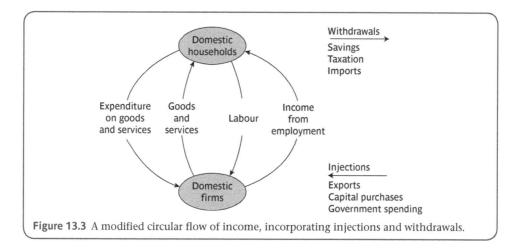

Figure 13.3 A modified circular flow of income, incorporating injections and withdrawals.

A revised model of the circular flow of income, incorporating these modifications, is shown in Figure 13.3.

This modified model of the economy still involves a number of fairly unrealistic assumptions (e.g. that consumers do not borrow money). In addition, it is unrealistic to assume that households earn income only from employment activity; they also receive it from returns on investments, property rentals and self-employment. However, it serves to stress the interdependence of the different sectors of the economy and the fact that, through this interdependence, changes in behaviour by one group can result in significant changes in economic performance as a whole. Of particular interest to government policy makers and businesses alike is the effect on total economic activity of changing just one element in the circular flow.

Another issue that is not fully reflected in this simple model is the role of the banking sector in circulating funds between and within the household and firm sectors. If firms rely on their own capital for growth, their growth would probably be very slow; therefore expanding economies have been associated with high levels of borrowing by firms. In the case of developing economies, this borrowing usually comes from overseas, representing a major injection to their national economies. If firms and banks do not feel confident about lending to each other (or do not feel confident about borrowing money), the circular flow of income will slow down. This was clearly seen in late 2007 when the so-called 'credit crunch' led to a liquidity crisis as banks became reluctant to lend money, both to firms and to private consumers. This led to a sharp downturn in consumer expenditure.

13.3.1 The multiplier effect

The **multiplier effect** can be compared to the effects of throwing a stone into a pool of water. The impact of the stone with the water will cause an initial wave to be formed, but beyond this will be waves of ever decreasing strength. The strength of these ripples will lessen with increasing distance from the site of original impact and with the passage of time. Similarly, injecting money into the circular flow of income will have an initial impact on households and businesses directly affected by the injection, but will also be indirectly felt by households and firms throughout the economy.

The multiplier effect can be illustrated by considering the effects of a major capital investment by private-sector firms or by government. The firm making the initial investment spends money buying in supplies from outside (including labour) and these outside suppliers in turn purchase more inputs. The multiplier effect of this initial expenditure can result in the total increase in household incomes being much greater than the original expenditure. A good example of the multiplier effect at work in the UK is provided by the Millennium Dome project at Greenwich, opened in 2000 (now known as the O_2). An important reason for the government supporting this project was the desire to regenerate an economically depressed part of London. Government expenditure initially created expenditure during the construction of the Dome and from employment within the Dome itself. This expenditure then rippled out to other business sectors, such as hotels and transport. The level of activity generated additional demand for local manufacturing industry – for example, visitors require food that may be produced locally, the producers of which may in turn require additional building materials and services to increase production facilities. On an even larger scale, the Mayor of London, supported by central government, successfully bid to host the 2012 Olympic Games, largely on the basis of the multiplier benefits that would result.

The extent of the multiplier effects of initial expenditure is influenced by a number of factors. Crucial is the extent to which recipients of this initial investment recirculate it back into the national economy. If large parts of it are saved by households or used to buy imported goods (whether by firms or by households), the multiplier effects to an economy will be reduced. In general, income that is received by individuals that have a high propensity to spend each additional pound on basic necessities is likely to generate greater multiplier benefits than the same money received by higher-income households that have a greater propensity to save it or to spend it on imported luxuries. The implications of this for government macroeconomic policy will be considered later.

The multiplier effect can be used to analyse the effects of withdrawals from the circular flow as well as injections. Therefore, if firms spend less on wages, household income will fall as a direct result, leading indirectly to lower spending by households with other domestic firms. These firms will in turn pay less to households in wages, leading to a further reduction in spending with firms, and so on.

Multiplier effects can be studied at a local as well as a national level. Government capital expenditure is often used with a view to stimulating areas of severe unemployment (as in the case of the Millennium Dome and grants given by Regional Development Agencies to support private-sector investment in Tyneside). The presence of a university in a town usually generates strong multiplier benefits – for example, one study in Wales estimated that the university in Newport, with a turnover of around £30 million per annum, and employing between 800 and 900 people, generated multiplier benefits to the local economy of around £80 million per annum in 2000. However, whether the local economy is helped will depend upon how much subsequent expenditure is retained within the area. In a study of the regional multiplier effects of siting a call centre for British Airways in a deprived part of Tyneside, it was found that a high proportion of the staff employed commuted in from other, more prosperous areas, thereby limiting the multiplier benefits to the deprived area.

As well as examining the general macroeconomic effects of spending by firms on household income, and vice versa, multiplier analysis can also be used to assess the impact of economic activity in one business sector upon other business sectors. Many economies suffer because vital economic infrastructure remains undeveloped, preventing productivity gains in other sectors. The availability of transport and distribution services has often had the effect of stimulating economic development at local and national levels – for example, following the improvement of rail or road services. The absence of these basic services can have a crippling effect on the development of the primary and manufacturing sectors – for instance, one reason for Russian agriculture not having been fully exploited has been the ineffective distribution system available to food producers.

One approach to understanding the contribution of one business sector to other sectors of the economy is to analyse input–output tables of production, and data on labour and capital inputs. In one study (Wood 1987), these were used to estimate the effects that productivity improvements in all the direct and indirect supply sectors had on the productivity levels of all other sectors. Thus, some apparently high-productivity sectors (such as chemicals) were shown to be held back by the low productivity of some of their inputs. On the other hand, efficiency improvements in some services, such as transport and distribution, were shown to have had widespread beneficial effects on the productivity contribution of other sectors. This is reflected in the common complaint among manufacturing businesses in the UK that their productivity is severely reduced by traffic congestion, which adds to their delivery costs and the costs of their supplies.

13.3.2 The accelerator effect

Changes in the demand for consumer goods can lead, through an **accelerator effect**, to a more pronounced change in the demand for capital goods. This accelerator effect occurs when, for instance, a small increase in consumer demand leads to a sudden large increase in demand for plant and machinery with which to satisfy that demand. When consumer demand falls by a small amount, demand for plant and machinery falls by a correspondingly larger amount.

The accelerator effect is best illustrated by reference to an example (Figure 13.4) based on consumers' demand for air travel and airlines' demands for new aircraft. In this simplified example, an airline operates a fleet of 100 aircraft and, during periods of stable passenger demand, buys ten new aircraft each year and retires ten older aircraft, retaining a stable fleet size of 100 aircraft. Then, some extraneous factor (e.g. a decline in the world economy) may cause the airline's passenger demand to fall by 3 per cent per annum. The airline responds to this by reducing its capacity by 3 per cent to 97 aircraft (we will assume, perhaps unrealistically, that it can reschedule its aircraft so that it is able to accommodate all its remaining passengers). The easiest way to achieve this is by reducing its annual order for aircraft from ten to seven. If it continued to retire its ten oldest aircraft, this would have the effect of reducing its fleet size to 97, in line with the new level of customer demand. What is of importance here is that while consumer demand has gone down by just 3 per cent, the demand facing the aircraft manufacturer has gone down by 30 per cent (from ten aircraft a year to seven). If passenger demand settles down at its new level, the airline will have no need to cut its fleet any further, so will revert to buying ten new aircraft a year and selling ten old ones. If passenger demand

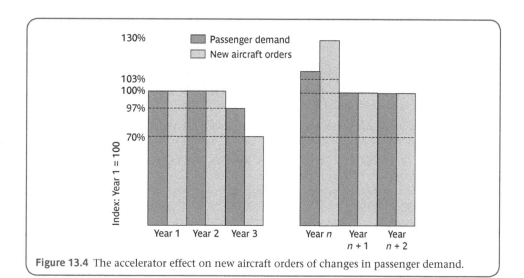

Figure 13.4 The accelerator effect on new aircraft orders of changes in passenger demand.

picks up once more, the airline may seek to increase its capacity by ordering not ten aircraft but, say, 13.

13.3.3 Inflation

It should be apparent that multiplier effects are associated with injections to the circular flow of income, causing more money to chase a fixed volume of goods and services available for consumption. This leads to the classic case of demand-pull **inflation**, when excessive demand for goods and services relative to their supply results in an increase in their market price level. Demand-pull inflation can result from an increase in the availability of credit, excessive spending by government, and tax cuts that increase consumers' disposable incomes, so allowing them to buy more goods and services.

An alternative cause of inflation is referred to as cost-push inflation. On the supply side, increases in production costs (such as higher wage costs, rising raw material costs, higher overheads and additional costs of health and safety legislation) may push up the price at which companies are prepared to supply their goods to the market, unless they are offset by increases in productivity.

An inflationary spiral can be created where higher wages in an economy result in greater spending power, leading to demand-pull inflation. The resulting higher cost of consumer goods leads workers to seek wage increases to keep them ahead of inflation, but these increases in wage costs add a further twist to cost-push inflation, and so on. Because markets are seldom perfectly competitive and therefore unable to correct for inflation, governments are keen to intervene to prevent inflationary processes building up in an economy (see below). The opposite of inflation – deflation – can occur where money is taken out of the circular flow, and a cycle can be created of falling prices for goods and services leading to lower income for households, resulting in turn to lower demand for goods and services, which causes their price to fall further.

13.3.4 Complex models of the economy

The simple **model** of the economy presented above is based on many assumptions, which need to be better understood if model making is to make a useful contribution to policy making. It is important for governments to have a reasonably accurate model of how the economy works so that predictions can be made about the effects of government policy. A model should be able to answer such questions as the following.

- What will happen to unemployment if government capital expenditure is increased by 10 per cent?
- What will happen to inflation if income tax is cut by 2p in the pound?
- What will be the net effect on government revenue if it grants tax concessions to firms investing in new capital equipment?

Companies supplying goods and services also take a keen interest in models of the economy, typically seeking to answer questions such as the following.

- What effect will a cut in income tax have on demand for new car purchases by private consumers?
- How will company buyers of office equipment respond to reductions in taxation on company profits?
- Will the annual budget create a feeling of confidence on the part of consumers, which is sufficiently strong for them to make major household purchases?

Developing a model of the economy is very different from developing a model in the natural sciences. In the latter case, it is often possible to develop closed models where all factors that can affect a system of interrelated elements are identifiable and can be measured. Predicting behaviour for any component of the model is therefore possible, based on knowledge about all other components. In the case of economic models, the system of interrelated components is open rather than closed. This means that not only is it difficult to measure components, but it can also be difficult to identify what elements to include as being of significance to a national economy. For example, few models accurately predicted that a sudden rise in oil prices by OPEC producers would have a major effect on national economies throughout the world. Furthermore, it is very difficult to develop relationships between variables that remain constant through time. Whereas the relationship between molecules in a chemistry model may be universally true, given a set of environmental conditions, such universal truths are seldom found in economic modelling. This has a lot to do with the importance of the attitudes of firms and consumers, which change through time for reasons that may not become clear until after the event. For example, a 2 per cent cut in income tax may have achieved significant increases in consumer expenditure on one occasion, but resulted in higher levels of savings or debt repayment on another. The first time round, factors as ephemeral as good weather and national success in an international football championship could have created a 'feel good' factor that was absent the next time round.

13.4 The business cycle

From the discussion in the previous sections, it should become quite apparent that national economies are seldom in a stable state. The situation where injections exactly equate with withdrawals can be described as a special case, with the normal state of affairs being for one of these to exceed the other. An excess of injections will result in economic activity increasing, while the opposite will happen if withdrawals exceed injections. This leads to the concept of the **business cycle**, which describes the fluctuating level of activity in an economy. Most developed economies go through cycles that have been described as:

- recession–prosperity
- expansion–contraction
- stop–go, and
- 'boom and bust'.

Business cycles vary in their length, and also in the difference between the top of the cycle and the bottom. Sometimes a fall in economic activity may be hardly noticed and rapidly self-correcting. At other times, such as the Great Depression of the 1930s, the depression can be long and deep. The descent into a recessionary phase can be quite rapid, as occurred in many western countries in 2008. Figure 13.5 shows the pattern of the business cycle for the UK, as measured by fluctuations in the most commonly used indicator of economic activity – gross domestic product (described below). Of course, it is relatively easy to draw such a graph with hindsight, but much more difficult to predict which way the graph is going to move next. In 2008, many economists were predicting a very long recession, but within two years, many indices of economic prosperity had already begun to improve.

13.4.1 Measuring economic activity

Gross domestic product (GDP) is just one indicator of the business cycle. In fact, there are many indicators of economic activity that may move at slightly different times to each other. Some 'leading' indicators may be used as early warning signs of an approaching economic recession or boom, with other indicators – if not corrected by government intervention – following a similar trend in due course. Some of the more commonly used indicators of the business cycle are described below.

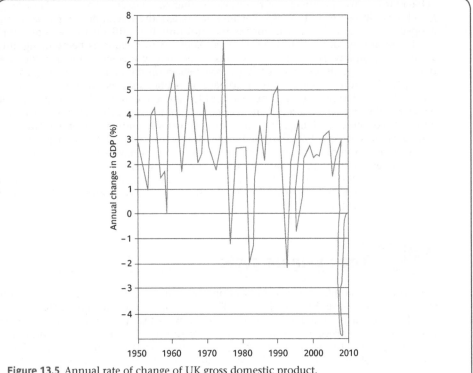

Figure 13.5 Annual rate of change of UK gross domestic product.

Source: based on *Annual Abstract of Statistics, London, Office for National statistics.*

Gross domestic product

This index measures the total value of goods and services produced within the economy, and can be used to compare economic performance over time and to compare performance between countries (see Figure 13.6). In a typical year, the economies of western European countries may expand by 2–3 per cent per annum, although this has reached 4–5 per cent in boom years, while GDP has fallen during recessionary periods. Much more rapid growth in GDP has been seen in emerging economies, such as China, where annual growth in GDP in the early years of the twenty-first century was averaging about 9 per cent a year. One derivative of the crude GDP figure is a figure for GDP per capita. Therefore, if GDP is going up by 2 per cent a year and the population is constant, it means that, on average, everybody is 2 per cent better off. Whether this is true in reality, of course, depends not only on how the additional income is distributed but also on an individual's definition of being better off (GDP takes no account of 'quality of life'). Since GDP depends on both prices and quantities, an increase in prices will also increase GDP (this is also referred to as nominal GDP). This is not a particularly good measure of economic well-being, so a GDP deflator removes the effects of price changes by calculating real GDP, expressed using a constant set of prices.

Unemployment rates

Because of the profound social and economic implications of high levels of **unemployment**, governments normally monitor changes in unemployment levels closely. Unemployment

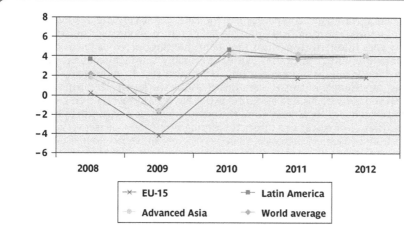

Figure 13.6 A comparison of GDP percentage annual growth rates for selected regions 2008–2012.

Source: IMF World Economic Outlook Database, October 2010; Eurostat; World Bank staff calculations.

Note: Advanced Asia refers to Korea, Hong Kong, Taiwan, and Singapore. Latin America refers to Latin America and the Caribbean. Figures for 2010, 2011 and 2012 are estimates made in 2009.

tends to rise as the economy enters a general economic recession and falls as it enters a period of recovery, although it typically lags behind changes in GDP. Unemployment occurs where firms are unable to sell their output and seek to scale back their workforce, either by laying off existing workers or not recruiting new ones. This results in less spending by the growing number of unemployed people, thereby exacerbating firms' sales difficulties. Actually measuring trends in unemployment over time can be difficult, as definitions used by governments frequently change. Cynics would say that this is done to hide the true level of unemployment – for example, by excluding people that are on job-training schemes.

Output levels

The output of firms is an important indicator of the business cycle, and is closely watched because of its effects on employment, and the multiplier effects of firms producing less and therefore spending less with their suppliers. In the UK, the government's Business Monitor publishes regular indicators of outputs for different sectors. Another widely quoted source of data on output is the Confederation of British Industry (CBI), which publishes monthly and quarterly surveys on industry's output, investment and stock levels. This provides a good indication of changes in different sectors of the economy, and possible future business trends. In addition to these widely used and formalized methods of measuring output, a number of ad hoc approaches have been used, which it is claimed give early indicators of an economic recovery or downturn. Examples include the following.

- Sales of first-class tickets by train operating companies, where a fall in sales is often an early indication of firms cutting back expenditure ahead of major cuts in output.
- The number of commercial vehicles crossing the Severn Bridge between England and Wales has been correlated with the output of the manufacturing sector in general.
- Rising sales of Ford Transit vans have been associated with a revival in fortunes by the small business sector, and rising sales of heavy trucks with growing confidence by firms to invest in capital equipment.

Stocks

During periods of boom, companies may be able to sell very quickly everything that they produce – indeed, waiting lists for some sought-after goods may by common. When the economy goes into recession, firms may continue their previous levels of production, and may not reduce output until they can be reasonably confident that the fall in demand for their products is not just a transient blip, but indicative of a more general slowdown in the economy. An example of this was seen with Scania trucks, which during the boom years of the 1990s and early 2000s had a waiting list of buyers. However, when recession set in from 2008, buyers reduced their orders and the company was left with stocks of unsold trucks.

The existence of stocks can affect the timing and extent of recovery in output. Even if demand from consumers increases, there may be no immediate increase in output by firms that may initially meet customer demands from stocks and increase their output level only when stocks decline to a normal level.

Average earnings

Unemployment figures record the extreme case of workers that have no employment. However, underemployment can affect the national economy just as significantly as unemployment, as workers are put on short-time working or lose opportunities for overtime working. Conversely, average earnings may rise significantly during the early years of a boom as firms increase overtime working and bid up wage rates in an attempt to take on staff with key skills. As the economies of many developed economies went into recession from 2008, there is a suggestion that many employers and trades unions agreed to reduce working hours, and hence the earnings of workers, rather than reduce the total workforce. One advantage of this approach is that companies could rapidly expand when demand improved, rather than having to wait to recruit new staff.

Disposable income

Average disposable income refers to the income that individuals have available to spend after taxation. It follows that, as taxes rise, disposable income falls. A further indicator of household wealth is discretionary income, which is a measure of disposable income less expenditure on the necessities of life, such as mortgage payments. Discretionary income can be significantly affected by sudden changes in the cost of mortgages and other items of expenditure, such as travel costs, which form a large component of household budgets.

Consumer spending

Trends in consumer spending may diverge from trends in discretionary income on account of changes in consumers' propensity to borrow or save. When consumer spending runs ahead of discretionary income, this can be explained by an increase in borrowing. Conversely, spending may fall faster than discretionary income, indicating that consumers are repaying debts and/or not borrowing additional money. There are numerous indicators of consumer spending, including the government's Family Expenditure Survey. More up-to-date information is supplied by the Credit Card Research Group (CCRG), an organization representing the main UK credit card issuers. After making a number of assumptions about changing card-using habits, CCRG is able to monitor changes in the volume of consumer spending using credit cards. It is also able to monitor consumer borrowing using credit cards and net repayments of credit card debts.

Savings ratio

The savings ratio refers to the proportion of individuals' income that is saved rather than spent. Saving/borrowing levels are influenced by a number of factors, including the distribution of income in society (poorer people tend to save less, therefore any redistribution of income to this group would have the effect of reducing net savings) and consumers' level of confidence about the future (see below). During periods of high consumer confidence, savings ratios tend to fall as consumer borrowing rises. During the period 1970–2008, the average household savings ratio was 7.6 per cent. It had fallen steadily during the boom years of the 2000s and reached 2.0 per cent in 2008, before rising again as the economy went into recession and households became reluctant to take on new debt and repaid old debt. Businesses look to a fall in savings ratios as an early indicator of increasing consumer confidence.

Confidence levels

Private individuals and businesses may have a high level of income and savings, but there is no guarantee that they will spend that money or take on new debt in making purchases of expensive items. They may only be happy about making major spending decisions if they feel confident about the future. Higher confidence levels may result, for example, from consumers feeling that they are not likely to be made unemployed, that their pay is going to keep up with inflation and that the value of their assets is not going to fall. A number of confidence indices are now published – for example, by Chambers of Commerce and the CBI, covering both private consumers and businesses. The organization GfK publishes a monthly Consumer Confidence Barometer for the European Commission.

Inflation rate

Inflation refers to the rate at which prices of goods and services in an economy are rising. It is not easy to measure inflation , as the effect of rising prices affects different groups of people in different ways. In the UK, there are two commonly used measures of inflation: the Consumer Prices Index (CPI) and the Retail Prices Index (RPI). The CPI is derived from a European measure of inflation. Like the RPI, it is based on information collected about the prices of goods and services consumed by an average household. These are commonly used 'headline' rates of inflation, which are frequently used by employees as a basis for wage negotiations and by the UK government for adjusting the value of a number of social security benefits.

A problem with general indices such as the CPI and RPI is that they may be too general to be of relevance to the spending patterns of specific groups of individuals. An average figure may mask differences in component elements, resulting in different groups of consumers experiencing quite different levels of inflation. For example, during a period of rising property prices, rising property rental fees and falling interest rates, the inflation rate of home owners may be quite different to that experienced by those who rent their property. To provide more detail about what is happening to inflation, there are numerous alternative indices covering specific sectors. Many building societies, for example, produce indices of house price inflation, while specialized indices are available for new car purchases and construction costs, among others. The government publishes a monthly producer prices index, which measures changes in the prices of goods bought by manufacturing firms. A rise in this indicator can signal later increases in the CPI when the components are incorporated into finished goods bought by households.

A 'normal' level of inflation is often considered to lie in the range of 1–3 per cent per annum. Where prices are falling, the opposite case of deflation occurs, which can have economic consequences just as serious as very high inflation. For several years from the mid-1990s, the Japanese economy experienced deflation, resulting in a reluctance of people to invest. Why invest today in an asset that will be cheaper in a year's time? Such attitudes can lead to a self-fulfilling prophecy. During the early years of recession from 2008, deflation occurred briefly in a number of west European countries.

Interest rates

Interest rates represent the price that borrowers have to pay to a lender for the privilege of using their money for a specified period of time. Interest rates tend to follow a cyclical pattern, which is partly a reflection of the level of activity in the economy. During periods of recession, the supply of funds typically exceeds demand for them (caused, for example, by consumers being reluctant to spend, thereby building up their savings, and by the unwillingness of consumers and firms to borrow to pay for major expenditure items). In these circumstances, interest rates have a tendency to fall. During a period of economic prosperity, the opposite holds true, and interest rates have a tendency to rise. Rates are also influenced by government intervention, as governments have frequently used them as a tool of economic management. In general, low interest rates are seen as desirable because they reduce the cost of firms' borrowings and increase consumers' level of discretionary income, especially through lower mortgage costs. However, during periods of unhealthily excessive demand in the economy, governments use high interest rates to try to dampen down demand from firms and consumers.

Overseas trade figures

The monthly overseas trade figures indicate the difference between a country's imports and exports. A lot of attention is given to the 'current account', which measures overseas transactions in goods and services but not capital (discussed further in Chapter 14). In general, a current account surplus is considered good for an economy, suggesting that an economy's production sector is internationally competitive. A detailed analysis of overseas trade figures indicates trends that can often be related to the business cycle and can be used to predict future levels of activity in the economy. At the height of a boom cycle, imports of manufactured goods may rise much faster than corresponding exports, possibly suggesting unsustainable levels of household consumption. Rising imports of capital equipment may give an indication that firms are ready to invest in additional domestic productive capacity following the end of a period of recession.

Exchange rates

The exchange rate is the price of one currency in terms of another (e.g. an exchange rate of £1 = $1.55 means that £1 costs $1.55). A number of factors influence the level of a country's exchange rate, but as an economic indicator the rate is often seen as an indication of the willingness of overseas traders and investors to hold that country's currency. Falling rates of exchange against other currencies may be interpreted as overseas investors losing their confidence in an economy or its government, leading them to sell their currency holdings and thereby depressing its price. The theory of exchange rate determination and the implications for business are discussed in more detail in Chapter 14.

Government borrowing

During periods of economic prosperity, government income streams from taxation tend to be buoyant, while many of its costs in respect of social welfare payment may be reduced, on account of lower levels of unemployment. The reverse tends to be true during periods of economic recession. In this sense, government borrowing is not so much an indicator of the business cycle, but rather a consequence of it. In the UK, national debt as a percentage of GDP fell steadily from 40 per cent in 1997 to 29 per cent by 2002, helped by buoyant tax receipts during a period of economic prosperity, which allowed the government to pay off debt. It then rose to 37 per cent in 2007, reflecting the government's decision to increase expenditure on health and education. Then, national debt as a percentage of GDP increased from 30 per cent in 2002 to 37 per cent in 2007. After 2008, government debt increased to a historic high of 64 per cent of GDP. This sharp increase was brought about by a combination of normal increases in expenditure associated with the onset of recession (higher spending on unemployment and welfare benefits, lower taxation revenue, etc.), but, exceptionally in this case, by government borrowing to rescue private-sector banks (Northern Rock, Lloyds TSB and Royal Bank of Scotland).

13.4.2 Tracking the business cycle

It is easy to plot business cycles with hindsight. However, businesses are much more interested in predicting the cyclical pattern in the immediate and medium-term future. If the economy is at the bottom of an economic recession, it is the ideal time for firms to begin investing in new productive capacity. In this case, accurate timing of new investment can have two important benefits.

1 Firms will be able to cope with demand as soon as the economy picks up. At the end of previous economic recessions, demand has often initially outstripped the restricted supply, leading many domestic firms and consumers to buy from overseas. Firms have often invested in new capacity only once overseas competitors have built up market share, and possibly created some long-term customer loyalty too.

2 At the bottom of the business cycle, resource inputs tend to be relatively cheap. This particularly affects wage costs and the price of basic raw materials such as building materials. Good timing can allow a firm to create new capacity at a much lower cost than it would incur if it waited until it was well into the upturn, when rising demand would push up resource costs.

Analysing **turning points** in the business cycle has therefore become crucial to marketers. To miss an upturn at the bottom of the recession can result in a firm missing out on opportunities when the recovery comes to fruition. On the other hand, reacting to a false signal can leave a firm with expensive excess stocks and capacity on its hands. A similar problem of excess capacity can result when a firm fails to spot the downturn at the top of the business cycle. It is extremely difficult to identify a turning point at the time it is happening. Unfortunately, it can be difficult to tell immediately whether a change is a short-term blip or part of a long-term trend. After a period of recession, a slight improvement in GDP could be interpreted as the start of a sustained economic recovery, or it could reflect restocking by firms with no significant long-term increase in demand from customers. Politicians are often keen to point to 'green shoots of recovery' in the hope that they will generate a feel-good factor and become a self-fulfilling prophecy. If the government doesn't believe that the economy is about to get better, why should consumers or investors?

Firms try to react to turning points as closely as possible in a number of ways.

■ Companies that are highly dependent on the business cycle frequently subscribe to the services of firms that have developed complex models of the economy and are able to make predictions about future economic performance. Some of these models (such as those developed by major firms of stockbrokers) are general in their application and based on models of the economy used by government policy makers in the Treasury. Specialized models seek to predict demand for more narrowly defined sectors, such as construction.

■ Companies can be guided by key lead indicators, which have historically been a precursor of a change in activity levels for the business sector. For a company manufacturing heavy trucks, the level of attendance at major truck trade exhibitions could indicate the number of buyers that are at the initial stages in the buying process for new trucks.

■ Instead of placing all their hopes in accurate forecasts of the economy, companies can place greater emphasis on ensuring that they are able to respond to economic change very rapidly when it occurs. At the bottom of the cycle, this can be facilitated by developing flexible production methods – for example, by retaining a list of trained part-time staff that can be called on at short notice, or having facilities to acquire excess capacity from collaborating firms overseas at very short notice. At the top of the cycle, the use of short-term contracts of employment can help a company to downsize rapidly at minimum cost. The development of 'efficient customer response' systems seeks to simplify supply chains so that orders can be fulfilled rapidly without the need to carry large stockholdings.

⟳ Thinking around the subject

Boom and bust for ever?

Throughout much of the later 1990s, growth of the US economy seemed almost unstoppable. In Britain it was described as the 'nice' decade (nice was an acronym for 'non inflationary continuous expansion'). Many people thought that this the dawn of a 'new economy' in which governments had managed to manipulate economies so effectively that the historical pattern of 'boom and bust' had become a thing of the past? Sadly, by 2007, the UK and US economies seemed to be coming back down to earth. By 2008, it seemed that the whole economy had gone into meltdown as share prices crashed, banks refused to lend to each other and GDP in most countries fell.

What causes such long and sustained booms, such as the UK and US economies had just enjoyed? Can we learn anything from previous booms that might help us to understand future business cycles?

The economic historian Angus Maddison undertook an analysis of the world economy over the past millennium and noted just three periods of rapid advance in incomes per head. The most rapid occurred from 1950 to 1973, when average global real incomes per head rose at a compound annual rate of 2.9 per cent. The other two periods were 1870–1913 and 1973 onwards. In the latter two periods, average real incomes per head rose at a compound average annual rate of 1.3 per cent.

Interestingly, these periods of prolonged economic boom appeared to have three things in common.

1 Each of these periods was associated with a process of rapid international economic integration, with trade and global capital flows growing faster than world output – for example, between 1973 and 1998, world exports rose from 10.5 per cent of world GDP to 17.2 per cent.

2 All three periods were associated with significant catching up by laggard economies with world-leading economies. Between 1870 and 1913, the catching up was by western Europe, the USA and some former European colonies, on the UK; between 1950 and 1973, it was by western Europe, Japan and a few small east Asian countries, on the USA; and from 1973, it was by much of the rest of Asia (including China), again on the USA. It was noted that the bigger the gap between the laggards and the leaders, the faster the rate of convergence has been.

3 The final feature of these periods has been a historically unprecedented rate of technological advance, generating rising real incomes per head in the world's most advanced economies.

The declining costs of transport and communications undoubtedly lie behind much of the development of the global economy over the last several centuries. The internet should be seen as just the latest innovation that continues a long historical sequence.

But what about the future? Over the past couple of decades, the world's two most populous countries, China and India, with 2.25 billion people between them (or just under 40 per cent of the total world population), have been growing faster than both the world as a whole and its economic leaders. Should this lead us to believe that economic growth will continue? Can the rate of technological advance be sustained? Between 1973 and 1995, the rate of US growth in labour productivity per hour fell to just under 1.5 per cent a year, from 3 per cent between 1950 and 1973. Even with the development of the internet, are rates of growth in productivity sustainable? Looking ahead, what new scientific and technological advances are likely to sustain a continued growth in productivity?

Thinking around the subject

Telltale signs of the recession around the home

Forget high-level statistics of GDP as an indicator of the economic prosperity of a nation. Just look at what is happening in your local high street and you will get an idea about whether consumers are feeling prosperous or digging in for a recession. In 2009, the research agency TrendSpotting (www.trendspotting.com) compiled a list of indicators that might help us to tell where we are in the business cycle. Among its findings was a lot of detail about how our spending patterns change as the economy goes into recession.

- Rather than eating out, many households choose to eat in. Sales of supermarkets' restaurant-style 'dine in for £10' meals boomed. Sales of cookbooks and basic ingredients increased. The supermarket chain Morrisons reported a 54 per cent year-on-year increase in sales of cake mix. At Waitrose, sales of essential herbs, oils and stocks were up 21 per cent, and the retailer stopped selling DVDs and CDs to increase sales space for its kitchen pans, knives and baking trays.

- When eating out, one in four people would rather eat cheaply than healthily, according to a *Which?* survey. Sales at McDonald's and KFC did not appear to be badly hurt by the recession, but consumption of fresh vegetables fell by 12 per cent.

- Shoppers had become more cautious, and this was reflected in a 20 per cent increase in the use of shopping lists, a tactic that could reduce the temptation to purchase goods on impulse. Shoppers had also become more canny in their use of discount vouchers cut from newspapers, up by 143 per cent at Christmas 2008 compared with the previous year.

- Fashion retailers noticed a change as consumers turned from high-profile fashion brands to retailers' own brands. Some even gave up buying clothes completely, and it was reported that knitting clubs had become popular and sales of sewing machines at John Lewis were up by 34 per cent.

- The nation's holiday habits were changing, with a rise in the number of people staying at home and having a 'staycation'. Rather than spending a lot of money getting a tan in the Caribbean, many chose a fake tan instead, and sales of fake tan brand St Tropez shot up 20 per cent in a year.

- A survey by Unilever revealed how the recession had affected life in the bathroom, when it reported that sales of shower gel had increased while those of bubble bath had fallen, the assumption being that showers are thriftier.

This examination of the minutiae of life might give some insight into the state of national prosperity. Changes in sales of some products might even be a lead indicator of changes in the business cycle – for example, if bubble bath sales start increasing again at the expense of shower gels, is this a sign that consumers are feeling more confident and likely to venture out to the shops to buy bigger-ticket items?

Of course, like all simple indicators, too much can be read in to those reported above. The onset of recession in 2008 coincided with increasing ecological concerns, so is being thrifty with clothes, water or energy a manifestation of economic recession or new-found concern for the ecological environment? If they are to be used as indicators of economic performance, they must assume that all other factors remain unchanged. The problem in the real world of economics is that it can be very unrealistic to assume that everything else remains unchanged – in the dynamic environment, economic change is usually associated with a wide range of social, political and technological change.

13.5 Macroeconomic policy

The national economy has been presented as a complex system of interrelated component parts. To free-market purists, the system should be self-correcting and need no intervention from governments. In reality, national economies are not closed entities and equilibrium in the circular flow can be put out of balance for a number of reasons, such as:

- increasing levels of competition in the domestic market from overseas firms that have gained a cost advantage
- changes in a country's ratio of workers to non-workers (e.g. the young and elderly)
- investment in new technology, which may replace firms' expenditure on domestic wages with payments for capital and interest to overseas companies.

Most western governments have accepted that the social consequences of free market solutions to economic management are unacceptable and they therefore intervene to manage the economy to a greater or lesser extent.

13.5.1 Policy objectives

This section begins by reviewing the objectives governments seek to achieve in their management of the national economy.

Maintaining employment

However unemployment is defined, its existence represents a waste of resources in an economy. Individuals who have the ability and willingness to work are unable to do so because there is no demand from employers for their skills. Workers' services are highly perishable in that, unlike stocks of goods, they cannot be accumulated for use when the economy picks up. Time spent by workers unemployed is an economic resource that is lost for ever. Most developed economies recognize that unemployed people must receive at least the basic means of sustenance, so governments provide unemployment benefit. Rising unemployment increases government expenditure. As well as representing a wasted economic resource, unemployment has been associated with widespread social problems, including crime, alcoholism and drug abuse. High levels of unemployment can create a divided society, with unemployed people feeling cut off from the values of society, while those in employment perceive many unemployed people as being lazy or unwilling to work.

In general, governments of all political persuasions seek to keep unemployment levels low in order to avoid the social and economic problems described above. However, many suspect that governments with right-wing sympathies are more likely to tolerate unemployment on the grounds that a certain amount of unemployment can bring discipline to a labour market that could otherwise give too much economic bargaining power to workers. An excess of labour supply over demand would result in wages paid to workers falling, at least in a free market. This may itself be seen as a desirable policy objective by lowering prices for consumers and increasing firms' competitiveness in international markets.

In their attempts to reduce unemployment, governments must recognize three different types of unemployment, each requiring a different solution.

1 Structural unemployment occurs where jobs are lost by firms whose goods or services are no longer in demand. This could come about through changing fashions and tastes (e.g. unemployment caused by the closure of many traditional UK seaside hotels); because of competition from overseas (for example, many jobs in the textile, shipbuilding and coal-mining industries have been lost to lower-cost overseas suppliers); or a combination of these factors. Where a local or national economy is very dependent upon one business

sector and workers' skills are quite specific to that sector, the effects of structural employment can be quite severe, as can be seen in the former shipbuilding areas of Tyneside or coal-mining areas of South Wales. Governments have tackled structural employment with economic assistance to provide retraining for unemployed workers and to attract new employers to areas of high unemployment.

2 Cyclical unemployment is associated with the business cycle and is caused by a general fall in demand, which may itself be a consequence of lower spending levels by firms. Some business sectors, such as building and construction, are particularly prone to cyclical patterns of demand, and hence cyclical unemployment. The long-term cure for cyclical employment is a pick-up in demand in the economy, which governments can influence through their macroeconomic policy.

3 Technological unemployment occurs where jobs are replaced by machines; it has had widespread implications in many industrial sectors, such as car manufacture, banking and agriculture. Governments have to accept this cause of unemployment, as failure to modernize will inevitably result in an industry losing out to more efficient competition. For this reason, attempts to subsidize jobs in declining low-technology industries are normally doomed as overseas competitors gain market share, and eventually lead to job losses that are greater than they would have been had technology issues been addressed earlier. Where a low-technology sector is supported by import controls, consumers will be forced to pay higher prices than would otherwise be necessary. Where the goods or services in question are necessities of life, consumers' discretionary income will effectively fall, leading to lower demand for goods and services elsewhere in the economy. Although technological unemployment may be very painful to the individuals directly involved, the increasing use of technology usually has the effect of making necessities cheaper, thereby allowing consumers to demand new goods and services. One manifestation of this has been the growth in services jobs, as consumers switch part of their expenditure away from food and clothing (which have fallen in price in real terms) towards eating out and other leisure pursuits.

Stable prices

Rapidly rising or falling prices can be economically, socially and politically damaging to governments.

Rapidly rising prices (inflation) can cause the following problems.

- For businesses, it becomes difficult to plan ahead when selling prices and the cost of inputs in the future are not known. In many businesses, companies are expected to provide fixed prices for goods and services, which will be made and delivered in the future at unknown cost levels.

- Governments find budgeting difficult during periods of high inflation. Although many government revenues rise with inflation (e.g. value added tax), this may still leave an overall shortfall caused by higher costs of employing government workers and higher contract costs for new capital projects.

- Inflation can be socially divisive as those on fixed incomes (e.g. state pensioners) fall behind those individuals who are able to negotiate wage increases to compensate for inflation. Inflation also discriminates between individuals that own different types of assets. While some physical assets, such as housing, may keep up with inflation, financial assets may be eroded by inflation rates that exceed the rate of interest paid. In effect, borrowers may be subsidized by lenders.

- High levels of inflation can put exporters at a competitive disadvantage. If the inflation level of the UK is higher than that of competing nations, UK firms' goods will become more expensive to export, while the goods from a low-inflation country will be much more attractive to buyers in the UK, all other things being equal. This will have an adverse effect on UK producers and on the country's overseas balance of trade (assuming that there is no compensating change in exchange rates).

High levels of inflation can create uncertainty in the business environment, making firms reluctant to enter into long-term commitments. Failure to invest or reinvest can ultimately be damaging for the individual firm as well as the economy as a whole.

This is not to say that completely stable prices (i.e. a zero rate of inflation) are necessarily good for a national economy. A moderate level of price inflation encourages individuals and firms to invest in stocks, knowing that their assets will increase in value. A moderate level of inflation also facilitates the task of realigning prices by firms. A price reduction can be achieved simply by holding prices constant during a period of price inflation. Where price inflation causes uncertainty for firms purchasing raw materials, this uncertainty can often be overcome by purchasing on the 'futures' market. Such markets exist for a diverse range of commodities, such as oil, grain and metals, and allow a company to pay a fixed price for goods delivered at a specified time in the future, irrespective of whether the market price for that commodity has risen or fallen in the meantime.

The opposite of inflation is deflation, and this too can result in social, economic and political problems.

- Individuals and firms that own assets whose value is depreciating perceive that they have become poorer and adjust their spending patterns accordingly. In Britain during 2008/2009, many individuals saw their most important asset – their house – falling in value as part of a general fall in property prices. In extreme cases, individuals felt 'locked in' to their house as they had borrowed more to buy it than the house was currently worth. They therefore had difficulty trading up to a larger house, thereby possibly also creating demand for home-related items such as fitted kitchens. More generally, falling property prices undermined consumer confidence, in sharp contrast to the early 2000s when rising house prices created a 'feel good' factor, fuelling spending across a range of business sectors.
- Individuals and firms will be reluctant to invest in major items of capital expenditure if they feel that, by waiting a little longer, they could obtain those assets at a lower price.
- Deflation can become just as socially divisive as inflation. Falling house prices can lead many people who followed government and social pressures to buy their house rather than rent to feel that they have lost out for their efforts.

Economic growth

Growth is a goal shared by businesses and governments alike. It was suggested in Chapter 9 that businesses like to grow, for various reasons. Similarly, governments generally pursue growth in GDP for many reasons.

- A growing economy allows for steadily rising standards of living, when measured by conventional economic indicators. In most western economies, this is indicated by increased spending on goods and services that are considered luxuries. Without underlying growth in GDP, increases in consumer spending will be short-lived.
- For governments, growth results in higher levels of income through taxes on incomes, sales and profits. This income allows government to pursue socially and politically desirable infrastructure spending, such as the construction of new hospitals or road improvements.
- A growing economy creates a 'feel good' factor in which individuals feel confident about being able to obtain employment and subsequently feel confident about making major purchases.

Economic growth in itself may not necessarily leave a society feeling better off, as economic well-being does not necessarily correspond to quality of life. There is growing debate about whether some of the consequences of economic growth, such as increased levels of pollution and traffic congestion, really leave individuals feeling better off. There is also the issue of how the results of economic growth are shared out between members of a society.

Thinking around the subject

Gross domestic product or gross national happiness?

A fairly universal indicator of how 'well' a country is doing is based on its index of gross gomestic product (GDP). There can be many adjustments to this figure – for example, by expressing it as GDP per capita or adjusting it for inflation. But, in recent years, there has been more fundamental questioning about whether the pursuit of higher levels of wealth expressed as GDP actually results in greater happiness for the citizens of a country. Even the newly elected UK Prime Minister, David Cameron, suggested that it was time the country concentrated not just on GDP but on GWB (general well-being).

The 'economics of happiness' has emerged as a new area of economics to challenge some of our assumptions about the performance of national economies. Naturally enough, when you get a group of economists together, you are likely to get as many views on the subject as there are economists. There is just as much debate about how you actually measure happiness, with suggestions for items to include in a National Happiness Index ranging from life expectancy to number and severity of mental illnesses and self-reported measures of happiness.

One question that is frequently asked is whether having more money makes people happier. One study reported in 2010 suggested that people's satisfaction with life generally increased as their income increased, but their day-to-day emotional well-being only rose with earnings up to an annual income of $75,000; beyond that level there was less effect (Holmes 2010).

One of the paradoxes of western developed economies is that, despite increased prosperity, people appear to be more stressed and increasingly unhappy. Despite better healthcare, rising incomes and labour-saving devices, surveys repeatedly show that people are no happier than they were in the 1950s. This seems far from the economist John Maynard Keynes' prediction in the 1930s that once the 'economic problem' of satisfying basic material needs was achieved, people would not have to work so hard and would devote their spare time to trying to live well.

People appear to be inconsistent in their statements about what would make them happy. They may say that a shorter travelling time to work would make them happy, yet more and more people travel longer distances to their place of employment in order to work harder to earn more money for more goods that, in the end, do not make them feel any better.

One explanation for this apparent paradox is that people compare themselves to others. If everyone is getting richer, people do not get happier – they do so only if they get richer relative to their peers. A BMW 3 series car can be a status symbol only if few people can afford it. When incomes rise and more people can afford the luxury brand, individuals become motivated to work harder to afford an even better model. This mechanism is a driving force behind economic growth, but it has the effect of constantly undermining the underlying benefit of economic progress.

Politicians tend to focus on economic growth figures, but should they instead be concentrating more on indices of happiness? Indices of depression and mental illness have been rising sharply in most western countries in the past couple of decades, and seem to be closely correlated with economic growth, and it has been argued that investment in therapy can yield more happiness than conventional economic investments (Boyce and Wood 2010) . According to Lord Layard, author of a book on happiness, one in six people in the UK is thought to suffer from some form of mental illness. He has argued that a course of cognitive behavioural therapy (CBT) can alleviate depression in 60 per cent of cases and typically costs about £1000. Is £1000 spent on relieving someone's depression, so they benefit in terms of happiness, a better investment by the government than £1000 spent increasing the competitiveness and efficiency of manufacturing industry?

Distribution of wealth

Left to market forces, it is likely that inequalities in wealth will be exacerbated as the wealthy use their dominant position to gather even more wealth, while the poor become relatively powerless and even poorer. This seems to have been true historically, and even today, countries with newly marketized economies, such as those of eastern Europe, appear to become more divided between a small very wealthy group and the large mass of people who own very few assets. In the past, inequalities of wealth and power have resulted in revolution, when the masses have risen in revolt against the few who have the dominant wealth and power. It could be argued that, in order to avoid tensions within society, governments – overtly and covertly – have objectives relating to the distribution of economic wealth between different groups in society. In the UK, the trend since the Second World War has been for a gradual convergence in the prosperity of all groups, as the very rich have been hit by high levels of income, capital gains and inheritance tax, while the poorer groups in society have benefited from increasing levels of social security payments. During periods of Labour administrations, the tendency has been for taxes on the rich to increase, tilting the distribution of wealth in favour of poorer groups. However, the period of the Conservative governments in the 1980s saw this process put into reverse as high-income groups benefited from the abolition of higher rates of income tax and the liberalization of inheritance taxes. At the same time, many social security benefits were withdrawn or reduced in scope or amount, leaving many lower- or middle-income groups worse off. Actually measuring distribution of wealth has been difficult with a variety of possible indicators. There has been argument about whether the post-1997 Labour government in the UK actually managed to redistribute wealth from the rich to the poor, and many indicators suggested that the reverse had actually happened.

The effects of government policy objectives on the distribution of income can have profound implications for an organization's marketing activities. During most of the post-war years, the tendency was for mid-market segments to grow significantly. In the car sector, this was associated with the success of mid-range cars such as the Ford Focus and Mondeo. During periods of Labour administration, the sale of luxury cars had tended to suffer. The boom of the late 1980s and early 2000s saw the rapid rise in income of the top groups in society, resulting in a significant growth in luxury car sales. Manufacturers such as BMW, Mercedes-Benz and Jaguar benefited from this trend.

Improving productivity

Productivity growth, alongside high and stable levels of employment, is central to long-term economic performance and rising living standards. Increasing the productivity of the economy has become a key objective of successive UK governments. Government approaches to improving long-term productivity have followed two broad strands: maintaining macroeconomic stability to enable firms and individuals to plan for the future, and implementing microeconomic reforms to remove the barriers that prevent markets from functioning efficiently. These microeconomic reforms address historic weaknesses in competitiveness, investment, research and development, innovation and entrepreneurship.

Stable exchange rate

A stable value of sterling in terms of other major currencies is useful to businesses that are thereby able to predict accurately the future cost of raw materials bought overseas and the sterling value they will receive for goods and services sold overseas. Stable exchange rates can also help consumers – for example, in budgeting for overseas holidays. It is, however, debatable just what the 'right' exchange rate is that governments should seek to maintain (this is discussed further in Chapter 14).

An important contributor to maintaining a stable exchange rate is the maintenance of the balance of payments. Governments avoid large trade deficits, which can have the effect of lowering the exchange rate. From a business perspective, balance of trade surpluses tend to benefit the economy through the creation of jobs, additional economic growth and a general feeling of business confidence. Surpluses created from overseas trade can be used to finance overseas lending and investment, which in turn generate higher levels of earnings from overseas in future years.

Government borrowing

Government borrowing represents the difference between what it receives in any given year from taxation and trading sources and what it needs in order to finance its expenditure programmes. The difference is often referred to as **public sector net borrowing (PSNB)**. The level of PSNB is partly influenced by political considerations, with right-wing free market advocates favouring a reduced role for the government, reflected in a low level of net borrowing. Advocates of intervention are happier to see the PSNB rise. Government borrowing tends to rise during periods of economic recession and fall during periods of boom. This can be explained by income (especially from income and profits taxes) rising relative to expenditure during a boom, and expenditure (especially on social security benefits) rising relative to income during a recession. Taxes and public spending tend to be quite cyclical, reflecting political ideology and the state of the national and international economy and trends, as discussed earlier (see Figure 13.7). Public-sector borrowing increased sharply in many countries following the banking crisis of 2008 when many governments borrowed money in order to support private-sector banks. In some cases, very high levels of government borrowing became unsustainable as lenders refused to lend to countries whose governments were considered to have excessive debt relative to their assets and earning power. This led many countries, such as Greece and Ireland, to implement emergency measures to cut public borrowing in order to satisfy the requirements of lenders who wanted reassurance that governments would not renege on their debts. Governments' efforts to cut public borrowing typically included raising taxes, reducing public-sector expenditure and selling off government-owned assets. Figure 13.7 shows a breakdown of total government budgeted income and expenditure by category for the year 2010–2011.

13.5.2 Government management of the economy

From government policy objectives come strategies by which these policy objectives can be achieved. This is an area where it can be possible to line up a dozen economists and get a dozen different answers to the same problem. Sometimes, political ideology can lead to the strategy being considered to be just as important as the policy objectives, with supporters of alternative strategies showing very strong allegiance to them.

In trying to reconcile multiple objectives, governments invariably face a dilemma in reconciling all of them simultaneously. Of the three principal economic objectives (maintaining employment, and controlling inflation and economic growth), satisfying objectives for any two invariably causes problems with the third (see Figure 13.8). It is therefore common for governments to shift their emphasis between policy objectives for political and pragmatic reasons. However, many surveys of business leaders have suggested that what they consider important above all else is stability in government policy. If the government continually changes the economic goalposts or its economic strategy, businesses' own planning processes can be thrown into confusion.

Sometimes, policy can be implemented in pursuit of one objective, only for adverse side effects to appear, leading to policy being directed to solving this second problem. During much of the 1990s, UK governments put the reduction in inflation as the top economic policy priority and achieved this through high interest rates and a strong value of sterling, among other things. However, high interest rates and a strong pound created recessionary conditions,

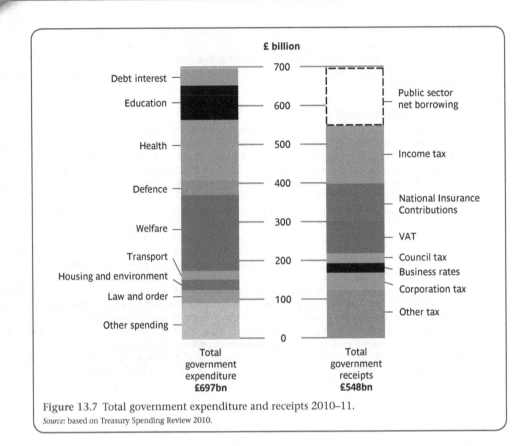

Figure 13.7 Total government expenditure and receipts 2010–11.
Source: based on Treasury Spending Review 2010.

signified by falling demand, rising unemployment and reduced levels of investment. Resolving these problems then became a priority for government policy.

Two commonly used approaches to economic management can be classified under the headings of:

1 *fiscal policy*, which concentrates on stimulating the economy through changes in government income and expenditure

2 *monetary policy*, which influences the circular flow of income by changes in the supply of money and interest rates.

Fiscal policy

Government is a major element of the circular flow of income, both as tax collector and as a source of expenditure for goods and services and payments to households. Increases in government spending have the effect of injecting additional income into the circular flow and, through the multiplier effect, thereby increasing the demand for goods and services. Reductions in government spending have the opposite effect. Changes in taxation can similarly affect the circular flow of income (e.g. a cut in income tax effectively injects more money into the economy).

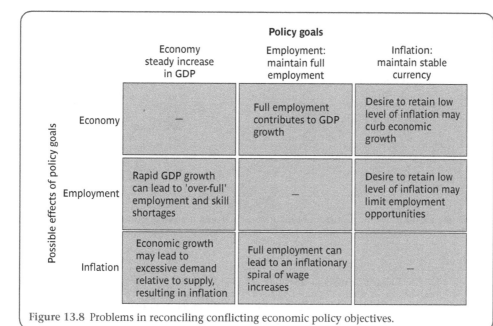

Figure 13.8 Problems in reconciling conflicting economic policy objectives.

The use of fiscal measures to regulate the economy achieved prominence with the economist John Maynard Keynes, whose followers are generally referred to as Keynsians. Keynes developed his ideas as a means of overcoming the high levels of unemployment and falling commodity prices that were associated with the Great Depression of the 1930s. Conventional economics had failed to return resource markets to equilibrium, largely because of rigidities that had built up in markets. Instead, Keynes advocated the use of fiscal policy to increase the level of aggregate demand within the economy. Through a multiplier effect, spending by workers employed on government 'pump-priming' projects would filter through to private-sector suppliers, who would in turn employ further workers, thereby eventually eradicating unemployment. If the economy showed signs of becoming too active, with scarcity in resource markets and rising price levels, suppression of demand through fiscal actions would have the effect of reducing inflationary pressures (Figure 13.9).

In the 1930s, fiscal measures were considered quite revolutionary and resulted in such projects as the electrification of railways and the construction of the National Grid being undertaken, not just for the end result but also for the multiplier benefits of carrying out the construction tasks. More recently, road-building and government-funded construction in general have been used as a regulator of the economy, on account of their high employment content and low levels of initial 'leakage' to imported supplies.

Critics of fiscal policy have argued that fiscal intervention is a very clumsy way of trying to return the economy to equilibrium and a method that achieves temporary rather than permanent solutions to underlying economic problems. Keynsian policies call for bureaucratic civil servants to make quasi-commercial decisions, which they are generally ill equipped to do. There is much evidence of failed fiscal policy at a local level where government grants and tax incentives have been given to attract industry to depressed areas, only for those industries to close down after a few years (e.g. car factories built in Northern Ireland, Merseyside and

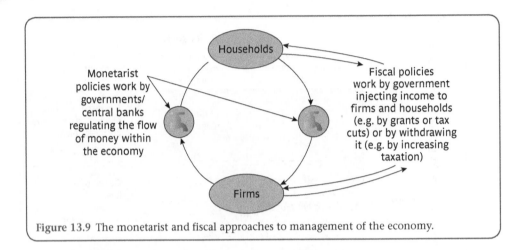

Figure 13.9 The monetarist and fiscal approaches to management of the economy.

Glasgow with government grants and tax concessions have often proved to be commercial failures). Many countries resorted to fiscal measures following the banking crisis of 2008 – for example, by reducing value added tax or giving grants to encourage consumers to purchase certain categories of product that are able to generate significant and rapid multiplier effects (see 'Thinking around the subject' for an example of one UK government fiscal imitative).

Critics of fiscal policy look to monetarist policies as an alternative.

⟳ Thinking around the subject

Money for old cars

When money is tight and buyers are fearful about the future, a new car is one purchase that can often be postponed, by businesses and private buyers alike. The car industry was a fairly early sector to suffer from the financial crisis of 2008. New car registrations in the UK fell sharply in the months after the collapse of Lehman Brothers, reaching just 112,000 new car registrations in January 2009, a 31 per cent fall compared to the same month one year previously. It seemed that car owners were using their cars less and, in 2009, the UK Department of Transport estimated that the average motorist drove 90 fewer miles than in the previous year. For the 34 million vehicles on Britain's roads, that was equivalent to 125,000 around-the-world trips, and the biggest decline in car use since records began. This may have been good for the environment, but one short-term consequence was that it had cost the government £165 million in reduced revenue from fuel duties. Furthermore, the Automobile Association (AA) reported that 52 per cent of drivers had consciously cut back on their car use and 67 per cent had changed the way they drove, typically driving slower to save fuel.

The car industry was facing a desperate plight and used arguments for fiscal stimulation to promote a plan for a 'car scrappage' scheme. Using this scheme, car owners who traded in a car over ten years old would receive a grant of £2000 towards a new one – half paid directly by the government and the other half by the industry. For government, the scheme was seen as a way of reviving economic activity in car dealers, manufacturers and component suppliers, and at the same time helping to get older, fuel-inefficient cars off the road and replaced with more efficient, environmentally friendly ones.

The scrappage scheme appeared to be a success with buyers, with over 400,000 old cars being traded in for new ones during 2009, bringing much needed activity back into car dealers' showrooms. Sales of small, fuel-efficient models were particularly popular with buyers. However, critics argued about just how successful the car scrappage scheme had been for the national economy, and even for the environment. It was pointed out that a high proportion of new cars purchased would have been manufactured in the Far East, bringing little benefit to the British economy. International trade rules prevented the government restricting grants to vehicles made in Britain or the EU. Environmentalists also challenged the green credentials of the scheme, pointing out that somebody could trade in a ten-year-old Ford Fiesta and buy a new gas-guzzling 4 × 4 vehicle.

The car scrappage scheme certainly helped to stimulate some aspects of the car industry that were facing a sharp decline in revenue and, in stimulating new car sales, generated some multiplier benefits through dealer networks and parts suppliers. However, critics pointed to the blunt nature of fiscal instruments such as the car scrappage scheme. Surely it had not been the intention of governments to encourage some buyers to purchase foreign-built 4 × 4 vehicles? Would many buyers of cars have purchased a new one anyway, therefore was the scrappage grant an unnecessary incentive and a waste of government money? And what was the cost of the paperwork associated with handling hundreds of thousands of claims? To the critics, this demonstrated the limitations of fiscal policy, compared to the simplicity of monetarist approaches to getting the economy going again.

Monetary policy

An alternative approach to managing the economy is through monetarist policies. Advocates of monetarism, including Adam Smith, Milton Friedman, Robert Lucas and Paul Samuelson, see money supply as the vital tool for managing the economy. The basic proposition of **monetarism** is that government need only regulate the supply of money in order to influence the circular flow of income. From this, adjustments in the economy happen automatically by market forces without the need for intervention by government in the running of business organizations. If government wishes to suppress demand in the economy, it would do this by restricting the volume of money in circulation in the economy. It could achieve this by raising interest rates, or by restricting the availability of credit. If it wished to stimulate the economy, in other words speed up the circular flow of income, it would increase the volume of money in circulation. Following the financial crisis of 2008, many governments adopted the monetarist strategy described as 'quantitative easing', but to some people it sounded more like 'printing money'. By this method, the central bank creates new money, which it uses to buy financial assets, including government bonds, mortgage-backed securities and corporate bonds, from banks and other financial institutions. The purchases give banks the excess reserves required for them to increase their lending capacity, and ultimately this leads to stimulation of the economy.

Monetarism appeals to free market purists because of the limited government hands-on intervention that is required. However, governments have found it politically unacceptable to pursue monetarist policies to their logical conclusion. For example, during a period of boom, suppressing demand by controlling the availability of money alone could result in unacceptably high levels of interest rates.

13.5.3 Limitations of government intervention in the national economy

At a practical level, critics of both monetarist and fiscal approaches to economic management have pointed to their failure to significantly influence the long-term performance of an economy. More recently, the fundamental concept of government intervention has been challenged in an emerging body of theoretical and empirical research, which is commonly referred to as rational expectations theory. Proponents of the theory claim that it is too simplistic to regard government economic intervention in terms of simple stimulus–response models. It is naive, for example, to assume that private companies will take an increase in government capital spending as a cue to increase their own productive capacity. Instead, firms rationally assess the likely consequences of government intervention. Therefore, an increase in government capital expenditure may lead to an expectation of eventually higher interest rates and inflation. Faced with this rational expectation, firms may decide to cut back their own expenditure, fearing the consequences for their own business of high inflation and interest rates. This is the opposite of the government's intended response. The theory of rational expectations holds that business people have become astute at interpreting economic signals and, because of this, government's ability to manage the national economy is significantly reduced.

13.5.4 The central bank

A nation's **central bank** plays an important role in the management of the national economy. In the UK, the Bank of England has responsibility for regulating the volume of currency in circulation within the economy. It was noted above that, following the credit crunch of 2008, the central banks in many countries intervened through a process of quantitative easing to create additional liquidity in national economies. The central bank has a duty to protect the stability of the banking sector. In 2007, the Bank of England was faced with the prospect of a major bank – Northern Rock – having to close down because it could not obtain ongoing credit to fund mortgages that it had lent to its domestic customers. This would have seriously affected the stability of the banking sector, and the reputation of the City of London as a financial centre, so the Bank of England intervened with emergency loans to the UK banking sector, effectively taking many of the banks into state control. When further banks failed, the Bank of England, along with the US Federal Reserve Bank and the European Central Bank, injected additional capital into the banking system in an attempt to lessen the effects of a credit shortage.

The central bank also has a role in maintaining the value of the nation's currency, which can be done by open-market operations – for example, selling the country's currency to keep its exchange rate low. Issues of exchange rate determination are discussed further in Chapter 14.

Countries differ in the extent to which the powers of the central bank are separated from those of government. In the USA, for example, granting the central bank quasi-autonomous status and allowing it freedom to make decisions on monetary policy has for a long time been regarded as a means of guaranteeing prudent management of the money supply against political intervention for possibly short-term opportunistic objectives. Against this, the argument is put forward that central banks should be politically accountable, and should be influenced by the social and political implications of their actions and not just the more narrowly defined monetary ones. In the UK, the Bank of England has traditionally been influenced by the Treasury, and seen to be effectively a branch of government decision making. However, the incoming Labour government in 1997 decided to give autonomy to much of the Bank's activity through a newly formed **Monetary Policy Committee (MPC)**, made up of a panel of eight economics experts plus the Governor of the Bank of England, who acts as Chair. The MPC is free to set interest rates at a level that it considers prudent and in the best interests of the country. Opinion remains divided on the relative merits of a politically influenced central bank and one that is above sectional political interests. While there is evidence that the MPC has acted with integrity, business leaders have sometimes accused it of being dominated by academics and financiers, who are unable to empathize with the problems faced by businesses. Employers' pressure groups, such as the CBI, feel less able to put pressure on the MPC than they previously could on Treasury ministers.

Throughout the EU, the development of a single currency has placed much greater control over monetary policy in the hands of the European Central Bank (ECB). The power of individual member states to determine their own interest rates and monetary policy is handed over to the ECB, which also handles member-states' currency reserves. The subject of the single European currency is discussed further in Chapter 14.

13.6 The international macroeconomic environment

So far, we have looked at the macroeconomic environment largely within the confines of a single national economic system. In reality, the economies of individual countries are becoming ever more closely linked with one another as goods, money and people pass between them. To understand the bases for these flows, we need to look at the underlying factors that cause them, leading some countries, such as China, to export more goods than it buys from foreign countries, leaving it with a cash surplus that it then invests in other countries. On the other hand, some countries, such as the USA, buy more goods from foreign countries than they export, and need to borrow money from foreign countries. The model of the circular flow of income that we looked at earlier in this chapter can be applied to flows between countries, so if country A reduces its purchases from country B, householders and firms in country B will have less income to buy goods from other countries, including imports from country A, whose producers pay less in wages to their employees, who in turn cut back their purchase of goods from country B.

During periods of worldwide recession, the slowdown in the flow of trade and money between countries can have serious consequences, in just the same way as a slowdown in the domestic circular flow of income can ultimately lead, through a vicious circle, to everybody being worse off. If one country's government sees the income of its firms fall, it may be tempted to keep more of its household incomes within the national economy by restricting imports from foreign companies. This can lead to retaliatory action by other countries, and the net result of this is that the flow of trade around the world is reduced. In recognition of this, a number of international institutions exist to facilitate the flow of trade, capital and people between countries, including the World Trade Organization, the World Bank and the International Monetary Fund (IMF). To give an example of where international institutions may be needed, the IMF came to the rescue of Ireland in 2011, when the Irish government found itself unable to repay the loans it had built up during the previous decade. The IMF provided an emergency loan (commonly referred to as a 'bail-out'), which restored some confidence to the companies and governments that traded with Ireland, and also to households and firms within Ireland.

The global economic environment is complex and is considered in more detail in Chapter 14.

Case study:
How sustainable is the Chinese economic boom?

Photo: Shanghai Skyline © Nikada

During the 1990s and 2000s, China's rate of GDP growth had astonished the rest of the world. While a growth rate of between 2 and 4 per cent would be considered normal for most western countries, the average annual growth rate of GDP for China during the 1990s was about 9 per cent. It had reached a peak of nearly 13 per cent in March 2007, before slowing down to a low point of 6.2 per cent in March 2009. This would have still been a very credible performance by most western countries' standards. However, this slowdown seemed to be short-lived, because GDP growth started climbing again, reaching 12 per cent by March 2010. More worryingly, other indicators were suggesting that the boom may ultimately be unsustainable. Property investment in China in 2009 was 10 per cent of GDP, up from 8 per cent in 2007. Much of this seems to be speculative investment by investors who simply thought that property prices would go even higher, therefore creating a self-fulfilling prophecy of rising prices. One survey in 2010 estimated that over 64 million apartments were standing empty, owned by investors who simply wanted to make a capital gain on their investment in a rising market. This was potentially very worrying, and analogies were drawn with the Japanese property bubble, which

many blamed for the subsequent long period of recession in Japan.

China has managed to combine very tight centralized political control by the Communist Party with thriving capitalism in its Special Economic Development Zones. Would this centralized control by the Communist Party be strong enough to prevent a western-style boom -and-bust cycle? Or had the country gone down the route of economic liberalization, which laid it open to the type of economic cycle that the West had experienced repeatedly during the previous century?

China traditionally adopted the sort of approach to economic management favoured in the West in the 1950s and 1960s, when currencies were fixed to the dollar and credit controls were used to regulate unemployment and inflation. As a result, China has been less prone to economic or financial crises than those emerging countries where financial liberalization allowed hot money to flow in and out of the country quickly, precipitating a currency crisis that eventually impacts on the rest of the economy.

China has a very high level of savings by households, which are typically invested in government-owned banks. But these state-run banks lend mainly to state-run firms without being subject to market-based disciplines. As a result, there was an evident massive overinvestment in productive capacity, with little regard for return on capital. It seemed that the Chinese economy, where state planning co-exists with market forces, had difficulty in adjusting to change. In the case of privately owned companies, when demand begins to fall (for example, in response to a fall in demand from western countries), the companies cut their investment. However, in the case of state-controlled companies, political factors can dominate and investment is not necessarily cut back when demand falls.

China's growing trade surplus – $183 billion in 2010 – has made its tightly managed currency the target of persistent complaints from the USA and Europe. At the G20 summit meeting in Seoul in November 2010, many countries accused China of using an artificially low exchange rate as a trade weapon to gain unfair advantage in overseas markets. Although the renminbi was depegged from the US dollar in mid-2005, and rose in value against the dollar during the following two years by 13 per cent, many western countries continued to complain that the renminbi was too strong.

A further sign of the possible unsustainability of the Chinese economic boom came with inflation figures, which in September 2010 had risen to 3.6 per cent, well above the year's target of 3 per cent and at a two-year high. This reflected increased pressure on resources, as Chinese manufacturers' seemingly insatiable appetite for raw materials sent prices higher. Even wage costs – traditionally a source of China's competitive advantage – appeared to be edging up. In 2007, the *Financial Times* reported that growth in the financial services sector was being held back by a shortage of skilled staff. Gradual liberalization of the financial services sector, and the appearance of international banks in China, had squeezed the pool of available staff, forcing up wages and making it harder for companies to hire and retain qualified staff (*Financial Times* 2007).

Although the Chinese economic boom of the 1990s was based on export-led growth, by the late 2000s there were strong signs that the economy was becoming increasingly driven by domestic demand. A growing number of middle-class people were now earning a level of income that triggered a range of purchases that had previously been considered unaffordable luxuries. Many very rich entrepreneurs had emerged from the period of economic boom. It seemed that the Chinese business cycle would increasingly be influenced by international and domestic market factors. The export-led nature of the economy had made the country quite dependent on the wealth of those countries that its manufacturers exported to. It was no coincidence that China's period of great economic growth also coincided with a period of great economic prosperity in the USA and Europe. But with the development of

the domestic economy, an additional cyclical factor would set in. Faced with falling export orders, domestic employment would be likely to fall, and consequently the number of people earning a level of income that triggers 'luxury' purchases would fall. There would therefore be not only a primary effect of falling exports, but also a secondary effect from falling demand for domestic producers.

Should the outside world have been concerned about China's huge trade surplus and strong currency? Would these issues be corrected by market forces, regardless of the actions of the Chinese government and international intergovernmental bodies? Over time, China's trade surplus will almost certainly go the same way as Britain's and the USA's once mighty surpluses, which were undermined by a combination of growing demand for imports and inflationary pressures that reduced the competitive edge of the countries' exporters.

As for the high value of the renminbi, this may fall in due course as domestic inflation rises and the trade surplus is moderated. Experience elsewhere has suggested that, in an international economic environment, it can be very difficult for a country to manage the value of its currency.

QUESTIONS

1 To what extent is it possible, or desirable, for governments to manage a national economy through centralized planning systems of the type that have traditionally been practised in China?

2 Summarize the macroeconomic factors that will influence demand in China for consumer durables such as cars and televisions over the next decade.

3 What are the key consequences for the Chinese economy of the business cycle?

Summary

This chapter has reviewed the structure of national economies and the flow of income between different elements of the economy. Producers, consumers and government are interrelated in the circular flow of income. Business cycles occur because the speed of the circular flow of income temporarily increases or decreases. Although governments seek to limit the magnitude of the business cycle, the cycle can pose problems (and opportunities) for business organizations. The rate at which an organization can grow can be constrained by the rate at which the national economy is growing (**Chapter 9**). This chapter has reviewed economic indicators that companies can read in order to better understand and predict the environment in which they operate. A good information system (**Chapter 4**) should be able to analyse leading indicators of the economy rapidly and effectively.

The state of the economic environment is very much influenced by politicians, and the interaction between the economic and political environments is developed further in **Chapter 2**. This chapter has recognized that the national economic environment is part of the international economic environment and international economic issues are discussed in **Chapter 14**.

Key Terms

Accelerator effect (423)	Interest rate (429)
Borrowing (430)	Invisible (417)
Business cycle (425)	Macroeconomic analysis (414)
Central bank (444)	Model (424)
Circular flow of income (419)	Monetarism (443)
Competitive cost advantage (417)	Monetary Policy Committee (MPC) (444)
Confidence level (429)	Multiplier effect (421)
Deflation (429)	Public sector net borrowing (PSNB) (439)
Disposable income (428)	Quantitative easing (443)
Economic structure (415)	Recession (417)
Exchange rate (430)	Retail Prices Index (RPI) (429)
Fiscal policy (441)	Savings ratio (428)
Gross domestic product (GDP) (425)	Turning point (431)
Inflation (424)	Unemployment (426)
Injection (420)	Withdrawal (420)

Online Learning Centre

To help you grasp the key concepts of this chapter, explore the extra resources posted on the Online Learning Centre at *www.mcgraw-hill.co.uk/palmer*. Among other helpful resources there are chapter-by-chapter test questions, revision notes and web links.

Chapter review questions

1 Identify some of the consequences for a UK vehicle manufacturer of a UK inflation rate of 5 per cent per annum, compared to an EU average of 2 per cent.

2 Contrast the effects of 'tight' fiscal and tight monetary policies on the construction sector.

3 In the context of 'rational expectations' theory, what evidence could you suggest to indicate that business people 'see through' the short-term implications of government economic policies?

Activities

1 You and your friends spend £200 on a night out at a nightclub, drinking beer, having a meal beforehand and taking a taxi home. Use a multiplier model to assess the effects on the local economy. What is the overall benefit locally? How much leaks out of the local economy?

2 Select a service sector from one of the following: restaurants; telecommunications; health services. Identify the effects of inflation on the sector. What steps could organizations take to try to overcome the effects of inflation?

3 Identify your government's current key economic policies. To what extent do you consider these policies to be good for business organizations?

Further reading

Macroeconomics can be a complex subject and this chapter has reviewed only the key elements of the macroeconomic system. For a fuller discussion of the subject, the following texts are useful.

Blanchard, O., Giavazzi, F. and Amighin, A. (2010) *Macroeconomics: A European Perspective,* Harlow Pearson Education.

Burda, M. and Wyplosz, C. (2009) *Macroeconomics: A European Text*, 5th edn, Oxford, Oxford University Press.

Griffiths, A. and Wall, S. (eds) (2009) *Economics for Business and Management*, 2nd edn, London, Prentice Hall.

For a review of the UK economy, the following statistical data are published regularly by the Office for National Statistics.

UK National Accounts (The Blue Book): the principal annual publication for national account statistics, covering value added by industry, the personal sector, companies, public corporations, central and local government.

Economic Trends: a monthly compendium of economic data, which gives convenient access from one source to a range of economic indicators.

References

Boyce, C.J. and Wood, A.M. (2010) 'Money or mental health: the cost of alleviating psychological distress with monetary compensation versus psychological therapy', *Health Economics, Policy and Law*, 5, 509–516, Cambridge Journals online, available at http://wrap.warwick.ac.uk/2528/(accessed 12 September 2011).

Eurostat (1998) *Eurostat Yearbook 1998*, Luxembourg, Statistical Office of the European Communities.

Eurostat (2006) *Eurostat Yearbook 2006*, Luxembourg, Statistical Office of the European Communities.

Financial Times (2007) 'HSBC highlights China staffing woes', London, *Financial Times*, 3 April, p. 15.

Holmes, R. (2010) 'Money can buy you happiness – up to a point', *New Scientist*, Vol. 17, September, No. 2777.

ILO (2008) *Global Employment Trends*, Geneva, International Labour Organization.

ONS (2010), *The Pink Book, United Kingdom Balance of Payments*, 2010 edn, Office for National Statistics online at: www.statistics.gov.uk/STATBASE/Product.asp?vink=1140 (accessed 6 March 2011).

Vargo, S.L. and Lusch, R.F. (2008) 'Service – dominant logic: continuing the evolution', *Journal of the Academy of Marketing Science*, Vol. 36, 1–10.

Wood, P.A. (1987) 'Producer services and economic change, some Canadian evidence', *Technological Change and Economic Policy*, K. Chapman and G. Humphreys (eds), London, Blackwell.

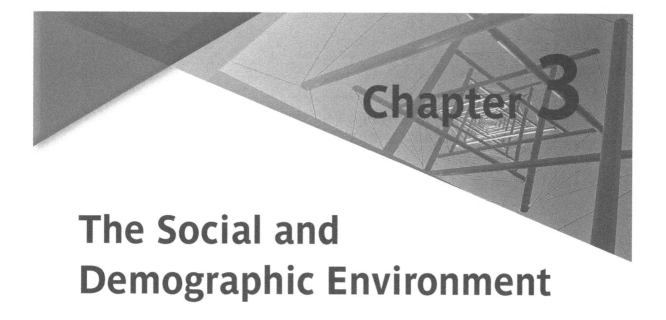

Chapter 3

The Social and Demographic Environment

Next time you are travelling on a bus or a train, look around at your fellow passengers. Reflect on how these people may be similar or different to you. Some differences may be obvious – for example, the age or gender of somebody may distinguish them from you. Some differences you may think are obvious, but actually may be quite complex to understand. You see a dark-skinned person and wonder if they are really any different to you with your white skin. Maybe their family was originally from India, but if they are third-generation immigrants to your country, are they really any different to you in the way they buy things in the shops? Then there are all sorts of differences that you cannot really tell simply by looking at people sitting on the bus, but the way people dress and the newspaper they are reading could give you some indication of the kind of lifestyle they lead, manifested in their interests, activities and the type of accommodation they live in. The passengers on the bus you are travelling in today are likely to be much more diverse than the passengers on the same bus 20 years ago, or a similar bus in another country. This chapter explores the nature of differences between individuals and the impacts diversity has on business organizations. Businesses can no longer afford to cater for the 'average' customer, but must understand the specific needs of different groups within society.

✓ Learning Objectives

This chapter will explain:

✓ How changing attitudes and lifestyles affect business organizations.

✓ The changing demographic composition of society and its effects on business organizations.

✓ Change in family composition and household structure.

✓ The effects on business of greater ethnic diversity.

✓ The two-way relationship between society and business.

3.1 Social change and its effects on business organizations

Consider the following recent social changes that have occurred in the UK and many other western countries:

- an increasing ethnic diversity, which is manifested in Asian and Indian communities in many towns of the UK
- a rising divorce rate, which is manifested in a rising number of single-person households and single-parent families
- a desire for instant gratification, manifested in individuals' desire to obtain goods and services 24 hours a day
- a workforce whose cultural diversity brings new challenges and opportunities to the workplace.

These are typical of changes that have concentrated the minds of business organizations as they attempt to supply goods and services that are of continuing relevance to the population. Companies that continue to base their efforts on the assumption of a typical white family unit, which is prepared to wait for a long time before a product is delivered, may find themselves targeting an increasingly small market segment.

As a result of social change, we have seen many goods and services become redundant, as they no longer satisfy a population whose needs, attitudes, values and behaviour have changed. The following are typical of goods and services that have disappeared or been greatly reduced in sales as a result of social change.

- Traditional drinking pubs have reduced in number as patterns of social relationships change and individuals seek more family-friendly pubs, which serve food in a pleasant environment.
- The number of butchers' shops has been sharply reduced as consumers opt for a healthier lifestyle, based on foods that do not contain meat.
- Local and regional newspapers have seen declining sales as people increasingly turn to web-based news providers and social networking sites for their source of news and views.

On the other hand, social change has resulted in tremendous growth for some goods and services.

- Microwave ovens and portable televisions have benefited from a move towards 'cellular' households, in which each member of the family operates in a much more independent manner than has traditionally been the case.
- Gyms and leisure facilities have benefited from individuals' increasing concern for health and personal fitness.
- Sales of organically produced food have increased as more consumers become suspicious about the effects of intensive farming and additives in their food.

It is very easy for an individual to take for granted the way they live. Furthermore, young people may imagine that people have always lived their lives that way. From one year to the next, social change may seem quite imperceptible, but when life today is compared with what it was like ten years ago, noticeable changes begin to appear. If comparisons are made with 20 or 50 years ago, it may seem as if two entirely different societies are being compared. Simply by looking at an old movie, major differences become apparent, such as attitudes to the family, leisure activities and the items commonly purchased by consumers.

⟳ Thinking around the subject

Government's official shopping basket reflects social change

New evidence of changing lifestyles sometimes emerges from the most unlikely sources. One interesting insight comes from the regular updating of the UK's Retail Prices Index (RPI), which is used by many organizations as a benchmark for inflation in the national economy. In principle, it is quite easy to take a typical shopping basket of consumers' purchases and to monitor what happens to the price of this basket from one year to the next. A problem occurs, however, because the contents of the basket are constantly changing as consumers' preferences and spending patterns change. For example, the proportion of the average consumer's expenditure allocated to food has reduced over time, leading to the RPI weighting for food dropping from over a third in 1956 to 10.5 per cent in 2007.

In 2010 the Office for National Statistics (ONS), which records the RPI (and also the related Consumer Prices Index (CPI)), carried out its annual updating of the average shopping basket, based on a survey of around 120,000 separate price quotations collected each month, covering some 650 representative consumer goods and services. The 2010 updating of the index saw bars of soap, lipstick and pitta bread being removed, while hair straighteners, garlic bread and cereal bars were added. Rapid changes in technology were reflected in the index, with items that were added to the index a few years ago now deleted because they had become obsolete. Disposable cameras were dropped, because so few were now being bought, because most people now owned a mobile phone that had a camera built into it. Among the new technology items added in 2010 were Blu-ray devices and a category that the ONS described as 'computer games involving accessories', following a boom in sales of games such as *Guitar Hero*.

It is not just changes in the actual products we buy that need to be reflected in the RPI index, but also how we buy them. The lowering of average grocery prices, which occurred as buyers moved from corner stores to supermarkets, and the lower prices available for many electrical goods bought online, are reflected in changes in the way the ONS samples points of purchase.

There still remains the problem that one person's shopping basket may be quite different to the next person's. Although the ONS weights its shopping basket according to the changing size of each population age group, an elderly person without a car and with no satellite navigation system may think that the RPI – on which their annual pension increase is based – does not reflect their own spending habits. Reflecting this diversity, the ONS has developed a personal inflation calculator (available at www.statistics.gov.uk/PIC/index.html), which individuals can use to calculate how inflation affects them personally. What is your own rate of inflation?

Change in society is also brought about by changes in its composition. Much recent attention has been given in many western European countries to the effects of an ageing population on society. Some commentators have seen major problems ahead (or, for some, opportunities) as an increasingly large dependent population has to be kept by a proportionately smaller economically active group in society. Some see this as challenging basic attitudes that individuals have towards the community and the family. At the very least, business organizations should be concerned about the effects of demographic change on patterns of demand for goods and services, and the availability of a workforce to produce those goods and services.

It is bad enough not to recognize social change that has happened in the past. It is much worse to fail to read the signs of social change that is happening now and to understand the profound effect this could have on the goods and services that people will buy in the future.

This chapter begins by examining what can loosely be described as a society's social and cultural values. These are what make people in the UK different today from how they were 20 years ago, or different from how people in Algeria or Indonesia are today. Social and cultural differences between countries focus on differences in attitudes, family structures and the pattern of interaction between individuals. Business organizations should understand the consequences of what may appear nebulous social changes for the types of things that consumers are likely to buy in the future.

3.1.1 Social influences on behaviour

The way an individual behaves as a consumer is a result of their unique physical and psychological make-up on the one hand, and a process of learning from experience on the other. The debate about the relative importance of nature and nurture is familiar to social psychologists. This chapter is concerned with the effects of learned behaviour on individuals' buying behaviour

An individual learns norms of behaviour from a number of sources (see Figure 3.1):

- the dominant cultural values of the society in which they live
- the social class to which they belong
- important reference groups, in particular the family.

Culture can be seen as an umbrella within which social class systems exist and reference groups exert influence on individuals or groups of individuals. The following sections consider the effects of each of these influences.

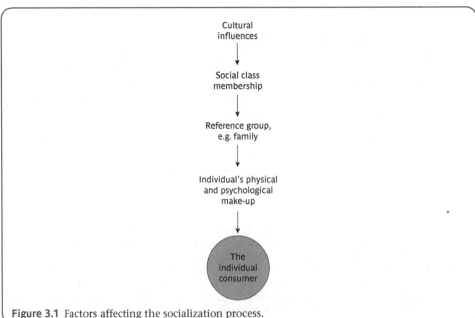

Figure 3.1 Factors affecting the socialization process.

3.2   The cultural environment

The *Oxford English Dictionary* defines **culture** as a 'trained and refined state of understanding, manners and tastes'. Central to culture is the concept of the learning and passing down of values from one generation to the next. A culture's values are expressed in a complex set of beliefs, customs and symbols, which help to identify individuals as members of one particular culture rather than another. The following are typical manifestations of cultural identity.

- Shared attitudes – for example, towards the role of women or children in society.
- Abstract symbols and rituals, which can be seen in historic cultures by such events as religious practices, harvest festivals and maypole dancing, and in more modern times by support for local football teams.
- Material manifestations – for example, the literature and art of a culture, or the style of decoration used in private houses.

It is common to distinguish between 'core' and 'secondary' cultural values.

- Core cultural values tend to be very enduring over time. In Britain, for example, the acceptance of monogamy represents a core belief and one that very few people would disagree with.
- Secondary cultural values are more susceptible to change over time. While there may be a core belief in the family, this does not prevent changes in attitudes towards the form that families should take, as is evident from the growing incidence of divorce and the increasing number of single-parent families. It is shifts in these secondary cultural values that it is particularly important for business organizations to monitor.

3.2.1 Effects of culture on business organizations

It is crucial for business organizations to appreciate fully the cultural values of a society, especially where an organization is seeking to do business in a country that is quite different from its own. The possible consequences of failing to do this can be illustrated by the following examples.

- When McDonald's entered the UK market, it initially found hostility from the British, who did not appreciate the brash, scripted, 'Have a nice day' mentality of its staff. The company subsequently adapted its style of business to cater for British preferences.
- The UK retailer Sainsbury's failed in its attempt to replicate supermarkets on the British model in Egypt, a country that had no tradition of supermarket shopping. Worse still, at the height of a Palestinian uprising, a story went round that Sainsbury's had Jewish connections, a rumour encouraged by local shopkeepers. After just two years, and losses of over £100 million, Sainsbury's pulled out of Egypt.
- Many UK businesses have set up operations overseas and gone about business in an open and above-board manner, only to find that corruption and the use of bribes is endemic in the local culture and essential for business success.

Cultural sensitivity affects many aspects of business planning and operations.

- Understanding processes of buyer behaviour (for example, the role of men in buying routine household goods varies between countries, leading sellers to adjust their product specification and promotional efforts to meet the needs of the most influential members of the buying unit).
- Some products may be unacceptable in a culture and must be adapted to be culturally acceptable (e.g. the original formulation for the McDonald's 'Big Mac' is unacceptable in Muslim cultures).

- Symbols associated with products, such as the design and colour of packaging, may be unacceptable in some cultures (e.g. the colour white is associated with purity in most western European cultures, but in other cultures it is associated with bereavement).
- Distribution channel decisions are partly a reflection of cultural attitudes, and not just economics and land use. Retailers and wholesalers may be seen as a vital part of a culture's social infrastructure and individuals may feel a sense of loyalty to their suppliers. Although it may appear economically rational for shoppers to buy in bulk, small local shops opening for long hours may be seen by consumers as an extension of their pantry.
- Advertising messages do not always translate easily between different cultures, reflecting culturally influenced standards of what is considered decent and appropriate.
- Methods of procuring resources can vary between cultures. In some Far Eastern countries, it is essential to establish a trusting relationship with a buyer before the buyer will even consider placing an order. Sometimes, it is essential to know personally the key decision maker or to offer a bribe, which is considered routine business practice in some cultures.
- Obtaining good-quality staff can be influenced by cultural factors. The notion of punctual timekeeping and commitment to the employer is often an unfamiliar set of values in cultures where commitment to the family comes very strongly first and timekeeping has little meaning.

Even in home markets, business organizations should understand the processes of gradual cultural change and be prepared to satisfy the changing needs of consumers. The following are examples of contemporary cultural change in western Europe and the possible business responses.

- Women are increasingly being seen as equal to men in terms of employment expectations and household responsibilities. According to the ONS, the proportion of women in employment has grown steadily. In 1971, 56 per cent of UK women were in employment, compared with 70 per cent in 2009 (ONS 2010). This compares with a similar-sized decrease in the employment rate for men over the same period, with the male employment rate falling from 92 per cent to 78 per cent. The growth in the number of career-orientated and financially independent women has presented opportunities for new goods and services – for example, childcare facilities and ready-prepared meals, which save time for busy working women who need to juggle work, family and social roles.
- Greater life expectancy is leading to an ageing of the population and a shift to an increasingly 'elderly' culture. This is apparent in product design, which reflects durability rather than fashionability.
- Leisure is becoming an increasingly important part of many people's lives, and businesses have responded with a wide range of leisure-related goods and services.
- Increasing concern for the environment is reflected in a variety of 'green' consumer products.

3.2.2 Cultural convergence

There has been much recent discussion about the concept of **cultural convergence**, referring to an apparent decline in differences between cultures. It has been argued that basic human needs are universal in nature and, in principle, capable of satisfaction with universally similar solutions. Companies have been keen to pursue this possibility in order to achieve economies of scale in producing homogeneous products for global markets. There is some evidence of firms achieving this – for example, the worldwide success of Coca-Cola and McDonald's. In the case of fast food, many western chains have capitalized on the deep-seated habits in some Far Eastern countries of eating from small hawkers' facilities by offering the same basic facility in a clean and hygienic environment.

The desire of a subculture in one country to imitate the values of those in another has also contributed to cultural convergence. This is nothing new. During the Second World War, many individuals in western Europe sought to follow the American lifestyle, and nylon stockings from the USA became highly sought-after cultural icons by some groups. The same process is at work today in many developing countries, where some groups seek to identify with western cultural values through the purchases they make. Today, however, improved media communications allow messages about cultural values to be disseminated much more rapidly. The development of satellite television and the internet hastens the process of creating shared worldwide values.

It can be argued that business organizations are not only responding to cultural convergence, they are also significant contributors to that convergence. The development of global brands backed up by global advertising campaigns has contributed to an increasing uniformity in goods and services offered throughout the world. Many commentators have described an 'MTV' generation that views global satellite television channels, and who converge in their attitudes to consumption. The internet, cheap telecommunications and air travel have contributed to this process of apparent global homogenization.

⟳ Thinking around the subject

New magazines for new men?

Until a few years ago, the shelves of most newsagents would have been loaded with many general interest women's magazines (e.g. *Woman's Own*, *Woman's Weekly*, *Cosmopolitan*), but very few general interest magazines aimed at men. Why? Some cynics might have argued that women were more likely to have spare time at home and could sit around reading, while 'busy' men were out at work, in the pub or watching sport, and did not have time to read magazines There may just have been a bit of truth in this, but the main reason has been that women's magazines have been popular with advertisers, who generally provide a high proportion of total income for a magazine publisher. In the traditional household, it has been women who have made decisions on a wide range of consumer goods purchases. Advertising the benefits of toothpaste, yoghurt or jam would have been lost on most men, who had little interest in which brand was put in front of them and may have played a very minor role in the buying process.

Take a look at the news-stand now and it will carry a wide range of men's general interest magazines, such as *FHM*, *Maxim*, *Nuts* and *Zoo*. Why have they suddenly mushroomed in number and in readership? Again, the answer lies in their attractiveness to advertisers. Talk of a male identity crisis may have spurred some sales. More importantly, it is evident that men are now involved in a much wider range of purchasing decisions than ever before, and therefore likely to be of much greater interest to advertisers. While some 'new men' may be taking a more active interest in the household shopping, many more are marrying later and indulging themselves in personal luxuries, an option that is less readily available to their married counterparts. With support from advertisers, the leading men's magazine in the UK, *FHM*, had a circulation of 192,596 copies per issue in 2010 (Audit Bureau of Circulation). Sales of all magazines – men's and women's – have suffered in recent years as more people seek out content online, but in the late 1990s, *FHM* magazine had even overtaken the leading women's monthly magazine, *Cosmopolitan*.

Critics of the trend towards cultural convergence have noted individuals' growing need for *identity* in a world that is becoming increasingly homogenized. Support for regional breakaway governments (e.g. by the Kurdish and Basque people) may provide some evidence of this. During the Iraq war in 2003, many consumers in Arab countries used purchases of Muslim products to identify themselves with an anti-American cause. Many western service brands have become despised by some groups as symbols of an alien identity. Banks in many Muslim countries have reported increased interest in sharia-based banking services, and many UK banks have developed bank accounts targeted specifically at Muslims.

In some countries, cultural convergence has been seen as a threat to the sense of local identity that culture represents. Governments have therefore taken measures in an attempt to slow down this process of cultural homogenization. This has achieved significance in France where legislation requires the use of the French language – an important means of creating identity for any culture – in packaging and advertising for products.

3.2.3 Multicultural, multi-ethnic societies

The UK, like many western countries, is increasingly becoming a culturally and ethnically diverse society (see Table 3.1). By ethnicity, we are talking about groups based on their common racial, national, tribal, religious, linguistic or cultural origin. An important reason for increasing ethnic diversity in most western countries is the growing numbers of immigrant people from overseas cultures, attracted by, among other things, economic prosperity in the host country, and motivated to leave their native country by the relative lack of opportunities available. Immigrants can bring with them a distinctive set of cultural and religious values, and adapting to the values of the host country can be a difficult task. In some countries, church and state may be closely linked, leading to an expectation that religious principles should be the basis for governance. For some religious groups, the power of a religious leader transcends any government institution. A lack of understanding from members of the host country may cause

Figure 3.2 How can Coca-Cola be sure that its brand name and product offer will be the object of aspiration for the dominant groups in a country, rather than a hated symbol of an alien system of capitalism? Coca-Cola is often at the top of league tables of global brands, and most people in the world have access to the company's beverages. But Coca-Cola has been challenged by numerous functionally similar cola drinks, which seek to appeal to consumers' need for cultural identity. By rejecting Coca-Cola in favour of Mecca Cola (shown here), individuals have made a statement about their sense of cultural identity. Mecca Cola has donated 10 per cent of its profits to fund humanitarian projects in Palestine, and a further 10 per cent to charities in the countries in which the drink is sold – mainly Arab countries, and European countries with significant Arab communities. An activist stance has been reflected in the company's slogan, which has appeared on all its products: 'Shake your Conscience', and in the company's pledge to support 'associations who work towards peace in the world and especially for peace in the conflict between Palestinians and fascist Zionist apartheid'.

Table 3.1 Population of Great Britain by religion, 2001.

Religion	Number (000)	% of total population	% of non-Christian religious population
Christian	41,015	71.8	
Muslim	1,589	2.8	51.9
Hindu	558	1.0	18.3
Sikh	336	0.6	11.0
Jewish	267	0.5	8.7
Buddhist	149	0.3	4.9
Others	159	0.3	5.2
All non-Christian religions			100.00
No religion	8,596	15.1	
Not stated	4,434	7.8	
Total	57,103	100.00	

Source: based on Census of Population (2001).

some immigrants to be seen as arrogant, lazy or lacking in humour by the standards of the host culture, but they may nevertheless be perfectly normal by the standards of their home culture. Where members of ethnic minorities are concentrated into distinct areas (within the UK this occurs in certain suburbs of London, Leicester and Bradford), their traditional cultural values may be strengthened and prolonged by mutual support and the presence of an infrastructure (such as places of worship and specialized shops) to support the values of the culture.

The presence of concentrations of ethnic subcultures in a town presents opportunities for businesses that cater for distinctive cultural preferences. In many towns catering for people of Asian origin, these include halal butchers, bureaux for arranged marriages, and travel agents specializing in travel to India and Pakistan. In some cases, completely new markets have emerged specifically for minority ethnic groups, such as the market for black sticking plasters. It has sometimes proved difficult for established businesses to gain access to immigrant segments. Many established companies have not adequately researched the attitudes and buying processes of these groups, with the result that, in markets as diverse as vegetables, clothing and travel, ethnic minorities have supported businesses run by fellow members of their minority group.

A report published in 2010 by the Institute of Practitioners in Advertising (IPA) identified a number of challenges in addressing the needs of ethnic minorities. It has been noted that consumers from these groups are typically younger, more likely to own a business than others, tend to live in large urban centres – creating opportunities for cost-effective marketing – and are close-knit, making word-of-mouth recommendation a powerful force. However, they tend to be very fragmented, with intergenerational differences, requiring that businesses commission professional research to gain in-depth understanding of their target markets.

As producers, members of ethnic minorities have contributed to the diversity of goods and services available to consumers in the host country. The large number of Indian restaurants in Britain, for example, can be attributed to the entrepreneurial skills of immigrants, while many food products (such as kebabs and Chinese food) have followed the example of immigrants.

Immigrants have tended to be of working age and have filled a vital role in providing labour for the economy. In 2004, the labour market in many parts of Britain was overheating, with labour shortages and a lack of people prepared to work in jobs involving unpleasant working conditions or anti-social hours. The opening of the UK labour market to migrants from the new EU member-states of eastern and central Europe helped to alleviate these shortages with a supply of hard-working and flexible workers. Some ethnic groups have brought vital entrepreneurial skills to the economy, often at a high cost economically and socially to the less developed countries they have left.

It must be recognized that there are great differences between ethnic subgroups. Entrepreneurship is much greater among the Chinese group, where 21 per cent were classified as self-employed by the ONS in the Annual Population Survey 2004, compared to 15 per cent for white Irish, 12 per cent for white British, but less than 10 per cent for mixed or black groups. The age structure of minority ethnic groups gives rise to differences in the proportion that are dependent. Within the Bangladeshi group, for example, 42 per cent are under 16 (compared to a figure of 20 per cent for whites), while only 20 per cent are in the economically most active group of 35–64 (compared with 37 per cent for whites). These figures are reversed for the Chinese community, where only 17 per cent are under 16 and 38 per cent are between 35 and 64.

3.2.4 Social class

In most societies, divisions exist between groups of people in terms of their access to privileges and status within that society. In some social systems, such as the Hindu caste system, the group that an individual belongs to exerts influence from birth and it is very difficult for the individual to change between groups. Western societies have class systems in which individuals are divided into one of a number of classes. Although the possibilities for individuals to move between social classes in western countries are generally greater than the possibilities of movement open to a member of a caste system, class values tend to be passed down through families. The very fact that it is seen as possible to move classes may encourage people to see the world in a different way from that which has been induced in them during their years of socialization.

While some may have visions of a 'classless' society that is devoid of divisions in terms of status and privileges, the reality is that divisions exist in most societies, and are likely to persist in some form. It is common in western societies to attribute individuals with belonging to groups that have been given labels such as 'working class' or 'middle class'. This emotional language of class is not particularly helpful to businesses that need a more measurable basis for describing differences within society, and later in this chapter we will look at some of the ways class is measured.

Why do business organizations need to know about the social grouping to which an individual belongs? The basic idea of a classification system is to identify groups that share common attitudes and behaviour patterns, and access to resources. This can translate into similar spending patterns. There are, for example, many goods and services that are most heavily bought by people who can be described as 'working class', such as the *Daily Star* newspaper and betting services, while others are more often associated with 'upper-class' purchasers, such as Jaguar cars, the *Financial Times* and investment management services.

Businesses need to take note of the changing class structure of society. As the size of each class changes, so market segments, which are made up of people who are similar in some important respects, also change. In the UK during the 1960s and 1970s it has been observed that more people were moving into the 'middle classes'. The effects of taxation, the welfare state and access to education had flattened the class structure of society. For car manufacturers, this translated into a very large demand for mainstream middle-of-the-road cars. However, during the 1980s and 1990s, both the upper and lower classes tended to grow in what had become a more polarized society. In terms of car sales, there was a growing demand for luxury cars such as Jaguars and BMWs at one end of the market and cheaper cars such as Kias at the other.

Thinking around the subject

How far can halal food go?

One consequence of the increasing cultural diversity in the UK is the emergence of a market in halal fresh meat and processed foods. Worldwide, a report published in 2010 by the consultancy firm AT Kearney estimated the value of the halal market to be £2 trillion a year. Halal means 'lawful and permitted', and, in food terms, products are not halal if they contain alcohol, any part of a pig, carnivorous animal meat or blood. Foods are also not halal if meat has not been slaughtered according to Islamic law.

The UK market for halal meat was estimated to have a value of £460 in a report by Mintel (Mintel 2002). The main market for halal food in the UK is the estimated 1.9 million Muslims who account for about 3.2 per cent of the population. However, Muslims have a varied ethnic background and in Britain are mainly drawn from Pakistan, Bangladesh, India and the Middle East, each with their own food preferences. Those from the Indian subcontinent are known to prefer hot, spicy food, while those from the Middle East have blander tastes, similar to those of native British people.

For butchers, who have had a hard time following a series of food scares and an increase in the number of vegetarian consumers, the emergence of the halal market offers a welcome opportunity. Mintel estimated that halal fresh meat accounted for 11 per cent of the value of all meat sales in the UK, but it appeared that just 3.2 per cent of the population was accounting for a disproportionate volume of halal meat sales.

Small independent butchers' shops have dominated halal meat sales. There have been problems in verifying the authenticity of halal meat, so trust is an important element of fresh meat supply, and it is likely that independent butchers' shops are used regularly as consumers have learned to trust the meat that they buy there. This is particularly true of older and more traditional Asian shoppers, who are much less likely to use supermarkets. Mintel observed that a large proportion of Muslim women play the traditional role of home-maker, which means that they have more time available for shopping in independent outlets – particularly those where their native language is spoken – and for preparing meals from scratch. However, it is unlikely that third-generation Muslims onwards will be satisfied with such a lifestyle. Third-generation Muslim women are more likely to have careers, and their busy lifestyles are likely to lead them to seek the convenience of one-stop shopping at supermarkets and online rather than using specialist small suppliers. They are also more likely to seek the convenience of ready-prepared meals, rather than cooking from raw ingredients as their parents did.

Already, halal brands have emerged, including Tahira (frozen, chilled, ambient foods) and Maggi (sauces and seasonings). Could other convenience food retailers further develop this market? Fast-food chains such as McDonald's are already experienced in catering for Muslim consumers in countries such as Malaysia – would there be a market for a halal burger in the UK?

Another intriguing question is whether the cultural traditions of Muslims may spread to the population generally. After all, Indian and Chinese restaurants now appeal to the UK population at large, rather than the narrow groups they initially served. Could halal food become mainstream rather than a niche market? One opportunity arises among the 3.4 million vegetarians in the UK, to whom meat-free halal foods are ideally placed to appeal.

⟳ Thinking around the subject

Equality is good for society, especially if you are on top

It is often claimed that one of the big trends in most western developed societies over the past few decades has been increased fairness, by reducing inequalities in life opportunities that result from differences in gender, age and ethnic background (among other things). However, a report published in 2010 by the UK's Equality and Human Rights Commission (EHRC) questioned the reality of equality in Britain today (EHRC 2010). The chairman of the EHRC, Trevor Phillips, noted that while British attitudes towards issues of race, gender and sexuality were now 'light years' ahead of previous generations, the reality on the ground had yet to fully catch up. Consequently, there were deep divisions in Britain's classrooms, different experiences of the criminal justice system, and a large pay gap between men and women. In full-time work, women in 2010 were still paid 16.4 per cent less than men, and in some sectors this was significantly worse (for example, the difference was 55 per cent in the finance sector).

The report noted that issues of inequality were often complex and interconnected, observing that 'Inequality and disadvantage don't come neatly packaged in parcels marked age, or disability, or gender, or race. They emerge often as a subset of a strand – not as a disability issue, but as a mental health issue; not as a generalised ethnic penalty, but as a result of being Pakistani; not a pay gap for working women, but a pay gap for working mothers.'

More worryingly, the report indicated that it appeared to have become increasingly difficult for children to escape from the social background into which they were born. Children born in to disadvantaged families faced a much greater struggle to succeed than those born into a more comfortable background. One example of this was seen in the way that young people from deprived backgrounds appear to be frozen out of top jobs because they are not well enough connected, or rich enough, to accept unpaid internships.

Societies function where people believe that, by working harder, they can improve their life chances. What are the implications for the business environment of a society where people feel increasingly trapped in their background? Is this exacerbated in a multimedia environment where the disadvantaged groups in society can easily become envious of other groups that they aspire to join, but see no realistic route to get there?

3.3   The family

The family represents a further layer in the socialization process. It is important that business organizations understand changes in family structures and values because change in this area can impact on them in a number of ways. Consider the following impacts of families on business organizations.

- Many household goods and services are typically bought by family units – for example, food and package holidays. When family structures and values change, consumption patterns may change significantly.
- The family is crucial in giving individuals a distinctive personality. Many of the differences in attitude and behaviour between individuals can be attributed to the values that were instilled in them by their family during childhood. These differences may persist well into adult life.
- The family has a central role as a transmitter of cultural values and norms, and can exercise a strong influence on an individual's buying behaviour.

3.3.1 Family composition

Many people still live with the idea that the typical family comprises two parents and an average of 2.4 children. In many western European countries this is increasingly becoming a myth, with single-person and single-parent households increasingly common. The following factors have contributed to changes in family composition:

- an increasing divorce rate, with about one-third of all marriages in the UK now ending in divorce
- marriage and parenthood are being put off until later; the average age of first marriage has increased by around five years since 1961, to 30 for men and 28 for women (based on UK 2001 Census)
- the gap between people leaving school, settling down to get married and starting a family has grown steadily, and young people are now enjoying freedom from parental responsibility for longer than ever before
- more people are living on their own outside a family unit, either out of choice or through circumstances (e.g. divorce, widowhood)
- family role expectations have changed, with an increasing number of career-orientated wives.

Changes in family composition have led firms to develop new goods and services that meet the changing needs of families, such as crèche facilities for working mothers and holidays for single parents. Advertising has increasingly moved away from portraying the traditional family group, which many individuals may have difficulty in identifying with. Examples that portray the new reality include an advertisement for McDonald's in which a boy takes his separated father to one of the company's restaurants, and one for Volkswagen in which a career-minded woman puts her car before her husband.

3.3.2 Family roles

As well as changing in composition, there is evidence of change in the way that families operate as a unit. Many household products have traditionally been dominated by either the male or female partner, but these distinctions are becoming increasingly blurred as family roles change.

A report by the Future Foundation showed that, in the UK, the proportion of couples in which the man has the final say in big financial decisions has fallen from 25 per cent in 1993 to 20 per cent in 2003 (Future Foundation 2004). This reflects an increase in the number of couples who claim that they have an equal say from 65 per cent to 69 per cent. The data also show that the number of couples where the female partner has the final say has risen from 10 per cent to 12 per cent. Men still make the major financial decisions in 40 per cent of couples aged over 65. Conversely, in couples under the age of 35, the woman is more likely to control major financial decisions. However, women still have the main responsibility for shopping in 47 per cent of couples, compared with 11 per cent of couples where men do it.

The scope for individual freedom of expenditure has increased significantly, and increasing affluence has widened the scope for discretionary spending in general. There are a number of markets, such as clothing, that benefit from this independent spending, although this finding is not consistent across the different age groups. Among couples aged over 65, a majority of men said their partner has at least an equal influence in the clothes they wear. This is lower in couples aged under 45, with only 19 per cent of men claiming that their partner mainly chooses their clothes for them. On the other hand, none of the women surveyed by Future Foundation said that their partner always chooses their clothes and a very small number indicated any significant influence.

The Future Foundation also highlighted a number of other changes in roles within family units.

- Cooking is still dominated by women, although men are increasingly sharing the task of preparing the main evening meal.
- Although men may say they believe household tasks should be shared, only 1 per cent say they always do the washing and ironing. Household cleaning is carried out mainly by women in nearly two-thirds of households, and this proportion has been falling gradually over the last two decades.
- The view that a man's task is to earn money, while a wife's job is to look after the family and home, has fallen consistently over the last decade.
- More women are stating that work and careers are more important than home and children.

There has been much debate about the fragmentation of families into **cellular households** in which family members essentially do their own activities independently of other members. This is reflected in individually consumed meals rather than family meals, and leisure interests that are increasingly with a family member's peer groups rather than other family members. Businesses have responded to the needs of the cellular household with products such as microwave ovens and portable televisions, which allow family units to function in this way. It can also be argued, however, that new product developments, combined with increasing wealth, are actually responsible for the fragmentation of family activities. The microwave oven and portable television may have lessened the need for families to operate as a collective unit, although these possible consequences were not immediately obvious when they were launched. The family unit can expect to come under further pressures as new products, such as online entertainment and information services, allow individual members to consume in accordance with their own preferences rather than the collective preferences of the family.

⟳ Thinking around the subject

Pocket-money pester power packs a punch

What role do children play in the purchase of the goods and services that they ultimately consume? In the UK, children aged just 7 to 14 years old receive an estimated £1.5 billion in pocket money and financial handouts, according to a report by Mintel (Mintel 2004). There has been considerable debate about the extent of 'pester power', where parents give in to the demands of children. Increasingly, advertisers are aiming their promotional messages over the heads of adults and straight at children. The ethics of doing this have been questioned by many, and some countries have imposed restrictions on television advertising of children's products. However, even with advertising restrictions, companies have managed to get through to children in more subtle ways – for example, by sponsoring educational materials used in schools and paying celebrities to endorse their products. When it comes to items such as confectionery and toys, just what influence do children exert on the purchase decision? And when football clubs deliberately change their strip every season, is it unethical for the clubs to expect fanatical children to pester their parents to buy a new one so that they can keep up with their peer group? Does the role of children in influencing purchase decisions say a lot about the structure of a society? In some cultures, children should be 'seen but not heard', but in others children may be treated as responsible adults from a much earlier age.

3.4   Reference groups

The family is not the only influence on an individual as they develop a view of the world. Just as individuals learn from and mimic the values of parents and close relations, so too they also learn from and mimic other people outside their immediate family. Groups that influence individuals in this way are often referred to as **reference groups**. These can be one of two types.

1 Primary reference groups exist where an individual has direct face-to-face contact with members of the group.

2 Secondary reference groups describe the influence of groups where there is no direct relationship, but an individual is nevertheless influenced by the group's values.

3.4.1 Primary reference groups

These comprise people with whom an individual has direct two-way contact, including those with whom an individual works, plays football and goes to church. In effect, the group acts as a frame of reference for the individual. Small groups of trusted colleagues have great power in passing on recommendations about goods and services, especially those where a buyer has very little other evidence on which to base a decision. For many personal services, such as hairdressing, word-of-mouth recommendation from a member of a peer group may be a vital method by which a company gains new business. If an individual needs to hire a builder, the first thing they are likely to do is ask friends if they can recommend a good one on the basis of their previous experience. For many items of conspicuous consumption, individuals often select specific brands in accordance with which brand carries most prestige with its primary reference group.

The development of social network media such as Facebook has brought new energy to the role of primary reference groups, as individuals post and read comments about what should be accepted as social norms among their circle of friends.

3.4.2 Secondary reference groups

These are groups with which an individual has no direct contact, but that can nevertheless influence a person's attitudes, values, opinions and behaviour. Sometimes, the individual may be a member of the group and this will have a direct influence on their behaviour patterns, with the group serving as a frame of reference for the individual member. Individuals typically belong to several groups that can influence attitudes and behaviour in this way – for example, university groups, trades unions and religious organizations. A member of a trades union may have little active involvement with the organization, but may nevertheless adopt the values of the union, such as solidarity.

At other times, an individual may not actually be a member of a group, but may aspire to be a member of it. Aspirational groups can be general descriptions of the characteristics of groups of people who share attitudes and behaviour. They range from teenage 'wannabes' who idolize pop stars through to businessmen who want to surround themselves with the trappings of their successful business heroes. Commentators have talked about a 'celebrity culture' in which individuals can be guided in their lives by the actions of celebrities in much the same way as followers of a religion are influenced by the icons and creeds associated with that religion. It can be difficult to identify just which aspirational groups are highly sought after at any one time. Middle-aged marketers marketing youth products may find it difficult to keep up with which pop stars and fashion models are currently in favour with teenagers.

The influence of secondary groups on purchases tends to vary between products and brands. In the case of products that are consumed or used in public, group influence is likely to affect not only the choice of product but also the choice of brand. (For example, training shoes are often sold using a 'brand spokesperson' to create an image for the shoe. There are some people who are so influenced by the images developed by famous athletes wearing a particular brand that they would not want to be seen wearing anything else.) For mass-market goods that are consumed less publicly (e.g. many grocery items), the effects of reference groups are usually less.

3.5 Values, attitudes and lifestyles

Many organizations have recognized that traditional indicators of social class are poor predictors of buyer behaviour. An analysis of changing attitudes, values and lifestyles is considered to be more useful.

3.5.1 Values

Values represent an individual's core beliefs, and tend to be deep-seated and relatively enduring. They tend to be learned at an early age and passed on through generations. They form an underlying framework that guides an individual's construction of the world and their response to events in it. Typical underlying value systems may include the belief that it is wrong to get into debt; a belief that family is more important than work; and that it is important to be the winner in any competitive event.

The term *values* should be distinguished from *value*. Economists describe value as the ratio of the benefit arising from a product relative to its cost. The distinction between values and value is that an individual's value system influences the value they place on any particular object. A person with a value system that rates security and reliability highly may place a high value on a car that is solidly built but not particularly attractive. Another person whose value system ranks recognition by others as being more important may place a higher value on a car that is not necessarily reliable, but has 'street cred'.

Although value systems tend to be deeply ingrained, they have a tendency to change through an individual's life cycle. So it follows that the value system of a teenager is likely to be different from that of a young adult parent, and different again from that of an elderly retired person.

3.5.2 Attitudes

Compared to values, attitudes are relatively transient sets of beliefs. Attitudes should be distinguished from the behaviour that may be manifested in a particular lifestyle. An individual may have an attitude about a subject, but keep their thoughts to themselves, possibly in fear of the consequences if these do not conform to generally accepted norms. A man may believe that it should be acceptable for men to use facial cosmetics, but be unwilling to be the first to actually change behaviour by using them.

It is important for businesses to study changes in social attitudes, because these will most likely eventually be translated into changes in buying behaviour. The change may begin with a small group of social pioneers, followed by more traditional groups who may be slow to change their attitudes and more reluctant to change their behaviour. They may be prepared to change only when something has become the norm in their society.

Businesses have monitored a number of significant changes in individuals' attitudes in western Europe – for example:

- healthy living is considered to be increasingly important
- consumers have a tendency to want instant results, rather than having to wait for things
- attitudes are increasingly based on secular rather than religious values.

Business organizations have been able to respond to these attitude changes creatively – for example:

- demand for healthy foods and gymnasium services has increased significantly; at first, it was only a small group of people whose attitude towards health led them to buy specialist products – now it is a mainstream purchase
- the desire for instant gratification has been translated into strategies to make stock always available, next-day delivery for mail-order purchases, instant credit approval and instant lottery tickets
- supermarkets in England have capitalized on the secularization of Sunday by opening stores and doing increasing levels of business on Sundays.

3.5.3 Lifestyles

Lifestyles are the manifestation of underlying value systems and attitudes. Lifestyle analysis seeks to identify groups within the population based on distinctive patterns of behaviour. It is possible for two people from the same social class carrying out an identical occupation to have very different lifestyles, which would not be apparent if businesses segmented markets solely on the basis of easily identifiable criteria such as occupation. Consequently, product development and marketing communications have often been designed to appeal to specific lifestyle groups. This type of analysis can be very subjective and quantification of numbers in each category within a population at best can only be achieved through a small sample survey.

Studies have indicated a number of trends in lifestyles, which have impacts on business organizations.

Figure 3.3 There can be a big difference between what people actually do, what they say they do, and what they would like to do. For businesses planning to offer new goods or services, it may be easy for a respondent to a survey to say that they would buy it, but when they have to get their money out, they may have other ideas. This gulf between attitudes and behaviour can be particularly great in the case of some health-related goods and services. Many people make 'new year's resolutions' to change their lifestyle, often after a Christmas of overindulgence, but their best intentions are not always matched by their actions. Many people believe that they should be fitter, perhaps based on reports about the effects of overeating and sedentary lifestyles. Many of these will simply rationalize away reasons for doing nothing to make themselves fitter ('I don't have time'; 'I get enough exercise anyway'; 'I don't want to risk the possibility of an injury while exercising'). Some will take positive action – for example, by joining a local gym; indeed, membership registrations rise sharply in January. However, industry research suggests that a high proportion of these people stop going to the gym after six months. Marketers face

a dilemma, because what people actually do is the best guide to what they spend their money on, but businesses are also continually trying to understand latent needs that have not yet been expressed in the form of actual purchases. How can a researcher tell whether a consumer's wish will be transformed into an actual purchase? (Photo reproduced with permission of Fitness First).

- A growing number of individuals are becoming money rich, but time poor. Such individuals quite commonly seek additional convenience from their purchases, even if this means paying a premium price. Businesses have responded with products such as gourmet ready-prepared meals.

- As individuals become financially more secure, their motivation to buy products typically changes from a need for necessities to a desire for the unusual and challenging. Businesses have responded with ranges of designer clothes, adventure holidays and personalized interior design services.

- With the increase in the number of single-person households, the symbolic meaning of the home has changed for many people. Businesses have responded with a range of home-related products such as widescreen home cinema systems and gas-fired barbecues.

Gaining knowledge of the current composition and geographical distribution of lifestyle segments is much more difficult than monitoring occupation-based segments, for which data are regularly collected by government and private-sector organizations. This is discussed again later in this chapter.

⟳ Thinking around the subject

A penny for your thoughts?

Businesses have become increasingly interested in individuals' deep-seated unconscious emotions, on the basis that these offer a much better guide to how they will actually behave than their considered responses to questions about their attitudes and beliefs. Enter the brave new world of 'neuro-marketing', which seeks to go straight to individuals' brains, rather than understanding them through what they say. One American organization, the Bright House Institute for Science, has used magnetic resonance imaging (MRI) to try to learn more about how marketing cues activate different parts of the brain.

The idea of trying to understand how people's brains function is not new, and has occupied scientists and criminologists, among others, for some time. The debate about the relative power of nature (a hard-wiring of the brain) versus nurture (the effects of socialization processes on our behaviour) is a long-running one. Marketers have already found some limited role for experimental methods of understanding deep-seated processing – for example, research into advertising effectiveness has used tachistoscopes to record individuals' unconscious eye movements.

Should neuro-marketing be regarded as a great hope for the future? Or is it overhyped? Critics have been quick to argue that it is one thing being able to identify a pattern of brain activity, but quite another to be able to infer causative links between brain patterns and buying behaviour. Some have dismissed neuro-marketing as a management fad, and a device used by research companies to get their foot in the door of the client, then selling more conventional research.

Is neuro-marketing ethical? To many people, neuro-marketing sounds like an Orwellian nightmare, which could play straight into the hands of the 'thought police'. Could an understanding of people's deep-seated thought processes potentially allow companies to wrongly exploit emotions that are against a consumer's best interest? Could food companies exploit an emotional need for high-calorie 'comfort' food at the expense of a more considered need for healthy food? At a broader level, what are the implications for democracy if politicians can understand and manipulate individuals' deep-seated attitudes?

Identifying and measuring social groups

So far we have discussed the changing composition of society in general terms, but now we need to turn our attention to possible methods by which organizations can identify specific groups within society. This is important if business organizations are to be able to target differentiated goods and services at groups that have quite distinctive sets of attitudes and lifestyles.

The aim of any system of social classification is to provide a measure that encapsulates differences between individuals in terms of their type of occupation, income level, educational background and attitudes to life, among other factors. There are three theoretical approaches to measuring social groupings.

1 *By self-measurement*: researchers could ask an individual which of a number of possible groups they belong to. This approach has a number of theoretical advantages for organizations, because how an individual actually sees him or herself is often a more important determinant of behaviour than an objective measure. If people see themselves as working class, they are probably proud of the fact, and will choose products and brands that accord with their own self-image. The danger of this approach is that many people tend to self-select themselves for 'middle-of-the-road' categories. In one self-assessment study, over two-thirds of the sample described themselves as 'middle class'.

2 *By objective approaches*: these involve the use of measurable indicators about a person, such as their occupation, education and spending habits, as a basis for class determination A number of these are discussed below.

3 *By asking third parties*: this combines the objective approach of indicators described above with a subjective assessment of an individual's behaviour and attitudes.

⟳ Thinking around the subject

Complicated lifestyles

Some indication of the minutiae of changing lifestyles, and their implications for marketing, was revealed in the report *Complicated Lives II – The Price of Complexity*, commissioned by Abbey National bank from the Future Foundation. The report brought together quantitative and qualitative research with extensive analysis of a range of trends affecting families and their finances. The findings show that, between 1961 and 2001:

- the average time women spent in a week doing cleaning and laundry fell from 12 hours and 40 minutes to 6 hours and 18 minutes
- the average time that parents spent helping their children with homework had increased from 1 minute a day to 15 minutes
- time spent caring for children increased from 30 minutes a day to 75 minutes
- the average amount of time spent entertaining went up from 25 minutes to 55 minutes per day
- time spent cooking has decreased for women, down from more than 1 hour and 40 minutes to just over an hour (73 minutes) per day; at the same time, men marginally increased their time in the kitchen from 26 to 27 minutes per day.

The growing number of money-rich, time-poor households presents new opportunities for businesses to provide convenient solutions to this group at a premium price. Sainsbury's was an early retailer to identify this opportunity and has developed a home delivery service that delivers customers' shopping to their home or place of work. The service has proved particularly popular with families who have difficulties in finding childminders, thereby avoiding the need to drag children round a supermarket. Some people have predicted the end of high-street shops as we know them, noting that internet-based distribution can be more efficient for a wide range of goods and services. However this overlooks the social needs that can be satisfied by a visit to a 'real' shopping centre – for example, a group of girls out shopping for clothes on a Saturday afternoon would probably consider online shopping to be a poor substitute, not only because of the technical limitations of the internet to convey properly the experiential values of clothes, but also because shopping with friends can be a social experience.

Social scientists have traditionally used the second of these approaches as a basis for defining social groupings, largely on account of its objectivity and relative ease of measurement. However, organizations must also recognize that an individual's attitudes can be crucial in determining buying behaviour, and have therefore been keen to introduce more subjective and self-assessed bases for classification. In the following sections we will review some bases commonly used by businesses for identifying social groups.

3.6.1 IPA classification system

One of the most long-standing and still widely used bases for social classification is the system adopted by the Institute of Practitioners in Advertising (IPA). It uses an individual's occupation as a basis for classification, on the basis that occupation is closely associated with many aspects of a person's attitudes and behaviour. The classes defined range from A to E, and Table 3.2 indicates the allocation of selected occupations to groups.

Table 3.2   IPA basis for social classification.

Class category	Occupation
A	Higher managerial, administrative or professional
B	Intermediate managerial, administrative or professional
C1	Supervisory or clerical, and junior managerial, administrative or professional
C2	Skilled manual workers
D	Semi- and unskilled manual workers
E	State pensioners or widows (no other earners), casual or lower-grade workers, or long-term unemployed

Such an attempt to reduce the multidimensional concept of social grouping to a single measure is bound to be an oversimplification, which limits its usefulness to business organizations. A person's occupation is not necessarily a good indicator of their buying behaviour – for example, an internet entrepreneur running a large business and a bishop would probably be put in the same occupational classification, but there are likely to be very significant differences in their spending patterns and the way they pass their leisure time. Nevertheless, the classification system described is widely used. Newspapers regularly analyse their readership in terms of membership of these groups, and go out of their way to show how many of the highly prized A/B readers they have.

3.6.2 Classification used for the UK Census

The data sets used by many organizations import data collected by the UK's Census of population. Since 1921, government statisticians have divided the population into six classes, based simply on their occupation. But the expansion of the number of workers in traditionally middle-class jobs such as finance and management led the government to increase the number of classes and to look more critically at an occupational title in terms of the life opportunities that it offers.

The Standard Occupational Classification used for the Census was first published in 1990, and updated in 2000. It uses two main concepts for classifying individuals:

1 the kind of work performed (that, is the job description)
2 the competence level required for the tasks and duties (the skills required for the job).

Changes introduced in 2000 reflected the need to improve comparability with the International Standard Classification of Occupations and the changing needs of users of census data, who were becoming increasingly dubious about the existing bases of classification. Revisions were influenced by innovations associated with technological developments and the redefinition of work, reflecting the educational attainment of those entering the labour market.

The main features of the revision included:

- a tighter definition of managerial occupations
- a thorough overhaul of computing and related occupations
- the introduction of specific occupations associated with the environment and conservation

- changes linked to the de-skilling of many manufacturing processes
- the recognition of the development of customer service occupations, and the emergence of remote service provision through the operation of call centres.

The major occupational groups defined by the Census are shown in Figure 3.4.

1 Managers and senior officials

2 Professional occupations

3 Associate professional and technical occupations

4 Administrative and secretarial occupations

5 Skilled trades occupations

6 Personal service occupations

7 Sales and customer service occupations

8 Process, plant and machine operatives

9 Elementary occupations

Figure 3.4 Major occupational groups used in UK Census data collection.

Each of these nine groups is broken down into further sub-groups so, for example, major group 2 (professional occupations) has a sub-major group (21) of science and technology professionals, which is broken down into a minor group (211) of science professionals, from which a unit (2111) of scientists can be identified.

In this revised system of classification there were risers and fallers. Teachers, librarians, nurses and police officers were among the risers, based on the skills and security of their job. Workers in call centres fell according to this system of classification.

3.6.3 Geodemographic classification system

A lot of research has shown a correlation between where a person lives and their buying behaviour. The type of house and its location says much more about an individual than can occupation alone. Income, the size of the family unit and attitudes towards city life/country living, as well as occupation, are closely related to residence. The classification of individuals in this way has come to be known as **geodemographic analysis**. A number of firms offer a geodemographic segmentation analysis, which allows a classification of small geographical pockets of households according to a combination of demographic characteristics and buying behaviour. One example of a widely used UK geodemographic segmentation system is MOSAIC, provided by Experian Ltd. By analysing a lot of sales data from people in each postcode area, it is possible to build up a good picture of the lifestyle and spending patterns associated with each classification (and also of individuals living at each address). It is also possible to see how the distribution of the population between different classifications changes over time (see Figure 3.5).

3.6.4 Lifestyle bases of classification

Geodemographic classification systems tell business a lot more about individuals than their occupation alone can, but this still misses much detail about the lifestyle of particular individuals, or the size of groups that share a similar lifestyle. A starting point for lifestyle segmentation is to understand where an individual is located in the family life cycle. Traditional models of family life cycles have portrayed individuals as going through a number of distinct and sequential stages, from

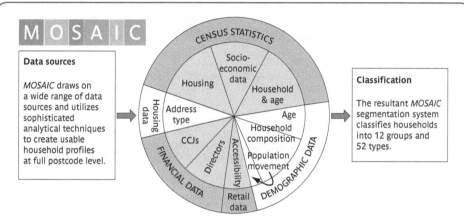

Figure 3.5 MOSAIC is a widely used method of geodemographic segmentation. Many companies are in the business of providing customer analysis services to help firms' segmentation, targeting and positioning strategies. One of the most widely used is Experian's MOSAIC consumer classification system. This gathers information about individuals from multiple sources under a number of headings, as shown in the diagram, and uses this to build up a picture of every household, as in the UK. From this information, each person has been assigned to one of 155 MOSAIC person types, aggregated into 67 household types (further aggregated into 15 broad groups). Each type has been given a distinctive and sometimes glib title, such as B05 'Mid-career climbers'; D16 'Side street singles' and I41 'Stressed borrowers' For a company planning a mailshot, or deciding on the best location for new service outlets, such information about consumer behaviour at the individual and household level can avoid waste by targeting the company's efforts at those groups who are most likely to respond to a proposition.
Source: Experian Ltd.

dependent child, through young adults, adults with dependent children, then with no dependent children ('empty nesters'), to solitary survivors. However, such simple linear models are no longer considered relevant to the increasing number of individuals who break this pattern through divorce, single parenthood, remarriage, and so on. The research company Mintel, for example, has advanced from the traditional family life cycle model by identifying a number of special categories that typify consumer habits in the early 2000s (see Table 3.3). Unlike the life stage groups, these groups represent only sections of the population and do not account for all adults.

Many research companies have developed much more subjective bases for defining lifestyle groups, which rely on a verbal description of the groups. Information to support the validity of these groups is hard to come by and generally relies on small sample surveys of the population. For this reason, such ideal-type classification systems are less well suited to monitoring social change than more objective systems based on quantifiable data.

Because of their subjectivity, there is a wide variety of lifestyle segmentation models, which tend to reflect the needs of the companies that created them. For example, one model developed by Young & Rubicam described four lifestyle groups to which members of a population could be allocated.

1 Conformers, comprising the bulk of the population, who typically may live in a suburban semi-detached house, drive a Ford Focus, shop at Sainsbury's and book a Thomson package holiday.

2 Aspirers, a smaller group who are ambitious, innovative and keen to surround themselves with the trappings of success. This group may typically live in a trendy mews house, drive a sports utility vehicle, shop for brand-name clothes and take adventure holidays.

Table 3.3 Consumer life stage and special categories as identified by Mintel.

Life stage groups	
Pre-family	those aged under 35 who are not parents
Family	those aged 15–54 with at least one child aged under 16 still at home
Empty nesters	no family/empty nesters aged 35–54 with no children [aged under 16]
Post-family	post-family/retired, those aged over 55/not working
Special category groups	
Benefit dependants	Es aged 35+ – those who are reliant solely on state benefits [around 10% of the adult population]
Families on a tight budget	working C2Ds with at least one child aged under 16 in the household – the majority have limited incomes that must be spent on a relatively large household [around 10% of the adult population]
Better-off families	working ABC1s with at least one child aged under 16 in the household [around 9% of the population]
Better-off empty nesters	ABC1s aged 35–64 who are working with no children [aged under 16] living at home. They are, therefore, the classic no family/ empty nesters with probably a high income that can be spent on themselves rather than on family [around 8% of the adult population]
Working managers	working ABs [around 9% of the population]
Working women	women in part- or full-time employment [around 21% of the adult population]

3 Controllers, by contrast, are comfortable in the knowledge that they have made it in life and do not feel the need to flaunt their success. They are more likely to live in a comfortable detached house, drive a Volvo, shop at Marks & Spencer and book their holiday through the local travel agent they trust.

4 Reformers have a vision of how life could be improved for everybody in society. At home they may be enthusiastic about DIY and energy conservation. They may see their car more as a means of transport than a status symbol, and buy own-label brands at the Co-op.

Of course, these are ideal types, and very few people will precisely meet these descriptions. However, they are a useful starting point for trying to understand who it is that a company is targeting. The numbers in each category have undoubtedly risen and fallen in the recent past. Aspirers seem to appear in great numbers during periods of economic boom, but become less conspicuous at the onset of a recession.

Many more informal, almost tongue-in-cheek, bases for segmenting lifestyle groups are commonly used. It has in the past, for example, been common to talk about lifestyle groups that have been labelled yuppies (young, upwardly mobile professionals), dinkys (dual income, no kids yet) and bobos (burnt out, but opulent), to name but a few. New descriptions emerge to describe new lifestyles. Again, these classifications are not at all scientific, but they give marketers a way of describing target markets.

Thinking around the subject

Sandwich statement

What does an individual's choice of sandwich say about them? The retailer Tesco undertook research that showed how complex the market for ready-made sandwiches had become, with clear segments emerging of people who sought quite different types of sandwich. In an attempt to define and target its lunch customers more precisely, the company found that well-paid executives invariably insisted on 'designer' sandwiches made from ciabatta and focaccia with sun-dried tomatoes and costing about £2.50. Salespeople and middle-ranking executives were more inclined to opt for meaty triple-deckers. Upwardly mobile women aged 25–40 chose low-calorie sandwiches costing around £1.49. Busy manual workers tended to grab a sandwich that looked affordable, simple and quick to eat, such as a ploughman's sandwich that Tesco sold for £1.15. Tesco's research claimed that sandwiches have become an important statement made by individuals, and need to be targeted appropriately. What do your snack meals say about you?

3.7 Demography

Demography is the study of populations in terms of their size and characteristics. Among the topics of interest to demographers are the age structure of a country, the geographic distribution of its population, the balance between males and females, and the likely future size of the population and its characteristics.

3.7.1 The importance of demographic analysis to business organizations

A number of reasons can be identified why business organizations should study demographic trends.

- First, on the demand side, demography helps to predict the size of the market that a product is likely to face. For example, demographers can predict an increase in the number of elderly people living in the UK and the numbers living in the south-west region of the country. Businesses can use this information as a basis for predicting, for example, the size of the market for retirement homes in the south-west.

- Demographic trends have supply-side implications. An important aim of business organizations is to match the opportunities facing an organization with the resource strengths that it possesses. In many businesses, labour is a key resource and a study of demographics will indicate the human resources that an organization can expect to have available to it in future years. Thus a business that has relied on relatively low-wage, young labour, such as retailing, would need to have regard to the availability of this type of worker when developing its product strategy. A retailer might decide to invest in more automated methods of processing transactions and handling customer enquiries rather than relying on a traditional but diminishing source of relatively low-cost labour.

- The study of demographics also has implications for public-sector services, which are themselves becoming more marketing orientated. Changing population structures influence the community facilities that need to be provided by the government. For example, fluctuations in the number of children have affected the number of schools and teachers required, while the increasing number of elderly people will require the provision of more specialized housing and hospital facilities suitable for this group.

■ In an even wider sense, demographic change can influence the nature of family life and communities, and ultimately affects the social and economic system in which organizations operate. The imbalance that is developing between a growing dependent elderly population and a diminishing population of working age is already beginning to affect government fiscal policy and the way in which we care for the elderly, with major implications for business organizations.

Although the study of demographics has assumed great importance in western Europe in recent years, study of the consequences of population change dates back a considerable time. T.R. Malthus studied the effects of population change in a paper published in 1798. He predicted that the population would continue to grow exponentially, while world food resources would grow at a slower linear rate. Population growth would be held back only by 'war, pestilence and famine' until an equilibrium point was again reached at which population was just equal to the food resources available.

Malthus's model of population growth failed to predict the future accurately and this only serves to highlight the difficulty of predicting population levels when the underlying assumptions on which predictions are based are themselves changing. Malthus failed to predict, on the one hand, the tremendous improvement in agricultural efficiency that would allow a larger population to be sustained and, on the other hand, changes in social and cultural attitudes that were to limit family size.

3.7.2 Global population changes

Globally, population has been expanding at an increasing rate. The world population level at AD 1000 has been estimated at about 300 million. Over the next 750 years, it rose at a steady rate to 728 million in 1750. Thereafter, the rate of increase became progressively more rapid, doubling in the following 150 years to 1550 million in 1900, and almost doubling again to 3000 million in the 62 years to 1962. The UN estimated total world population in 2007 to be 6.6 billion, and predicted that this would rise to 9.1 billion by 2050 (UNFPA 2009). The growth of world population has not been uniform, with recent growth being focused on the world's poorer countries, especially Korea and China, as well as South America. Within the EU countries, the total population in recent times has increased at a natural rate of about 1 per 1000 population (that is, for every 1000 deaths, there are 1001 births). However, this hides a range of rates of increase with, at each extreme, Ireland having a particularly high birth rate and Germany a particularly low one. This has major implications for future age structures and consumption patterns (see below). Much faster population growth is expected to occur in Africa and Latin America.

An indication of the variation in population growth rates is given in Figure 3.6. It should, however, be noted that there is still considerable debate about future world population levels, with many predictions being revised downwards.

A growth in the population of a country does not necessarily mean a growth in business opportunities, for the countries with the highest population growth rates also tend to be those with the lowest gross domestic product (GDP) per head. Indeed, in many countries of Africa, total GDP is not keeping up with the growth in population levels, resulting in a lower GDP per head. On the other hand, the growth in population results in a large and low-cost labour force, which can help to explain the tendency for many European-based organizations to base their design capacity in Europe but relatively labour-intensive assembly operations in the Far East.

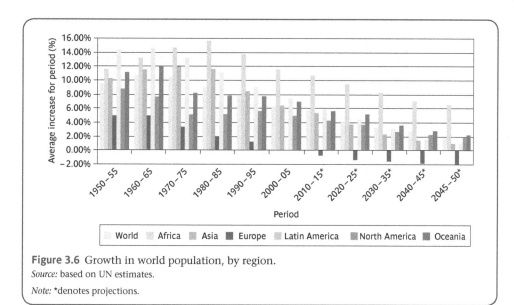

Figure 3.6 Growth in world population, by region.

Source: based on UN estimates.

Note: *denotes projections.

3.7.3 Changes in UK population level

The first British Census was carried out in 1801 and the subsequent ten-yearly Census provides the basis for studying changes in the size of the British population. A summary of British population growth is shown in Table 3.4.

The fluctuation in the rate of population growth can be attributed to three main factors: the birth rate, the death rate, and the difference between inward and outward migration. The fluctuation in these rates is illustrated in Figure 3.7. These three components of population change are described below.

3.7.4 The birth rate

The **birth rate** is usually expressed in terms of the number of live births per 1000 population. Since the Second World War, the birth rate of the UK has shown a number of distinct cyclical tendencies. The immediate post-war years are associated with a 'baby boom', followed by a steady decrease in the number of births until 1956. Following this, the rate rose again until the mid-1960s during a second, but lesser, baby boom. The birth rate then fell until the mid-1970s, rising again in recent years. Worldwide, the UN has estimated that the average birth rate per female has fallen from 5 in 1953 to 2.56 in 2007 (UNFPA 2009). Of the 44 countries in the developed world, all except Albania were reported to have birth rates below the natural replacement rate of 2.1 per female (the level needed to maintain a stable population level).

In order to explain these trends, it is necessary to examine two key factors:

1 the number of women in the population who are of childbearing age

2 the proportion of these women who actually give birth (this is referred to as the fertility rate).

Table 3.4 Population growth, England, Wales and Scotland, 1801–2031.

Year	Population of England, Wales and Scotland (000)	Average increase per decade (%)
1801	10,501	13.9
1871	26,072	9.4
1911	40,891	4.5
1941	46,605	5.8
1971	54,369	0.8
1981	54,814	2.4
1991	55,831	2.8
2001	57,424	2.3
2011	58,794	1.7 (projected)
2031	58,970	0.5 (projected)

Source: based on *Annual Abstract of Statistics*, Government Actuary's Department and population censuses.

The peak in the birth rate of the early 1960s could be partly explained by the 'baby boom' children of the immediate post-war period working through to childbearing age. Similarly, the children of this group have themselves reached childbearing age, accounting for some of the recent increase in the birth rate. Greater doubt hangs over reasons for changes in the fertility rate, usually expressed in terms of the number of births per 1000 women aged between 16 and 44. This has varied from a peak of 115 at the beginning of the twentieth century to a low point of 56.8 in 1983 (see Table 3.5).

There are many possible explanations for changes in fertility rates and it is our difficulty in understanding the precise nature of these changes that makes population forecasting a difficult task. Some of the more frequently suggested causes of the declining fertility rate are described below.

- A large family is no longer seen as an insurance policy for future parental security. The extended family has declined in importance and state institutions have taken over many of the welfare functions towards elderly members of the family that were previously expected of children. Furthermore, infant and child mortality has declined, and consequently the need for large numbers of births has declined. Alongside this falling need for large numbers of children has come a greater ability to control the number of births.

- Children use household resources that could otherwise be used for consumption. The cost of bringing up children has been increasing as a result of increased expectations of children and the raising of the school leaving age. Although in many western countries this is partly offset by financial incentives for having children, the cost of child rearing has increased relative to consumer purchases in general. According to a survey carried out by the UK's largest friendly society, LV, parents typically spend £9610 a year to feed, clothe and educate each of their children. The total cost of raising a child to the age of 21 was estimated to be £201,809, excluding private school fees (Smithers 2010).

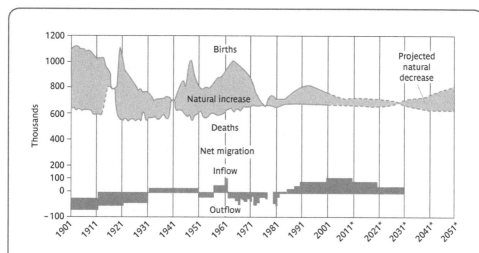

Figure 3.7 Changes in the UK birth rate, death rate and level of net migration, 1901–2051.

Source: Office of Population Censuses and Surveys (OPCS), Government Actuary's Department, © Crown copyright.

Note: *denotes projections.

- In addition to diverting household resources from the consumption of other goods and services, caring for children also has the effect of reducing the earning capacity of the household. Women may also seek additional status and career progression by having fewer children or spacing them over a shorter period of time.
- Birth rates tend to be related to current economic conditions, falling significantly in response to temporary economic recession and rising in response to a period of economic boom.

Table 3.5 General fertility rate: total births per 1000 women aged 15–44, UK.

Year	Fertility rate
1900	115.0
1933	81.0
1951	73.0
1961	90.6
1971	84.3
1981	62.1
1991	64.0
2001	54.5

Source: based on OPCS/Census of Population data.

The effects of variation in birth rates can be felt for a long time after the variation itself. In the UK, a post-war peak in births resulted in a large 'baby boomer' generation having a high number of children in the 1960s, and their children in turn made up a large cohort of mothers who raised the birth rate again when they had children 20 to 30 years later. Although these cycles become progressively less pronounced over time, businesses should nevertheless be able to predict them and adjust their capacity accordingly.

3.7.5 The death rate

Death rates are normally expressed as the number of people in the country that die in a year per 1000 of the population. This is sometimes called the crude death rate; the age-specific death rate takes account of the age of death and is expressed as the number of people per 1000 of a particular age group that die in a year.

In contrast to the volatility of the birth rate during the post-war period, the death rate has been relatively stable and has played a relatively small part in changing the total population level. The main feature of mortality in the UK has been a small decline in age-specific death rates, having the effect of increasing the survival chances of relatively old people. The age-specific death rate of women has fallen more significantly than for men. The main reasons for the decline in age-specific death rates are improved standards of living, a better environment and better awareness of health issues, and an improvement in health services. While age-specific death rates have been falling in most advanced industrial countries, the UK has generally experienced a slower fall than most other EU member-states.

3.7.6 Migration

If immigration is compared with emigration, a figure for net migration is obtained. In general, net immigration tends to be greatest during periods of economic prosperity, while net emigration tends to be greatest during periods of economic recession. During most periods of the twentieth century, the UK experienced a net outflow of population, the main exceptions being: the 1930s, caused by emigrants to the Commonwealth returning home during the depression; the 1940s when a large number of refugees entered the UK from Nazi Europe; and the late 1950s/early 1960s when the prosperity of the British economy attracted large numbers of immigrants from the new Commonwealth. Emigration has tended to peak at times of economic depression in the UK. The prosperity of the UK during the 1990s and 2000s increased the number of immigrants. The enlargement of the EU in 2004, to include former eastern European countries, brought a large number of migrants to Britain from the new member-states; some estimates put this as high as one million between 2004 and 2007. This has put pressure on public facilities in some areas, and provided opportunities for businesses targeting these new immigrants (for example, Lloyds TSB Bank announced in 2006 that it would open a business unit employing Polish-speaking staff, specifically to target Polish immigrants).

3.7.7 The age structure of the population

It was noted earlier that the total population of the UK – and indeed most countries of the EU – is fairly stable. However, within this stable total, there has been a more noted change in the composition of particular age groups, with Ireland having a particularly high birth rate and Germany a particularly low one (see Table 3.6). This has major implications for future age structures and consumption patterns. By 2030, people over 65 in Germany will account for almost half the adult population, compared with one-fifth in 2000. And unless the country's birth rate recovers from its present low of 1.3 per woman, over the same period its population of under-35s will shrink about twice as fast as the older population will grow. The net result

Table 3.6 A comparison of the population structure of EU member countries.

Country	Total population 1 Jan 2005 (000)	% aged 0–14	% aged 15–24	% aged 25–64	% aged 65+
Austria	8,206	16.1	12.3	55.6	16.0
Belgium	10,445	17.2	12.1	53.5	17.2
Bulgaria	7,761	13.8	13.7	55.3	17.1
Czech Republic	10,220	14.9	13.4	57.7	14.0
Cyprus	749	19.2	15.9	53.0	11.9
Denmark	5,411	18.8	11.0	55.1	15.0
Estonia	1,347	15.1	15.6	52.5	16.5
Finland	5,236	17.5	12.4	54.2	15.9
France	60,561	18.5	13.0	52.2	16.4
Germany	82,500	14.5	11.7	55.2	18.6
Greece	11,075	14.4	12.4	55.1	18.1
Hungary	10,097	15.6	13.1	55.6	15.6
Ireland	4,109	20.7	15.5	52.6	11.2
Italy	58,462	14.2	10.5	55.9	19.4
Latvia	2,306	14.8	15.6	53.1	16.5
Lithuania	3,425	17.1	15.4	52.5	15.1
Luxembourg	455	18.7	11.5	55.5	14.2
Malta	402	17.6	14.5	54.5	13.3
Netherlands	16,305	18.5	12.0	55.6	14.0
Poland	38,173	16.7	16.5	53.7	13.1
Portugal	10,529	15.6	12.6	54.7	17.0
Romania	21,658	15.9	15.5	53.9	14.7
Slovakia	5,384	17.1	16.1	55.2	11.6
Slovenia	1,997	14.4	13.4	56.9	15.3
Spain	43,038	14.5	12.3	56.4	16.8
Sweden	9,011	17.6	12.2	53.0	17.2
UK	60,034	18.1	13.1	52.9	16.0

Source: compiled from *Eurostat Yearbook 2006–07* (Population Statistics) (Eurostat 2007).

will be that the total population, now 82 million, will decline to 70–73 million, and the number of people of working age will fall by a quarter, from 40 million today to 30 million. In Japan, the population is expected to have peaked in 2005, at around 125 million and, by around 2030, the share of over-65s in the adult population will have grown to about half (*The Economist* 2001).

The changes that have affected the size of age-specific segments in the UK are illustrated in Figure 3.8.

What are the implications for business organizations of an ageing of the population structure?

- There is a growing imbalance between the shrinking size of the working population and an increasingly large dependent population. Government statistics show that, between 1961 and 2003, the number of people of working age in the UK available to support the retired population decreased from 4.1 per pensioner to 3.3. This figure is expected to fall again slightly to 2020 but then fall again sharply as those in the baby boom generation start to become eligible for their pensions. The ratio of those contributing to the pensions that sustain the retired population is smaller still, to take account of the fact that although many people of working age are available to work, many are either unemployed or pay no taxes. By 2020, each pensioner will be supported by the contributions of two tax-paying workers. This is expected to fall to 1.6 by 2040.

- For businesses that have offered their employees a 'final salary' pension scheme, the cost of paying pensions has increased markedly, as longevity has resulted in a lengthening stream of pension payments. The current profitability of many companies has been reduced as they divert profits to fill this pension gap.

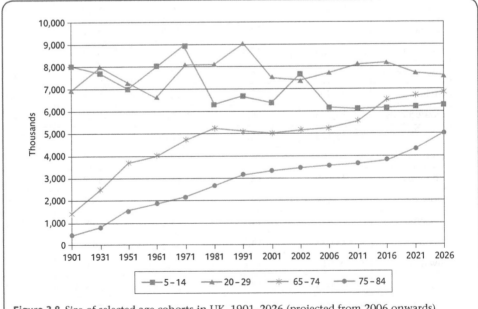

Figure 3.8 Size of selected age cohorts in UK, 1901–2026 (projected from 2006 onwards).
Source: based on Office of Population Censuses and Surveys estimates.

- With the number of younger people declining as a proportion of the workforce, employers are increasingly looking to older people to fill their vacancies.

- The growing proportion of older people in the population may change the values of a youth-orientated culture. For example, the emphasis on fashion and short-life products

🔄 Thinking around the subject

How to defuse a demographic time bomb

The term demographic time bomb is often used to describe the effects of the increasing average age of populations in the EU. What will the effects of this 'time bomb' be on the business environment?

In 2005, the European Commission published a Green Paper on demographic change, which claimed that, from 2005 until 2030, the EU would lose 20.8 million (6.8 per cent) people of working age. By 2030, Europe would have 18 million fewer children and young people than in 2005. By 2030, the number of 'older workers' (aged 55 to 64) would have risen by 24 million as the baby boomer generation become senior citizens, and the EU would have 34.7 million citizens aged over 80 (compared to 18.8 million in 2005). Average life expectancy has also risen by five years since 1960 for women and nearly four years for men. The number of people aged 80+ is expected to grow 180 per cent by 2050. At the same time, the EU's fertility rate fell to 1.48 in 2003, below the level needed to replace the population (2.1 children per woman). As a result of these demographic changes, the proportion of dependent young and old people in the population will increase from 49 per cent in 2005 to 66 per cent in 2030.

For many people, the most pressing consequence of an ageing population focuses on pensions provision, but according to the European Employment and Social Affairs Commissioner, Vladimir Spidla, the looming crisis raises issues that are much broader. 'This development will affect almost every aspect of our lives – for example, the way businesses operate and work is organized, our urban planning, the design of houses, public transport, voting behaviour and the infrastructure of shopping possibilities in our cities,' he said.

The EU report noted that modern Europe has never experienced economic growth without rising birth rates, and suggested that 'ever larger migrant flows may be needed to meet the need for labour and to safeguard Europe's prosperity'.

How can Europe increase the size of its working population to serve the growing proportion of the population that is dependent? One strategy is to ensure that all people who are of working age and able to work actually do so. This would entail eliminating unemployment through retraining and changes to government social payments. Another strategy to increase long-term employment levels is to promote a higher birth rate. But there is an apparent contradiction here, because there is evidence that pressure on families to work harder has been having the effect of reducing the birth rate. The EU report found that Europe's low birth rate is largely the result of constraints on families' choices – late access to employment, job instability, expensive housing and lack of

⤵

family-focused incentives (such as parental leave and childcare). Incentives of this kind can have a positive impact on the birth rate and increase employment, especially female employment.

A further way of expanding the workforce is to rely on immigration, but this raises a number of issues. First, there is the emotive issue to many people of diluting a national culture. More significantly, from a demographic perspective, what happens when these immigrant workers themselves get old and become dependent? They will need yet more immigrants to look after them. There is also a moral issue associated with immigration, because a common source of immigrants is the developing world. Given that many immigrants are the better-educated members of the society that they come from, is it morally right for the prosperous West to deprive developing countries of trained staff, such as doctors and nurses?

In presenting the EU report, Commissioner Spidla noted that 'Politics alone cannot solve the problem . . . they have to go hand in hand with a picture in society that does not stamp women who re-enter the labour market after maternity leave as "bad mothers" and men that take care of children as "softies".' Why do some cultures find this challenge insurmountable, whereas others readily accept working mothers as a valuable addition to the workforce? Is this the best way to defuse the 'demographic time bomb'?

may give way to an emphasis on quality and durability as the growing numbers in the older age groups increasingly dominate cultural values.

3.7.8 Household structure

Reference was made earlier in this chapter to the changing role and functions of family units, and this is reflected in an analysis of **household structure** statistics. A number of important trends can be noted.

- First, it was noted above that there has been a trend for women to have fewer children. From a high point in the 1870s, the average number of children for each woman born in 1930 was 2.35, 2.2 for those born in 1945, and it is projected to be 1.97 for those born in 1965. There has also been a tendency for women to have children later in life. In the UK, the average age at which women have their first child moved from 24 years in 1961 to 28 in 2001. There has also been an increase in the number of women having no children. According to the Office of Population Census and Surveys, more than one-fifth of women born in 1967 are expected to be childless when they reach the age of 40, compared with 13 per cent of those born in 1947.

- Alongside a declining number of children has been a decline in the average household size. The total number of dwellings in the UK is estimated to have risen by 9 per cent between 1992 and 2002, significantly outstripping population growth, which was 2.3 per cent for the same period. The result is a reduction in the number of people per household, falling continuously from an average of 3.1 people in 1961 to 2.4 in 2001 (Mintel 2003). There has been a particular fall in the number of very large households with six or more people (down from 7 per cent of all households in 1961 to under 2 per cent in 2001) and a significant increase in the number of one-person households (up from 14 per cent to 30 per cent over the same period). A number of factors have contributed to the increase in one-person households, including the increase in solitary survivors, later marriage and an increased divorce rate. The business implications of the growth of this group are numerous, ranging from an increased demand for smaller units of housing to the types and size of groceries purchased. A single-person household buying for him or herself is likely to use different types of retail outlet compared to the household buying as a unit – the single person may be more likely to use a niche retailer than the (typically) housewife buying for the whole family, whose needs may be better met by a department store. Mintel showed a number of ways in which the spending patterns of single-person households deviate from the average. For example, compared to the British average, a person living in a single-person household spends 49 per cent more on tobacco, 26 per cent more on household services and 23 per cent less on meat (Mintel 2003).

■ There has been an increase in other non-traditional forms of household. Households comprising lone parents with children have increased, and in 2001, 20 per cent of all households in England and Wales with dependent children comprised only one adult. Further variation is provided by house sharers, who live independent lives within a household, pragmatically sharing the cost of many household items, while retaining the

⟳ Thinking around the subject

More elderly people, so why are homes for the elderly closing?

Ageing of the population is a major opportunity for many organizations. However, the link between growth in size of the elderly population and demand for a company's products can be complex. Nursing homes may expect a boom in demand as the population ages. However, during the period 1995–2004, the number of elderly people in residential care in the UK fell, and many care homes and their operators went out of business, despite a growth in the number of elderly people during this period. Trying to forecast future demand for care homes is complicated by uncertainty over the future health needs of elderly people – will the elderly people of the future be healthier and able to look after themselves for longer? Will they make greater efforts to live in their own homes, rather than in a residential care home? Some care homes, such as this one, have spotted this trend and now offer an outreach service to care for people in their own homes. Costs of operating residential care homes are likely to increase, fuelled

by increasing government regulations, and wages rising in real terms, reflecting a scarcity of people of working age relative to the number of elderly people. How much will elderly people and their relatives be able or willing to pay for residential care home accommodation? How much will the government be prepared to pay towards care? The Scottish Parliament announced in 2003 that it would provide financial support for elderly people in residential care homes, making the sector more attractive to operators in Scotland compared with the rest of the UK.

independence of mind more typical of a single-person household. The number of shared households has increased as young people find themselves priced out of the property market, and shared ownership (or shared rental) offers lifestyle opportunities that may otherwise be closed to a single person. In some cases, two families have shared the cost of a house, living as separate units within it.

■ Very significant differences occur throughout the EU in home ownership patterns, with implications for demand for a wide range of home-related services. The proportion of households living in owned accommodation ranges from 57 per cent in Germany to 74 per cent in the UK and Belgium (Eurostat 2007).

3.7.9 Geographical distribution of population

The population density of the UK of 231 people per square kilometre is one of the highest in the world. However, this figure hides the fact that the population is dispersed very unevenly between regions, and between urban and rural areas. The distribution of population is not static.

Regional distribution

The major feature of the regional distribution of the UK population is the dominance of the south-east of England, with 30 per cent of the population. By contrast, the populations of Scotland, Wales and Northern Ireland account in total for only 17 per cent of the UK population.

Movement between the regions tends to be a very gradual process. In an average year, about 10 per cent of the population will change address, but only about one-eighth of these will move to another region. Nevertheless, there have been a number of noticeable trends. First, throughout the twentieth century there had been a general drift of population from the north to the Midlands and south. More recently, there has been a trend for population to move away from the relatively congested south-east to East Anglia, the south-west and the Home Counties. This can be partly explained by the increased cost of industrial and residential location in the south-east, the greater locational flexibility of modern industry and the desire of people for a pleasanter environment in which to live. The inter-regional movement of population is illustrated in Figure 3.9.

Urban concentration

Another trend has been a shift in the proportion of the population living in urban areas. Throughout most of western Europe, the nineteenth and twentieth centuries have been associated with a drift from rural areas to towns. In the UK, this has resulted in the urban areas of Greater London, Greater Manchester, Merseyside, Greater Glasgow, the West Midlands, West Yorkshire and Tyneside having just one-thirtieth of the UK's surface area, but nearly one-third of the total population. From the 1960s, the trend towards urbanization was partly reversed, with many of the larger conurbations experiencing a decline in population, combined with a deterioration in many inner-city areas. Those moving out have tended to be the most economically active, leaving behind a relatively elderly and poor population. Much of the movement from the conurbations has been towards the rural areas just beyond the urban fringe. For example, London has lost population to the Home Counties of Berkshire, Buckinghamshire, Hertfordshire and Essex. The increasingly large dormitory population of these areas remains dependent on the neighbouring conurbation. Movement from urban to rural areas has brought about a change in lifestyle, which has implications for businesses. Higher car ownership in rural areas has led more households to make fewer shopping trips for household goods, to travel

Figure 3.9 Percentage population change by region, 2002–2011 projections.

Source: based on information published by the Office of Population Censuses and Surveys, General Register Office (Scotland) and General Register Office (Northern Ireland).

further to the shop that best suits their lifestyle and to spend more on each trip. In this changed shopping pattern, the decision-making unit may comprise more members of the household than in an urban area where the (typically) wife may have made more frequent trips to the local supermarket by herself.

More recently, there has been a trend for young professional people to move back into town centres. For this group, having the facilities of a town centre close at hand without the need for increasingly expensive and time-consuming commuting has proved attractive. Town centres, which were once deserted in the evening, have often been brought back to life, helped by this group's patronage of wine bars, restaurants and all-night convenience stores.

The geographical distribution of the population differs between EU member-states. For example, EU statistics show that the proportion of the population living within metropolitan areas varies from 13 per cent in Italy to 44 per cent in France. The resulting differences in lifestyles can have implications for goods and services as diverse as car repairs, entertainment and retailing.

Case study:
A journey through Liverpool – European Capital of Culture 2008

By Damian Gallagher, University of Ulster

Photo reproduced with permission of Liverpool City Council.

To many people, Liverpool's culture is characterized by the 'Scouser', an individual with a jovial, happy-go-lucky sense of humour, a strong, distinct accent and sense of community spirit. The Scouser's love of music and entertainment is epitomized by Liverpool being the birthplace of the Beatles, and home to one of the world's greatest football teams. But scratch beneath the surface of Scouser culture and you will find a number of subcultures. It has always been that way, and a historical excursion through the city's culture demonstrates how the evolution of Scouser culture has influenced the business environment of Liverpool.

In 1660, the population of Liverpool was a modest 1200, but over the course of the next three centuries this was to change dramatically in the face of unrelenting urban and commercial growth. By 1775 the culture of Liverpool was dominated by commerce and the population had increased to 35,000; by 1801 this had doubled to more than 82,295 as more people were drawn to its ever developing port facilities and transport links, and it grew to become one of the most important ports in the world, trading in almost everything, including sugar, tobacco, grain, cotton and even people.

As well as growing in size, the population had grown in its cultural diversity. Between 1830 and 1930 Liverpool became a centre for transcontinental migration as almost 9 million people used its port as a gateway to a new life. Many sought escape from the events of their own countries of origin, such as the Irish famine and social unrest in eastern Europe, via emigration to Canada, the USA, Australia, New Zealand, South Africa and South America. Many immigrant seafarers settled in the area and others moved from neighbouring agricultural areas attracted by the work available. Between 1845 and 1849, 1.25 million Irish people used Liverpool in this way, but many had to stay, as they could not afford to go any further. By 1851, 25 per cent of Liverpool's population was Irish.

By the mid-nineteenth century, Liverpool had become a city of social extremes. There was a distinctly unequal distribution of wealth, headed by the wealthy elite of merchant traders, bankers and shipping agents who benefited from Liverpool's prospering port and invested heavily in the city's architecture, but very little in the education, housing or healthcare of its workers. This allowed ghetto-like segregation to develop in the city, with lots of poverty and deprivation. As the population increased, the city's boundaries expanded, but its infrastructure struggled to cope with the sheer number of people, and many poor Irish, Caribbean, Chinese, Dutch, German, Jewish, Welsh, Filipino and African working-class slum areas developed around the Scotland Road and Sebastapol Dock areas. Houses built to accommodate 19 were often found to contain over 90 people, where typhus, dysentery, cholera and lack of adequate sanitation saw average life expectancy at only 38 for women and 37 for men compared to the national averages of 42 and 40 respectively.

In the years prior to the Second World War, Liverpool's population peaked at 867,000. However, the twentieth century saw massive changes in the world's economic order, with many political and commercial changes having a negative impact upon Liverpool. As the century drew to a close, the last of the working docks had closed and the once thriving port was a shadow of its former self. The population fell to 439,473, with many having chosen to leave the city in the face of rising unemployment.

High unemployment has often played a major role in the life of Liverpool. Manufacturing, which had boomed in the early post-war years, declined in the 1970s and 1980s. The docks were also shrinking rapidly and many of the inner-city docks closed, with the once strong workforce being replaced by machinery and new technologies. This led to much social and political unrest as answers and solutions were sought by the 22 per cent of the male population who were unemployed (compared to the national average of 10 per cent). In some areas of Liverpool, unemployment was as high as 90 per cent. In 1981, social unrest exploded into the notorious Toxteth riots. While racial tensions between the police and black youths provided the spark, it is now widely accepted that this was not a 'race riot'. Many underlying social issues lay at the heart of the problems in the form of chronic unemployment, bad housing and poor education. Many white youths from neighbouring areas saw the riots as an excuse to vent their frustrations and joined in the fierce battles that raged for most of that summer, causing millions of pounds' worth of damage and leading to over 500 arrests.

Many people in these areas also blamed the recently elected Thatcher Conservative government for making their problems worse, seeing no role for the working classes in its policies of free-market enterprise and the reduced role of trades unions. This gave birth in the mid-1980s to a radical militant local government in the city. Based on the Far Left of the Labour Party, it was seen by many as a revolt against Thatcherism as it embarked upon largely confrontational policies that were detached from the central Conservative government. In challenging the Conservative government's house-building policies, among others, the socialist government of Liverpool appeared to be riding on a wave of popular support from the disadvantaged Scousers who had lost out in the economic and social reforms of the Thatcher government.

This militancy was seen by many as a hangover from the working-class labour organizations of the docks that were opposed to the aims of the Conservative government. Negative media images of a city with many social and economic problems did little to attract inward investment to the city or alleviate the sense of decline felt by its inhabitants.

By the 1990s, while the extremes of wealth and poverty still existed in Liverpool, though perhaps not as pronounced as in earlier years, a substantial middle-class population had also emerged. A new generation of young affluent and well-educated professionals with ambition and drive for success helped to fuel the social and economic regeneration of the city – some even point out with irony that these were the products of the Thatcherism that was once so reviled by the traditional Scouser. The smart coffee bars that this group gravitates to today are in another world compared with the rough pubs and ale houses of their predecessors.

An aerial view of Liverpool today reveals a city that is symbolized by its two cathedrals, one Catholic and one Anglican, standing at opposite ends of Hope Street. However, this hides the underlying multicultural make-up of the city, which remains from its days as a successful trading port. The Irish influence on the city remains strong, with many Scousers being fourth- and fifth-generation Irish, and the city often being referred to as the 'capital of Ireland'! Muslims, Jews, Hindus, Sikhs, Buddhists and Taoists of Europe's second-largest Chinese community still play a substantial role in the city. From 2004 onwards, many Poles headed for Liverpool, following the expansion of the EU to eastern Europe. Many businesses specifically target these ethnic and cultural groups, whose cultures are celebrated in events such as the annual Chinese New Year celebrations, the Irish Festival, the Caribbean Carnival and the Liverpool Welsh Choral Union, as well as the recent gay, lesbian, bisexual and transsexual Homotopia festivals.

In 2008, the city of Liverpool was named European Capital of Culture. It was looking to its Capital of Culture celebrations as a key driver for economic and social regeneration in the same way as previous hosts had experienced (e.g. Glasgow in 1990). With unemployment at its lowest rate for 30 years as a good starting point, the city saw many benefits to be obtained before, during and after 2008; The docks area that temporarily lay derelict has been subject to regeneration and redevelopment, and is now home to many expensive luxury apartments and trendy bars, shops, restaurants and cafes, art galleries and museums. In 2004, Liverpool's Pier Head was even designated a UNESCO World Heritage site.

A monitoring study undertaken by the University of Liverpool reported in 2010 that there had been 9.7 million additional visits specifically influenced by the Capital of Culture celebrations generating direct expenditure of £753.8 million across the north-west in 2008 alone. Researchers also found, for the first time in decades, positive stories about the city's cultural assets dominated over the traditional, negative emphasis on social issues. By the end of 2008, 85 per cent of Liverpool residents agreed that the city was a better place to live than before the European Capital of Culture award. The researchers also found that 99 per cent of visitors to the city liked the 'atmosphere' and 'welcoming' feel of the city, well above the response in other UK popular tourist destinations and previous years' findings for Liverpool.

Will such an influx bring about further change in the composition of Liverpool's cultural groups? And will the traditional working-class solidarity derived from the days of the docks survive in an era of consumerism and competitive service industry employment?

Sources: Liverpool Capital of Culture website, **www.liverpool08.com/**; University of Liverpool, IMPACTS 08 - European Capital of Culture Research Programme, at www.liv.ac.uk/impacts08/.

QUESTIONS

1 Summarize the changes in the cultural composition of Liverpool that have occurred during the last two centuries, and explain why business organizations should be interested in understanding these changes.

2 The case describes periods of social unrest in Liverpool that resulted from rising levels of unemployment following the decline of many traditional industries. Should business organizations seek to address issues of social exclusion such as that which occurred in Liverpool in the 1980s? If so, how could they help?

3 Identify the possible effects on businesses in Liverpool resulting from being European Capital of Culture 2008.

Summary

Societies are not homogeneous and this chapter has explored the processes by which individuals develop distinct social and cultural values. The concepts of social class, lifestyles, reference groups, family structure and culture are important reference points for businesses, and change in these must be monitored and addressed. Population totals and structures change, and this chapter has reviewed the impact of demographic change on the marketing of goods and services. A changing population structure also has implications for the availability of employees.

There is a close link between this chapter and **Chapter 5**, where we look at the social responsibility of businesses. As attitudes change, there has been a trend for the public to expect business organizations to act in a socially more acceptable manner. There are close links between the social environment and the political environment (**Chapter 2**), with the latter reflecting changes in the former. It has also been noted that technology can have a two-way effect with the social environment, and understanding the complexity of society's changing needs calls for an information system that is comprehensive and speedy (**Chapter 4**). When a company enters an overseas market, it is likely to face a quite different set of cultural values (**Chapter 14**).

Key Terms

Age structure (111)	Census of population (103)
Attitude (89)	Cultural convergence (88)
Birth rate (109)	Culture (87)
Cellular household (96)	Demography (108)
Ethnic minorities (91)	Migration (112)
Family roles (95)	Reference group (97)
Geodemographic analysis (104)	Role (95)
Household structure (116)	Social class (92)
Life stage (105)	Subculture (89)
Lifestyle (99)	Values (98)

Online Learning Centre

To help you grasp the key concepts of this chapter, explore the extra resources posted on the Online Learning Centre at *www.mcgraw-hill.co.uk/palmer*. Among other helpful resources there are chapter-by-chapter test questions, revision notes and web links.

Chapter review questions

1 Examine the ways in which the different culture of a less developed country may affect the marketing of confectionery that has previously been marketed successfully in the UK.

2 In what ways are the buying habits of a household with two adults and two children likely to change when the children leave home?

3 Critically assess some of the implications of an increasingly aged population on the demand for hotel accommodation in the UK.

Activities

1 Postcodes can reveal a lot about the social and economic composition of an area. If you live in the UK, go to the *Up My Street* website (www.upmystreet.com) and enter a selection of postcodes that you are familiar with. You will be given a range of information about each area – for example, house prices, nearby schools and crime levels. Click on the demographics button and you will be presented with a description of the area based on its ACORN code classification. How well do the ACORN classifications match the characteristics of inhabitants that you are familiar with?

2 If you live in a multi-ethnic area, examine advertising material for businesses catering for distinctive ethnic groups. What, if any, differences can you spot in how these businesses have differentiated their product, compared to similar goods and services offered by other companies to the indigenous population? To what extent do you see evidence of common underlying needs, but distinct cultural manifestations?

3 Consider a recent case when you went out with a group of friends to a restaurant, a bar or cinema. Critically examine the processes involved in deciding between the alternatives available. Explore the effects of the attitudes, values and lifestyles of the individuals concerned. What was the effect of social pressure on the final decision?

Further reading

Social classification has been discussed widely and the following texts are useful in a marketing context.

Devine, F., Savage, M., Scott, J. and Crompton, R. (2004) *Rethinking Class: Cultures, Identities and Lifestyles*, Basingstoke, Palgrave Macmillan.

Mihić, C. and Ćulina, G. (2006) 'Buying behavior consumption: social class versus income', *Management*, Vol. 11, No. 2, pp. 77–92.

For further discussion of market segmentation methods, the following texts show practical application of methods to identify groups within society that have similar consumption patterns.

Dibb, S. and Simkin, L. (2007) *Market Segmentation Success: Making it Happen!*, New York, Haworth Press.

McDonald, M. and Dunbar, I. (2010) *Market Segmentation: How to Do It, How to Profit from It*, Oxford, Butterworth-Heinemann.

Yankelovich, D. and Meer, D. (2006) 'Rediscovering market segmentation', *Harvard Business Review*, February, pp. 1–10.

For statistics on the changing structure of UK society and its habits, the following regularly updated publications of the Office for National Statistics (ONS) provide good coverage.

Family Expenditure Survey: a sample survey of consumer spending habits, providing a snapshot of household spending, published annually.

Population Trends: statistics on population, including population change, births and deaths, life expectancy and migration.

Regional Trends: a comprehensive source of statistics about the regions of the UK, allowing regional comparisons.

Social Trends: statistics combined with text, tables and charts, which present a narrative of life and lifestyles in the UK, published annually.

References

Census of Population (2001), UK Office for National Statistics.

Economist, The (2001) 'The new demographics', *The Economist*, Vol. 361, No. 8246, 11 March, Special Section, pp. 5–8.

EHRC (2010), *How Fair is Britain?* London, Equality and Human Rights Commission.

Eurostat (2007) *Eurostat Yearbook 2006–07*, Luxembourg, Statistical Office of the European Communities.

Future Foundation (2004) *Changing Lives*, London, Future Foundation.

IPA (2010) *The Marketing Opportunities for Advertisers and Agencies in Multi-cultural Britain*, London, Institute of Practitioners in Advertising.

Mintel (2002) *Halal Foods – UK*, London, Mintel.

Mintel (2003) *British Lifestyles*, London, Mintel.

Mintel (2004) *Pocket Money – Food and Drink in the UK 2004*, London, Mintel.

ONS (2010) Annual Survey of Hours and Earnings, London, Office for National Statistics.

Smithers, R. (2010) 'Cost of raising child breaks £200,000', *Guardian*, 23 February.

UNFPA (2009) *State of World Population Report 2009*, New York, United Nations Population Fund.

Chapter 4

The Technological and Information Environment

You probably take for granted that you can book a cheap airline flight at 2 o'clock in the morning from the comfort of your home, and pay no more than the cost of a pair of jeans to fly away to somewhere exciting. Just 20 or 30 years ago, this might have seemed an impossible dream, but the dream has become a reality, and advances in technology have been a major contributor to this. New fuel-efficient aircraft, using many new lightweight materials, and information technology to make booking a seat more efficient have had a big impact on the market. But airlines still need to be thinking about what the next generation of customers will want to buy in 10 or 20 years' time. What about trips into outer space? A dream today, but like previous dreams of cheap transatlantic travel, could this dream become an everyday affordable reality? Or will issues of climate change and the depletion of natural resources make travel an unaffordable luxury, fuelling further innovation to make 'virtual' tourism an acceptable and enjoyable treat for all? Companies cannot afford to stand still, but the future is invariably uncertain. It is easy to look back at successful innovations, but much more difficult to predict the future. This chapter will explore not only the technological uncertainties about the future, but also the interaction between the technological environment and the social, economic and political environment.

✓ Learning Objectives

This chapter will explain:

☑ The diversity of technological impacts on business.

☑ The increasing speed of technological development.

☑ Innovation as a source of companies' and countries' competitive advantage.

☑ The effects of the social environment on technology acceptance.

☑ The impact of the internet on communication between organizations and their environment.

4.1   What is technology?

The word 'technology' can easily be misunderstood as simply being about computers and high-tech industries such as aerospace. In fact, technology has a much broader meaning and influences our everyday lives. It impacts on the frying pan (Teflon-coated for non-stick), the programmable central heating timer, cavity wall insulation, the television, DVD player, washing machine, car – in fact, just about everything in the home. The impact at work can be even greater, as technology changes the nature of people's jobs, creating new jobs and making others redundant. It influences the way we shop, our entertainment, leisure, the way we work, how we communicate, and the treatment we receive in hospital. The aim of this chapter is to explore the many ways in which technology impacts on business, and will focus on:

- the development of new or better products
- reduction in the cost of making existing products
- improvements in the distribution of goods and services
- new methods of communicating with customers and suppliers.

Technology is defined in the *Longman Modern English Dictionary* as 'the science of technical processes in wide, though related, fields of knowledge'. Technology therefore embraces mechanics, electrics, electronics, physics, chemistry and biology, and all the derivatives and combinations of them. The **technological fusion** and interaction of these sciences is what drives the frontiers of achievement forward. It is the continuing development, combination and application of these disciplines that give rise to new processes, materials, manufacturing systems, products and ways of storing, processing and communicating data. The fusion and interaction of knowledge and experience from different sciences is what sustains the 'technological revolution' (see Figure 4.1).

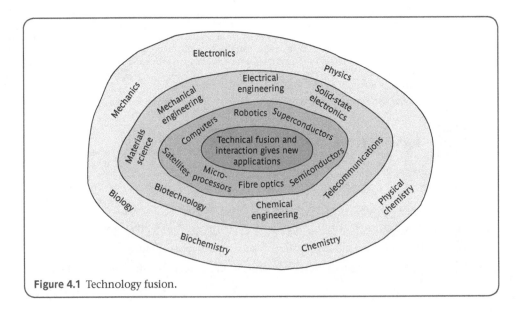

Figure 4.1 Technology fusion.

The term **demand-technology life cycle** is used to help explain the relevance to businesses of technological advances. Products are produced and marketed to meet some basic underlying need of individuals. An individual product or group of products may be only one way of meeting this need, however, and indeed is likely to be only a temporary means of meeting this need. The way in which the need is met at any period is dependent on the level of technology prevailing at that time. Kotler (1997) cited the need of the human race for calculating power. The need has grown over the centuries with the growth of trade and the increasing complexity of life. This is depicted by the 'demand life cycle' in Figure 4.2, which runs through the stages of emergence (E), accelerating growth (G_1), decelerating growth (G_2), maturity (M) and decline (D).

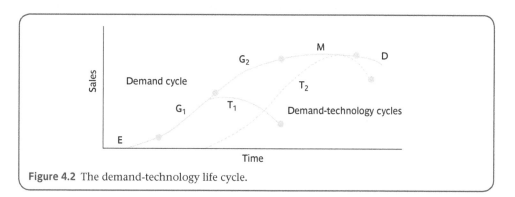

Figure 4.2 The demand-technology life cycle.

Over the centuries, the need for calculating power has been met by finger-counting, abacuses, ready-reckoners, slide rules, mechanical adding machines (as big as an office desk), electrical adding machines (half the size of an office desk), electric calculators (half the size of a typewriter), battery-powered hand calculators and now palm-sized computers. Kotler suggests that 'each new technology normally satisfies the need in a superior way'. Each technology has its own 'demand-technology life cycle', shown in Figure 4.2 as T_1 and T_2, which serves the demand cycle for a period of time. Each demand-technology life cycle will have a history of emergence, rapid growth, slower growth, maturity and decline, but over a shorter period than the more sustainable longer-term demand cycle.

Business organizations should watch closely not only their immediate competitors but also emerging technologies. Should the demand technology on which their product is based be undermined by a new demand technology, the consequences may be dire. If the emerging demand technology is not recognized until the new and superior products are on the market, there may be insufficient time and money available for the firm to develop its own products using the competing technology. Companies making mechanical typewriters, slide rules, gas lights and radio valves all had to adjust rapidly or go out of business. One way executives can scan the technological environment in order to spot changes and future trends is to study technology transfer.

The term **technology transfer** can be used in a number of contexts. It is used to refer to the transfer of technology from research establishments and universities to commercial applications. It may also be used in the context of transfers from one country to another, usually from advanced to less advanced economies. Transfers also occur from one industry to another; technology then permeates through the international economy from research into commercial applications in industries that can sustain the initially high development and production costs. As the costs of the new technology fall, new applications become possible. Applications of technology first developed for the US space programme, for example, may now be found in many domestic and industrial situations. NASA (the National Aeronautics and

Space Administration) established nine application centres in the USA to help in transferring the technology that was developed for space exploration to other applications.

4.2   Impacts of technology on business operations

From the previous discussion, it should be clear that technology has widespread impacts on business organizations. In extreme cases, technological development could be the reason for companies coming into existence in the first place (think of start-up companies created in the field of biotechnology), or the reason for a company's death (e.g. UK-based car manufacturers who, among other things, were slower than their Japanese competitors in adopting low-cost, high-quality manufacturing systems). In this chapter, we will explore a number of ways in which technological development has had impacts on the way organizations do business:

- product design and development
- manufacturing and processing
- supply chain management
- point of sale, order and payment processing
- communicating with customers
- managing customer relationships
- performance measurement
- the ecological environment.

Of course, many of these themes overlap – for example, performance measurement is an important aspect of most companies' efforts at managing relationships with customers – databases allow the company to identify who are the most profitable customers. In the following sections we will introduce general principles for assessing technology. In a later section, we will look specifically at the impact of the internet.

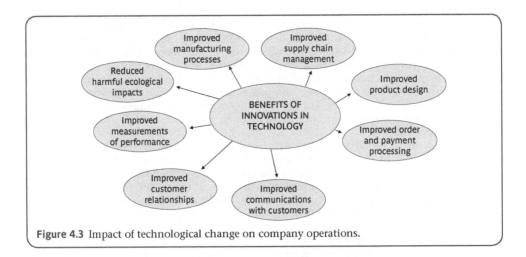

Figure 4.3 Impact of technological change on company operations.

Technology and society

At a broader level, business organizations are affected by the rate at which technology permeates the business world generally. Product life cycles are typically becoming shorter. Expertise in a particular technology may no longer be a barrier preventing competitors from entering an industry. New entrants into an industry may benefit from the falling costs of technology or may be able to bypass the traditional technology by using some new and alternative technology.

Businesses managers should be interested in the degree to which technology influences their business. Consider some historical antecedents: Bic produces a disposable plastic razor to challenge Wilkinson and Gillette; the fountain pen is challenged by the ballpoint, and in turn the ballpoint is challenged by the fibre-tip. Failure to identify changes in technology soon enough may cause severe and sometimes terminal problems for companies. Although there can be sudden changes in technology that impact on an industry, it is the gradual changes that creep through the industry that may be harder to detect. Companies that anticipate, identify and successfully invest in emerging technologies should be able to develop a strategic advantage over the competition. As the demand-technology life cycle goes through the stage of rapid growth, they will grow with it. As growth slows and the cycle matures, competitors will find it increasingly hard to gain a foothold in the new and by now dominant technology.

Our lives are affected by the interaction between technological changes and the social, economic and political systems within which we live and work. Over the last half-century the life of a mother has changed dramatically. With washing machines, tumble dryers, dishwashers, fridge-freezers and microwave ovens, modern textiles that are easier to wash and iron, convenience foods, and possibly the use of a car, the time devoted to household chores is much reduced. Partly as a result of these innovations, women are better educated and more likely to be in paid employment, and thus contributing to an increased disposable income. Also flowing from these developments, shopping patterns change from daily shopping in small local shops, limited to what can be carried and with transport via the bus, to weekly shopping (perhaps even on a Sunday or in the middle of the night) using the car or online grocery shopping with home delivery. The lives of schoolchildren also change, with even the youngest being introduced to the computer. Business people now have a truly mobile office with a laptop computer, PDA and mobile phone, which have merged into integrated 'smartphones'. They may be working from the car, from home, or even from a client's office. We are experiencing the casualization of communications, with people using personal phones, faxes, email and SMS text messages and expecting immediate responses but of a less formal nature. Within the family, life can become more dysfunctional as individual members pursue their own lives and activities. With more TV channels and choice, there is a greater need for additional TVs, at least one of which is likely to be linked to a games console. Space will also need to be found for at least one computer.

The impacts of technological development can differ between countries. In some newly industrializing countries people may view the rush in western economies to automated self-service as perplexing. In India and other Asian countries, where labour is relatively cheap and plentiful, the rising incomes of the middle classes would be used to employ more domestic help rather than to buy a washing machine or vacuum cleaner, for example. Consumers in different parts of the world will have different priorities according to wealth and circumstances. In China, where the opportunity to buy your own home or car is more limited than in the UK, consumers with rising incomes are more likely to spend on TVs and mobile phones.

4.4   Forecasting new technologies

It can be very difficult to forecast the development and take-up of new technologies. Those nations and companies that are first to develop a technological lead will grow, as the technology is embedded in new industries and products. Early developments in biotechnology in the USA and UK, for example, in the mid-1980s have developed into a billion-dollar global industry impacting on agriculture, pharmaceuticals, health and chemicals. Developments in the software industry transformed Silicon Valley, California, in the 1980s and 1990s, just as the car industry transformed Detroit, USA, in the 1950s. The interaction between a favourable political and social climate, higher education and research, and entrepreneurial individuals, may transform a whole economy and have a global impact.

There is a complex relationship between customers' demand for new technology and the ability of private and governmental organizations to supply it. There are many well-documented examples of new technologies that emerged through 'blue sky' research, in which technological advancement arose from scientific curiosity rather than a clearly identified customer demand. In recent years, the development of Post-it notes and music cassette players did not arise because of a careful analysis of customer demand, but nevertheless they went on to become great commercial successes.

Many new technologies experience initial scepticism from consumers, sometimes referred to as a 'hype cycle'. At first, many thought that bank ATM machines would never become popular with customers, who would prefer to deal with bank staff face to face. Of course, ATMs have now become the routine method of withdrawing cash from a bank account. Similar voices of scepticism were raised with internet banking. So how does a company try to predict the take-up of new technologies by consumers?

Models of technology adoption have their origins in the disciplines of psychology, information systems and sociology. The Technology Acceptance Model (TAM) (Davis, Bagozzi and Warshaw 1989), based on the Theory of Reasoned Action (Ajzen and Fishbein 1980; Fishbein and Ajzen 1975), has become well established as a model for predicting acceptance of new IT-based services. The model (Figure 4.4) introduces two specific beliefs that are relevant for technology usage, namely perceived usefulness (U) and perceived ease of use (E). Actual behaviour is determined by behavioural intention (BI); however, behavioural intention is jointly determined by the individual's attitude towards a technology (A) and perceived usefulness (U). Finally, perceived ease of use (E) is a direct determinant of attitude (A) and perceived usefulness (U). In the case of older bank customers, where there is often nothing to be gained by switching to computer-mediated banking because other banking methods are available, it is likely that perceived ease of use would have a stronger influence on behavioural intentions than would perceived usefulness. However, in a business banking context, perceived usefulness is likely to be a stronger predictor of behavioural intention than attitude. There is considerable evidence that young people have been more ready to adopt new technologies than older people (O'Cass and Fenech 2003).

Sometimes, consumers are faced with the simultaneous emergence of two new competing technologies, and it can be difficult at the outset to predict which one will win out. In the 1970s, video recording became a mass-market possibility, but although the Betamax format was claimed to offer higher quality, it was the VHS format that eventually became dominant. Once a new technology passes a tipping point, with backing from key stakeholders, it can acquire an unstoppable momentum. The battle of technology formats came to a head again in 2008 in the struggle between two alternative versions of high-definition DVD recorders. Walt Disney, 20th Century Fox and Metro Goldwyn Mayer had lined up behind Blu-ray while Universal supported the competing HD-DVD format. The costlier Blu-ray accounted for an estimated three-quarters of world-wide sales in 2007, but how long could this last? The film-makers were desperate for a new format to emerge in order to revive sales of DVDs, which had begun to slow down. However,

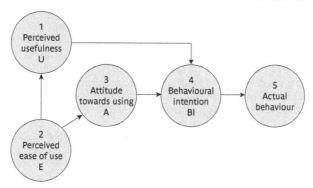

Figure 4.4 Companies often encourage their customers to adopt new self-service technologies, thereby reducing their costs, especially staffing costs. They may also promote the fact that service users can obtain additional benefits by using an automated form of service delivery. However, many service users may remain deeply sceptical, failing to see the benefits to themselves, and influenced by horror stories in the media of how the new technology has previously let customers down (for example, many people remain cautious about giving their credit card details over the internet, although, rationally, this is safer than giving details over the telephone). When planning the expansion of self-service facilities, companies need to be able to estimate the take-up rate, so that queues do not form or capacity remain unused. This model has been developed to explain the influences of perceived usefulness and attitude on consumers' intention to use, and actual use of new technology.
Source: based on Davis, Bogazzi and Warshaw (1989, p. 985).

they were concerned that consumers' confusion could lead to deferred purchases, and eventually high-definition DVD technology could lose out to digital downloads or video-on-demand. In this war of the formats, the winner would be the format with support from the majority of film studios and equipment manufacturers. The losing format would probably become increasingly marginalized and eventually go the way of Betamax.

Demand forecasting for new technologies often begins by trying to predict general changes in the macro-marketing environment. This in itself can be very difficult; for example, economists frequently disagree in their forecasts of economic growth during the year ahead. When it comes to predicting macroenvironmental change, larger companies often retain expert consultants, such as the Future Foundation (www.futurefoundation.net) and Trendspotting (www.trendspotting.com), which employs economists, sociologists and psychologists, among others, to try to build a picture of the world as it will evolve. Such macro-level forecasts can inform more detailed forecasts about market size, growth rates, market share, and so on.

The UK government's 'Foresight Programme', which brings together industry, academia and government to consider how the UK can take advantage of opportunities to promote wealth creation through innovation. Foresight, and its associated 'horizon scanning centre', aims to provide challenging visions of the future, and to develop effective strategies for meeting them. It does this by providing a core of skills in science-based future projects and access to leaders in government, business and science. Foresight operates through a rolling programme that looks at three or four areas at any one time. The starting point for a project area is either a key issue where science holds the promise of solutions, or an area of cutting-edge science where the potential applications and technologies have yet to be considered and articulated. In 2009, active projects included land use futures, global food and farming futures, global environmental migration and international dimensions of climate change (Foresight 2009).

When it comes to forecasting demand for completely new technologies, simply asking potential buyers whether they would buy the product can be fraught with difficulties. And simply asking somebody what they would use a new product for is likely to be limited to the scope of respondents' imagination. In the context of developing a low-cost car, Henry Ford once famously commented that if he had asked people what they wanted, they would have simply replied 'faster horses', rather than being able to imagine ever owning a car. For intangible services, the problem of consumers' limited vision can be even greater, requiring more sophisticated research methods that seek to understand deep-seated needs and motivators. Where possible, companies have sought to experiment with new products targeted at trial groups, before committing themselves to large-scale provision. This may be a valid approach where capital commitments are high and the market is relatively stable, but in fast-moving markets, too much time spent trying to understand consumer behaviour may allow competitors to gain a lead in an emerging new service sector. In the early days of the internet, many new online services were developed with very little research; indeed, in those days, the problem of Henry Ford's horses was ever more present, with most consumers having little idea of how they might use the internet. So, in order to be first to market and have 'first mover' advantage, the process of understanding customers and forecasting demand was often based more on intuition and judgement than on a rigorous analysis.

⟳ Thinking around the subject

Too many chips in the kitchen?

How does a company developing high-technology consumer products predict whether a new product is going to be a hit with consumers or a miserable failure? One very simple, but naive, solution would be to ask target consumers whether they would purchase the proposed new product. But, for radically new technologies, consumers may have very little idea of what the product involves and how it would fit in to their lives. They would probably have difficulty articulating their thoughts about the product to a researcher. Is it any wonder then that an estimated 80 per cent of new products fail?

One method used by companies to try to predict better the likely take-up of new products is based on ethnographic research. This involves supplying participating households with prototype versions of the product and watching how they actually use and interact with the product. In return for an incentive, a family may be filmed and a diary recorded of their activities, typically over a two- or three-week period.

Researchers have been curious to understand how automation, and the internet, can be brought into the domestic kitchen. The Korean firm LG developed an 'intelligent fridge' that used bar code readers to record items put into the fridge, and then taken from it and used up. This was linked to a simple stock-control programme, which drew up a shopping list for the household, which in turn could be sent through the internet to the household's preferred online grocer. In principle, the household need not worry about shopping or running out of any of its favourite grocery items. But the developers of the intelligent fridge didn't take account of the loss of a sense of control felt by the household. Ethnographic researchers pointed out that what appeared to be a technologically neat solution did not meet the lifestyle requirements of households.

The electronics companies Electrolux and Ericsson joined forces for another study involving human guinea pigs and their use of domestic refrigerators. They wanted to test the concept of a 'screen fridge', which allowed the user to download recipe ideas from the internet, store shopping lists and had a built-in video camera to record messages. Among the questions that they sought answers to were: To what extent are households adventurous in their use of recipes? What is the typical number of recipes that a household relies on when cooking family meals? Who would show most interest in the technology – male members of the household who like gizmos, or the women who do most of the cooking?

The idea of being watched by television cameras throughout the house might seem very Orwellian. However, a rash of reality television shows such as Big Brother have made many people more open to the idea of being watched. However, the question is often asked – as it has been for the Big Brother series – whether what is being seen is reality or the actions of a self-selecting idiosyncratic group who like to be watched? There is apparently no shortage of individuals and households who are willing to be filmed, and stories abound of semi-professional people who make a decent part-time living through such research. But is this really research that represents the population as a whole?

Source: based on Jones (2004).

Figure 4.5 Would you ever want to travel into outer space? Would you invest millions in developing space tourism? In 2001, the world's first space tourist, Dennis Tito, paid a reported $20 million for a visit to the International Space Station. Already a number of companies are looking at the possibilities for mass-market space tourism. Although the price of travelling into space may still appear prohibitive, analogies have been drawn with the early days of transatlantic air travel. In 1939, it cost the equivalent of £79,000 in today's inflation-adjusted money to make a return flight from Britain to the USA, something which can be routinely done today for around £400. Sir Richard Branson's Virgin Galactic plans to begin commercial passenger flights into space, departing from Spaceport America in New Mexico. The flights will allow the public to experience the thrill of weightlessness outside the Earth's atmosphere, gain their astronaut wings and witness spectacular views of the planet at a cost of £120,000 per ticket. Virgin Galactic has already taken several hundred reservations and tens of millions of dollars in deposits, but will space tourism

© *Getty Images*

go the same way as transatlantic air travel by eventually becoming mass-market? What would be the price at which space tourism really begins to grow? Who will be the innovators, and just how many people in the later adopter groups really want to have the space experience? Of greater uncertainty in planning for the future is the effect of aircraft emissions on global warming. Could these lead to prohibitively high taxes on operations, or a feeling of guilt by potential passengers about the effects of their travel into space on climate change?

Source: www.virgingalactic.com.

4.5   Expenditure on research and development

Technological advancement derives from investment in research and development. **Research and development (R&D) expenditure is often classified into three major types: basic, applied and experimental.**

1 Basic or fundamental research is work undertaken primarily for the advancement of scientific knowledge without a specific application in view.

2 Applied research is work undertaken with either a general or specific application in mind.

3 Experimental development is the development of fundamental or applied research with a view to introduction of new, or the improvement of existing, materials, processes, products, devices and systems.

Classification is also often carried out on a sectoral basis, e.g. public or private, and by type of industry. The International Standard Industrial Classification Code (ISIC) is often used.

International comparisons of R&D expenditure should be used with caution. Difficulties in comparing statistics stem from:

- differences in the basic definitions of R&D and the boundaries between R&D and education, training, related scientific expenditure and administration costs
- differences in counting numbers employed in R&D; e.g. definitions of full-time/part-time, directly or indirectly employed, qualifications and occupation
- discrepancies in the sources and destination of funds; e.g. private and commercial organizations receive some public funds, but public bodies also receive some funding from private sources; this makes it difficult to calculate the proportion of R&D expenditure financed by governments as compared to that financed by the private sector; university expenditure is typically a mix of the two, for instance
- difficulties in distinguishing the R&D element of large-scale defence programmes
- difficulties in assessing R&D funds flowing between countries, particularly between the components of multinational firms (Young 1993); the consolidated accounts of a multinational may show R&D expenditure, but in which country was it spent?
- R&D expenditure undertaken by small firms is not usually recorded by government agencies (Lopez-Bassols 1998).

In order to overcome these difficulties, economists at the Organization for Economic Co-operation and Development (OECD) issue guidelines in the form of the *Frascati Manual* for use by government statisticians. This helps to ensure that statistics are collected by each country on a similar basis, thereby aiding international comparison. The manual is also updated regularly to take account of new issues, such as software R&D expenditure, for example. However, caution still needs to be exercised when using international comparative statistics. Variations in exchange rates, purchasing power of the currency in the domestic market, and the reliability and comparability of the statistics all give grounds for caution.

R&D expenditure across all OECD countries averaged 2.28 per cent of GDP in 2007, which is higher than the average for the EU countries (1.77 per cent) (OECD 2010a). Finland, Japan, Korea and Sweden were the only OECD countries in which the R&D-to-GDP ratio exceeded 3 per cent, well above the OECD average. Since the mid-1990s, R&D expenditure in real terms has been growing faster in turkey and Portugal, both with average annual growth rates above 10 per cent.

Some emerging countries have robust and growing budgets for R&D – for example, according to the OECD, China increased its R&D intensity from 0.9 per cent in 2000 to 1.44 per cent in 2007, and its growth in real R&D spending since 2000 has exceeded 20 per cent per year.

An alternative approach to comparing countries' R&D activities is to measure the number of people employed in R&D activities. Researchers are individuals engaged in the conception and creation of new knowledge, products, processes, methods and systems, as well as those who are directly involved in the management of projects. They include researchers working in both civil and military research in government, universities and research institutes, as well as in the business sector. In the OECD area, around 4 million people were employed in R&D in 2006. Approximately two-thirds of these were engaged in the business sector. In 2006, there were about 7.6 researchers per 1000 of employed people in the OECD area, compared with 5.9 per thousand employed in 1995. This indicator has increased steadily over the last two decades. Among the major OECD areas, Japan has the highest number of researchers relative to total employment, followed by the USA and the EU (OECD 2010).

The UK's R&D figures do not make happy reading for the country's industrialists and politicians, with expenditure in manufacturing being particularly bad, and declining R&D expenditure in almost every sector. In real terms the UK's R&D expenditure has declined in recent years in mechanical engineering, electronics, electrical engineering, motor vehicles and aerospace. Increases in expenditure have occurred in chemicals, other manufactured products and non-manufactured products. The UK is well down the international league table on expenditure. Add to this the controversy surrounding cuts in science research budgets affecting UK universities and the picture looks even worse. Research and development is the seedcorn for the new technologies, processes, materials and products of the future. Failure in this area is likely to mean that UK companies are less competitive in the future.

According to the OECD, the UK's expenditure on R&D between 1981 and 2007 declined from 2.4 per cent of gross domestic product (GDP) to 1.82 per cent (EU average 1.77 per cent) (OECD 2010). The UK's ranking against other major industrial nations (Group of Seven, or G7, nations), except Italy, has slipped (see Figure 4.6).

Spending on R&D is not the only indicator of technological innovation. The number of patents registered in a country is also a reflection of a healthy R&D culture and advanced economy. As might be expected, the USA and Japan lead the way in patent registrations, but Europe is also a significant contributor via the European Patent Office. However, with multinationals conducting

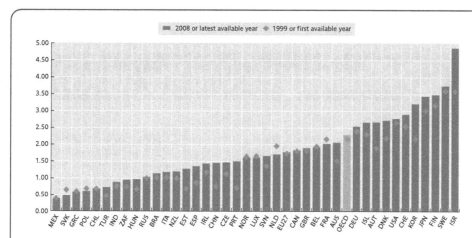

Figure 4.6 Gross domestic expenditure on research and development as a percentage of GDP for OECD countries, 2008.
Source: based on OECD (2010a).

research in many countries and with multiple international registrations, it is becoming more difficult to track expenditure and patents by country.

Having taken the broad macro view of technology, the rest of this chapter looks more specifically at how technology impacts on a business and where it may be applied to improve business operations. The following areas of technology application will be discussed: product design, manufacturing and processing systems, storage and distribution, order and payment processing, materials handling, document handling, computerized information and communications, and office automation (see Figure 4.7).

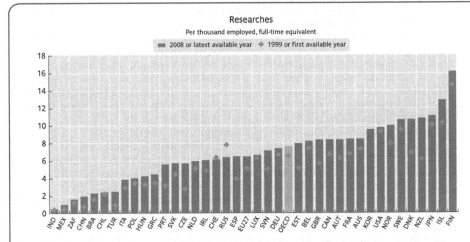

Figure 4.7 Researchers per thousand employed, full-time equivalent, for selected OECD countries.

Source: based on OECD Factbook (2010b).

⟳ Thinking around the subject

Soap powder companies – All washed up?

The soap powder companies are popularly attributed with having invented modern marketing and have continuously been at the forefront of new sales and marketing techniques. But could their progress be undone by recent developments in technology? A South Korean firm, Kyungwon Enterprise Company, is reported to have developed a washing machine that does not use detergent to clean clothes.

According to the company, a device inserted into a washing machine is able to transform water into electrically charged liquid that cleans with the same results as a conventional synthetic detergent. Water is transformed inside the machine by forcing it through layers of special catalysts planted between electrodes. The system utilizes the natural tendency of water to return to a stable state and harnesses it for laundering, deodorizing and killing viruses. The system also promises to cut water consumption and reduce the growing problem of water pollution by detergents. The developers of the system have applied for patents in over 60 countries. How are existing washing machine and detergent manufacturers likely to react? The washing machine manufacturer Hotpoint is reported to have been monitoring developments closely and would doubtless seek a licence to use the technology, or develop an alternative technology not covered by patent.

But what about the detergent manufacturers? Their market is unlikely to disappear overnight. The new system has still to be proven and, even if it is shown to be effective, important segments for detergent could remain out of inertia or simply because the new technology does not cope with all tasks as well as traditional methods. The detergent companies may also embrace the new technology by developing ranges of complementary products, such as fragrant conditioners. Another possibility is that the detergent companies might seek to buy the patents to the new process and then not use them. The inventor of the technology would receive a payout and the detergent companies would continue to sell detergent, but what would be the effects on consumers?

4.6 Product design and development

It is often argued that the life expectancy of products has tended to shorten as technology has advanced. It took radio 30 years, from 1922 to 1952, to reach 50 million users. Television required 13 years to do the same thing. Cable television became available in 1974 and achieved this level of worldwide take-up in ten years. It took the internet approximately five years to reach an estimated 100 million users (*Harris Interactive:* www.harrisinteractive.com). The increasingly rapid pace of technological change means that nearly all companies must have a strategy for developing new products, to replace those that become redundant. Typewriter manufacturers who did not embrace the move towards electronic word processing eventually saw their sales decline sharply. Central to companies' understanding of change in their technological environment is the concept of the **product life cycle** (PLC). This is a means of plotting sales and profits of a product over time (see Figure 4.8) in such a way that different stages in the life cycle can be identified and appropriate marketing strategies applied.

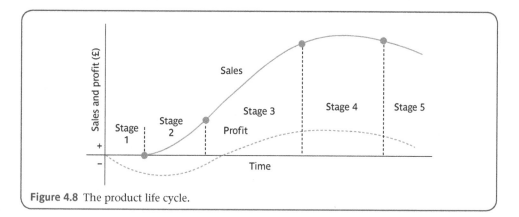

Figure 4.8 The product life cycle.

Five stages in the product life cycle can be identified.

1 *Product development prior to launch:* at this point, sales are zero, and development and investment costs are rising. The new technology may as yet be unproven, so this can be a very risky stage.

2 *Introduction of the product into the market:* this means expensive launch costs and promotion. Profitable sales may take some time to develop.

3 *Growth stage:* this is when the product is fully accepted into the market and healthy profits begin to materialize on the strength of increasing sales.

4 *Maturity:* this refers to the period over which sales growth begins to slow and eventually stop. Profits may begin to decline as increasing competition puts pressure on prices and forces up promotional expenses to defend the market share. New technologies are now mature, and easy for competitors to copy. Patents may have expired.

5 *Decline:* at this point sales begin to fall off and profits decline due to a lower volume of production. New technologies are likely to have appeared that take sales away from the product.

⟳ Thinking around the subject

Do patents encourage or stifle innovation in business?

Patents grant their owner a limited monopoly on the 'idea' defined by the patent. Such monopoly rights restrict competition for the length of the patent, which some may argue is socially harmful (the example of drugs companies pricing AIDS-related drugs out of the reach of most people in developing countries is often mentioned). On the other hand, a patent helps the owner to achieve a return on the research expenditures that went into the discovery of the patented idea. This makes large expenditures for easily copied products, such as pharmaceuticals, easier to justify, arguably increasing research and development activity throughout an industry.

But could granting of patents slow down, rather than encourage, technological development? And are there cases where it may be considered immoral to grant patents for knowledge that should be freely available to all?

One of the biggest public concerns voiced in recent times against the patent system is in relation to the granting of patents by the United States Patent Office (USPTO) for inventions in biotechnology, especially those based on genetic information. The Human Genome Project has sought to identify the structure of DNA, sometimes referred to as the building blocks of life. An understanding of human genes offers the prospect of new medical treatments. But can and should gene sequences be patented? It is reported that, by 2005, four leading private companies had already patented about 750 human genes between them and had applications for a further 20,000 pending. If all of these pending patents were awarded (which is unlikely), those four private companies could own half of the human genome.

There have been conflicting results in studies of the impact on research of gene patents. Is there a risk that a lack of reasonable access to the genetic codes will stifle further basic research? Will it slow down the development of commercial products? In one study, it is reported that

25 per cent of US university and commercial laboratories were refraining from providing genetic tests or continuing with some of their research for fear of breaching patents or because they lacked the funds to pay licence fees or royalties. Patents appeared to be challenging the traditional academic approach to a shared community of knowledge (Press and Washburn 2003).

On the other hand, turning genetic research into marketable treatments implies a long-term investment, for which there is no certainty of success. In a report on genetics patents, the OECD suggested that patents have the effect of making 'knowledge a tradable commodity which both encourages the circulation of new information and promotes a division of labour'. It found little evidence that growth in the number and complexity of biotechnology patents had caused a breakdown in the patent system or prevented access to inventions by researchers and health service providers. In fact patents and licences for genetic inventions appeared to have stimulated research, knowledge flows and the entry of new technology into markets (OECD 2002).

A distinction can be made between product category (say computers), product forms (e.g. networked, desktop PC, laptop, notebook and PDA) and brands (individual product brands offered by particular manufacturers such as Dell, Toshiba and Apple). Product categories tend to have the longest life cycles and stay in the mature stage for very long periods. They may begin to decline only with significant and fundamental changes in technology (as when typewriters come to be replaced by personal computers) or major shifts in consumer preferences. Product forms tend to show a more classical PLC, with each subsequent form showing a similar history to the previous one. For example, manual typewriters moved through the stages of introduction, growth and maturity, and entered decline as electronic typewriters were introduced. These then followed a similar history until they began to decline as personal computers were introduced. The old product category entered a decline stage as the new product category of personal computers went through a growth stage, and indeed has since gone into maturity. Individual brands follow the shortest life cycle, as companies are constantly attempting to update their products to keep abreast of changes in technology, fashion, customer preferences and competitors' offerings. Rapid advances in technology may mean shortening product life cycles in some industries. In consumer electronics, for example, advances in technology have allowed manufacturers to add more and more product features, and to reduce prices as costs have fallen. Consumer electronic products may have a life expectancy of only 18 months before they are withdrawn and replaced.

Managing the development of new products is a complex and risky business. While many textbooks will identify a linear process, usually comprising about five stages, the reality involves a complex interaction between a number of forces. These external forces comprise technological developments, market demand, competitor activity and possibly government influence. The internal organizational factors include management culture, research and development capabilities, engineering skills, production experience, management competence, access to finance, and marketing ability.

The linear model of the **new-product development (NPD)** process can be seen in Figure 4.9.

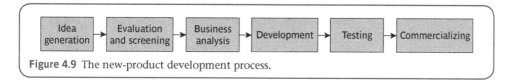

Figure 4.9 The new-product development process.

The process starts with idea generation, which involves the search for new ideas. The next step is evaluation and screening, during which the ideas are assessed for potential. If the company has a short-term planning horizon and a conservative culture, then revolutionary and innovative ideas may be dropped at this stage. As the company focuses on the short term and operates in its comfort zone it may reduce risks but it may also be producing 'me too' products. In doing so it may also miss innovative developments and technological shifts and, as a result, jeopardize its long-term competitive position or even its survival. The purpose of this stage is to reduce the number of ideas and to focus on the further development of those with potential. Before engaging in expensive research and development an initial business analysis should be undertaken to assess the market potential of new ideas. For products involving minor innovation, and aimed at an existing well-defined market, estimating total market potential should be relatively straightforward. But what will be the share taken by a completely new product, especially if it is aimed at a new group of buyers? How will consumers take to the new product? Will distributors like the product? How will competitors react? Will competitors launch a similar product? What price should be charged and how will this affect demand? Is the new product likely to cost more, the same or less than the existing product to make? These are all questions that need to be considered when calculating potential sales and profit.

For those products remaining, the next stage is development. This is where the expenses, mainly associated with research and development and/or engineering, are heaviest. Can the idea and new technology be developed into a workable product that can be produced in volume, at a reasonable cost, and that is practicable for the consumer? The testing stage may involve a number of activities. Testing the functional capabilities of the product may include technical tests, reliability tests and performance tests. Market testing involves testing consumers' and dealers' attitudes to the product. The final decision as to whether to launch the product is made at this stage.

Commercializing is the last stage, and can involve the highest expenditure as the product is prepared for manufacture and launch into the market. Decisions on expected sales, what volume to manufacture, what to contract out and what to manufacture in-house can all be critical. Product decisions, such as the final form of the product, the number of variants to offer, features, size, colours, branding and packaging, all have to be made, as have decisions on pricing and dealer margins. Promotional strategies have to be finalized, and the timing and logistics of the launch planned.

These stages are often presented as sequential linear activities with one stage being completed before the next commences. In reality not all of the new product ideas come together and start the process at the same time. Ideas are generated at odd times and come from a wide variety of sources. The company needs to capture and evaluate these as and when they arise. From here on the company will have a number of products at different stages in the process at any one time. The development of some may be speeded up or slowed down as priorities are reassessed. Neither is the process completed in separate and distinct stages as described above. Some new ideas may come from the company's blue-sky (speculative) research, so a certain amount of 'development' will have been done before the 'evaluation and screening' stage. 'Testing' is likely to begin before the 'development' stage is finished, and planning for 'commercialization' will commence before 'testing' is finished. The important point to note is that there should be formal reviews and reappraisal at regular intervals. Transition periods between the stages identified in the NPD process are appropriate times for such reviews.

There are of course internal barriers to the adoption of new technology-based products. Individuals may be resistant to change in the organizational setting. They may have a fear of new technology itself, or for their job, or the disruption that change may bring. Change may disturb existing management structures, departmental power bases, individual authority and working relationships.

Products should be designed with a view to keeping material, manufacturing, handling and storage costs to a minimum. These issues should be considered at the outset of the design brief and not as an afterthought. Reducing product costs by 5 or 10 per cent can mean huge savings over the life of a product. In many industries **computer-aided design (CAD)** gives more flexibility and a speedier response to customer needs. As production methods may now give greater flexibility, it is possible to produce a wider variety of styles, colours and features based on a basic product. These planned variations should be designed in at the initial design stages, even though they may not be offered for sale until much later.

The new product development process can be extremely complex, with many examples of cost overruns and delayed results (Kim and Wilemon 2003). A key to more effective new-product development activity is close working relationships between marketing and operational functions. Even simple administrative matters such as rapid communication following the results of one stage can help to speed up the process. The complexity of the new-product development process has often led to companies outsourcing the whole process to specialist companies that have developed an expertise in product development and market testing (Howley 2002). The use of an outside consultancy can also be useful where a company's ethos is production orientated and it seeks to bring on board broader marketing skills. It has been noted that brilliant inventors do not necessarily make good marketers of a new product (Little 2002).

4.7 Manufacturing and processing

Technology impacts on manufacturing and processing systems, particularly in computerized numerical control (CNC) machine tools, **computer-aided manufacturing (CAM)**, integrated manufacturing systems (IMS) and **just-in-time (JIT) systems**. With CNC, a machine tool is directly linked to a computer so that the instructions can be stored and repeated. This gives greater reliability and quicker changeover times. CAM involves linking computers to a number of machine tools and assembly robots that are interfaced with computer-controlled material handling systems. Sections of the manufacturing process are thus integrated into the same production control system. CAD/CAM (computer-aided design/computer-aided manufacturing) is where parts designed on a computer can be programmed directly into the machine tool via the same computer system. These systems can save many hours over previous methods involving the separate activities of design, building models and prototypes, and then programming separate machines for production.

Integrated manufacturing systems (IMS) enable a number of CAM sub-systems to be integrated together within a larger computer-controlled system. A number of manufacturers are attempting to integrate the total manufacturing process. This, however, is very difficult to do in practice, as plant and equipment are often of different ages, were designed by different companies and use different control systems. While it is possible to design a total IMS from scratch, the investment costs are likely to be prohibitive for most companies.

JIT systems are designed to limit stockholding and handling costs. A supplier is often expected to deliver components to the right delivery bay, on a specific day and at a specific time. There may be heavy penalties for failing to deliver on time. Components can then be moved directly on to the production floor ready for use on the line. This requires close cooperation between the manufacturer and supplier, and usually is made possible only by the use of computerized information systems and data links.

These developments in technology impact on small companies and large, and on traditional industries such as textiles and shoes, as well as on new ones. Generally speaking, modern manufacturing systems allow production lines to be run with greater flexibility and higher quality, making it easier to produce product variations and allowing a speedier changeover between products, thus minimizing downtime.

Developments in production technology present companies with a number of opportunities for gaining a competitive advantage. First, developments in these areas are likely to contribute to a reduction in costs. Aiming to be a low-cost manufacturer should help in achieving a higher return on investment by allowing a higher margin and/or a higher volume of sales at lower prices. Second, modern manufacturing techniques allow for greater flexibility in production; thus, a wider variety of product variations may be produced without incurring onerous cost penalties. Recent advances in integrated manufacturing systems using computer-controlled industrial robots have meant that carmarkers, for example, can produce totally different models on the same production line. Third, lead times between orders and delivery can be improved. Finally, it is possible to ensure that the quality of the products is more consistent and of a higher standard.

4.8 Supply chain management

The storage and distribution of goods has also benefited from advances in technology. In particular, the increased capacity and reliability of computerized data processing and storage combined with improved data transmission and computer-controlled physical handling systems have led to reductions in costs and improvements in service. It is now possible to hold less stock at all stages in the distribution chain for a given product variety. From a retailer's perspective the amount of stock kept on the sales floor and in the back room can be greatly reduced.

As companies come to rely very heavily on IT systems, any problems in the system can have an adverse effect on logistical and financial operations. During 2001, the children's goods retailer Mothercare opened a new UK distribution centre at Daventry. The aim was to increase the efficiency and effectiveness of deliveries to the company's nationwide store network. In reality, poor implementation of IT systems caused stock to be lost within its system. Instead of getting 'hot' products quickly to the shelves where customers were eager to buy them, they arrived at the shop only after market preferences had changed and the goods had to be sold at discounted 'clearance' prices. As a direct result of its distribution problems, the company was forced to issue a series of profit warnings and its share price slumped, threatening the continued independent existence of the company (Keers 2002).

Retail groups acquiring competitor companies now face a much more difficult task in integrating the newly acquired stores. Previously the takeover focused on re-branding with the new company's logo and house style, selling off old stock and replacement with new, and refurbishment of some stores. Now all tills and local computer systems are likely to need replacing, the newly acquired stores must be networked into the group computer, information and communication systems, and staff need to be trained in the new systems (see Figure 4.10).

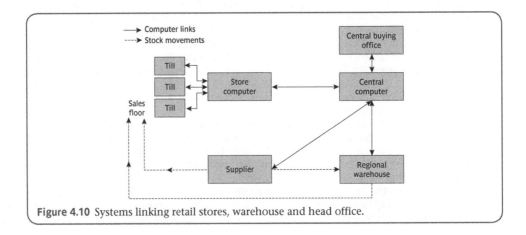

Figure 4.10 Systems linking retail stores, warehouse and head office.

4.8.1 Efficient consumer response

Partnerships between producers and intermediaries are evident in the Efficient Consumer Response (ECR) initiative. This involves members of the total supply chain working together to respond to customers' purchasing patterns, thereby ensuring the right products are delivered to store shelves at the right time. Rather than seeing one retailer competing against another, it may be more realistic to see one supply chain competing against another supply chain. The implications of ECR for IT in enhancing the flow of information between participants are discussed later in this chapter. However, it should be noted that the implementation of ECR could require considerable investment from manufacturers to change corporate structures and culture, and to improve IT links between participants. Efficient consumer response can be further facilitated by 'just-in-time' (JIT) methods of production, which require close cooperation between firms and rapid sharing of data. We will return to JIT relationships in Chapter 8.

4.8.2 Article numbering/bar codes

Efficient response to consumer demands depends on each individual product having a unique code number and the equipment at the point of sale being able to read that number. Manufacturers, retailers and other interested parties cooperated under the auspices of the global umbrella of GS1 (formed from an alliance of the Article Number Association, Electronic Commerce Association and e-Centre UK) to devise an article numbering system, to allocate numbers and set standards for the use of what have become known as 'bar codes'. GS1 is a non-profit-making member organization with representation globally. According to GS1, over 1 million organizations in 133 countries adhere to its standards. Recently the organization has also extended its work to radio frequency identification (RFId) for use in tracking goods in transit.

GS1 issues its members with sets of globally unique numbers, which form the basis of this identification and communication system. Each product item is allocated a unique global traded item number (referred to as the GTIN), so that each product variation by size and colour can be identified by the manufacturer. For example, a 430 g can of peas has a different number from a 300 g can. Nearly all grocery products now carry a bar code on their packaging. A product is simply passed over the scanner at the checkout so that the computerized till can read its bar code.

Bar code scanning systems are used throughout the distribution chain. Outer cases are referred to as 'traded units' and can include pallets. GS1 coordinates the allocation of numbers that are used for traded units as well as consumer units. These bar codes for the 'traded units' are also machine-readable, so the outer case can be monitored more at every stage in the distribution channel, from the manufacturer to the retailer or customer; every traded unit that differs by the nature or quantity of its contents must have a different number (see Figure 4.11).

Developments in RFId technology are allowing tags to be attached to products, transmitting information to nearby receivers without the need for a bar code to be manually scanned. RFId tags were first used to track bulk containers and cartons of products, but falling costs and improved reliability are allowing individual products to be fitted with tags. This has the potential to remove the need manually to scan groceries at a supermarket checkout, as the tag would immediately transmit full details of products contained in a shopping basket. However, RFId tags are still too expensive for widespread application to low-value, high-volume products.

For a national retailer, improved service and reduction in costs are achieved by linking computerized tills to a central computer and a stock control system that connects all stores and warehouses (Figure 4.11). In many cases large suppliers are also linked directly into the system. At the end of the day's trading, or periodically during the day, the central computer checks on the sales through each till. Replacement orders can then be placed with the nearest warehouse, and if necessary the warehouse stock will be replenished by calling off further orders from the supplier. In the warehouse, orders can be processed overnight or the next day, and delivered the following evening or early the next morning. Fast-selling lines can be identified using sales data and projections of sales made; further orders can then be placed with the supplier. This may be based on the first few days of a line being placed on sale. On delivery to the store, most of the items will be placed directly on to the sales floor, thus considerably reducing the need for back-room storage. This allows for a greater range of items to be stocked in a given floor space, as the stock held for each item is reduced. Stockholding by the individual store may be as low as two days' sales, compared with a week in the late 1970s. The space previously given over to back-room storage can now be opened up as part of the sales floor. Thus, the total selling space is increased, sales turnover per square metre is increased and the range of items carried is increased. There is less overstocking, fewer out-of-stock situations and less shrinkage. The tighter financial control, higher sales turnover and increased profits help pay for the investment in computers, new out-of-town warehousing, transport and physical handling systems. Electronic point of sale (EPOS) systems, which are an important source of information for the supply chain, are discussed later in this chapter.

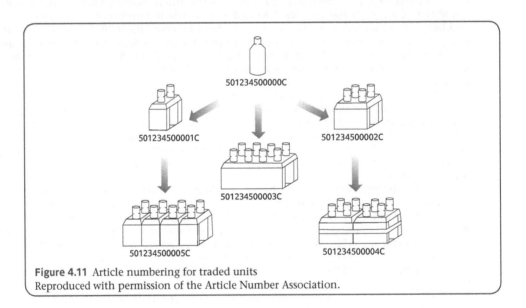

Figure 4.11 Article numbering for traded units
Reproduced with permission of the Article Number Association.

At each stage of the distribution process electronic communications between seller, distributor and buyer keep all the individual organizations' systems up to date. Electronic despatch documents, shipping documents and goods received documents form the basis of electronic invoicing and payment systems (see below). These systems are not only invaluable in tracking items through the supply chain but can be used to trace products in the event of a product recall. This is known as 'traceability' and is an essential requirement in a world of global trade.

Figure 4.12 It is not just the supply chains of manufacturing companies that have been radically improved advances in by technology. Services companies do not generally need to move large volumes of physical stock, but they nevertheless often deal with their final consumers through intermediaries. For a typical insurance broker or travel agent, this may have meant handling and storing large volumes of documents as policies and tickets passed from the service principal, to the agent and on to the customer. Electronic forms of communication have greatly speeded up this process, and reduced the amount of paper needing to be moved. More significantly, for some highly intangible services, the internet has allowed a company to deal directly with its customers, rather than having to deal with them through intermediaries. An airline such as easyJet now has the technology to deal directly with millions of individual customers quickly and cheaply, something that might have been unthinkable in earlier paper-based systems of distribution. Credit cards and electronic ticketing have allowed easyJet to simplify its distribution channel, so that now over 90 per cent of its tickets are sold directly, rather than through an agent. However, such 'disintermediation' is not universal, because technology has also allowed internet-based intermediaries to flourish. Instead of booking directly with airlines such as easyJet, some travellers may prefer to use an intermediary such as Expedia or Opodo, which offer a choice of airlines. By linking airlines' and agents' databases, a customer can rapidly compare prices and availability for a selection of airlines.
(Illustration reproduced with permission of easyJet Airline Company Ltd.)

With products and processed food manufactured from components and ingredients sourced throughout the world, traceability back through the supply chain is necessary to isolate the cause of any problems.

4.9 Point of sale, order and payment processing

This chapter continues to explore specific methods by which technology has been used to improve the efficiency and effectiveness of transactions within a supply chain. In particular, organizations must aim to cut the cost of stockholding, yet still be able to respond efficiently and effectively to customers' requests.

In the previous section we considered the impact of computer systems and data links on storage and distribution. The combination of bar codes, scanners, computerized tills, data links and powerful computers with remote terminals has much improved the control of stock. Systems are constantly being improved, as is the reliability and speed with which the systems operate. These systems can also be expensive to install and run. However, as the technology improves and competition increases between suppliers of systems, we can expect the costs to come down.

EPOS (electronic point of sale) systems allow each till to total the goods purchased by individual customers and record the transaction in the normal way. In addition to the daily cash analysis, however, EPOS systems may provide stock reports and an analysis of sales figures, and improve control over each till and the staff using it. The retailer no longer has to price each individual item, as the price needs to be displayed only on the shelf or rack. This saves labour and allows for easier price changes. The customer benefits from itemized till receipts, a faster checkout, greater choice and fewer items out of stock (Figure 4.13).

Improved management information
Store-by-store comparison of states
Direct product profitability analysis
Sales-promotion effectiveness

Operational efficiency
Better stock control
Quicker stocktaking
Reduced shrinkage
No item pricing
Faster price changes

Improved customer service
Faster checkout service
Fewer queues
Itemized sales receipts
Reduced operator error

Figure 4.13 Benefits of EPOS.
Source: adapted from Fletcher (1995, p. 367).

EFTPOS (electronic funds transfer at point of sale) extends the benefits of EPOS to include electronic funds transfer. This means that the computerized till is now fitted with a card reader, and data links into the banking system can transfer funds electronically. The convenience for customers and retailers is enhanced, the accuracy of transactions is increased, cash handling is reduced and the costs of processing the sale are also significantly reduced (Figure 4.14). For the future, it is likely that mobile phones will emerge as ubiquitous payment devices, allowing a customer to pay for goods simply by entering a pin code on their mobile phone.

In business-to-business transactions the speed at which orders can be captured and processed by a company's systems is related to the speed at which orders and invoices can be despatched and payment collected. Closely associated and inseparable from the ordering system is a document handling system, which includes orders, manufacturing dockets, picking notes, despatch/delivery notes, invoices and statements.

Benefits to retailers
Reduced paperwork
Single system for all cards
Reduction in volume and cost of cash handling
Reduced security risk
Reduction in fraud
Faster checkout time
Faster payment into retailer's account

Benefits to customers
Less need to carry large amounts of cash
More choice in methods of payment
No £50 limit as with cheques
Itemized receipts and statements easy to check
Faster checkout time

Figure 4.14 Benefits of EFTPOS.
Source: adapted from Fletcher (1995, p. 367).

4.10 Communicating with customers

A number of long-term trends in the technological impacts on communication can be noted.

- There has been a gradual proliferation of communication media available for companies to send messages to customers. In the early twentieth century, advertisers' choices were largely limited to printed media, but, since then, a variety of alternative media have become available, including radio, television and the internet.

- There has been a long-term reduction in the cost of communicating with customers – for example, internet communication reduces the need for costly printing and physical distribution of messages.

- The time taken to get a message to its audience has been reduced. Instead of waiting for the next daily, weekly or monthly edition of a newspaper or magazine, electronic media allow almost instantaneous generation and distribution of messages. This can be particularly important in dynamic environments – for example, airlines routinely update the price message they send to individual enquirers at their websites, depending upon the current level of availability of seats.

- Technology has allowed much more precise targeting of messages. In the early days of printed media, targeting was essentially limited to the regional geographical coverage of local newspapers, or the readership profile of national dailies. Modern database marketing allows companies to send quite different messages to individuals, depending upon their interests. A company such as Amazon makes very little use of impersonal broadcast media, but instead builds up a picture of its customers and uses this to send quite specific messages. For example, a customer who has a long record of buying Harry Potter books is likely to be particularly receptive to a message about a new book by the author J.K. Rowling. One aspect of improved targeting is that companies are increasingly able to target customers by specific location and time. Communication based on GPS data can allow a target customer to receive a message just at the time and place where they will be most receptive to a message (e.g. a restaurant with spare capacity sending messages to customers' phones when they are known to be near to a restaurant).

■ Communication between a company and its customers has become increasingly interactive. With very simple technology, a company could communicate with its customers but it was difficult for them to reply immediately through the limited media available (e.g. the dominant media of newspaper and television advertising may have required the customer to send away a coupon or make a telephone call). Improvements in technology allowed customers to respond immediately and directly (e.g. through interactive TV or the internet). Further developments in communications technology have allowed real-time interaction not only between the company and its customers, but between customers themselves. This peer-to-peer communication has the potential to spread good and bad news stories about the company very rapidly, and organizations are still learning how to manage this communication.

⟳ Thinking around the subject

Telecoms companies are particularly bad at communicating, says report

The phenomenal development of telecommunications over the past couple of decades should have opened up tremendous new opportunities for two-way communication between a company and its customers – actual and potential – but there is still evidence that companies can be slow to embrace the interactive communication abilities of the telephone and internet. Research undertaken in 2006 by the e-services provider Transversal showed that the UK telecoms sector – which should have been at the forefront of the telecommunications revolution – was actually performing badly at communication. The report found phone companies to be among the slowest at answering their phones, with some, such as Carphone Warehouse, apparently being overwhelmed at their call centres. Answering a phone is generally more expensive than having customers communicating through a website, entering all the data themselves and using their time rather than a call centre operator's time to search for results. But the phone companies didn't seem to do well here either. The report found that only a third provided an online customer search function, down from 70 per cent in 2005. Furthermore, the telephone companies' websites could answer an average of just two out of ten most basic customer questions, such as 'How do I upgrade my phone?' Online users who sent an email to the company to resolve a problem would typically wait 48 hours for a reply, and many email requests for information simply did not get answered.

It is easy to say that telecommunications improve the ability of companies to communicate with their customers, but technology alone will not improve communication. Telecommunications companies should be at the leading edge when it comes to the enabling technology, but did they have the management abilities to put the technology to good use? Or were they simply victims of their own success, and as they grew their capacity to handle calls continually lagged behind customer demand? Had the communications revolution led to higher expectations by customers, who may have been happy to wait several days for an answer, but now want an instant response, 24/7? And with communication costing money, could facilitating easier communication simply result in more calls from customers, adding to a company's costs and putting it at a disadvantage in a price-sensitive market?

4.11   Managing customer relationships

The information-gathering and analysis power of the internet has allowed companies to build a much clearer picture of their markets in general, and individual customers in particular. This has resulted in improvements in efficiency (for example, fewer wasted mailshots that are sent to un-interested target buyers), as well as improvements in effectiveness (improving the content of the mailshot so that it addresses specific target buyers' principal concerns).

Whatever the reason for a customer first making a purchase from a company, an important role in sustaining an ongoing business relationship is likely to be played by information held about customers. A small business owner, such as a small shopkeeper or guest house owner may have the ability to keep in their head all the information they need in order to deliver a high quality of relationship. But, in a large organization, information about individual customers must be shared, so that, for example, a customer of a hotel chain will find their personal details readily available every time they deal with one of the chain's hotels or reservations offices. We are probably all familiar with companies where customer information seems to be very poor – the hotel reservation that is mixed up, the delivery that does not happen as specified, or junk mail that is of no interest at all. On the other hand, customers may revel in a company that delivers the right service at the right time and clearly demonstrates that it is knowledgeable about all aspects of the transaction.

Customer relationship management (CRM) has become a generic term to describe processes that essentially seek to join up a company's customer-focused information systems and to track dealings with individual customers throughout the relationship life cycle. Many companies offer technological solutions that promise integrated information management. However, technology is of little value if management does not give the leadership and create a culture that is conducive to integrated systems. Indeed, it is not uncommon to find firms that have invested heavily in IT systems to handle customer information, only to find that the information may actually hinder, rather than help, the task of creating more effective customer relationships.

There are many definitions of CRM, which reflect the varying scope of CRM within different companies. It is defined here as:

> **"**The systems and processes used by an organization to integrate all sources of information about a customer so that the organization can meet individual customers' needs more effectively and efficiently.**"**

One reason for the variation in definitions is that organizations may pay differing levels of attention to the different components of CRM. The basic, but interrelated components can be described as follows.

- Data collection and management – ensuring that data are captured accurately and speedily during all points of contact with a customer. Data collection can also include buying in records from third-party sources.

- Customer analysis and profiling – developing algorithms to analyse a customer database and identify customer/product profitability and to identify opportunities for new product development (see the 'Thinking around the subject' box on page p.152).

- Computer-aided sales support – providing members of the salesforce with information about an actual or prospective customer so that they can conduct sales negotiations from a position of knowledge about the customer's history and preferences.

- Customer information and service – providing information to customers about a product that they have bought, or may be considering buying – for example, a warranty claim or a product recall.

How much data should a company collect about its customers? A trade-off has to be made between the cost and inconvenience of collecting information and the associated benefits to the company. Is it really worthwhile for a company to ask questions to a prospective customers the first time they call? Will this be regarded as too intrusive? Will it add to costs by slowing down the process of taking customers' orders? Will the information actually be used to profitably improve sales and service delivery? Or is the information crucial to ensure that the prospective customer's needs – vital for the long-term development of a relationship – are correctly diagnosed?

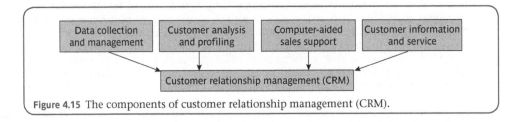

Figure 4.15 The components of customer relationship management (CRM).

Merging and updating databases can be a very complex task, especially where a company has multiple points of access by customers. It is quite common to find telephone sales and internet sales databases, for example, not linked to each other. The problem of linkages is particularly great where companies have merged or been acquired, and the resulting 'legacy' systems do not interface easily with each other. It is reported that when Lloyds Bank merged with Trustee Savings Bank (TSB), it took over two years for both banks' customer databases to be effectively integrated.

⟳ Thinking around the subject

Any excuse for a pint?

Companies are able to capture ever-increasing amounts of information in order to build up a better picture of their customers' buying behaviour. The retailer Tesco is one of many companies that gather large volumes of data from till receipts, loyalty card data and other bought-in data, to give previously unimaginable insights into consumer behaviour. The story has frequently been told of an exercise undertaken by the company using data-mining techniques, which apparently discovered a correlation between sales of beer and sales of nappies. The two products were not in any way complementary to each other, so why should their sales appear to be associated? Was this just another spurious correlation, to be binned along with other gems of information such as a previously reported correlation between an individual's shoe size and their propensity to use a gym? The company didn't give up, and refined its analysis to study the correlation for different categories of store and by different times of day. Where it also had details of customers' demographic characteristics (gathered through its Clubcard loyalty programme) it was able to probe for further insights. The company was edging towards a better understanding of why the sales of these two products should be closely correlated, but it took further qualitative analysis techniques to provide a fuller explanation. It appeared that men were offering to run a household errand to the shops in order to buy babies' nappies. This was an excuse to leave the family home in order to buy more beer for their own consumption. The company is claimed to have learned from this exercise and subsequently positioned the two products closer together in selected stores.

The story of Tesco's analysis of beer and nappy sales may have become distorted with telling, and may even come close to being an urban myth. But should it take data mining to reveal these insights to buyers' behaviour? The landlord of the traditional Irish pub spotted this type of behaviour long ago, with pubs doubling up as the local post office, bookseller or grocer, giving the Irish drinker plenty of good excuses to visit the pub. He would have had none of the technology available to today's businesses, just a good set of ears and eyes. Do we sometimes look for complex technological solutions to understand buyer behaviour, when the answer might be much easier to find using more traditional judgements?

4.12 Performance measurement

It has been suggested that measurability – an inherent aspect of IT applications in business – has led to a change in organizational culture, from one based on a lot of intuition and judgement, to one where the measurement of targets, processes and outcomes is key. IT makes it increasingly easy for companies to measure their:

- Efficiency – that is, the extent to which they are performing their activities using the minimum amount of inputs relative to outputs (e.g. what proportion of banner ads results in a click-through or a sale?)
- effectiveness – that is, the extent to which the company is doing the right things in the first place (e.g. how satisfied are its customers with the products they buy?)

Shared information through a distribution channel can also help to improve each member's measurement of business performance. Intermediaries can conduct direct product profitability (DPP) analysis of individual items, through the use of EPOS data. DPP attempts to identify all the costs that are attached to a product or an order as it moves through the distribution channel. Thus, after the gross margin has been calculated, costs such as warehousing, transportation, retail space allocation and stocking labour are subtracted to give the product's net profit contribution to a business. It is in a manufacturer's interest to determine how it might lower the cost element to the retailer by, say, redesigning a product's packaging, and thus influencing the retailer's purchase decision more favourably. Because shelf-space is often a limiting factor, the key performance measure becomes DPP per square metre. A typical store may find that the figure for ready–prepared meals is over twice that of basic items such as rice.

4.13   Technology and the ecological environment

Increasingly, there is concern about the ecological environment, but is technology a friend or enemy of the environment? In many people's minds, technology may be associated with ecological problems. The Industrial Revolution that took place in England in the nineteenth century is associated with harmful ecological effects, including pollution of water courses, and the emission of noxious substances into the atmosphere. Industrialization has been associated with many techniques that have depleted natural resources in an unsustainable manner. Instead of small-scale fishing, trawlers with large nets and detecting equipment are able to locate and quickly catch large volumes of fish, contributing to a decline in fish stocks available in the North Sea.

The harmful ecological consequences of industrialization are not confined to western countries during their periods of rapid industrial development. Similar effects can be seen today in rapidly developing economies such as India and China. In these countries, standards of ecological protection tend to be lower than in the developed West, with manufacturers able to undertake production processes that would no longer be allowed in the developed western world. Some in the West have sought measures to restrict emerging countries from polluting the ecological environment, although others have argued that it is morally wrong for the West, which has already made its wealth, to seek to restrict the activities of emerging economies that have yet fully to develop their wealth. Furthermore, it has been argued that much of the damage caused in emerging economies is indirectly caused by western consumers demanding cheap manufactured goods from their polluting industries.

Technology can also help solve ecological problems, and ecological concerns present opportunities for the development of new technologies. Among the examples of 'problems' given above, it could be argued that some of these could in fact be solutions. In the case of genetically modified (GM) crops, the ability to improve yields could be seen as a solution to the problem of finite farming resources, against a background of rising population. There are many examples of technology leading to the development of substitute products that have reduced the demand for finite suppliers of natural resources – for example, composite materials have provided an alternative to scarce ivory.

Whether a technological development is good or bad for the environment can be the subject of endless debate, with uncertain facts often being mixed with personal and political prejudice. Debate over nuclear power typifies this dilemma. In Britain, early development of nuclear power was generally seen as harmful to the environment, and emphasis was placed on the risk of emissions into the atmosphere and water courses. Incidents involving nuclear power plants, such as that at Chernobyl in 1986, heightened concerns about the harmful effects of nuclear power generation. However, in recent years, nuclear power plants have been seen as a solution to problems of global warming. With fewer CO_2 emissions than electricity generated from gas or coal, nuclear energy has been rehabilitated in many people's minds, including some elements of the 'green' movement, which have traditionally been vehemently opposed to nuclear power. Recall also the case study in Chapter 1 about the ecological impacts of civil aviation. While many would see cheap 'no-frills' airlines as an enemy of the ecological environment, the chief executive of Ryanair nevertheless claimed that his airline was a friend of the environment, by using the latest technology in its engines and control systems to reduce emissions.

Many companies have seen ecological concern as an opportunity to develop new technologies. Wind turbines, lightweight vehicle batteries and technologies for carbon capture and storage are recent examples. By 2010 it appeared that the UK had lost any competitive advantage in the design and construction of wind turbines, but the government seemed determined to support innovative carbon capture and storage technologies in the hope that a strong home market would provide the basis for global competitive advantage.

The internet and electronic business

We may be tempted to think that the use of information technology to communicate between organizations began with the development of the internet. In fact, organizations had already developed proprietary systems through which orders and payments could be processed. In this section, we will explore the diversity of forms of electronic business. One underlying theme of the development of electronic business has been the reduced cost of handling transactions electronically, rather than through paper-based systems. Alongside this, the speed of communication has allowed business to be transacted much quicker, and the data generated through electronic business systems has given managers a much better understanding of the marketing and operational aspects of their organization. It can be easy with hindsight to trace technological development, but businesses also need to develop a good idea about future developments – for example, the use of mobile phones as payment devices.

4.14.1 The internet

The **internet**, or World Wide Web (www), is an open system that anyone can access via a computer and a modem. No one person, organization or government controls or owns the internet. It developed as a means of transferring large volumes of information between academic and government research centres in the USA. Soon people were sending messages via electronicmail (email). More universities hooked up and commercial companies became involved. As the personal computer developed so did the software, browsers, search engines, etc., to interface between the user and the internet. Messages and information are relayed quickly via servers and hubs to their final destination.

Initially the system was used by technical experts to send data, and text messages followed subsequently. Commercial companies began to post web pages on the internet so those interested could browse through the information. Soon websites were developed that provided more information, which eventually led to the development of interactive sites. With the development of protocols for encoding financial and other sensitive information, the internet is now routinely used to make purchases using a credit card.

Of course, it is not just in business-to-consumer markets that the internet is reshaping distribution channels. In business-to-business channels, the internet (and intranets and extranets) has replaced previous **electronic data interchange** (EDI) systems for handling transactions between businesses. Government and not-for-profit organizations have also incorporated the internet into their distribution channels, both for procuring purchases (Timmins 2003) and making services available to users (e.g. NHS Direct makes medical advice available to the public through call centres and the internet).

Intranet systems are private internal systems (as opposed to open and public systems) constructed using internet technology. A company's intranet can link together an organization that is geographically dispersed, and facilitate links between the organization and its business partners such as suppliers and distributors. Such a system is often described as an 'extranet'.

The deregulated nature of the internet, operating across international boundaries, has posed new challenges as it developed from an information service, to a promotional tool, and now a sales and distribution channel. A number of particular challenges for e-business can be identified: confidentiality of individual information; security of the operating system against attack or major failure; consumer protection for those purchasing goods and services; under which legal system a transaction takes place; and concern over the difficulty of governments collecting sales taxes.

Some people have argued that the internet has represented a step-change in methods of conducting business, whereas others would place the internet that we know today in a more gradual process of evolution. The processes of industrialization using electronic methods, including some of those described earlier in this chapter, provided an evolutionary basis for modern internet service delivery. So, in the case of banking, ATM machines provided some of the benefits to customers (e.g. 24/7 access to account information and availability in a wide range of locations) and to banks (reduced cost of face-to-face contacts), which have evolved into online banking. Insurance companies that had moved from distribution through branches to distribution through call centres saw the development of online sales as a natural evolution. Even the whole concept of the internet has evolved during its so far still brief history. Early applications using the internet were relatively static and largely sought to replicate the telephone and printed media they replaced. As the internet has developed into what has become known as 'Web 2.0', there has been much greater interactivity between service providers and consumers, and between fellow consumers. There has been a lot of discussion about whether further developments in the interactive consumer-to-consumer abilities of the internet will lead to consumers setting the agenda for the internet environment, rather than commercial

⟳ Thinking around the subject

To boldly go where no computer has gone before?

You want to go for a short break to Paris to explore its museums and architecture, but can't face the hassle of flying there, and can't really afford the cost of the flights or the accommodation. If you simply wanted to see Paris, the offer of a virtual tour might suddenly seem attractive. Is it realistic to expect that virtual tourism will ever take over from the real thing? A report, *Tomorrow's Tourist*, published in 2010 by the Future Foundation, claimed that young people are increasingly likely to play computer games and indulge in social networking rather than enjoy leisure activities outside. As 3D technology improves, will more people be tempted to sightsee from the comfort of their own home instead of actually visiting other places?

Dr Ian Yeoman, author of *Tomorrow's Tourist* and a consultant on the report, pointed to what had happened in Japan. The Japanese, it seems, had over the last ten years spent more on in-home entertainment and technology rather than travelling the world. The technologies that the Japanese adopt today are likely to be those adopted by the rest of the world before too long.

The report shows that spending on out-of-home leisure activities fell during the Japanese recession of the late twentieth century, but sales of in-home electronics had grown, and since 2000 had increased by 2.5 times in real terms. It also seemed that people had been gaining increasing enjoyment from in-home activities such as socializing via social networking websites.

Some of the hype about virtual tourism may not seem so far-fetched when it is remembered that, 10 or 20 years ago, many said that children would not give up kicking a football around in favour of computer games. Since then, the number of children taking part in sports has fallen while many sit for hours playing virtual-reality games on their PlayStations. As virtual reality systems improve, and the cost, hassle and security risks of travel increase, there may well be a scenario in which people decide that the virtual world of Paris is better than the reality. What else could trigger this transformation? Could the technology improve to the point where friends can have virtual meetings in Paris quite effortlessly? How can the experiential values of virtual reality systems be improved so that users get a greater sense of actually being there? Will virtual tourism become an aspirational first choice, or will it only ever become the second choice when real travel becomes too difficult and expensive? Will the availability of virtual tours whet people's appetites, so that in fact instead of being a substitute for travel, it will encourage even more travel to explore real destinations? If you were managing a museum or gallery in a tourist town, how could you adapt to the needs of virtual tourists?

In this evolving role for the internet, some see a greater need for government control, or at least influence in the development of the internet. The OECD Sacher Report identified three priority areas for governments. The first is for governments actively to support the development of electronic commerce by encouraging the development of the infrastructure. Governments have traditionally controlled telecommunications and television industries by either direct ownership or licensing. Technologies in computing, telecommunications, data networks and television are now converging rapidly. The report recommends that governments should encourage this by modifying regulatory regimes where necessary and by working to commonly agreed international protocols.

organizations. The development of peer-to-peer sites such as youtube and Facebook have challenged many assumptions about the role of traditional advertising, for example. Customer review sites are increasingly becoming an important source of evaluation in the buying decision process, but such sites are much more difficult to control than conventional paid-for advertising. There is also some evidence of websites being used to 'educate' a customer prior to a face-to-face encounter with an organization. For example, one study of medical practitioners showed how patients engaged in virtual, parallel service encounters through the internet, changing the nature of their appointment with the doctor and presenting challenges to medical professionals both in terms of doctor–patient relationships and their professional judgement (Hogg, Laing and Winkelman 2003).

The second recommendation was that all governments should 'raise the visibility of electronic commerce and promote new partnerships with the private sector in order to coordinate technical, economic and political choices'. It is suggested that governments may seek to appoint a Chief Information Officer to coordinate these activities.

The third recommendation was that governments themselves should acquire the skills to participate in the electronic information age. Regulatory issues need to be dealt with urgently and as they arise. Legal issues surrounding the 'definitions, practices and structures' of electronic commerce are now being addressed. International protocols need to be further developed for dealing with consumer protection, fraud, crime prevention, the protection of intellectual property, electronic identity, definitions of residence, liability, auditing, and the control, unauthorized use and protection of databases. The issue of taxation is also of concern, particularly for taxes based on sales. Sales taxes are often refunded to exporters at despatch but re-applied on receipt in the country of importation. These issues have not been fully resolved for internet transactions.

The Economist Intelligence Unit (EIU), working in collaboration with IBM, publishes annual 'e-readiness' ratings for countrie (Economist Intelligence Unit 2010). It defines 'e-readiness' as a measure of the quality of a country's information and communications technology (ICT) infrastructure, and the ability of its customers, businesses and governments to use ICT to their benefit. When a country uses ICT to conduct more of its activities, the economy can become more transparent and efficient. E-readiness takes into account a wide range of factors, which include connectivity and technology infrastructure (20 per cent), business environment (15 per cent), social and cultural environment (15 per cent), legal environment (10 per cent), government policy and vision (15 per cent), and consumer and business adoption (25 per cent) (Economist Intelligence Unit 2010). Denmark reclaimed the world's e-readiness leadership in the EIU's 2009 rankings, a position it had relinquished to the USA in the previous year. According to the 2009 e-readiness rankings, Scandinavian countries have, among other attributes, high levels of ICT usage – following Denmark's first ranking were Sweden (second), Norway (fourth) and Finland (tenth). The UK was in 13th position (Table 4.1).

Table 4.1   E-readiness of top ten ranked countries, 2009.

Country	Rank
Denmark	1
Sweden	2
Netherlands	3
Norway	4
USA	5
Australia	6
Singapore	7
Hong Kong	=8
Canada	=8
Finland	10

Source: based on Economist Intelligence Unit: e-readiness rankings 2009, the usage imperative, http://graphics.eiu.com/pdf/E-readiness%20rankings.pdf

4.14.2 Governments and the development of a knowledge-based economy

Although no single individual organization can own or control the internet, there have been calls for governments to become involved in promoting, managing and regulating the internet environment. Some countries with a tradition of government media censorship, such as China, Iran and North Korea, have no qualms about regulating use of the internet by their citizens. There have, for example, been many documented cases of the Chinese government seeking to block access to search engines such as Google. In western countries with a democratic tradition, the issue of government involvement in the internet can be much more complex. In the early days of the internet, many western governments were reluctant to interfere with the free-market nature of the internet, besides which the borderless nature of the internet made it very difficult for individual countries to regulate it. As an example, gambling is restricted in many American states, and the US government has found it very difficult to prevent American citizens getting access to gambling websites, most of which are located in foreign countries and made available to US citizens through the internet. The US Constitution and operational difficulties have made it almost unthinkable that the US government would try to block access to gambling sites, therefore it has resorted to trying to control them through indirect means – for example, by making it illegal for American banks to use credit cards to pay for online gambling services, or prosecuting the owners of offshore gambling sites when they set foot in American territory.

Nevertheless, there are many measures that governments can take to encourage the development of e-business. A report by the UK research and consultancy group Gartner identified a number of pressing challenges for the EU in its attempts to create an e-commerce friendly environment.

- Anti-trust authorities will have to resolve, more rapidly than at present, complex competition issues raised by mergers in the media and telecoms sectors, electronic marketplaces, wireless portals and public service providers.

- Enterprises will need more flexible employment schemes and laws to cope with skills shortages in the information technology sector. Employers need the ability to import and outsource skills as required, and a clearer legislative framework for teleworking.

- Tax regulations need to be brought up to date, to recognize the presence of internet transactions. The Gartner study predicted that the difference between European and US internet tax schemes would become a major source of friction in international trade.

- In order to boost consumers' trust in e-commerce and reduce legal uncertainty for enterprises, governments need to develop privacy laws that are relevant to the internet.

The report painted a picture of national governments throwing money at the microenvironment of **electronic commerce (e-commerce)**, such as grants for computer training, often displacing money that could readily be provided by the private sector. Developing the macroenvironment for e-commerce throughout the EU is a much bigger challenge. The question remains as to just what it is possible for governments to do to create an e-commerce-friendly environment. Is responsibility for achieving it best left to the EU rather than national governments? Or is even the EU too small a unit for making decisions, when the internet is progressively breaking down national boundaries?

⟳ Thinking around the subject

The internet and the law of unintended consequences

'The world will never be the same again.' This was the bold message being proclaimed by many pundits at the dawn of the internet age. In one sense, they were quite right, because the internet has had significant effects on how individuals have gone about their lives. Business processes have been transformed, often resulting in great cost savings and improvements in service to customers. But, in many respects, the nature of the change that has resulted from the development of the internet has not quite been what was expected. The complex interaction between the technological, social and economic environments has produced some unexpected consequences of technological development.

Consider the following predictions, which were made in 2000 when 'dotcom' mania was at its height.

- Predictions were made that there would be less commuting as people would work from home, using the internet to communicate with their work colleagues. Traffic congestion would disappear and commuter rail services would lose customers. In fact, technology has allowed many people to choose a pleasant residential environment and to live much further away from their work, because they now have to travel to the office on only a couple of days each week rather than every day. Overall, the travelling distances of many people in this situation have actually increased, resulting in more rather than less total commuting.

- Conferences were predicted to disappear in favour of videoconferencing. Why bother travelling to a meeting or conference when you could meet 'virtually' from the comfort of your own desk or armchair, and at lower cost? However, face-to-face conferences have continued to prosper. The technology that causes many people to work in isolation may have indirectly contributed to a desire to counter this with more face-to-face meetings with a greater social content.

- High-street shops were being written off in 2000 when, quite extraordinarily, the pure internet company lastminute.com had a market capitalization value far in excess of the 110-outlet Debenhams store. The convenience of shopping in the high street or at out-of-town shopping centres, and the problems of arranging the home deliveries of internet suppliers were underestimated by advocates of internet-based shopping.
- Pre-dating all of these predictions has been the expectation that we will need to work fewer hours, as we live in a world of leisure where machines do the work, leaving consumers with more leisure time. In reality, average working hours have tended to increase in recent years, not fall.

We seem to have an inherent tendency to overstate the short-term effects of technological change, but to understate the long-term effects on our behaviour. With the development of new technologies enabling high-speed mobile internet services, further predictions were being made in 2008. Would we really want to download full-length feature films to watch on our mobile phones? Would we really want to surf the net while travelling on a train? Would there be unforeseen 'killer applications' such as SMS text messaging, which was almost left out of the specification of first-generation mobile phones because no useful role for it was foreseen? Perhaps the long-term effects of the internet may be more subtle by contributing to individuals' sense of connectedness with narrowly selected commercial and social groups, no matter where they may be located, while the sense of community with diverse groups of people forced to live together in close proximity may be reduced.

The unforeseen consequences of the internet emphasize how difficult it can be for organizations to understand the consequences of new technologies. These examples demonstrate the importance of understanding the linkages between different elements of the business environment, so developments in the technological environment can be sensibly understood only in conjunction with changes in the social environment.

4.14.3 E-retailing

At the height of the dotcom boom in 2000, the hype cycle in relation to e-retailing had reached its peak. At that time, predictions were being made that conventional shops would soon be eclipsed by online shopping. Why would a retailer want to incur the costs of running a network of shops in expensive retail locations? And why would customers struggle through traffic jams and crowded car parks to buy something that they could order from the comfort of their own home? The appeal of e-retailing might have seemed irresistible to some, and indeed there has been remarkable growth in the value of retail sales through the internet, although there is now some sign that the rate of increase is slowing down (Table 4.2). Some retailers have closed a number of branches or reduced their salesforce, and instead offer customers access to their product range via a website. Several UK suppliers of books, music, computer games and flowers have the logistical support to develop their businesses on the internet.

While e-retailing can offer cost savings to the seller and added convenience to the buyer, a number of challenges remain:

- small orders
- high transport costs

Table 4.2   Value of online retail sales for selected countries for 2009 and 2010.

	Online sales 2009 (bn)	Online sales 2010 (bn)	% increase 2009 vs 2010	Online sales per customer per year	Average number of items purchased per year	Online share of retail trade 2009
UK	£38.0	£42.7	12.4%	£1,101	37	9.5%
Germany	£29.7	£34.8	17.2%	£680	22	6.9%
France	£22.0	£28.9	31.4%	£884	20	4.9%
Benelux	£7.4	£9.0	22.8%	£630	16	3.5%
Italy	£7.3	£8.8	20.5%	£830	17	0.8%
Spain	£5.6	£7.0	25.0%	£692	12	1%
Denmark	£3.5	£4.1	17.9%	£1,078	24	6.1%
Sweden	£3.4	£4.0	18.0%	£712	20	4.8%
Switzerland	£3.4	£4.0	21.0%	£771	19	4.8%
Norway	£2.9	£3.5	20.7%	£979	13	6.3%
Finland	£2.3	£2.8	23.0%	£867	18	4.9%
Poland	£2.2	£3.0	36.4%	£321	10	2%
Total/Avg	£127.7	£152.8	19.6%	£774	20	4.7

Source: adapted from A.C. Nielson Global Trends in Online Shopping (June 2010).

- goods not compatible with the letter/mail box
- difficulty in offering a timed delivery window
- most economical delivery times for companies are 9 am to 5 pm, Monday to Friday, when the customer is most likely to be out
- difficulty of returning goods.

The delivery of goods to the final consumer has not shown the productivity gains that internet-based ordering has achieved (see Yrjölä 2001). This is probably not surprising when it is remembered that home delivery remains a labour-intensive activity in which two of the main costs – labour and transport – are likely to continue to increase in real terms. We should not forget that, in the UK, the milkman has almost disappeared because efficiency of delivery could not be improved relative to the cost of consumers collecting milk from large, efficient supermarkets. The problem of buyers being at home to accept goods is also one that has been slow to resolve. Retailers have experimented with 24-hour collection points at local convenience stores, and delivery companies have experimented with evening and weekend deliveries. In the UK, the Royal Mail announced in October 2010 that it was to experiment with evening deliveries of mail to cater for busy professionals who are out at work all day and unable to receive deliveries at the time when retailers and delivery companies have traditionally made their deliveries.

There are also many high-involvement goods where buyers feel more comfortable being able to see and feel the goods before they commit to a purchase. When buying clothes, many buyers would prefer to try the items on and to feel the texture of the clothes. Some retailers have introduced 'virtual reality' systems to help simulate the shop buying experience – for example, some retailers allow customers to develop their personal avatar, which they can then use to judge how an item of clothing would look on them. Despite a lot of hype about the potential of virtual reality systems, and hope that these could be used in a peer-to-peer environment, progress appears to have been slow. Uptake of the virtual reality social network website 'Second Life' is reported to be lower than original expectations predicted.

Retailing often fulfils a social function – for example, a group of friends may 'have a day out shopping', which might include stopping for coffee, having a meal and sharing experiences of new purchases. Many have doubted the ability of the internet to replace this social function, even with further development of virtual reality peer-to-peer networks.

As e-retailing has developed, customers' expectations have risen. When ordering online, they expect to have prices and stock confirmed, as well as a delivery date and preferably the time. Customers also expect to be told of any delays, particularly when they are waiting in for the delivery.

Although many companies have set up internet retail sites in an attempt to cut out intermediaries, routes to market for e-retailers have become increasingly complex. E-retailing can be extremely competitive, with customers being just a click away from a competitor – they don't even have to make the effort of walking into a competitor's shop. Getting a customer into your site increasingly involves the use of online intermediaries, including search engines, affiliate sites and price comparison sites. These would usually seek a percentage of the sales revenue, or a payment per 'click-through' in return for providing the link to the retailer's site.

4.15 Data security and privacy

Technology has undoubtedly allowed businesses to do things that were previously unimaginable – for example, in the way that data are handled and analysed. While much of this development has been beneficial to companies and their customers, some commentators have pointed to more harmful consequences for personal privacy and security.

Data protection has become a very big issue, as it is not just companies that can easily collect and manipulate information – so too can criminals. There is also concern on the part of some consumers that their personal data may be misused, if not in a criminal way certainly in a way that they would consider unethical. These concerns have grown with developments in technology. When personal records were entirely paper based, it was difficult to appropriate data for improper uses. If paper records were lost, they were probably only likely to turn up in a rubbish skip or a place that only a small number of people have access to. The bank customer could be reasonably confident that their personal information would not get out of their local branch, and it would be difficult for anybody else to get hold of their records. Today, their personal information is likely to be held on servers that are accessible remotely by a range of authorized employees.

Unfortunately, unauthorized people may be able to access personal information held on databases. Instead of having to break in laboriously to several bank branches to obtain large volumes of customer data, there have been many reported cases (and probably many more unreported) of skilled hackers being able to get into a bank's database and view the records of thousands or even millions of customers. Where customer information is held on transportable discs, huge amounts of data can accidentally or deliberately end up in the wrong hands. In November 2007, many people in the UK were concerned to hear that the government had 'lost' two CDs containing personal information on 25 million recipients of government benefits. There was concern that this information could be used by criminals wrongly to impersonate another person and obtain credit or benefits to which they were not entitled.

Within the EU, the 1981 European Convention for Individuals with regard to Automatic Processing of Personal Data, implemented through Directive 95/46/EC provides a framework for data privacy and security. This has been implemented in the UK in the 1988 Data Protection Act, and policed by the Data Protection Commissioner. The Act covers electronically stored data, which can be used to identify a living person, including names, birthday and anniversary dates, addresses, telephone numbers, fax numbers, email addresses, etc. A number of principles guide companies' use of data, and require, among other things, that personal data shall be processed fairly and lawfully, and shall not be used for any purpose that is not compatible with the original purpose. There is a requirement for companies to keep accurate records that are not unnecessarily excessive in detail, and data shall not be kept for longer than is necessary for the purpose of collecting them. Appropriate technical and organizational measures must be taken against unauthorized or unlawful processing of personal data and against its accidental loss or destruction. The Data Protection Act 1988 and the Freedom of Information Act 2000 give some rights of access to data.

The internet has created problems for consumers in verifying who they are actually dealing with. There have been many cases of sham online companies that have set up in business with enticing offers, but have rapidly disappeared without trace. Some have been set up to obtain customers' personal information, which has then been used fraudulently, after the company has disappeared. But it is not just customers who should be wary of rogue companies, companies also need to be wary of rogue customers. In a real-life environment, a company can see who is coming into its site and remove visibly disruptive elements, such as drunks disturbing the atmosphere of a restaurant. In the case of online service processes, it can be much more difficult to judge whether visitors to a company's website are benign or malicious. Malicious visitors may disrupt a company's service processes by planting viruses, bombing it with mass emails or disrupting the codes of its operating system. The reasons for this action may be a grudge against the company, or simply the challenge for a computer hacker of beating a system. Where a company is dependent on online transactions for the bulk of its revenue, the effects of such malicious intrusions can be devastating, not only resulting in a short-term loss of revenue, but long-term harm to its brand reputation where customers' details are obtained or used in an unauthorized way. In designing the online environment, companies must strike a balance between making a site easily accessible to all, and difficult for those with malicious intentions.

Case study:
Will the bank of the future be 'mobile'?

By Nicole Koenig-Lewis, Swansea University, and Alexander Moll, Visual Identity AG

© David Clark

Internet banking is now taken for granted by many people, who may be relieved at not having to visit a bank branch or use a telephone call centre to undertake many banking transactions. Mobile banking ('m-banking') is probably ten years behind internet banking in its development. In ten years' time, will we be taking mobile banking similarly for granted?

Whenever any new banking technology comes along, there are sceptics who doubt that the new technology will catch on with the public. When ATM machines first appeared, many people thought they would never be popular because people liked to go in to a branch and deal with a human being. In the late 1990s, when the internet was only beginning to catch the public's imagination, doubters expressed major concerns about privacy, security, download speeds and access to the internet. When Egg bank launched its then revolutionary online banking service in 1998, even Egg itself turned out to have been unduly cautious as prospective customers appeared in unexpectedly high numbers, crashing its servers and swamping its telephone lines.

Mobile phones have become an essential part of our lives. We have adopted the phone as a personal organizer, as a camera and music player to consume and share music, pictures, games, ringtones, etc. A report by Juniper, for example, highlighted that many young people would not leave home without their mobile phone (Wilcox 2009b). But what is happening with mobile banking?

More recently, high hopes have been held for m-banking, following the more general development of mobile commerce, which in turn has been helped by the appearance of sophisticated, easy-to-use smartphones such as the iPhone. M-banking enables customers to access their bank accounts through mobile devices to check their balance or to conduct financial transactions. The range of services that can be undertaken while mobile is likely to increase, and many have suggested that mobile phones are likely to evolve as ubiquitous payment devices, allowing a mobile phone to be used in a similar way to a credit card (Wilcox 2009a). But will the growth of m-banking be as swift as the previous growth of online banking? Some critics have argued that banks have less to gain from promoting m-banking than they had from promoting the first generation of internet banking. It has been claimed that m-banking does not provide significant cost saving benefits for banks in comparison to those that can be achieved by migrating customers from traditional banking methods to online banking (Laukkanen *et al.* 2007). If consumers do not see advantages in m-banking, will banks significantly increase the allocation of resources to support it?

Although phones have now achieved very high levels of ownership in most developed countries (with more mobile phones than people in the UK), doubters have pointed out that most users of smartphones (and not-so-smart phones) rarely use them to their full capacity, and the majority of phones that are capable of internet browsing are never actually connected to the internet (ICT Statistics 2009).

Forecasting the likely uptake of new technologies is vital for the rapidly changing communication sector, where new applications/services appear daily. However, these forecasts are very difficult to make and there are many cases of inaccurate forecasting. For example, in the 1980s many experts failed to predict the rapid adoption of mobile phones. Also the uptake of texting was completely unexpected. On the other hand, picture phones and video calling have largely failed to take off, while Bluetooth adoption has been much slower than predicted.

In the short life of m-commerce, forecasters appear to have had only limited success in accurately predicting take-up of m-banking, which reportedly still does not meet industry expectations (Kim *et al.* 2009). Forrester Research reported in 2009 that only 4 per cent of the nearly 25 million Bank of America online customers were active users of m-banking (Khan 2008). A recent study by the Mobile Marketing Association revealed that, while m-banking is gaining popularity, it is still far away from becoming mainstream, as only 14 per cent of UK adult consumers, and 9 per cent of French and German consumers, use mobile phones for banking, with SMS being the most popular medium for viewing account balances (Mobile Marketing Association and Lightspeed Research 2010). However, these figures are higher for young consumers aged between 18 and 34, with 24 per cent of UK young people and 20 per cent of German young people already engaging in m-banking (Mobile Marketing Association and Lightspeed Research 2010). It seems that young people are more predisposed to adopt m-commerce services in general than other internet users because these services are usually low-cost entertainment services (e.g. ringtones, songs), which fit with their lifestyle (Bigne *et al.* 2005).

Many predictions of the likely take-up of m-banking have been made. For example, Juniper Research in 2007 suggested that, worldwide, the number of consumers using m-banking would reach 816 million by 2011, which would be a tenfold increase on the number using these services in 2007 (Goode 2008). In addition, it has been predicted that by the end of 2011 more than 150 million subscribers worldwide would have used their mobile phone not only for banking information services but also for transactional m-banking services (Wilcox 2009b). In making predictions, analysts have tried to draw comparisons with previous adoption patterns for new technology, which have typically got off to a slow start as they target relatively high-income, innovative segments and eventually become affordable to all. In an attempt to improve forecasts, models of consumer adoption have been applied, most notably the Technology Acceptance Model (TAM) and Innovation Diffusion Theory (IDT). These models are not without their problems – for example, it has been pointed out that the TAM typically explains only about 40 per cent of variance in purchase intention (Venkatesh and Davis 2000).

In western countries, m-banking adoption has been moving slowly and it might therefore at first sight seem surprising that the West lags far behind some developing countries such as Kenya and South Africa. In Kenya, about 7 million people use the M-Pesa service, which was launched by Safaricom in partnership with Vodafone in 2007 and allows customers to use their mobile phone to pay bills, deposit cash and send cash to other mobile phone users. The adoption of the M-Pesa service has been speedy, with 11,000 new registrations per day during 2009. Even though the average transaction per person is very small, $1.9 billion have been moved in person-to-person transactions since the launch of the service (Mwangi 2009).

This rapid adoption of the M-Pesa service in Kenya can be largely explained by the lack of a landline telephone network and a poorly developed banking infrastructure. The Financial Access Survey 2009 shows that only 23 per cent of the Kenyan adult population have a bank account but 48 per cent own a mobile phone, with the rate of ownership rising to 72.8 per cent in urban areas and 80.4 per cent in Nairobi (FSD Kenya and Central Bank of Kenya 2009). Furthermore, Africans with bank accounts have to pay high charges for moving cash around. M-Pesa provides a service that allows the safe transfer of cash without facing high costs. Setting up an account is straightforward. Similar successful m-banking examples exist in other non-western countries – for example, Globe Telecom's GCash service is available in the Philippines, which transforms the mobile phone into a virtual wallet for secure, quick and convenient money transactions.

In Europe the situation is different with fewer incentives to use m-banking services as there are a range of digitized payment methods already accessible for bank customers. Thus there is a trend for banks to offer services that are unique to m-banking customers. NatWest, for example, launched a mobile banking service that allows Polish workers in the UK to send money home (Montia 2008). According to one survey, other m-banking services of interest to customers are geo-location, which leads customers to their nearest ATM or bank branch, and the use of the mobile phone to make in-store payments, and to receive deposit and withdrawal notices (Mobile Marketing Association and Lightspeed Research 2010).

The mobile phone is the one piece of technology that most people worldwide own. Technology providers and financial institutions believe that m-banking will one day reach a critical tipping point, after which it will become mainstream. But what will it take to reach this tipping point? Will it be the availability of even more sophisticated, useful phones? Will it occur when consumers overcome their fears about the security of mobile banking and recognize a new generation of phones as really easy to use? Will widespread adoption occur only when mobile phones become widely used as easy payment devices, making it easy for a customer to use their phone to pay for a bus ticket or a drink in a bar? Or will the tipping point occur only when banks put serious resources into the further development of m-banking?

QUESTIONS

1 Discuss the causes of uncertainty in forecasts of levels of consumer adoption of new technology-based services such as m-banking.

2 Identify methods by which a bank could seek to improve the accuracy of its forecasts of take-up of m-banking.

3 Discuss the concept of a 'tipping point' in the adoption of new technology-based services. What factors do you consider would contribute to a tipping point for m-banking? How are these likely to differ between western and non-western countries?

Summary

This chapter has considered technological change from the macro perspective and examined the impact of technology on different aspects of business at the micro level. In both instances the relevance of technological change to business success has been stressed. At the macro level of technological change, the key points to remember concern the demand-technology life cycle. This will be influenced by the level of R&D expenditure, not only in a particular industry but also in related and sometimes unrelated industries. The fusion and interaction of different technologies results in new applications and processes which eventually may give rise to whole new industries. Technology permeates through from academic and research institutions into industry, from one industry to another, and from one economy to another.

At the micro level, this chapter has considered the impact of technology on a company's products and operations: product design and development, manufacturing and processing; storage and distribution; order and payment processing; and information and communication systems via electronic business. Managers should seek to improve the efficiency of business operations and also to ensure that the benefits are passed on to the customer. These customer benefits may include better pre-order services, such as product availability and specification, information, faster quotations, quicker design customization and shorter delivery times.

The technological environment is a constantly changing one. In many industries during the 2000s and beyond, change will be the norm rather than the exception. Companies that focus on customer needs, competitor activity and technological developments, rather than simply aiming to sell what the factory makes, are more likely to succeed.

There is a close link between this chapter and **Chapter 8**, which looks at networks and relationships between companies. The use of technology to improve supply chain efficiency is often a key element of business-to-business relationships. The interrelationship between technology and society is stressed in **Chapter 3** and this chapter has explored not only technology's response to changes in society, but also the effects of changing technology on social values.

Technology has opened up many opportunities for businesses to enter global markets, and these are discussed in more detail in **Chapter 14**.

Finally, issues of privacy and security surrounding new technologies have attracted the attention of the law (**Chapter 6**) and raised ethical concerns (**Chapter 5**).

Key Terms

Article numbering (145)

Computer-aided design (CAD) (143)

Computer-aided manufacturing (CAM) (143)

Demand-technology life cycle (129)

Electronic commerce (e-commerce) (159)

Electronic data interchange (EDI) (155)

Electronic point of sale (EPOS) (146)

Hype cycle (132)

Internet (155)

Just-in-time (JIT) system (143)

New product development (NPD) process (141)

Product life cycle (139)

Research and development (R&D) (136)

Technological fusion (128)

Technology transfer (129)

Online Learning Centre

To help you grasp the key concepts of this chapter, explore the extra resources posted on the Online Learning Centre at *www.mcgraw-hill.co.uk/palmer*. Among other helpful resources there are chapter-by-chapter test questions, revision notes and web links.

Chapter review questions

1 Discuss the extent to which marketing managers should be involved in the R&D process. What should their role be?

2 Critically discuss the role of governments in fostering an R&D culture and in encouraging technological development?

3 Using examples, discuss ways in which new technologies have altered social relationships.

Activities

1 Assume you are working for a multinational manufacturer of electrical goods. Your main retailer in the UK has had a number of your vacuum cleaners returned recently with a serious malfunction. It appears to be a problem with the on/off switch. The product is assembled at the company's plant in Spain, but the on/off switch is manufactured in China. However, the miniature circuit board in the vacuum could have been made in Japan or Korea (two suppliers). It may be just one batch of switches or circuit boards that was faulty. To recall all the products sold in the UK in recent months would be extremely expensive. Also it is not known as yet if the vacuums sold in other countries are affected, or if other products (such as hair-dryers) use the same switch or other switch designs with the same circuit board.

    How would you trace the identity of the batch of vacuums and other products affected before enacting a product recall?

2 In the pub one Friday evening two men were overheard discussing electronic shopping. Both men worked in the computer industry, had lots of 'kit' at home, and had been connected to the World Wide Web for some time. They were exchanging views about the latest developments on the internet, and getting quite excited about the possibilities of buying their weekly groceries over the net and having them delivered. This would take the drudgery out of supermarket shopping, they agreed. Both men worked long hours and when asked the last time they had seen the inside of a supermarket, neither could remember. Both were married. One wife, although quite capable of holding a good job, did not work at all, had no need to work, and was quite happy to look after the family (two children) and do the supermarket shopping. The other was in a very similar position, although she had taken up part-time work, as the children were a little older. Neither woman was much taken with computers and thought that being tied to a computer all day and half the evening would be a life of drudgery.

    Discuss the advantages and limitations of online grocery shopping in the social context described above.

3 Now revisit the case of online shopping and identify the technological innovations that have made this method of shopping a sustainable business model. Think carefully about technology innovation at all points in the supply chain.

Further Reading

The following provide contemporary insights into the role of innovation in organizations and the relationship between business and R&D.

Crawford, C.M. and Di Benedetto, A. (2011) *New Product Management*, 10th edn, Boston, MA, McGraw-Hill Higher Education.

Dodgson, M. Gann, D. and Salter, A. (2008), *Management of Technological Innovation: Strategy and Practice*, Oxford, Oxford University Press.

Javi, R. Triandis, H.C. and Weick, C.W. (2010) *Managing Research, Development and Innovation: Managing the Unmanageable*, 3rd edn, New Jersey, John Wiley & Sons.

McGourty, J. Tarshis, L.A. and Dominick, P. (2009) Managing innovation: lessons from world class organizations', *International Journal of Technology Management*, Vol. 11, No. 3/4, pp. 354–368.

Trott, P. (2008) *Innovation Management and New Product Development*, 4th edn, London, FT Prentice Hall.

There are now lots of books about e-business, ranging from textbooks to quick 'how to' books.

Chaffey, D. (2009) *E-business and E-commerce Management*, 4th edn, London, FT Prentice Hall.

Damani, C. and Damani, R. (2007) *Ecommerce 2.0: The Evolution of Ecommerce*, London, Imano.

Laudon, K. and Traver, C. (2009) *E-Commerce 2010: Business, Technology, Society*, International Version, 6th edn, Englewood Cliffs, NJ, Prentice Hall.

The management of the new service development process is explored further in the following articles.

Droege, H., Hildebrand, D. and Heras Forcada, M.A. (2009) 'Innovation in services: present findings, and future pathways', *Journal of Service Management*, Vol. 20, No. 2, pp. 131–155.

Seegy, U., Gleich, R.,Wald, A., Mudde, P. and Motwani, J. (2008) 'The management of service innovation: an empirical investigation', *International Journal of Services and Operations Management*, Vol. 4, No. 6, pp. 672–686.

Storey, C. and Hull, F.M. (2010) 'Service development success: a contingent approach by knowledge strategy', *Journal of Service Management*, Vol. 21, No. 2, pp. 140–161.

Consumer adoption processes for innovative technologies are discussed in the following.

Hossain, L. and de Silva, A. (2009) 'Exploring user acceptance of technology using social networks', *Journal of High Technology Management Research*, Vol. 20, pp. 1–18.

Vlachos, P.A. and Vrechopoulos, A.P. (2008) 'Determinants of behavioral intentions in the mobile internet services market', *Journal of Services Marketing*, Vol. 22, No. 4, pp. 280–291.

Walker, R.H. and Johnson, L.W. (2006) 'Why consumers use and do not use technology enabled services', *Journal of Services Marketing*, Vol. 20, No. 2, pp. 126–135.

The methods used by organizations to search for new service ideas are discussed in the following.

Olsen, N.V. and Sallis, J. (2006) 'Market scanning for new service development', *European Journal of Marketing*, Vol. 40, No. 5/6, pp. 466–484.

Toivonen, M. and Tuominen, T. (2009) 'Emergence of innovations in services', *Service Industries Journal*, Vol. 29, No. 7, pp. 887–902.

The role of social network media in new product development is discussed in the following.

Füller, J., Matzler, K. and Hoppe, M. (2008) 'Brand community members as a source of innovation', *Journal of Product Innovation Management*, Vol. 25, pp. 608–619.

Blazevic, V. and Lievens, A. (2008) 'Managing innovation through customer coproduced knowledge in electronic services: an exploratory study', *Journal of the Academy of Marketing Science*, Vol. 36, pp. 138–151.

References

Ajzen, I. and Fishbein, M. (1980) *Understanding Attitudes and Predicting Social Behaviour*, Englewood Cliffs, NJ, Prentice Hall.

Bigne, E., Ruiz, C. and Sanz, S. (2005) 'The impact of internet user shopping patterns and demographics on consumer mobile buying behaviour', *Journal of Electronic Commerce Research*, Vol. 6, No. 3, pp. 193–209.

Davis, F.D., Bagozzi, R.P. and Warshaw, P.R. (1989) 'User acceptance of computer technology: a comparison of two theoretical models', *Management Science*, Vol. 35, No. 8, pp. 982–1003.

Economist Intelligence Unit (2010), *E-readiness Rankings*, London, EIU.

Fishbein, M. and Ajzen, I. (1975) *Belief, Attitude, Intention and Behaviour: An Introduction to Theory and Research*, Reading, MA, Addison-Wesley.

Fletcher, K. (1995) *Marketing Management and Information Technology*, 2nd edn, London, Prentice-Hall International.

Foresight (2009) *Foresight Annual Review 2009*, online at: www.bis.gov.uk/foresight/publications/annual-reviews (accessed 17 September 2010).

FSD Kenya and Central Bank of Kenya (2009) 'Results of the finaccess national survey: dynamics of Kenya's changing financial landscape', online at www.fsdkenya.org/finaccess/documents/09-06-10%20FinAccess%20FA09%20Brochure.pdf (accessed 29 March 2010).

Goode, A. (2008) 'Press release: Juniper Research forecasts over 800 million consumers to use mobile banking services by 2011, but cautions that key hurdles are yet to be overcome', online at http://juniperresearch.com (accessed 20 July 2009).

Hogg, G., Laing, A. and Winkelman, D. (2003) 'The professional service encounter in the age of the internet: an exploratory study', *Journal of Services Marketing*, Vol. 17, No. 5, pp. 476–494.

Howley, M. (2002) 'The role of consultancies in new product development', *Journal of Product and Brand Management*, Vol. 11, No. 6/7, pp. 447–458.

ICT Statistics (2009) 'International Telecommunication Union', online at www.itu.int (accessed 30 July 2009).

Jones, H. (2004) 'Up close and personal', *The Marketer*, Issue 7, November.

Keers, H. (2002) 'Mothercare slips into red as warehouse woes grow', *Daily Telegraph*, 22 November.

Khan, M.A. (2008) 'Consumers are apathetic about mobile banking', online at www.mobilemarketer.com/cms/news/research/1561.html, Forrester Research (accessed 3 November 2009).

Kim, G., Shin, B. and Lee, H.G. (2009) 'Understanding dynamics between initial trust and usage intentions of mobile banking', *Information Systems Journal*, Vol. 19, No. 3, pp. 283–311.

Kim, J. and Wilemon, D. (2003) 'Sources and assessment of complexity in NPD projects', *R&D Management*, Vol. 33, No. 1, pp. 16–30.

Kotler, P. (1997) *Marketing Management: Analysis, Planning, Implementation and Control*, 9th edn, Englewood Cliffs, NJ, Prentice-Hall.

Laukkanen, T., Sinkkonen, S., Kivijärvi, M. and Laukkanen, P. (2007) 'Innovation resistance among mature consumers', *Journal of Consumer Marketing*, Vol. 24, No. 7, pp. 419–427.

Little, G. (2002) 'Inventors don't always make great marketers', *Design Week*, Vol. 17, No. 27, p. 15.

Lopez-Bassols, V. (1998) *The OECD Observer*, No. 213, August–September, pp. 16–19.

Mobile Marketing Association and Lightspeed Research (2010) 'Europeans opt for mobile banking in increasing numbers', online at http://mmaglobal.com/news/europeans-opt-mobile-banking-increasing-numbers (accessed 29 March 2010).

Montia, G. (2008) 'NatWest launches Polish mobile money transfer service', online at www.bankingtimes.co.uk/2008/12/23/natwest-launches-polish-mobile-money-transfer-service/ (accessed 29 March 2010).

Mwangi, B. (2009) 'M-Pesa-transforming the lives of Kenyans', online at www.safaricom.co.ke/fileadmin/M-PESA/Documents/Presentations/09.05.05%20-%20MMT%20Conference%20(SA).pdf (accessed 29 March 2010).

O'Cass, A. and Fenech, T. (2003) 'Web retailing adoption: exploring the nature of Internet users' web retailing behaviour', *Journal of Retailing and Consumer Services*, Vol. 10, No. 2, pp. 81–94.

OECD (2002) *Short Summary of the Workshop on Genetic Inventions, Intellectual Property Rights and Licensing Practices*, Paris, OECD.

OECD (2010a) *OECD Factbook 2010: Economic, Environmental and Social Statistics, Science and Technology, Research and Development, Expenditure on R&D*, pp. 150–151.

OECD (2010b) *Economic, Environmental and Social Statistics, Science and Technology, Research and Development, Researchers*, pp. 152–153.

Press, E. and Washburn, J. (2003) 'Secrecy and science', *The Atlantic Online*, online at www.theatlantic.com/issues/2000/03/press2 htm (accessed April 2005).

Timmins, N. (2003) 'A bid to save money for the government: online auctions', *Financial Times*, 29 January, p. 12.

Venkatesh, V. and Davis, F.D. (2000) 'A theoretical extension of the technology acceptance model: four longitudinal field studies', *Management Science*, Vol. 46, No. 2, pp. 186–204.

Wilcox, H. (2009a) 'Press release: mobile banking users to exceed 150m globally by 2011 according to Juniper Research', Juniper Research, online at http://juniperresearch.com/shop/viewpressrelease.php?pr=120 (accessed 2 September 2009).

Wilcox, H. (2009b) 'Banking on the mobile (White Paper)', Juniper Research, online at www.juniperresearch.com (accessed 23 October 2009).

Young, A. (1993) 'What goes into R&D?', *OECD Observer*, No. 183, August–September.

Yrjölä, H. (2001) 'Physical distribution considerations for electronic grocery shopping', *International Journal of Physical Distribution and Logistics Management*, Vol. 31, No. 10, pp. 25–38

Chapter 1
Accounting and decision making in business

LO Learning objectives

After studying Chapter 1, you should be able to:
1 Describe what managers do and why they need accounting information
2 Appreciate the key characteristics of management accounting information
3 Review the impact on business of organizational and technological change, managing for value, the sustainability agenda and corporate governance
4 Appreciate that management accounting principles can be useful irrespective of who applies them or where they are located in an organization

Concepts in Context

We will see in this chapter how management accounting practices have had to respond to changes in the business environment. For example, airlines such as easyJet have developed a business model enabled by new technology and deregulation in the airline industry. According to the company website, easyJet keeps costs low by eliminating the unnecessary costs and 'frills' which characterize 'traditional' airlines. This is done in a number of ways: 1. Use of the internet to reduce distribution costs; 2. Maximizing the utilization of the substantial assets thus reducing unit cost;

© Paul Trendell

3. Ticketless travel which helps to reduce significantly the cost of issuing, distributing, processing and reconciling millions of tickets each year; 4. No free lunch – eliminating free catering on-board reduces cost and unnecessary bureaucracy and management; 5. Efficient use of airports – easyJet flies to main destination airports throughout Europe, but gains efficiencies through rapid turnaround times, and progressive landing charge agreements with the airports; 6. Paperless operations – the management and administration of the company is undertaken entirely on IT systems which can be accessed through secure servers from anywhere in the world enabling huge flexibility in the running of the airline.[1]

What is management accounting?

LO 1

Planning

In simple terms, management accounting provides information that may be used to plan, direct, motivate and control an organization. Although it is predominantly used by managers in an organization, management accounting information might also be the basis of a business plan that can be presented to outside interested parties such as banks or potential private investors. Among other data, potential investors look at the *sales volumes*, *profit margins* and *costs*. They will also consider the *cash* needs of the business. Going forward, the plan should indicate not just long-term projections of profit but suggest a way of co-ordinating and controlling the business so that it is 'kept on track'.

The plans of management are often expressed formally in budgets, and the term budgeting is applied generally to describe this part of the planning process. Typically, budgets are prepared annually and represent management's plans in specific, quantitative terms. These data will be collected, analysed and summarized for management use in the form of budgets. Although they may be prepared annually, ever cheaper and more powerful computer packages now mean that actual outturns can be checked against the planned budget with great frequency and with a high level of detail, with data that can be 'sliced and diced'.

Directing and motivating

In addition to planning for the future, managers must oversee day-to-day activities and keep the organization functioning smoothly. This requires the ability to motivate and effectively direct people. Managers assign tasks to employees, arbitrate disputes, answer questions, solve on-the-spot problems, and make many small decisions that affect customers and employees. In effect, directing is that part of the managers' work that deals with the routine and the here and now. Management accounting data, such as daily sales reports, are often used in this type of day-to-day decision making.

Controlling

In carrying out the control function, managers seek to ensure that the plan is being followed. Feedback, which signals whether operations are on track, is the key to effective control. In sophisticated organizations this feedback is provided by detailed reports of various types. One of these reports, which compares budgeted to actual results, is called a performance report. Performance reports suggest where operations are

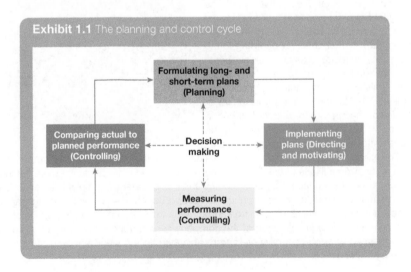

Exhibit 1.1 The planning and control cycle

Formulating long- and short-term plans (Planning)

Comparing actual to planned performance (Controlling)

Decision making

Implementing plans (Directing and motivating)

Measuring performance (Controlling)

Focus on Business Practice

Business planning: Eco-hotel

© Sashi Ono

James has a proposal to build an 'Eco-hotel' on an island in the Red Sea. The project involves renovating a historic site using local labour and materials and the latest 'green' sustainable technologies. In order to attract investors, James has produced a prospectus which includes detailed forecasts of revenues, costs and profits for the next ten years. In the prospectus, he has also explained what assumptions he has made about likely visitor numbers and possible competitors for the main recreational activity in the area, which is scuba diving in the warm and spectacular waters of the Red Sea.

James has produced a business *plan* but this plan can also form the basis of a *control model*. Once the project is under way, James can check whether his plans are being realized – are the costs over-running? Are the visitor numbers coming through? Are there any actions that need to be taken to keep the project on track? Or maybe the plans have to be modified?

Exercise: Refer to Exhibit 1.1 and see how the hotel project matches up to the planning and control features of the model in the exhibit.

not proceeding as planned and where some parts of the organization may require additional attention. As we shall see in following chapters, providing this kind of feedback to managers is one of the central purposes of management accounting.

The planning and control cycle

The work of management can be summarized in a model such as the one shown in Exhibit 1.1. The model, which depicts the planning and control cycle, illustrates the smooth flow of management activities from planning through directing and motivating, controlling, and then back to planning again. All of these activities involve *decision making*, so it is depicted as the hub around which the other activities revolve.

An overview of management accounting principles

LO 2

Financial accounting is mandatory; that is, it must be done. Various outside parties such as the Stock Exchange regulators and the tax authorities require periodic financial statements. Management accounting, on the other hand, is not mandatory. A company is completely free to do as much or as little as it wishes. Since management accounting is completely optional, the important question is always, 'Is the information useful?' rather than, 'Is the information required?' With these criteria in mind, management accounting is characterized by:

- **An emphasis on the future.** Since planning is such an important part of the manager's job, management accounting has a strong future orientation. In contrast, financial accounting primarily provides

summaries of past financial transactions. Changes are constantly taking place in economic conditions, customer needs and desires, competitive conditions and so on.

- **Relevance and flexibility of data.** Managers want information that is relevant even if it is not completely objective or verifiable. By relevant, we mean appropriate for the problem at hand. The management accounting information system should be flexible enough to provide whatever data are relevant for a particular decision.

- **Emphasis on timeliness rather than precision.** Timeliness is often more important than precision to managers. If a decision must be made, a manager would much rather have a good estimate now than wait a week for a more precise answer. A decision involving tens of millions of pounds does not have to be based on estimates that are precise down to the penny, or even to the pound. Management accounting increasingly places considerable weight on non-monetary data. For example, information about customer satisfaction is of tremendous importance even though it would be difficult to express such data in a monetary form. If customers are dissatisfied then the future revenues and profits of the organization might be at risk.

- **Focus on the segments of an organization.** Financial accounting is primarily concerned with reporting for the company as a whole. By contrast, management accounting focuses much more on the parts, or segments, of a company. These segments may be product lines, sales territories, divisions, departments, or any other categorization of the company's activities that management finds useful.

Focus on Business Practice

Accounting in human resources

© Andresr

Human resources (HR) professionals often say 'people are our greatest asset', but might not understand what an asset is, or forget to look at the profit and loss account to see what payroll and related costs are. According to a recent article in *People Management*, not many HR professionals have sufficient basic accounting knowledge to understand basic accounting principles. They need to be familiar with the basic financial statements – the profit and loss account (income statement), balance sheet and cash flow statement – as well as understand costs. The article suggests accounting is a communication medium, a language indeed, that not everyone understands. While HR professionals may not think they require fluency in accounting, they do need to make business decisions which are underpinned by sound financial information, for example hiring someone, or approving redundancy packages. Having an understanding of accounting information (rather than just accepting it from accountants) would benefit HR managers and staff. Certainly, management accountants within an organization could provide some help by training HR staff in the basics of accounting and costs.[2]

Exercise: Can you think of how other sections of an organization (like product design, for example) might use accounting information?

Management accounting: responding to challenges in the business environment

LO 3

New business processes and technologies

The last three decades have been a period of tremendous ferment and change in the business environment. Competition in many industries has become worldwide in scope, and the pace of innovation in products and services has accelerated. This has been good news for consumers, since intensified competition has generally led to lower prices, higher quality and more choices. However, the last two decades have been a period of wrenching change for many businesses and their employees. Many managers have learned that cherished ways of doing business do not work any more and that major changes must be made in how organizations are managed and in how work gets done.

Another significant influence on management accounting is new and ever-changing technology, especially in computers and telecommunications. These technologies have not just resulted in the automation of existing manual management accounting systems but have enabled the restructuring of whole industries and economies. Even if some of the hype surrounding the internet has died down a little since the heady days of the late 1990s, the internet has, and is, changing the way business is done. Production philosophies pioneered in manufacturing such as lean production are now applied in service as well as manufacturing activities.

Enterprise resource planning systems

Some technological changes have not just affected the environment of management accounting but have had a direct impact on the collection and dissemination of management information.[3] The increasing use of sophisticated real time information systems known as enterprise resource planning (ERP) provided by companies such as SAP, Oracle, J.D. Edwards and Baan, has changed the nature of management accounting work and the role of the finance function.[4] One of the emerging implications for the management accountant is that there is more emphasis on business support rather than routine information gathering. Furthermore, not only is there a greater dispersion of finance personnel into process areas, but accounting information itself has become more dispersed throughout the organization as it becomes more accessible to non-accounting personnel.

More emphasis on business ethics

If ethical standards in business were not generally adhered to, there would be undesirable consequences for everyone. Essentially, abandoning ethical standards would lead to a lower standard of living with lower-quality goods and services, less to choose from, and higher prices. In short, following ethical rules is not just a matter of being 'nice'; it is absolutely essential for the smooth functioning of an advanced market economy. The single-minded emphasis placed on short-term profits in some companies may make it seem as if the only way to get ahead is to act unethically. When top managers say, in effect, that they will only be satisfied with bottom-line results and will accept no excuses, they are asking for trouble, as recent collapses in the banking sector illustrate.

The increased importance of service sector management

Management accounting has expanded its influence from its traditional base in manufacturing to service sectors, which themselves have become increasing sources of employment and income in many economies. Many traditional management accounting approaches to issues such as costing were developed with manufacturing industry in mind. In comparison with traditional manufacturing where the product is easy to see

and touch, products in service industries are less tangible. A bank may offer a number of different 'products' such as types of account or loans which are defined by dimensions such as accessibility or repayment terms, secured or unsecured and so on. Services cannot be stored in inventory so that managers in banks and other service industries may be less interested in *product* cost but, rather, which *customers* are profitable and which customers are not. Service industries provide new challenges and opportunities for management accounting information, particularly as competitive success is especially dependent on intangible assets such as employee expertise and customer relations.

Not only are service activities becoming more important relative to manufacturing but they are increasingly subject to reorganization in both public and private sectors.[5] In particular, we have seen the emergence of shared service centres where the support services of an entire corporation are concentrated in a single geographical location. Other companies have gone a stage further by sub-contracting them to independent companies in a practice known as outsourcing.[6]

Management accounting's spread into the public sector is driven by government demands for new measures of performance and new delivery systems. Although its precise form and motivation varies in different countries, this phenomenon, often referred to as the 'New Public Management',[7] may be seen as a global movement.[8] These developments are not without controversy, especially where there is an attempt to apply, in the not-for-profit, public sector organizations, the same management philosophies and techniques that were originally developed for private, profit-making organizations.

Managing for value

Traditionally, accountants were portrayed as 'bean-counters' or 'corporate policemen' with an emphasis on past performance and organizational control. While these functions are still part of an accountant's role, the trend recently has been to emphasize the creation and management of value. Pressures from corporate raiders and new sources of capital, such as private equity, mean that managers have to be increasingly aware of shareholder value. There are challenges both to *measure* shareholder value and to discover how to *create* it through the adoption and implementation of corporate strategies. Managers are also aware of the importance of *customer value* and its relationship to shareholder value. Managing for value has to balance the possible

Focus on Business Practice

New IT and business analysis

© Greg Nicholas

Rachel has trained as a management accountant and is now director of divisional finance in a large restaurant and public house chain. The company has an advanced accounting system in which transactions recording and reporting has been automated. Freed up from routine data gathering, Rachel liaises between the regional operational managers and the company's board as she and her team of analysts monitor and manage the financial performance of the many restaurant and pub brands that make up the business.

Exercise: Note how advances in IT have automated the 'score-keeping' aspects of accounting and enabled managers not only to have more up-to-the-minute business intelligence but also freeing up their time for value creation.

gains to short-run profitability arising from cost-cutting exercises to possible long-run damage to shareholder value as costs may be cut at the expense of customer satisfaction. For the management accountant the challenge is not just to devise appropriate financial and non-financial metrics to measure value but to try and understand cause-and-effect relationships.[9]

Managing for environmental sustainability

While concern about the environment has been around for some decades, the threat of rapid man-induced climate change has raised the profile of a whole range of environmental sustainability issues. Even managers focusing on shareholder value may be concerned about the environment for three main reasons. First, there is a compliance motive – companies may find that they are forced through regulation and green taxes to manage environmental resources more carefully. Second, eco-efficiency not only may save the planet but reduce business costs. Finally, there may be strategic reasons – companies may have customers who demand green business policies and who are increasingly suspicious of 'environmental window dressing' through environmental reporting. Environmental management accounting is not just about reporting but collecting and analysing *physical* information on flows of energy, water and other materials as well as *monetary* information on environmental costs and benefits in order to make environmentally sensitive decisions.[10]

The practice of management accounting LO 4

Management accounting principles may be useful for non-specialists as well as specialists

Although management accounting has traditionally been practised by professionals in a specialized finance function, one of the results of the changes discussed above in technology and organizational processes, has meant that it is not just finance workers but other-finance specialists (such as engineers, doctors and many other professionals) who have become more 'finance literate' and aware of the importance of management accounting data. The spread of management accounting practices to non-accounting managers has been influenced by the changes such as privatization. New information technology has also played a part by 'de-centring' accounting knowledge. Some academics have coined the term 'hybrid accountants' to describe individuals who 'may be accountants (but are) ... more likely people from other functions who are financially literate'.[11] The result is that management accounting practices are not simply located in a specialist finance function but are dispersed throughout all levels in many functional areas of the organization.[12]

The sources of business knowledge

The practice and principles of management accounting have been developed over many decades, even centuries. In the early days the main source of practice was practitioners such as early industrialists at Josiah Wedgewood's potteries or at Alfred Sloan's General Motors. More recently other inputs have come from business schools, management consultants and even management gurus.[13] In the particular case of accounting other contributors to managerial knowledge production include professional bodies. Managerial and business knowledge may be visualized as being produced via a circulation of ideas and practices as shown in Exhibit 1.2.

Yet the processes that impact on the production and circulation of managerial knowledge should not be seen as infallible. Academic theories may be rejected by practitioners on the grounds of 'irrelevance' and practices may develop that weaken rather than enhance long-run business performance.[14] The latest practices may not really be 'best practice' but rather introduced because of managerial fashions and fads. One of the aims of this book is to enable the reader to develop a *critical* understanding of the principles behind management accounting so that faulty practices may be recognized even if they cannot always be changed in a particular organizational setting.

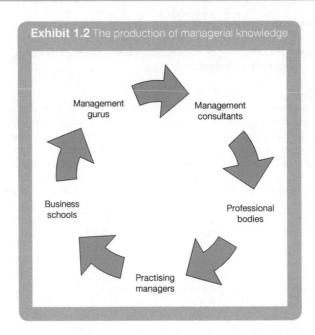

Exhibit 1.2 The production of managerial knowledge

Management gurus

Management consultants

Professional bodies

Practising managers

Business schools

Summary

- Management accounting assists managers in carrying out their responsibilities, which include planning, directing and motivating, and controlling.

- Since management accounting is geared to the needs of the manager rather than to the needs of outsiders, it differs substantially from financial accounting. Management accounting is oriented more towards the future, places less emphasis on precision, emphasizes segments of an organization (rather than the organization as a whole), is not governed by generally accepted accounting principles, and is not mandatory.

- Most organizations are decentralized to some degree. Accountants perform a staff function – they support and provide assistance to others inside the organization.

- The business environment in recent years has been characterized by increasing competition and a relentless drive for continuous improvement. Organizations have also restructured with outsourcing and relocation of company activities. Reformed public sectors are increasingly applying management accounting techniques.

- Management accounting principles and practices may be useful for non-finance specialists and may be useful in many parts of the organization outside the finance function.

Key terms

At the end of each chapter, a list of key terms for review is given, along with the definition of each term. (These terms are highlighted in colour.) Carefully study each term to be sure you understand its meaning, since these terms are used repeatedly in the chapters that follow. The list for Chapter 1 follows.

Budget A detailed plan for the future, usually expressed in formal quantitative terms (p. 4).

Control The process of instituting procedures and then obtaining feedback to ensure that all parts of the organization are functioning effectively and moving towards overall company goals (p. 4).

Environmental management accounting is the collection and analysis of physical and monetary information on environmental costs and benefits in order to make environmentally sensitive decisions (p. 9).

Feedback Accounting and other reports that help managers monitor performance and focus on problems and/or opportunities that might otherwise go unnoticed (p. 4).

Management accounting The phase of accounting concerned with providing information to managers for use in planning and controlling operations and in decision making (p. 4).

Performance report A detailed report comparing budgeted data to actual data (p. 4).

Planning and control cycle The flow of management activities through planning, directing and motivating, and controlling, and then back to planning again (p. 5).

Endnotes

1 Adapted from the easyJet company website, 24 March 2005.

2 *People Management*, July 2009.

3 See Scapens, Ezzamel, Burns and Baldvinsdottir (2003).

4 See May (2002).

5 See, e.g., Bain and Taylor (2000).

6 Hayward (2002); CIMA Technical Briefing (2001a).

7 Hood (1995).

8 Olson, Guthrie and Humphrey (1998).

9 For a historical view on value based management see Ittner and Larcker (2001). For a very recent attempt to analyse the cost of customer satisfaction see Cugini, Caru and Zerbini (2007).

10 See IFAC (2005).

11 Burns and Scapens (2000).

12 May (2002).

13 Thrift (2005).

14 Johnson and Kaplan (1987) and Seal (2010).

When you have read this chapter, log on to the Online Learning Centre for *Management Accounting for Business Decisions* at **www.mcgraw-hill.co.uk/ textbooks/seal**, where you'll find multiple choice questions, practice exams and extra study tools for management accounting.

Assessment

Questions

[Instructors note: these are non-technical exercises that might be used for either individual or group work]

connect

1-1 Preparing a business plan

Imagine that you are a newly qualified chef and that you want to set up your own restaurant. You need to raise some funds from the bank. Draw up a list of the financial and non-financial information that you would need in order to present a credible business case to the bank.

1-2 Ethics on the job

Ethical standards are very important in business, but they are not always followed. If you have ever held a job – even a summer job – describe the ethical climate in the organization where you worked. Did employees work a full day or did they arrive late and leave early? Did employees honestly report the hours they worked? Did employees use their employer's resources for their own purposes? Did managers set a good example? Did the organization have a code of ethics and were employees made aware of its existence? If the ethical climate in the organization you worked for was poor, what problems, if any, did it create?

1-3 Relevance of management accounting principles

Imagine that you are:

1   A medical doctor
2   An engineer
3   A lawyer
4   An accountant in professional practice
5   A head teacher
6   A local government manager
7   A manager in a job centre
8   A film producer

In each case suggest when and why management accounting concepts and practices may impact on some aspects of your work.

Glossary

Absorption costing A costing method that includes all manufacturing costs – direct materials, direct labour and both variable and fixed overhead – as part of the cost of a finished unit of product. This term is synonymous with full cost (p. 106).

Activity An event that causes the consumption of overhead resources in an organization (p. 123).

Activity-based costing (ABC) A costing method based on activities that is designed to provide managers with cost information for strategic and other decisions that potentially affect capacity and therefore fixed costs (p. 122).

Activity cost pool A 'bucket' in which costs are accumulated that relate to a single activity in the activity-based costing system (p. 126).

Activity measure An allocation base in an activity-based costing system; ideally, a measure of the amount of activity that drives the costs in an activity cost pool (p. 127).

Administrative costs All executive, organizational and clerical costs associated with the general management of an organization rather than with manufacturing, marketing or selling (p. 17).

Allocation base A measure of activity such as direct labour-hours or machine-hours that is used to assign costs to cost objects (p. 108).

Avoidable cost Any cost that can be eliminated (in whole or in part) by choosing one alternative over another in a decision-making situation. In managerial accounting, this term is synonymous with relevant cost and differential cost (p. 76).

Attribute costing Costing the product attributes that appeal to customers (p. 260).

Balanced scorecard (BSC) An integrated set of performance measures that is derived from and supports the organization's strategy (p. 263).

Batch-level activities Activities that are performed each time a batch of goods is handled or processed, regardless of how many units are in a batch. The amount of resource consumed depends on the number of batches run rather than on the number of units in the batch (p. 126).

Benchmarking A comparison with organizations that are the best at performing specific activities or producing particular products in order to learn how they achieve their relatively high performance (p. 309).

Bill of materials A listing of the quantity of each type of material required to manufacture a unit of product (p. 208).

Bottleneck A machine or process that limits total output because it is operating at capacity (p. 89).

Break-even point The level of sales at which profit is zero. The break-even point can also be defined as the point where total sales equals total expenses or as the point where total contribution margin equals total fixed expenses (p. 45).

Budget A detailed plan for the future, usually expressed in formal quantitative terms (p. 4).

Budget committee A group of key management persons who are responsible for overall policy matters relating to the budget programme and for co-ordinating the preparation of the budget (p. 182).

Business process A series of steps that is followed in order to carry out some task in a business (p. 302).

Business process re-engineering involves mapping and then redesigning business processes in order to eliminate unnecessary steps, reduce opportunities for errors, and lower costs. (p. 313).

Capital budgeting The process of planning significant outlays on projects that have long-term implications, such as the purchase of new equipment or the introduction of a new product (p. 234).

Cash budget A detailed plan showing how cash resources will be acquired and used over some specific time period (p. 183).

Constrained management style A management approach that concentrates on easy to measure events and lacks flexibility (p. 195).

Constraint A limitation under which a company must operate, such as limited machine time available or limited raw materials available that restricts the company's ability to satisfy demand (p. 88).

Continuous or perpetual budget A 12-month budget that rolls forward one month as the current month is completed (p. 180).

Contribution approach A profit statement format that is geared to cost behaviour in that costs are separated into variable and fixed categories rather than being separated according to the functions of production, sales and administration (p. 25).

Contribution margin The amount remaining from sales revenue after all variable expenses have been deducted (p. 25).

Contribution margin method A method of computing the break-even point in which the fixed expenses are divided by the contribution margin per unit (p. 51).

Contribution margin ratio (CM ratio) The contribution margin as a percentage of total sales (p. 47).

Control The process of instituting procedures and then obtaining feedback to ensure that all parts of the organization are functioning effectively and moving towards overall company goals (p. 4).

Conversion cost Direct labour cost plus manufacturing overhead cost (p. 17).

Cost behaviour The way in which a cost reacts or responds to changes in the level of business activity (p. 22).

Cost centre A business segment whose manager has control over cost but has no control over revenue or the use of investment funds (p. 281).

Cost driver A factor, such as machine-hours, beds occupied, computer time, or flight-hours, that causes overhead costs (p. 108).

Cost leadership Aiming to be the lowest cost producer in an industry (p. 260).

Cost of capital The overall cost to an organization of obtaining investment funds, including the cost of both debt sources and equity sources (p. 238).

Cost-plus pricing A pricing method in which a predetermined mark-up is applied to a cost base to determine the target selling price (p. 150).

Cost–volume–profit (CVP) graph The relations between revenues, costs and level of activity in an organization presented in graphic form (p. 52).

Customer-level activities Activities that are carried out to support customers but that are not related to any specific product (p. 126).

Decentralized organization An organization in which decision making is not confined to a few top executives but rather is spread throughout the organization (p. 280).

Defender A company which concentrates on reducing costs and/or improving quality in existing markets/products (p. 260).

Degree of operating leverage A measure, at a given level of sales, of how a percentage change in sales volume will affect profits. The degree of operating leverage is computed by dividing contribution margin by profit (p. 57).

Delivery cycle time The amount of time required from receipt of an order from a customer to shipment of the completed goods (p. 268).

Differential cost Any cost that differs between alternatives in a decision-making situation. In managerial accounting, this term is synonymous with avoidable cost and relevant cost. Also see Incremental cost (p. 26).

Differential revenue The difference in revenue between any two alternatives (p. 26).

Direct labour Those factory labour costs that can easily be traced to individual units of product. Also called touch labour (p. 16).

Direct labour budget A detailed plan showing labour requirements over some specific time period (p. 186).

Direct materials Those materials that become an integral part of a finished product and can conveniently be traced into it (p. 16).

Direct materials budget A detailed plan showing the amount of raw materials that must be purchased during a period to meet both production and stock needs (p. 186).

Direct method The allocation of all of a service department's costs directly to operating departments without recognizing services provided to other service departments (p. 111).

Economic value added (EVA) A concept similar to residual profit (p. 288).

Environmental management accounting is the collection and analysis of physical and monetary information on environmental costs and benefits in order to make environmentally sensitive decisions (p. 9).

Executional drivers Cost factors such as work force involvement, quality management capacity utilization, plant lay-out efficiency, product configuration effectiveness, and exploitation of linkages (p. 261).

Feedback Accounting and other reports that help managers monitor performance and focus on problems and/or opportunities that might otherwise go unnoticed (p. 4).

Finished goods stock budget A budget showing the cost expected to appear on the balance sheet for unsold units at the end of a period (p. 189).

First-stage allocation The process by which overhead costs are assigned to activity cost pools in an activity-based costing system (p. 128).

Fixed cost A cost that remains constant, in total, regardless of changes in the level of activity within the relevant range. If a fixed cost is expressed on a per unit basis, it varies inversely with the level of activity (p. 23).

Full cost See Absorption costing (p. 107).

High-low method A technique for separating mixed costs into fixed and variable components (p. 61).

Ideal standards Standards that allow for no machine breakdowns or other work interruptions and that require peak efficiency at all times (p. 207).

Incremental analysis An analytical approach that focuses only on those items of revenue, cost and volume that will change as a result of a decision (p. 49)

Incremental cost An increase in cost between two alternatives. Also see Differential cost (p. 26).

Indirect labour The labour costs of caretakers, supervisors, materials handlers, and other factory workers that cannot conveniently be traced directly to particular products (p. 16).

Indirect materials Small items of material such as glue and nails. These items may become an integral part of a finished product but are traceable to the product only at great cost or inconvenience (p. 16).

Intermediate market A market in which a transferred product or service is sold in its present form to outside customers (p. 164).

Internal rate of return The discount rate at which the net present value of an investment project is zero;

thus, the internal rate of return represents the interest yield promised by a project over its useful life. This term is synonymous with time-adjusted rate of return (p. 238).

Investment centre A business segment whose manager has control over cost and over revenue and that also has control over the use of investment funds (p. 281).

Job-order costing system A costing system used in situations where many different products, jobs or services are produced each period (p. 107)

Just-in-time A production system in which materials are purchased and produced only as needed to meet actual customer demand so that stocks are reduced to the minimum and in some cases to zero (p. 303).

Kaizen budgeting Rather than base budgets on historical standards, kaizen budgeting plans for incremental improvements in efficiency and reduction in costs (p. 158).

Kaizen costing The reduction of cost during production through continuous gradual improvements that reduce waste and increase efficiency (p. 158).

Labour efficiency variance A measure of the difference between the actual hours taken to complete a task and the standard hours allowed, multiplied by the standard hourly labour rate (p. 218).

Labour rate variance A measure of the difference between the actual hourly labour rate and the standard rate, multiplied by the number of hours worked during the period (p. 217).

Lean production The identification of a value stream and challenging all forms of waste or non-value adding activity (p. 303).

Life-cycle costing Analyses costs incurred throughout the life of a product from development through to full production (p. 260).

Make or buy decision A decision as to whether an item should be produced internally or purchased from an outside supplier (p. 85).

Management accounting The phase of accounting concerned with providing information to managers for use in planning and controlling operations and in decision making (p. 4).

Management by exception A system of management in which standards are set for various operating activities, with actual results then compared to these standards. Any differences that are deemed significant are brought to the attention of management as 'exceptions' (p. 206).

Manufacturing cycle efficiency (MCE) Process (value-added) time as a percentage of throughput time (p. 271).

Manufacturing overhead All costs associated with manufacturing except direct materials and direct labour (p. 16).

Manufacturing overhead budget A detailed plan showing the production costs, other than direct materials and direct labour, that will be incurred over a specified time period (p. 187).

Margin Net operating profit divided by sales (p. 284).

Margin of safety The excess of budgeted (or actual) sales over the break-even volume of sales (p. 54).

Market price The price being charged for an item on the open (intermediate) market (p. 164).

Marketing mix Price is one element in product competitiveness together with product, promotion and place (p. 260).

Marketing or selling costs All costs necessary to secure customer orders and get the finished product or service into the hands of the customer (p. 17).

Mark-up The difference between the selling price of a product or service and its cost. The mark-up is usually expressed as a percentage of cost (p. 150).

Master budget A summary of a company's plans in which specific targets are set for sales, production, distribution, and financing activities and that generally culminates in a cash budget, budgeted profit and loss account, and budgeted balance sheet (p. 183).

Materials price variance A measure of the difference between the actual unit price paid for an item and the standard price, multiplied by the quantity purchased (p. 214).

Materials quantity variance A measure of the difference between the actual quantity of materials used in production and the standard quantity allowed, multiplied by the standard price per unit of materials (p. 215).

Material requirements planning (MRP) An operations management tool that uses a computer to help manage materials and stocks (p. 186).

Multiple predetermined overhead rates A costing system in which there are multiple overhead cost pools with a different predetermined rate for each cost pool, rather than a single predetermined overhead rate for the entire company. Frequently, each production department is treated as a separate overhead cost pool (p. 109).

Negotiated transfer price A transfer price agreed on between buying and selling divisions (p. 159).

Net operating profit Profit before interest and profit taxes have been deducted (p. 283).

Net present value The difference between the present value of the cash inflows and the present value of the cash outflows associated with an investment project (p. 235).

Non-value-added activities are activities in an organization that do not add value to that organization's products or services. (p. 313).

Operating assets Cash, debtors, inventory, plant and equipment, and all other assets held for productive use in an organization (p. 283).

Operating department A department or similar unit in an organization within which the central purposes of the organization are carried out (p. 109).

Operating leverage A measure of how sensitive profit is to a given percentage change in sales. It is computed by dividing the contribution margin by profit (p. 57).

Opportunity cost The potential benefit that is given up when one alternative is selected over another (p. 27).

Organization-sustaining activities Activities that are carried out regardless of which customers are served, which products are produced, how many batches are run, or how many units are made (p. 126).

Overhead application The process of charging manufacturing overhead cost to job cost sheets and to the work in progress account (p. 108).

Participative budget See Self-imposed budget (p. 180).

Payback period The length of time that it takes for a project to recover its initial cost out of the cash receipts that it generates (p. 242).

Performance report A detailed report comparing budgeted data to actual data (p. 4).

Period costs Those costs that are taken directly to the profit and loss account as expenses in the period in which they are incurred or accrued; such costs consist of selling (marketing) and administrative expenses (p. 17).

Plan-do-check-act cycle is a systematic, fact-based approach to continuous improvement (p. 309).

Planning and control cycle The flow of management activities through planning, directing and motivating, and controlling, and then back to planning again (p. 5).

Plantwide overhead rate A single predetermined overhead rate that is used throughout a plant (p. 109).

Practical standards Standards that allow for normal machine downtime and other work interruptions and that can be attained through reasonable, though highly efficient, efforts by the average worker (p. 208).

Predetermined overhead rate A rate used to charge overhead cost to jobs in production; the rate is established in advance for each period by use of estimates of total manufacturing overhead cost and of the total allocation base for the period (p. 108).

Price elasticity of demand A measure of the degree to which the volume of unit sales for a product or service is affected by a change in price (p. 150).

Prime cost Direct materials cost plus direct labour cost (p. 17).

Product costs All costs that are involved in the purchase or manufacture of goods. In the case of manufactured goods, these costs consist of direct materials, direct labour, and manufacturing overhead. Also see Stock-related costs (p. 17).

Product differentiation Aims to maintain a price premium based on superior product quality (p. 261).

Product-level activities Activities that relate to specific products that must be carried out regardless of how many units are produced and sold or batches run (p. 126).

Production budget A detailed plan showing the number of units that must be produced during a period in order to meet both sales and stock needs (p. 185).

Profit centre A business segment whose manager has control over cost and revenue but has no control over the use of investment funds (p. 281).

Prospector A company that is continually searching for market opportunities (p. 260).

Range of acceptable transfer prices The range of transfer prices within which the profits of both the selling division and the purchasing division would increase as a result of a transfer (p. 160).

Raw materials Any materials that go into the final product (p. 16).

Relaxing (or elevating) the constraint Increasing the capacity of a bottleneck (p. 307).

Relevant cost A cost that differs between alternatives in a particular decision. In managerial accounting, this term is synonymous with avoidable cost and differential cost (p. 76).

Relevant range The range of activity within which assumptions about variable and fixed cost behaviour are valid (p. 23).

Required rate of return The minimum rate of return that an investment project must yield to be acceptable (p. 239).

Residual income The net operating profit that an investment centre earns above the required return on its operating assets (p. 288).

Responsibility centre Any business segment whose manager has control over cost, revenue or the use of investment funds (p. 281).

Return on investment (ROI) Net operating profit divided by average operating assets. It also equals margin multiplied by turnover (p. 283).

Sales budget A detailed schedule showing the expected sales for coming periods; these sales are typically expressed in both pounds and units (p. 183).

Sales mix The relative proportions in which a company's products are sold. Sales mix is computed by expressing the sales of each product as a percentage of total sales (p. 58).

Second-stage allocation The process by which activity rates are used to apply costs to products and customers in activity-based costing (p. 133).

Segment Any part or activity of an organization about which the manager seeks cost, revenue or profit data (p. 281).

Self-imposed budget A method of preparing budgets in which managers prepare their own budgets. These budgets are then reviewed by the manager's supervisor, and any issues are resolved by mutual agreement (p. 180).

Selling and administrative expense budget A detailed schedule of planned expenses that will be incurred in areas other than manufacturing during a budget period (p. 189).

Service department A department that provides support or assistance to operating departments and that does not engage directly in production or in other operating activities of an organization (p. 110).

Shared service centres Organizations which specialize in the delivery of the routine trans-actions of support services that are required by the operating units of large organizations (p. 314).

Simple rate of return The rate of return computed by dividing a project's annual accounting profit by the initial investment required (p. 243).

Six sigma An approach that focuses on the variation from the mean rather than average times (p. 311).

Special order A one-time order that is not considered part of the company's normal on-going business (p. 87).

Standard cost card A detailed listing of the standard amounts of materials, labour and overhead that should go into a unit of product, multiplied by the standard price or rate that has been set for each cost element (p. 206).

Standard cost per unit The standard cost of a unit of product as shown on the standard cost card; it is computed by multiplying the standard quantity or hours by the standard price or rate for each cost element (p. 210).

Standard hours allowed The time that should have been taken to complete the period's output as computed by multiplying the actual number of units produced by the standard hours per unit (p. 212).

Standard hours per unit The amount of labour time that should be required to complete a single unit of product, including allowances for breaks, machine downtime, cleanup, rejects, and other normal inefficiencies (p. 209).

Standard price per unit The price that should be paid for a single unit of materials, including allowances for quality, quantity purchased, shipping, receiving, and other such costs, net of any discounts allowed (p. 208).

Standard quantity allowed The amount of materials that should have been used to complete the period's output as computed by multiplying the actual number of units produced by the standard quantity per unit (p. 211).

Standard quantity per unit The amount of materials that should be required to complete a single unit of product, including allowances for normal waste spoilage, rejects and similar inefficiencies (p. 208).

Standard rate per hour The labour rate that should be incurred per hour of labour time, including employment taxes, fringe benefits and other such labour costs (p. 209).

Stock-related costs (also known as inventoriable costs) Synonym for product costs (p. 19).

Strategic choice Choosing not only which industries and products to compete in but also how a company plans to compete (p. 260).

Strategic management accounting The use of management accounting information to help managers choose where and how to compete (p. 260).

Structural drivers Factors such as scale, scope, experience, technology and complexity (p. 261).

Sub-optimization An overall level of profitability that is less than a segment or a company is capable of earning (p. 159).

Sunk cost Any cost that has already been incurred and that cannot be changed by any decision made now or in the future (p. 27).

Target costing The process of determining the maximum allowable cost for a new product and then developing a prototype that can be profitably manufactured and distributed for that maximum target cost figure (p. 157).

Theory of constraints (TOC) A management approach that emphasizes the importance of managing constraints (p. 307).

Throughput accounting (TA) Ranking products by calculating the throughput accounting ratio (p. 309).

Throughput time The amount of time required to turn raw materials into completed products (p. 270).

Time-adjusted rate of return This term is synonymous with internal rate of return (p. 238).

Total quality management An approach to quality that focuses on serving customers and using teams made up of frontline workers to aim for zero defects (p. 309).

Transfer price The price charged when one division or segment provides goods or services to another division or segment of an organization (p. 159).

Turnover The amount of sales generated in an investment centre for each pound invested in operating assets. It is computed by dividing sales by the average operating assets figure (p. 284).

Unit-level activities Activities that arise as a result of the total volume of goods and services that are produced, and that are performed each time a unit is produced (p. 126).

Value chain The major business functions that add value to a company's products and services (p. 261).

Variable cost A cost that varies, in total, in direct proportion to changes in the level of activity. A variable cost is constant per unit (p. 21).

Variable overhead efficiency variance The difference between the actual activity (direct labour-hours, machine-hours, or some other base) of a period and the standard activity allowed, multiplied by the variable part of the predetermined overhead rate (p. 220).

Variable overhead spending variance The difference between the actual variable overhead cost incurred during a period and the standard cost that should have been incurred based on the actual activity of the period (p. 219).

Variance The difference between standard prices and quantities on the one hand and actual prices and quantities on the other hand (p. 211).

Vertical integration The involvement by a company is more than one of the steps from production of basic raw materials to the manufacture and distribution of a finished product (p. 85).

Working capital The excess of current assets over current liabilities (p. 237).

Yield A term synonymous with internal rate of return and time-adjusted rate of return (p. 238).

Yield management A practice of achieving high capacity utilization through varying prices according to market segments and time of booking (p. 153).

Yield percentage A performance metric calculated by dividing actual revenue by the maximum potential revenue (p. 153).

Zero-based budgeting A method of budgeting in which managers are required to justify all costs as if the programmes involved were being proposed for the first time (p. 196).

Chapter 5
The principles of cost allocation: full costing

LO Learning objectives

After studying Chapter 5, you should be able to:
1 Understand the need for job-costing in a variety of industries
2 Compute predetermined overhead rates
3 Compute product cost in a simple manufacturing operation
4 Analyse the allocation of service department costs
5 Consider some pitfalls in the allocation of costs

Concepts in Context

In a film studio, each film produced by the studio is a 'job', and costs for direct materials (costumes, props, film, etc.) and direct labour (actors, directors and extras) are accounted for and charged to each film's job cost sheet. A share of the studio's overhead costs, such as utilities, depreciation of equipment, salaries of maintenance workers, and so forth, is also charged to each film. However, there is considerable controversy about the methods used by some studios to distribute overhead costs among films, and these controversies some-times result in lawsuits. Some authors who have

© AFP/Getty Images

signed 'net profit' contracts may see virtually nothing from films that gross millions at the box office and millions more in merchandising. In the business, this is known as 'Hollywood Accounting'.[1]

We should keep in mind that the essential purpose of any managerial costing system should be to provide cost data to help managers plan, control, direct and make decisions. Nevertheless, external financial reporting and tax reporting requirements often heavily influence how costs are accumulated and summarized on managerial reports. This is true of product costing.

Recall from Chapter 2 with variable costing, only those costs of production that vary with output are treated as product costs. This would generally include direct materials, direct labour and the variable portion of manufacturing overhead. Fixed manufacturing overhead is not treated as a product cost under this method. Rather, fixed manufacturing overhead is treated as a period cost and, like selling and administrative expenses, it is charged off in its entirety against revenue each period. Consequently, the cost of a unit of product in stock or in cost of goods sold under the variable costing method contains no element of fixed overhead cost.

Variable costing is sometimes referred to as direct costing or marginal costing. The term *direct costing* was popular for many years, but is slowly disappearing from day-to-day use. The term *variable costing* is more descriptive of the way in which product costs are computed when a contribution profit and loss account is prepared.

In contrast, absorption costing assigns both variable and fixed costs to products – mingling them in a way that makes it difficult for managers to distinguish between them. In one form or another, most countries require absorption costing for both external financial reporting and for tax reporting. *In addition, the vast majority of companies throughout the world also use absorption costing for management accounting purposes.*

Focus on Business Practice

Full costing for municipal waste management

© Ben Blankenburg

Full costs are often used by public sector bodies as well as service/manufacturing concerns. In the United States, for example, the Environmental Protection Agency (EPA) has produced a handbook to help municipal authorities calculate the full cost of dealing with solid waste (i.e. household and commercial waste). The handbook states that full cost accounting for such waste 'takes into account past and future outlays, overhead (oversight and support service) costs, and operating costs'. With full costs on hand, municipal authorities can use the cost data to monitor service costs and improve efficiency. But what kind of overhead costs might be incurred in managing municipal waste? To give an example, the EPA manual lists four possible paths solid waste can take: disposal, recycling, waste-to-energy and composting. Thinking about each of these paths, it is easy to visualize administrative and support staff for each path. Other support type costs include education and outreach projects, legal costs, records management, facility services, supervision, and so on. By taking into account such support costs as well as operating costs, and then deducting revenues from sales of some recyclable materials and energy, a municipal authority can report figures like an average cost per household. If authorities can agree what is included in full cost, comparisons are also possible, a point which the EPA handbook views as good management practice.[2]

Exercise: In a related area, many countries charge households for water supply. Can you think of the full costs to a local authority of providing clean, treated water?

Absorption costing treats *all* costs of production as product costs, regardless of whether they are variable or fixed. The cost of a unit of product under the absorption costing method therefore consists of direct materials, direct labour, and both variable and fixed overhead. Thus, absorption costing *allocates* a portion of *fixed manufacturing overhead cost* to each unit of product, along with the variable manufacturing costs. Because absorption costing includes all costs of production as product costs, it is frequently referred to as the full cost method.

Record-keeping and cost assignment problems are more complex when a company sells many different products and services than when it has only a single product. Since the products are different, the costs are typically different. Consequently, cost records must be maintained for each distinct product or job. For example, a lawyer in a large criminal law practice would ordinarily keep separate records of the costs of advising and defending each of her clients.

Job-order costing: an overview

LO 1

A job-order costing system is used in situations where many *different* products are produced each period. In a job-order costing system, costs are traced and allocated to jobs and then the costs of the job are divided by the number of units in the job to arrive at an average cost per unit.

Recall from Chapter 2 that companies generally classify manufacturing costs into three broad categories: (1) direct materials, (2) direct labour, and (3) overhead. As the names imply, direct labour and direct costs are those costs that can be easily and directly traced to a particular job. The key issues in this chapter and in Chapter 6 are related to the issues of the allocation of overhead and other common costs that cannot easily be traced to a product of a department. In full costing, the convention adopted is to allocate costs by choosing an *overhead base*.

Job-order costing can be used in service organizations such as law firms, film studios, hospitals and repair shops, as well as in manufacturing companies. In a law firm, for example, each client represents a 'job', and the costs of that job are accumulated day by day on a job cost sheet as the client's case is handled by the firm. Legal forms and similar inputs represent the direct materials for the job; the time expended by lawyers represents the direct labour; and the costs of secretaries, clerks, rent, depreciation, and so forth, represent the overhead. An example of a job costing approach for a legal firm is shown in Exhibit 5.1.

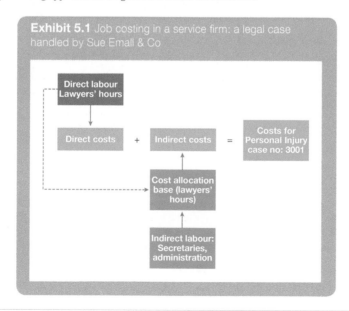

Exhibit 5.1 Job costing in a service firm: a legal case handled by Sue Emall & Co

In total, the reader should be aware that job-order costing is a versatile and widely used costing method, and may be encountered in virtually any organization where there are diverse products or services.

LO 2 Choice of an allocation base for overhead cost

An allocation base should be used that is a *cost driver* of overhead cost. A cost driver is a factor, such as machine-hours, beds occupied, computer time, or flight-hours, that causes overhead costs. If a base is used to compute overhead rates that does not 'drive' overhead costs, then the result will be inaccurate overhead rates and distorted product costs. Overhead must be included with direct materials and direct labour on the job cost sheet since overhead is also a product cost. However, assigning overhead to units of product can be a difficult task. There are three reasons for this.

1 Overhead is an *indirect cost*. This means that it is either impossible or difficult to trace these costs to a particular product or job.
2 Overhead consists of many different items ranging from the grease used in machines to the annual salary of the senior managers.
3 Even though output may fluctuate due to seasonal or other factors, overhead costs tend to remain relatively constant due to the presence of fixed costs.

Given these problems, about the only way to assign overhead costs to products is to use an allocation process. This allocation of overhead costs is accomplished by selecting an *allocation base* that is common to all of the company's products and services. An allocation base is a measure such as direct labour-hours (DLH) or machine-hours (MH) that is used to assign overhead costs to products and services.

The most widely used allocation bases are direct labour-hours and direct labour cost, with machine-hours and even units of product (where a company has only a single product) also used to some extent.

The allocation base is used to compute the predetermined overhead rate in the following formula:

$$\text{Predetermined overhead rate} = \frac{\text{Estimated total overhead cost}}{\text{Estimated total units in the allocation base}}$$

Note that the predetermined overhead rate is based on *estimated* rather than actual figures. This is because the *predetermined* overhead rate is computed *before* the period begins and is used to apply overhead cost to jobs throughout the period. The process of assigning overhead cost to jobs is called overhead application. The formula for determining the amount of overhead cost to apply to a particular job is:

$$\text{Overhead applied to a particular job} = \text{Predetermined overhead rate} \times \\ \text{Amount of allocation base incurred by the job}$$

So, for example, if the predetermined overhead rate is £8 per direct labour-hour, then £8 of overhead cost is *applied* to a job for each direct labour-hour incurred by the job. When the allocation base is direct labour-hours, the formula becomes:

$$\text{Overhead applied to a particular job} = \text{Predetermined overhead rate} \times \\ \text{Actual direct labour hours charged to job}$$

LO 3 Job costing: an example

Classic Brass Ltd makes finely machined brass fittings for a variety of applications including stanchions, cleats and helms for luxury yachts. The company has decided to use machine-hours as the predetermined allocation base. The total estimated overheads of the company total £1,000,000 and the total number of estimated machine hours is 20,000. Therefore, the predetermined overhead rate per machine-hour is:

$$\frac{\text{Total manufacturing overhead, £1,000,000}}{\text{Total machine-hours, 20,000}} = £50 \text{ per machine-hour}$$

Let us now consider the costing of two products: *Standard stanchions* and *Custom compass housing* which have the following design and cost characteristics:[3]

Standard stanchions

1 This is a standard design that does not require any new design resources.
2 Four hundred units were ordered during the year, comprising two separate orders.
3 Each stanchion required 0.5 machine-hours, for a total of 200 machine-hours.
4 Direct materials for 400 units totalled £2,110.
5 Direct labour for 400 units totalled £1,850.

Custom compass housing

1 This is a custom product that requires new design resources.
2 There was only one order for a single unit during the year.
3 The compass housing required 4 machine-hours.
4 Direct materials were £13.
5 Direct labour was £50.

From these data and using machine-hours as an overhead allocation base, we can determine the costs of different job-orders (400 standard stanchions and one custom compass housing) as shown in Exhibit 5.2.

Multiple predetermined overhead rates

In the above example, we have assumed that there is a single predetermined overhead rate for an entire factory called a **plantwide overhead rate**. This is, in fact, a common practice – particularly in smaller companies. In larger companies, multiple predetermined overhead rates are often used. In a **multiple predetermined overhead rate** system there is usually a different overhead rate for each production department. Such a system, while more complex, is considered to be more accurate, since it can reflect differences across departments in how overhead costs are incurred. We now consider the issue of how the overhead represented by *service department costs* may be allocated.

Service and operating departmental costing: selecting allocation bases

LO 4

Departments within an organization can be divided into two broad classes: (1) operating departments and (2) service departments. **Operating departments** include those departments or units where the central purposes of the organization are carried out. Examples of such departments or units would include the Surgery

---

Exhibit 5.2 Basic job-order costing using machine-hours as allocation base

Job 1: 400 standard stanchions

Cost:

Direct materials	£2,110
Direct labour	1,850
Manufacturing overhead (400 units × 0.5 machine-hours per unit × £50 per machine-hour*)	10,000
	13,960

Job 2: One custom compass housing

Cost:

Direct materials	13
Direct labour	50
Manufacturing overhead (1 unit × 4.0 machine-hours Per unit × £50 per machine-hour)	200
	263

Department in hospitals and producing departments such as Milling, Assembly, and Painting in manufacturing companies.

Service departments, by contrast, do not engage directly in operating activities. Rather, they provide services or assistance to the operating departments. Examples of service departments include Cafeteria, Internal Auditing, Personnel, Cost Accounting, and Purchasing. Although service departments do not engage directly in the operating activities of an organization, the costs that they incur are generally viewed as being part of the cost of the final product or service, the same as are materials, labour and overhead in a manufacturing company or medications in a hospital.

The major question we consider here is: How much of a service department's cost is to be allocated to each of the units that it serves? This is an important question, since the amount of service department cost allocated to a particular unit can have a significant impact on the computed cost of the goods or services that the unit is providing and can affect an operating unit's performance evaluation.

Many companies use a two-stage costing process. In the first stage, costs are assigned to the operating departments; in the second stage, costs are assigned from the operating departments to products and services. Costs are usually assigned from a service department to other departments using an allocation base, which is some measure of activity. The costs being allocated should be 'driven' by the allocation base. Ideally, the total cost of the service department should be proportional to the size of the allocation base. Managers also often argue that the allocation base should reflect as accurately as possible the benefits that the various departments receive from the services that are being provided. For example, most managers would argue that the square metres of building space occupied by each operating department should be used as the allocation base for janitorial services since both the benefits and costs of janitorial services tend to be proportional to the amount of space occupied by a department. Examples of allocation bases for some service departments are listed in Exhibit 5.3. A given service department's costs may be allocated using more than one base. For example, data processing costs may be allocated on the basis of CPU minutes for mainframe computers and on the basis of the number of personal computers used in each operating department.

Although the previous paragraph explains how to select an allocation base, another critical factor should not be overlooked. The allocations should be clear and straightforward and easily understood by the managers to whom the costs are being allocated.

Exhibit 5.3 Examples of bases used in allocating service department costs

Service Department	Bases (cost drivers) Involved
Laundry	Kilos of laundry
Airport Ground Services	Number of flights
Cafeteria	Number of employees; number of meals
Medical Facilities	Cases handled; number of employees; hours worked
Materials Handling	Hours of service; volume handled
Data Processing	CPU minutes; lines printed; disk storage used; number of personal computers
Custodial Services (building and grounds)	Square metres occupied
Cost Accounting	Labour-hours; clients or patients serviced
Power	KWh used; capacity of machines
Human Resources	Number of employees; employee turnover; training hours
Receiving, Shipping, and Stores	Units handled; number of requisitions; space occupied
Factory Administration	Total labour-hours
Maintenance	Machine-hours

The direct method

The direct method is the simplest cost allocation method. It ignores the services provided by a service department to other service departments and allocates all costs directly to operating departments. Even if a service department (such as Personnel) provides a large amount of service to another service department (such as the cafeteria), no allocations are made between the two departments. Rather, all costs are allocated directly to the operating departments. Hence the term *direct method*.

To provide an example of the direct method, assume that Mountain View Hospital has two service departments and two operating departments as shown below:

| | Service department | | Operating department | | |
	Hospital administration	Custodial services	Laboratory	Daily patient care	Total
Departmental costs before allocation	£360,000	£90,000	£261,000	£689,000	£1,400,000
Employee hours	12,000	6,000	18,000	30,000	66,000
Space occupied (square metres)	10,000	200	5,000	45,000	60,200

In the allocations that follow, Hospital Administration costs will be allocated on the basis of employee-hours and Custodial Services costs will be allocated on the basis of square metres occupied.

The direct method of allocating the hospital's service department costs to the operating departments is shown in Exhibit 5.4. Several things should be carefully noted in this exhibit. First, even though there are employee-hours in both the Hospital Administration Department itself and in the Custodial Services Department, these employee-hours are ignored when allocating service department costs using the direct method. *Under the direct method, any of the allocation base attributable to the service departments themselves is ignored; only the amount of the allocation base attributable to the operating departments is used in the allocation.* Note that the same rule is used when allocating the costs of the Custodial Services Department. Even though the Hospital Administration and Custodial Services departments occupy some space, this is ignored when the Custodial Services costs are allocated. Finally, note that after all allocations have been completed, all of the

Exhibit 5.4 Direct method of allocation

| | Service department | | Operating department | | |
	Hospital administration	Custodial services	Laboratory	Daily patient care	Total
Departmental costs before allocation	£360,000	£90,000	£261,000	£689,000	£1,400,000
Allocation:					
Hospital Administration costs ($^{18}/_{48}$, $^{30}/_{48}$)*	(360,000)		135,000	225,000	
Custodial Services costs ($^{5}/_{50}$, $^{45}/_{50}$)†	————	(90,000)	9,000	81,000	
Total costs after allocation	£ –0–	£ –0–	£405,000	£995,000	£1,400,000

*Based on the employee-hours in the two operating departments, which are 18,000 hours + 30,000 hours = 48,000 hours.
†Based on the space occupied by the two operating departments, which is 5,000 square metres + 45,000 square metres = 50,000 square metres.

departmental costs are contained in the two operating departments. These costs will form the basis for preparing overhead rates for purposes of costing products and services produced in the operating departments.

Some cautions in allocating service department costs

Pitfalls in allocating fixed costs

Rather than allocate fixed costs in predetermined lump-sum amounts, some firms allocate them by use of a *variable* allocation base that fluctuates from period to period. This practice can distort decisions and create serious inequities between departments. The inequities will arise from the fact that the fixed costs allocated to one department will be heavily influenced by what happens in *other* departments or segments of the organization.

To illustrate, assume that Kolby Products has a car service centre that provides maintenance work on the fleet of cars used in the company's two sales territories. The car service centre costs are all fixed. Contrary to good practice, the company allocates these fixed costs to the sales territories on the basis of actual miles driven (a variable base). Selected cost data for the last two years follow:

	Year 1	Year 2
Car service centre costs (all fixed)	£120,000 (a)	£120,000 (a)
Western sales territory (miles driven)	1,500,000	1,500,000
Eastern sales territory (miles driven)	1,500,000	900,000
Total miles driven	3,000,000 (b)	2,400,000 (b)
Allocation rate per mile, (a)/(b)	£0.04	£0.05

Notice that the Western sales territory maintained an activity level of 1,500,000 miles driven in both years. On the other hand, the Eastern sales territory allowed its activity to drop off from 1,500,000 miles in Year 1 to only 900,000 miles in Year 2. The car service centre costs that would have been allocated to the two sales territories over the two-year span using actual miles driven as the allocation base are as follows:

Year 1:	
Western sales territory: 1,500,000 miles at £0.04	£60,000
Eastern sales territory: 1,500,000 miles at £0.04	60,000
Total cost allocated	£120,000

Year 2:	
Western sales territory: 1,500,000 miles at £0.05	£75,000
Eastern sales territory: 900,000 miles at £0.05	45,000
Total cost allocated	£120,000

In Year 1, the two sales territories share the service department costs equally. In Year 2, however, the bulk of the service department costs are allocated to the Western sales territory. This is not because of any increase in activity in the Western sales territory; rather, it is because of the decrease in activity in the Eastern sales territory. Even though the Western sales territory maintained the same level of activity in both years, the use of a variable allocation base has caused it to be penalized with a heavier cost allocation in Year 2 because of what has happened in another part of the company.

This kind of inequity is almost inevitable when a variable allocation base is used to allocate fixed costs. The manager of the Western sales territory undoubtedly will be upset about the inequity forced on his territory, but he will feel powerless to do anything about it. The result will be a loss of confidence in the system and considerable ill feeling.

Beware of sales as an allocation base

Over the years, sales have been a favourite allocation base for service department costs. One reason is that a sales base is simple, straightforward, and easy to work with. Another reason is that people tend to view sales as a measure of well-being, or 'ability to pay', and, hence, as a measure of how readily costs can be absorbed from other parts of the organization.

Unfortunately, sales are often a very poor allocation base, for the reason that sales vary from period to period, whereas the costs being allocated are often largely fixed in nature. As discussed earlier, if a variable base is used to allocate fixed costs, inequities can result between departments, since the costs being allocated to one department will depend in large part on what happens in *other* departments. For example, a let-up in sales effort in one department will shift allocated costs off that department and onto other, more productive departments. In effect, the departments putting forth the best sales efforts are penalized in the form of higher allocations, simply because of inefficiencies elsewhere that are beyond their control. The result is often bitterness and resentment on the part of the managers of the better departments.

Consider the following situation:

A large men's clothing store has Suits, Shoes and Accessories Departments. The Service costs total £60,000 and are allocated to the three sales departments according to monetary sales figures. A recent period showed the following allocation:

	Department			
	Suits	Shoes	Accessories	Total
Sales by department	£260,000	£40,000	£100,000	£400,000
Percentage of total sales	65%	10%	25%	100%
Allocation of service department costs, based on percentage of total sales	£39,000	£6,000	£15,000	£60,000

In a following period, the manager of the Suits Department launched a very successful programme to expand sales by £100,000 in his department. Sales in the other two departments remained unchanged. Total service department costs also remained unchanged, but the allocation of these costs changed substantially, as shown below:

	Department			
	Suits	Shoes	Accessories	Total
Sales by department	£360,000	£40,000	£100,000	£500,000
Percentage of total sales	72%	8%	20%	100%
Allocation of service department costs, based on percentage of total sales	£43,200	£4,800	£12,000	£60,000
Increase (or decrease) from prior allocation	4,200	(1,200)	(3,000)	–

The manager of the Suits Department complained that as a result of his successful effort to expand sales in his department, he was being forced to carry a larger share of the service department costs. On the other hand, the managers of the departments that showed no improvement in sales were relieved of a portion of the costs that they had been carrying. Yet there had been no change in the amount of services provided for any department.

The manager of the Suits Department viewed the increased service department cost allocation to his department as a penalty for his outstanding performance, and he wondered whether his efforts had really been worth while after all in the eyes of top management.

This example illustrates how sales should be used as an allocation base only in those cases where there is a direct causal relationship between sales and the service department costs being allocated.

Summary

- Job-order costing is used in situations where the organization offers many different products or services, such as in furniture manufacturing, hospitals, accounting and legal firms.

- Overhead costs are assigned to jobs through use of a predetermined overhead rate. The predetermined overhead rate is determined before the period begins by dividing the estimated total overhead cost for the period by the estimated total allocation base for the period.

- The most frequently used allocation bases are direct labour-hours and machine-hours. Overhead is applied to jobs by multiplying the predetermined overhead rate by the actual amount of the allocation base used by the job.

- In order to allocate the costs of service departments, many companies use a two-stage costing process. In the first stage, costs are assigned to the operating departments; in the second stage, costs are assigned from the operating departments to products and services.

- Costs are usually assigned from a service department to other departments using an allocation base, which is some measure of activity.

Key terms

Absorption costing A costing method that includes all manufacturing costs – direct materials, direct labour and both variable and fixed overhead – as part of the cost of a finished unit of product. This term is synonymous with full cost (p. 106).

Allocation base A measure of activity such as direct labour-hours or machine-hours that is used to assign costs to cost objects (p. 108).

Cost driver A factor, such as machine-hours, beds occupied, computer time, or flight-hours, that causes overhead costs (p. 108).

Direct method The allocation of all of a service department's costs directly to operating departments without recognizing services provided to other service departments (p. 111).

Full cost See Absorption costing (p. 107).

Job-order costing system A costing system used in situations where many different products, jobs or services are produced each period (p. 107)

Multiple predetermined overhead rates A costing system in which there are multiple overhead cost pools with a different predetermined rate for each cost pool, rather than a single predetermined overhead rate for the entire company. Frequently, each production department is treated as a separate overhead cost pool (p. 109).

Operating department A department or similar unit in an organization within which the central purposes of the organization are carried out (p. 109).

Overhead application The process of charging manufacturing overhead cost to job cost sheets and to the work in progress account (p. 108).

Plantwide overhead rate A single predetermined overhead rate that is used throughout a plant (p. 109).

Predetermined overhead rate A rate used to charge overhead cost to jobs in production; the rate is established in advance for each period by use of estimates of total manufacturing overhead cost and of the total allocation base for the period (p. 108).

Service department A department that provides support or assistance to operating departments and that does not engage directly in production or in other operating activities of an organization (p. 110).

Endnotes

1 Getlin (2008).

2 US Environmental Protection Agency (1997).

3 Note that the Classic Brass example will be used again in the next chapter to illustrate activity-based costing.

When you have read this chapter, log on to the Online Learning Centre for *Management Accounting for Business Decisions* at **www.mcgraw-hill.co.uk/ textbooks/seal**, where you'll find multiple choice questions, practice exams and extra study tools for management accounting.

Assessment

Questions

connect™

5-1 Why are actual overhead costs not traced to jobs as are direct materials and direct labour costs?

5-2 What is a predetermined overhead rate, and how is it computed?

5-3 Explain why some production costs must be assigned to products through an allocation process. Name several such costs. Would such costs be classified as direct or as indirect costs?

5-4 Why do firms use predetermined overhead rates rather than actual manufacturing overhead costs in applying overhead to jobs?

5-5 What factors should be considered in selecting a base to be used in computing the predetermined overhead rate?

5-6 If a company fully allocates all of its overhead costs to jobs, does this guarantee that a profit will be earned for the period?

5-7 What is the difference between a service department and an operating department? Give several examples of service departments.

5-8 How are service department costs assigned to products and services?

Exercises

connect™

E5-1 ⏱ Time allowed: 20 minutes

Kingsport Containers Ltd of Dublin experiences wide variation in demand for the 200-litre steel drums it fabricates. The leakproof, rustproof steel drums have a variety of uses from storing liquids and bulk materials to serving as makeshift musical instruments. The drums are made to order and are painted according to the customer's specifications – often in bright patterns and designs. The company is well known for the artwork that appears on its drums. Unit costs are computed on a quarterly basis by dividing each quarter's manufacturing costs (materials, labour and overhead) by the quarter's production in units. The company's estimated costs, by quarter, for the coming year follow:

	Quarter			
	First	Second	Third	Fourth
Direct materials	€240,000	€120,000	€60,000	€180,000
Direct labour	128,000	64,000	32,000	96,000
Manufacturing overhead	300,000	220,000	180,000	260,000
Total manufacturing costs	€668,000	€404,000	€272,000	€536,000
Number of units to be produced	80,000	40,000	20,000	60,000
Estimated cost per unit	€8.35	€10.10	€13.60	€8.93

Management finds the variation in unit costs to be confusing and difficult to work with. It has been suggested that the problem lies with manufacturing overhead, since it is the largest element of cost. Accordingly, you have been asked to find a more appropriate way of assigning manufacturing overhead cost to units of product. After some analysis, you have determined that the company's overhead costs are mostly fixed and therefore show little sensitivity to changes in the level of production.

Required

1 The company uses a job-order costing system. How would you recommend that manufacturing overhead cost be assigned to production? Be specific and show computations.
2 Recompute the company's unit costs in accordance with your recommendations in Question 1 above.

E5–2 Time allowed: 15 minutes

Estimated cost and operating data for three companies for the upcoming year follow:

	Company		
	X	Y	Z
Direct labour-hours	80,000	45,000	60,000
Machine-hours	30,000	70,000	21,000
Direct materials cost	£400,000	£290,000	£300,000
Manufacturing overhead cost	536,000	315,000	480,000

Predetermined overhead rates are computed using the following bases in the three companies:

Company	Overhead rate based on:
X	Direct labour-hours
Y	Machine-hours
Z	Direct materials cost

Required

Compute the predetermined overhead rate to be used in each company during the upcoming year.

E5–3 Time allowed: 25 minutes

The Ferre Publishing Company has three service departments and two operating departments. Selected data from a recent period on the five departments follow:

The company allocates service department costs by the direct method in the following order: A (number of employees), B (space occupied), and C (hours of press time). The company makes no distinction between variable and fixed service department costs.

	Service department			Operating department		
	A	B	C	1	2	Total
Overhead costs	£140,000	£105,000	£48,000	£275,000	£430,000	£998,000
Number of employees	60	35	140	315	210	760
Square metres of space occupied	15,000	10,000	20,000	40,000	100,000	185,000
Hours of press time	–	–	–	30,000	60,000	90,000

Problems

connect™

Required
Assuming that the company uses the direct method, how much overhead cost would be allocated to each operating department?

P5–4 Cost Allocation: Direct Method

ⓘ Time allowed: 30 minutes

The Sendai Co. Ltd of Japan has budgeted costs in its various departments as follows for the coming year:

Factory administration	¥270,000,000
Custodial services	68,760,000
Personnel	28,840,000
Maintenance	45,200,000
Machining – overhead	376,300,000
Assembly – overhead	175,900,000
Total cost	¥965,000,000

The Japanese currency is the yen, denoted by ¥. The company allocates service department costs to other departments in the order listed below.

Department	Number of employees	Total labour-hours	Square metres of space occupied	Direct labour-hours	Machine-hours
Factory administration	12	–	5,000	–	–
Custodial services	4	3,000	2,000	–	–
Personnel	5	5,000	3,000	–	–
Maintenance	25	22,000	10,000	–	–
Machining	40	30,000	70,000	20,000	70,000
Assembly	60	90,000	20,000	80,000	10,000
	146	150,000	110,000	100,000	80,000

Machining and Assembly are operating departments; the other departments all act in a service capacity. The company does not make a distinction between fixed and variable service department costs. Factory administration is allocated on the basis of labour-hours; Custodial services on the basis of square metres occupied; Personnel on the basis of number of employees; and Maintenance on the basis of machine-hours.

Required
1. Allocate service department costs to departments using the direct method. Then compute predetermined overhead rates in the operating departments using a machine-hours basis in Machining and a direct labour-hours basis in Assembly.
2. Assume that the company does not want to bother with allocating service department costs but simply wants to compute a single plantwide overhead rate based on total overhead costs (both service department and operating department) divided by total direct labour-hours. Compute the overhead rate.

3   Suppose a job requires machine and labour time as follows:

	Machine-hours	Direct labour-hours
Machining department	190	25
Assembly department	10	75
Total hours	200	100

Using the overhead rates computed in (1) and (2), compute the amount of overhead cost that would be assigned to the job if the overhead rates were developed using the direct method and the plantwide method.

P5–5 Plantwide and Departmental Overhead Rates

⏱ **Time allowed:** 40 minutes

'Blast it!' said David Wilson, CEO of Teledex Company. 'We've just lost the bid on the Koopers job by €2,000. It seems we're either too high to get the job or too low to make any money on half the jobs we bid.'

Teledex Company manufactures products to customers' specifications and operates a job-order cost system. Manufacturing overhead cost is applied to jobs on the basis of direct labour cost. The following estimates were made at the beginning of the year:

	Department			
	Fabricating	Machining	Assembly	Total plant
Direct labour	€200,000	€100,000	€300,000	€600,000
Manufacturing overhead	350,000	400,000	90,000	840,000

Jobs require varying amounts of work in the three departments. The Koopers job, for example, would have required manufacturing costs in the three departments as follows:

	Department			
	Fabricating	Machining	Assembly	Total plant
Direct materials	€3,000	€200	€1,400	€4,600
Direct labour	2,800	500	6,200	9,500
Manufacturing overhead	?	?	?	?

The company uses a plantwide overhead rate to apply manufacturing overhead cost to jobs.

Required

1   Assuming use of a plantwide overhead rate:
    (a) Compute the rate for the current year.
    (b) Determine the amount of manufacturing overhead cost that would have been applied to the Koopers job.

2   Suppose that instead of using a plantwide overhead rate, the company had used a separate predetermined overhead rate in each department. Under these conditions:
    (a) Compute the rate for each department for the current year.
    (b) Determine the amount of manufacturing overhead cost that would have been applied to the Koopers job.
3   Explain the difference between the manufacturing overhead that would have been applied using the plantwide rate in question 1 (b) above and using the departmental rates in question 2 (b).
4   Assume that it is customary in the industry to bid jobs at 150% of total manufacturing cost (direct materials, direct labour, and applied overhead). What was the company's bid price on the Koopers job? What would the bid price have been if departmental overhead rates had been used to apply overhead cost?

Chapter 3
Short-term decision making: cost–volume–profit relationships

LO Learning objectives

After studying Chapter 3, you should be able to:

1 Explain how changes in activity affect contribution margin and profit
2 Compute the contribution margin ratio (CM ratio) and use it to compute changes in contribution margin and profit
3 Show the effects on contribution margin of changes in variable costs, fixed costs, selling price and volume
4 Compute the break-even point by both the equation method and the contribution margin method
5 Prepare a cost–volume–profit (CVP) graph and explain the significance of each of its components
6 Use the CVP formulas to determine the activity level needed to achieve a desired target profit
7 Compute the margin of safety and explain its significance
8 Compute the degree of operating leverage at a particular level of sales and explain how the degree of operating leverage can be used to predict changes in profit
9 Compute the break-even point for a multiple product company and explain the effects of shifts in the sales mix on contribution margin and the break-even point.

Concepts in Context

Since CVP analysis shows that levels of activity can have a big effect on profits, choices on the best way of compensating salespersons must be chosen with a great deal of care. Digital Equipment Corporation's founder, Kenneth Olsen, believed that salespersons should never sell customers something they do not need and, accordingly, Digital paid them salaries rather than sales commissions. This approach worked fine for many years because 'Digital's products were the hottest alternative to expensive mainframe computers, and because they were cheaper, they almost sold themselves. But when competition arrived, the Digital sales staff was hopelessly outclassed.' When commissions were introduced in an attempt to stem the tide, the new system backfired. 'Some salesmen sold product at little or no profit to pump up volume – and their commission.'[1]

© Getty Images

Cost–volume–profit (CVP) analysis is one of the most powerful tools that managers have at their command. It helps them understand the interrelationship between cost, volume and profit in an organization by focusing on interactions between the following five elements:

1   Prices of products
2   Volume or level of activity
3   Per unit variable costs
4   Total fixed costs
5   Mix of products sold.

Because CVP analysis helps managers understand the interrelationship between cost, volume and profit, it is a vital tool in many business decisions. These decisions include, for example, what products to manufacture or sell, what pricing policy to follow, what marketing strategy to employ, and what type of productive facilities to acquire.

The basics of cost–volume–profit (CVP) analysis

Recall the discussion on cost behaviour in Chapter 2 and how we showed that the contribution profit and loss account emphasizes the behaviour of costs and therefore is extremely helpful to a manager in judging the impact on profits of changes in selling price, cost or volume. Let us consider the case of Acoustic Concepts which has the following contribution profit and loss account:

Acoustic Concepts Ltd Contribution profit and loss account For the month of June		
	Total	Per unit
Sales (400 speakers)	£100,000	£250
Less variable expenses	60,000	150
Contribution margin	40,000	£100
Less fixed expenses	35,000	
Profit	£5,000	

Notice that sales, variable expenses and contribution margin are expressed on a per unit basis as well as in total. This is commonly done on profit and loss accounts prepared for management's own use, since, as we shall see, it facilitates profitability analysis.

Contribution margin

Contribution margin is the amount remaining from sales revenue after variable expenses have been deducted. Thus, it is the amount available to cover fixed expenses and then to provide profits for the period. Notice the sequence here – contribution margin is used *first* to cover the fixed expenses, and then whatever remains goes towards profits. If the contribution margin is not sufficient to cover the fixed expenses, then a loss occurs for the period. To illustrate with an extreme example, assume that by the middle of a particular month Acoustic Concepts has been able to sell only one speaker. At that point, the company's profit and loss account will appear as follows:

	Total	Per unit
Sales (1 speaker)	£250	£250
Less variable expenses	150	150
Contribution margin	100	£100
Less fixed expenses	35,000	
Net loss	£(34,900)	

For each additional speaker that the company is able to sell during the month, £100 more in contribution margin will become available to help cover the fixed expenses. If a second speaker is sold, for example, then the total contribution margin will increase by £100 (to a total of £200) and the company's loss will decrease by £100, to £34,800:

	Total	Per unit
Sales (2 speakers)	£500	£250
Less variable expenses	300	150
Contribution margin	200	£100
Less fixed expenses	35,000	
Net loss	£(34,800)	

If enough speakers can be sold to generate £35,000 in contribution margin, then all of the fixed costs will be covered and the company will have managed to at least *break even* for the month – that is, to show neither profit nor loss but just cover all of its costs. To reach the break-even point, the company will have to sell 350 speakers in a month, since each speaker sold yields £100 in contribution margin:

	Total	Per unit
Sales (350 speakers)	£87,500	£250
Less variable expenses	52,500	150
Contribution margin	35,000	£100
Less fixed expenses	35,000	
Profit	£0	

Computation of the **break-even point** is discussed in detail later in the chapter; for the moment, note that the break-even point can be defined as the level of sales at which profit is zero.

Once the break-even point has been reached, profit will increase by the unit contribution margin for each additional unit sold. If 351 speakers are sold in a month, for example, then we can expect that the profit for the month will be £100, since the company will have sold one speaker more than the number needed to break even:

	Total	Per unit
Sales (351 speakers)	£87,750	£250
Less variable expenses	52,650	150
Contribution margin	35,100	£100
Less fixed expenses	35,000	
Profit	£100	

If 352 speakers are sold (2 speakers above the break-even point), then we can expect that the profit for the month will be £200, and so forth. To know what the profits will be at various levels of activity, therefore, it is not necessary for a manager to prepare a whole series of profit and loss accounts. The manager can simply take the number of units to be sold over the break-even point and multiply that number by the unit contribution margin. The result represents the anticipated profits for the period. Or, to estimate the effect of a planned increase in sales on profits, the manager can simply multiply the increase in units sold by the unit contribution margin. The result will be the expected increase in profits. To illustrate, if Acoustic Concepts is currently selling 400 speakers per month and plans to increase sales to 425 speakers per month, the anticipated impact on profits can be computed as follows:

Increased number of speakers to be sold	25
Contribution margin per speaker	× £100
increase in profit	£2,500

These calculations can be verified as follows:

	Sales volume			
	400 speakers	425 speakers	Difference 25 speakers	Per unit
Sales	£100,000	£106,250	£6,250	£250
Less variable expenses	60,000	63,750	3,750	150
Contribution margin	40,000	42,500	2,500	£100
Less fixed expenses	35,000	35,000	0	
Profit	£5,000	£7,500	£2,500	

To summarize the series of examples given above, if there were no sales, the company's loss would equal its fixed expenses. Each unit that is sold reduces the loss by the amount of the unit contribution margin. Once the break-even point has been reached, each additional unit sold increases the company's profit by the amount of the unit contribution margin.

Focus on Business Practice

Green regulation and fixed costs

© AFP/Getty Images

The recent alliance between Renault/Nissan and Daimler was driven by the high fixed costs of developing new low emission technology and rules about average carbon emissions within car groups: '"these technologies are utterly expensive and almost impossible to shoulder alone for carmakers like Daimler or BMW," said Gregor Matthies, partner with the consultancy Bain & Co.'[2] Clearly the strategy for carmakers is to spread the higher fixed costs of new technology over higher volumes of cars.

Exercise: What might be a strategic risk for Daimler in this sort of deal?

Contribution margin ratio (CM ratio)

LO 2

In addition to being expressed on a per unit basis, sales revenues, variable expenses, and contribution margin for Acoustic Concepts can also be expressed as a percentage of sales:

	Total	Per unit	Percentage of sales
Sales (400 speakers)	£100,000	£250	100
Less variable expenses	60,000	150	60
Contribution margin	40,000	£100	40
Less fixed expenses	35,000		
Profit	£5,000		

The contribution margin as a percentage of total sales is referred to as the contribution margin ratio (CM ratio). This ratio is computed as follows:

$$CM \ ratio = \frac{Contribution \ margin}{Sales}$$

For Acoustic Concepts, the computations are as follows:

$$\frac{Total \ contribution \ margin, \ £40,000}{Total \ sales, \ £100,000} = 40\%$$

or

$$\frac{Per \ unit \ contribution \ margin, \ £100}{Per \ unit \ sales, \ £250} = 40\%$$

The CM ratio is extremely useful since it shows how the contribution margin will be affected by a change in total sales. To illustrate, notice that Acoustic Concepts has a CM ratio of 40%. This means that for each pound increase in sales, total contribution margin will increase by 40 pence (£1 sales × CM ratio of 40%). Profit will also increase by 40 pence, assuming that there are no changes in fixed costs.

As this illustration suggests, *the impact on profit of any given pound change in total sales can be computed in seconds by simply applying the CM ratio to the pound change.* If Acoustic Concepts plans a £30,000 increase in sales during the coming month, for example, management can expect contribution margin to increase by £12,000 (£30,000 increased sales × CM ratio of 40%). As we noted above, profit will also increase by £12,000 if fixed costs do not change.

This is verified by the following table:

	Sales volume		Increase	Percentage of sales
	Present	Expected		
Sales	£100,000	£130,000	£30,000	100
Less variable expenses	60,000	78,000*	18,000	60
Contribution margin	40,000	52,000	12,000	40
Less fixed expenses	35,000	35,000	0	
Profit	£5,000	£17,000	£12,000	

*£130,000 expected sales/£250 per unit = 520 units. 520 units × £150 per unit = £78,000.

Some managers prefer to work with the CM ratio rather than the unit contribution margin figure. The CM ratio is particularly valuable in those situations where the manager must make trade-offs between

more pound sales of one product versus more pound sales of another. Generally speaking, when trying to increase sales, products that yield the greatest amount of contribution margin per pound of sales should be emphasized.

Some applications of CVP concepts

If we want to see how the concepts developed on the preceding pages of this text can be used in planning and decision making, we can use the following basic data:

	Per unit	Percentage of sales
Sales price	£250	100
Less variable expenses	150	60
Contribution margin	£100	40

Recall that fixed expenses are £35,000 per month, these data can show the effects of changes in variable costs, fixed costs, sales price and sales volume on the company's profitability.

Change in fixed cost and sales volume

Acoustic Concepts is currently selling 400 speakers per month (monthly sales of £100,000). The sales manager feels that a £10,000 increase in the monthly advertising budget would increase monthly sales by £30,000. Should the advertising budget be increased?

The following table shows the effect of the proposed change in monthly advertising budget:

	Current sales	Advertising budget	Sales with additional difference	Percentage of sales
Sales	£100,000	£130,000	£30,000	100
Less variable expenses	60,000	78,000	18,000	60
Contribution margin	40,000	52,000	12,000	40
Less fixed expenses	35,000	45,000*	10,000	
Profit	£5,000	£7,000	£2,000	

*£35,000 plus additional £10,000 monthly advertising budget = £45,000.

Assuming there are no other factors to be considered, the increase in the advertising budget should be approved since it would lead to an increase in profit of £2,000. There are two shorter ways to present this solution. The first alternative solution follows:

Expected total contribution margin:	
£130,000 × 40% CM ratio	£52,000
Present total contribution margin:	
£100,000 × 40% CM ratio	40,000
Incremental contribution margin	12,000
Change in fixed costs:	
Less incremental advertising expense	10,000
Increased profit	£2,000

Since, in this case, only the fixed costs and the sales volume change, the solution can be presented in an even shorter format, as follows:

Incremental contribution margin:	
£30,000 × 40% CM ratio	£12,000
Less incremental advertising expense	10,000
Increased profit	£2,000

Notice that this approach does not depend on a knowledge of previous sales. Also notice that it is unnecessary under either shorter approach to prepare a profit and loss account. Both of the solutions above involve an incremental analysis in that they consider only those items of revenue, cost and volume that will change if the new programme is implemented. Although in each case a new profit and loss account could have been prepared, most managers would prefer the incremental approach. The reason is that it is simpler and more direct, and it permits the decision maker to focus attention on the specific items involved in the decision.

Change in variable costs and sales volume

Refer to the original data. Recall that Acoustic Concepts is currently selling 400 speakers per month. Management is contemplating the use of higher-quality components, which would increase variable costs (and thereby reduce the contribution margin) by £10 per speaker. However, the sales manager predicts that the higher overall quality would increase sales to 480 speakers per month. Should the higher-quality components be used?

The £10 increase in variable costs will cause the unit contribution margin to decrease from £100 to £90. So the solution is:

Expected total contribution margin with higher-quality components:	
480 speakers × £90	£43,200
Present total contribution margin:	
400 speakers × £100	40,000
Increase in total contribution margin	£3,200

Yes, based on the information above, the higher-quality components should be used. Since fixed costs will not change, profit should increase by the £3,200 increase in contribution margin shown above.

Change in fixed cost, sales price and sales volume

Refer to the original data and recall again that the company is currently selling 400 speakers per month. To increase sales, the sales manager would like to cut the selling price by £20 per speaker and increase the advertising budget by £15,000 per month.

The sales manager argues that if these two steps are taken, unit sales will increase by 50% to 600 speakers per month. Should the changes be made?

A decrease of £20 per speaker in the selling price will cause the unit contribution margin to decrease from £100 to £80. The solution is:

Expected total contribution margin with lower selling price:	
600 speakers × £80	£48,000
Present total contribution margin:	
400 speakers × £100	40,000
Incremental contribution margin	8,000
Change in fixed costs:	
Less incremental advertising expense	15,000
Reduction in profit	£(7,000)

No, based on the information above, the changes should not be made. The same solution can be obtained by preparing comparative profit and loss accounts:

	Present 400 speakers per month		Expected 600 speakers per month		
	Total	Per unit	Total	Per unit	Difference
Sales	£100,000	£250	£138,000	£230	£38,000
Less variable expenses	60,000	150	90,000	£150	30,000
Contribution margin	40,000	£100	48,000	£80	8,000
Less fixed expenses	35,000		50,000*		15,000
Profit (loss)	£5,000		£(2,000)		£(7,000)

*£35,000 + Additional monthly advertising budget of £15,000 = £50,000.

Notice that the effect on profit is the same as that obtained by the incremental analysis above.

Change in variable cost, fixed cost and sales volume

Refer to the original data. As before, the company is currently selling 400 speakers per month. The sales manager would like to place the sales staff on a commission basis of £15 per speaker sold, rather than on flat salaries that now total £6,000 per month. The sales manager is confident that the change will increase monthly sales by 15% to 460 speakers per month. Should the change be made?

Changing the sales staff from a salaried basis to a commission basis will affect both fixed and variable costs. Fixed costs will decrease by £6,000, from £35,000 to £29,000. Variable costs will increase by £15, from £150 to £165, and the unit contribution margin will decrease from £100 to £85.

Expected total contribution margin with sales staff on commissions:	
460 speakers × £85	£39,100
Present total contribution margin:	
400 speakers × £100	40,000
Decrease in total contribution margin	(900)
Change in fixed costs:	
Add salaries avoided if a commission is paid	6,000
Increase in profit	£5,100

Yes, based on the information above, the changes should be made. Again, the same answer can be obtained by preparing comparative profit and loss accounts:

	Present 400 speakers per month		Expected 600 speakers per month		
	Total	Per unit	Total	Per unit	Difference: increase or (decrease) in profit
Sales	£100,000	£250	£115,000	£250	£15,000
Less variable expenses	60,000	150	75,900	165	(15,900)
Contribution margin	40,000	£100	39,100	£85	(900)
Less fixed expenses	35,000		29,000		6,000
Profit	£5,000		£10,100		£5,100

Change in regular sales price

Refer to the original data where Acoustic Concepts is currently selling 400 speakers per month. The company has an opportunity to make a bulk sale of 150 speakers to a wholesaler if an acceptable price can be worked out. This sale would not disturb the company's regular sales. What price per speaker should be quoted to the wholesaler if Acoustic Concepts wants to increase its monthly profits by £3,000? The solution is:

Variable cost per speaker	£150
Desired profit per speaker:	
£3,000/150 speakers	20
Quoted price per speaker	£170

Notice that no element of fixed cost is included in the computation. This is because fixed costs are not affected by the bulk sale, so all additional revenue in excess of variable costs goes to increasing the profits of the company.

Importance of the contribution margin

As stated in the introduction to the chapter, CVP analysis seeks the most profitable combination of variable costs, fixed costs, selling price and sales volume. The above examples show that the effect on the contribution margin is a major consideration in deciding on the most profitable combination of these factors. We have seen that profits can sometimes be improved by reducing the contribution margin if fixed costs can be reduced by a greater amount. More commonly, however, we have seen that the way to improve profits is to increase the total contribution margin figure. Sometimes this can be done by reducing the selling price and thereby increasing volume; sometimes it can be done by increasing the fixed costs (such as advertising) and thereby increasing volume; and sometimes it can be done by trading off variable and fixed costs with appropriate changes in volume. Many other combinations of factors are possible.

The size of the unit contribution margin figure (and the size of the CM ratio) will have a heavy influence on what steps a company is willing to take to improve profits. For example, the greater the unit contribution margin for a product, the greater is the amount that a company will be willing to spend in order to increase unit sales of the product by a given percentage. This explains in part why companies with high unit contribution margins (such as car manufacturers) advertise so heavily, while companies with low unit contribution margins (such as dishware manufacturers) tend to spend much less for advertising.

In short, the effect on the contribution margin holds the key to many decisions.

Break-even analysis

CVP analysis is sometimes referred to simply as break-even analysis. This is unfortunate because break-even analysis is only one element of CVP analysis – although an important element. Break-even analysis is designed to answer questions concerning how far sales could drop before the company begins to lose money.

Break-even computations

LO 4

Earlier in the chapter we defined the break-even point to be the level of sales at which the company's profit is zero. The break-even point can be computed using the *contribution margin method*.

The contribution margin method

The contribution margin method centres on the idea discussed earlier that each unit sold provides a certain amount of contribution margin that goes towards covering fixed costs. To find how many units must be sold to break even, divide the total fixed costs by the unit contribution margin:

$$\text{Break-even point in units sold} = \frac{\text{Fixed expenses}}{\text{Unit contribution margin}}$$

Each speaker generates a contribution margin of £100 (£250 selling price, less £150 variable expenses). Since the total fixed expenses are £35,000, the break-even point is as follows:

$$\frac{\text{Fixed expenses}}{\text{Unit contribution margin}} = \frac{£35,000}{£100} = 350 \text{ speakers}$$

A variation of this method uses the CM ratio instead of the unit contribution margin. The result is the break-even point in total sales in pounds rather than in total units sold.

$$\text{Break-even point in total sales} = \frac{\text{Fixed expenses}}{\text{CM ratio}}$$

In the Acoustic Concepts example, the calculations are as follows:

$$\frac{\text{Fixed expenses}}{\text{CM ratio}} = \frac{£35,000}{40\%} = £87,500$$

This approach, based on the CM ratio, is particularly useful in those situations where a company has multiple product lines and wishes to compute a single break-even point for the company as a whole. More is said on this point in a later section on the concept of sales mix.

Focus on Business Practice

Costing in event management

Laura is the manager of a company that specialises in events organizing. She is in a very competitive industry and usually sets the price per person for an event with reference to market rates. Each event has some fixed costs and she must try to work out how many tickets must be sold before these costs are covered. She can spend more money on publicity and advertising but this will push up the fixed costs of the event. Will the extra revenue from more delegates justify the increased expenditure on promotion?

© Digital Hallway

Exercise: Is advertising a fixed or variable cost?

LO 5 CVP relationships in graphic form

The relationships among revenue, cost, profit and volume can be expressed graphically by preparing a cost–volume–profit (CVP) graph. A CVP graph highlights CVP relationships over wide ranges of activity and can give managers a perspective that can be obtained in no other way. We can prepare a CVP graph for Acoustic Concepts.

Preparing the CVP graph

Preparing a CVP graph (sometimes called a *break-even chart*) involves three steps. These steps are keyed to the graph in Exhibit 3.1:

1 Draw a line parallel to the volume axis to represent total fixed expenses. For Acoustic Concepts, total fixed expenses are £35,000.

2 Choose some volume of sales and plot the point representing total expenses (fixed and variable) at the activity level you have selected. In Exhibit 3.1, at a volume of 600 speakers, the total expenses at that activity level would be as follows:

Fixed expenses	£35,000
Variable expenses (600 speakers × £150)	90,000
Total expenses	£125,000

After the point has been plotted, draw a line through it back to the point where the fixed expenses line intersects the pounds axis.

3 Choose some volume of sales and plot the point representing total sales pounds at the activity level you have selected. In Exhibit 3.1, at a volume of 600 speakers, sales at that activity level total £150,000 (600 speakers × £250). Draw a line through this point back to the origin.

The interpretation of the completed CVP graph is given in Exhibit 3.2. The anticipated profit or loss at any given level of sales is measured by the vertical distance between the total revenue line (sales) and the total expenses line (variable expenses plus fixed expenses).

The break-even point is where the total revenue and total expenses lines cross. The break-even point of 350 speakers in Exhibit 3.2 agrees with the break-even point obtained for Acoustic Concepts in earlier computations.

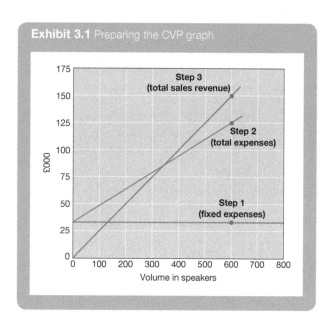

Exhibit 3.1 Preparing the CVP graph

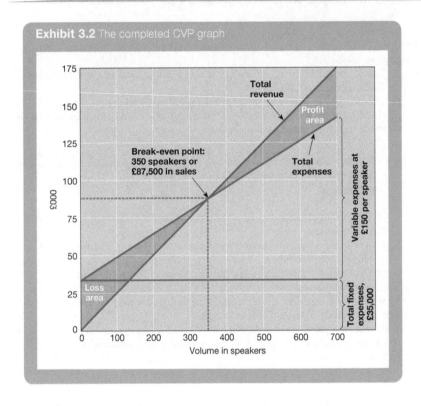

Exhibit 3.2 The completed CVP graph

LO 6 Target profit analysis

CVP formulas can be used to determine the sales volume needed to achieve a target profit. Suppose that Acoustic Concepts would like to earn a target profit of £40,000 per month. How many speakers would have to be sold?

We may expand the contribution margin formula to include the target profit:

$$\text{Units sold to attain the target profit} = \frac{\text{Fixed expenses} + \text{Target profit}}{\text{Unit contribution margin}}$$

$$= \frac{\text{£35,000 fixed expenses} + \text{£40,000 target profit}}{\text{£100 contribution margin per speaker}} = 750 \text{ speakers}$$

LO 7 The margin of safety

The **margin of safety** is the excess of budgeted (or actual) sales over the break-even volume of sales. It states the amount by which sales can drop before losses begin to be incurred. The formula for its calculation is as follows:

Margin of safety = Total budgeted (or actual) sales − Break-even sales

The margin of safety can also be expressed in percentage form. This percentage is obtained by dividing the margin of safety in pound terms by total sales:

$$\text{Margin of safety percentage} = \frac{\text{Margin of safety in pounds}}{\text{Total budgeted (or actual) sales}}$$

The calculations for the margin of safety for Acoustic Concepts are as follows:

Sales (at the current volume of 400 speakers) (a)	£100,000
Break-even sales (at 350 speakers)	87,500
Margin of safety (in pounds) (b)	£12,500
Margin of safety as a percentage of sales,(b)/(a)	12.5%

This margin of safety means that at the current level of sales and with the company's current prices and cost structure, a reduction in sales of £12,500, or 12.5%, would result in just breaking even.

In a single-product firm like Acoustic Concepts, the margin of safety can also be expressed in terms of the number of units sold by dividing the margin of safety in pounds by the selling price per unit. In this case, the margin of safety is 50 units (£12,500/£250 per unit = 50 units).

CVP considerations in choosing a cost structure

We stated in the preceding chapter that *cost structure* refers to the relative proportion of fixed and variable costs in an organization. We also stated that an organization often has some latitude in trading off between fixed and variable costs. Such a trade-off is possible, for example, by automating facilities rather than using direct labour workers. In this section, we discuss various considerations involved in choosing a cost structure.

We look first at the matter of cost structure and profit stability, and then we discuss an important concept known as *operating leverage*.

Cost structure and profit stability

When a manager has some latitude in trading off between fixed and variable costs, which cost structure is better – high variable costs and low fixed costs, or the opposite? No categorical answer to this question is possible; there may be advantages either way, depending on the specific circumstances. To show what we mean by this statement, refer to the profit and loss accounts given below for two blackberry farms. Bogside Farm depends on migrant workers to pick its berries by hand, whereas Sterling Farm has invested in expensive berry-picking machines. Consequently, Bogside Farm has higher variable costs, but Sterling Farm has higher fixed costs:

	Bogside Farm		Sterling Farm	
	Amount	%	Amount	%
Sales	£100,000	100	£100,000	100
Less variable expenses	60,000	60	30,000	30
Contribution margin	40,000	40	70,000	70
Less fixed expenses	30,000		60,000	
Profit	£10,000		£10,000	

The question as to which farm has the better cost structure depends on many factors, including the long-run trend in sales, year-to-year fluctuations in the level of sales, and the attitude of the owners toward risk. If sales are expected to be above £100,000 in the future, then Sterling Farm probably has the better cost structure. The reason is that its CM ratio is higher, and its profits will therefore increase more rapidly as sales increase. To illustrate, assume that each farm experiences a 10% increase in sales without any increase in fixed costs. The new profit and loss accounts would be as follows:

	Bogside Farm		Sterling Farm	
	Amount	%	Amount	%
Sales	£110,000	100	£110,000	100
Less variable expenses	66,000	60	33,000	30
Contribution margin	44,000	40	77,000	70
Less fixed expenses	30,000		60,000	
Profit	£14,000		£17,000	

Sterling Farm has experienced a greater increase in profit due to its higher CM ratio even though the increase in sales was the same for both farms.

What if sales drop below £100,000 from time to time? What are the break-even points of the two farms? What are their margins of safety? The computations needed to answer these questions are carried out below using the contribution margin method:

	Bogside Farm	Sterling Farm
Fixed expenses	£30,000	£60,000
Contribution margin ratio	÷40%	÷70%
Break-even in total sales pounds	£75,000	£85,714
Total current sales (a)	£100,000	£100,000
Break-even sales	75,000	85,714
Margin of safety in sales pounds (b)	£25,000	£14,286
Margin of safety as a percentage of sales,(b)/(a)	25.0%	14.3%

This analysis makes it clear that Bogside Farm is less vulnerable to downturns than Sterling Farm. We can identify two reasons why it is less vulnerable. First, due to its lower fixed expenses, Bogside Farm has a lower break-even point and a higher margin of safety, as shown by the computations above. Therefore, it will not incur losses as quickly as Sterling Farm in periods of sharply declining sales. Secondly, due to its lower CM ratio, Bogside Farm will not lose contribution margin as rapidly as Sterling Farm when sales fall off. Thus, Bogside Farm's profit will be less volatile. We saw earlier that this is a drawback when sales increase, but it provides more protection when sales drop.

To summarize, without knowing the future, it is not obvious which cost structure is better. Both have advantages and disadvantages. Sterling Farm, with its higher fixed costs and lower variable costs, will experience wider swings in profit as changes take place in sales, with greater profits in good years and greater losses in bad years. Bogside Farm, with its lower fixed costs and higher variable costs, will enjoy greater stability in profit and will be more protected from losses during bad years, but at the cost of lower profit in good years.

Operating leverage

LO 8

A lever is a tool for multiplying force. Using a lever, a massive object can be moved with only a modest amount of force. In business, *operating leverage* serves a similar purpose. Operating leverage is a measure of how sensitive profit is to percentage changes in sales. Operating leverage acts as a multiplier. If operating leverage is high, a small percentage increase in sales can produce a much larger percentage increase in profit.

Operating leverage can be illustrated by returning to the data given above for the two blackberry farms. We previously showed that a 10% increase in sales (from £100,000 to £110,000 in each farm) results in a 70% increase in the profit of Sterling Farm (from £10,000 to £17,000) and only a 40% increase in the profit of Bogside Farm (from £10,000 to £14,000). Thus, for a 10% increase in sales, Sterling Farm experiences a much greater percentage increase in profits than does Bogside Farm. Therefore, Sterling Farm has greater operating leverage than Bogside Farm.

The degree of operating leverage at a given level of sales is computed by the following formula:

$$\text{Degree of operating leverage} = \frac{\text{Contribution margin}}{\text{Profit}}$$

The degree of operating leverage is a measure, at a given level of sales, of how a percentage change in sales volume will affect profits. To illustrate, the degree of operating leverage for the two farms at a £100,000 sales level would be as follows:

$$\text{Bogside Farm:} \frac{£40,000}{£10,000}$$
$$= 4$$

$$\text{Sterling Farm:} \frac{£70,000}{£10,000}$$
$$= 7$$

Since the degree of operating leverage for Bogside Farm is four, the farm's profit grows four times as fast as its sales. Similarly, Sterling Farm's profit grows seven times as fast as its sales. Thus, if sales increase by 10%, then we can expect the profit of Bogside Farm to increase by four times this amount, or by 40%, and the profit of Sterling Farm to increase by seven times this amount, or by 70%.

	1 Percentage increase in sales	2 Degree of operating leverage	3 Percentage increase in profit (1 × 2)
Bogside Farm	10	4	40
Sterling Farm	10	7	70

What is responsible for the higher operating leverage at Sterling Farm? The only difference between the two farms is their cost structure. If two companies have the same total revenue and same total expense but different cost structures, then the company with the higher proportion of fixed costs in its cost structure will have higher operating leverage. Referring back to the original example on page 55, when both farms have sales of £100,000 and total expenses of £90,000, one-third of Bogside Farm's costs are fixed but two-thirds of Sterling Farm's costs are fixed. As a consequence, Sterling's degree of operating leverage is higher than Bogside's.[3]

The degree of operating leverage is greatest at sales levels near the break-even point and decreases as sales and profits rise. This can be seen from the tabulation below, which shows the degree of operating leverage for Bogside Farm at various sales levels.

Sales	£75,000	£80,000	£100,000	£150,000	£225,000
Less variable expenses	45,000	48,000	60,000	90,000	135,000
Contribution margin (a)	30,000	32,000	40,000	60,000	90,000
Less fixed expenses	30,000	30,000	30,000	30,000	30,000
Profit (b)	£0	£2,000	£10,000	£30,000	£60,000
Degree of operating leverage, (a)/(b)	∞	16	4	2	1.5

Thus, a 10% increase in sales would increase profits by only 15% (10% × 1.5) if the company were operating at a £225,000 sales level, as compared to the 40% increase we computed earlier at the £100,000 sales level. The degree of operating leverage will continue to decrease the farther the company moves from its break-even point. At the break-even point, the degree of operating leverage will be infinitely large (£30,000 contribution margin/£0 profit = ∞).

A manager can use the degree of operating leverage quickly to estimate what impact various percentage changes in sales will have on profits, without the necessity of preparing detailed profit and loss accounts. As shown by our examples, the effects of operating leverage can be dramatic. If a company is near its break-even point, then even small percentage increases in sales can yield large percentage increases in profits.

This explains why management will often work very hard for only a small increase in sales volume. If the degree of operating leverage is five, then a 6% increase in sales would translate into a 30% increase in profits.

The concept of sales mix

The preceding sections have given us some insights into the principles involved in CVP analysis, as well as some selected examples of how these principles are used by the manager. Before concluding our discussion, it will be helpful to consider one additional application of the ideas that we have developed – the use of CVP concepts in analysing sales mix.

The definition of sales mix

The term **sales mix** means the relative proportions in which a company's products are sold. Managers try to achieve the combination, or mix, that will yield the greatest amount of profits. Most companies have several products, and often these products are not equally profitable. Where this is true, profits will depend to some extent on the company's sales mix. Profits will be greater if high-margin rather than low-margin items make up a relatively large proportion of total sales.

Changes in the sales mix can cause interesting (and sometimes confusing) variations in a company's profits. A shift in the sales mix from high-margin items to low-margin items can cause total profits to decrease even though total sales may increase. Conversely, a shift in the sales mix from low-margin items to high-margin items can cause the reverse effect – total profits may increase even though total sales decrease. It is one thing to achieve a particular sales volume; it is quite a different thing to sell the most profitable mix of products.

Sales mix and break-even analysis

If a company sells more than one product, break-even analysis is somewhat more complex than discussed earlier in the chapter. The reason is that different products will have different selling prices, different costs and different contribution margins. Consequently, the break-even point will depend on the mix in which the various products are sold. To illustrate, consider Sound Unlimited, a small company that imports CD-ROMs from France for use in personal computers. At present, the company distributes the following to retail computer stores: the Le Louvre CD, a multimedia free-form tour of the famous art museum in Paris; and the Le Vin CD, which features the wines and wine-growing regions of France. Both multimedia products have sound, photos, video clips, and sophisticated software. The company's September sales, expenses and break-even point are shown in Exhibit 3.3.

As shown in the exhibit, the break-even point is £60,000 in sales. This is computed by dividing the fixed costs by the company's *overall* CM ratio of 45%. But £60,000 in sales represents the break-even point for the company only as long as the sales mix does not change. *If the sales mix changes, then the break-even point will also change*. This is illustrated by the results for October in which the sales mix shifted away from the more profitable Le Vin CD (which has a 50% CM ratio) towards the less profitable Le Louvre CD (which has only a 25% CM ratio). These results appear in Exhibit 3.4.

Although sales have remained unchanged at £100,000, the sales mix is exactly the reverse of what it was in Exhibit 3.3, with the bulk of the sales now coming from the less profitable Le Louvre CD. Notice that this shift in the sales mix has caused both the overall CM ratio and total profits to drop sharply from the prior month – the overall CM ratio has dropped from 45% in September to only 30% in October, and profit has dropped from £18,000 to only £3,000. In addition, with the drop in the overall CM ratio, the company's break-even point is no longer £60,000 in sales. Since the company is now realizing less average contribution margin per pound of sales, it takes more sales to cover the same amount of fixed costs. Thus, the break-even point has increased from £60,000 to £90,000 in sales per year.

In preparing a break-even analysis, some assumption must be made concerning the sales mix. Usually the assumption is that it will not change. However, if the manager knows that shifts in various factors (consumer tastes, market share and so forth) are causing shifts in the sales mix, then these factors must be explicitly considered in any CVP computations. Otherwise, the manager may make decisions on the basis of outmoded or faulty data.

Exhibit 3.3 Multiple-product break-even analysis

	Le Louvre CD		Le Vin CD		Total	
	Amount	Per cent	Amount	Per cent	Amount	Per cent
Sales	£20,000	100	£80,000	100	£100,000	100
Less variable expenses	15,000	75	40,000	50	55,000	55
Contribution margin	£5,000	25	£40,000	50	45,000	45
Less fixed expenses					27,000	
Profit					£18,000	

Sound Unlimited
Contribution profit statement
For the month of September

Computation of the break-even point:

$$\frac{\text{Fixed expenses, } £27,000}{\text{Overall CM ratio, } 45\%} = £60,000$$

Verification of the break-even:

	Le Louvre CD		Le Vin CD		Total	
Sales	£12,000	100	£48,000	100	£60,000	100
Less variable expenses	9,000	75	24,000	50	33,000	55
Contribution margin	£3,000	25	£24,000	50	27,000	45
Less fixed expenses					27,000	
Profit					£0	

Exhibit 3.4 Multiple-product break-even analysis: a shift in sales mix (see Exhibit 3.3)

Sound Unlimited
Contribution profit statement
For the month of October

	Le Louvre CD		Le Vin CD		Total	
	Amount	Per cent	Amount	Per cent	Amount	Per cent
Sales	£80,000	100	£20,000	100	£100,000	100
Less variable expenses	60,000	75	10,000	50	70,000	70
Contribution margin	£20,000	25	£10,000	50	30,000	30
Less fixed expenses					27,000	
Profit					£3,000	

Computation of the break-even point:

$$\frac{\text{Fixed expenses, £27,000}}{\text{Overall CM ratio, 30%}} = £90,000$$

Focus on Business Practice

Making the labour force more flexible

© Mike Liu

Geoff is the general manager of a large resort hotel. Geoff has a sophisticated forecasting model which tells him what the balance of demand is likely to be for each holiday package. For example, a 'Motown' weekend will mean a lot of extra demand at the bar. He has trained his workforce to multi-task which makes his costs more flexible for the different mixes of demand that relate to the expected preferences of his guests.

Exercise: Are the hotel's labour costs now more variable with respect to total guest numbers or just more variable in respect of sales mix?

Assumptions of CVP analysis

A number of assumptions typically underlie CVP analysis:

1   Selling price is constant throughout the entire relevant range. The price of a product or service will not change as volume changes.
2   Costs are linear throughout the entire relevant range, and they can be accurately divided into variable and fixed elements. The variable element is constant per unit, and the fixed element is constant in total over the entire relevant range.
3   In multiproduct companies, the sales mix is constant.
4   In manufacturing companies, stocks do not change. The number of units produced equals the number of units sold.

While some of these assumptions may be technically violated, the violations are usually not serious enough to call into question the basic validity of CVP analysis. For example, in most multiproduct companies, the sales mix is constant enough for the results of CVP analysis to be reasonably valid.

Perhaps the greatest danger lies in relying on simple CVP analysis when a manager is contemplating a large change in volume that lies outside the relevant range. For example, a manager might contemplate increasing the level of sales far beyond what the company has ever experienced before. However, even in these situations a manager can adjust the model as we have done in this chapter to take into account anticipated changes in selling prices, fixed costs and the sales mix that would otherwise violate the assumptions. For example, in a decision that would affect fixed costs, the change in fixed costs can be explicitly taken into account as illustrated earlier in the chapter in the Acoustic Concepts example on page 48.

Separation of costs into fixed and variable elements: the high-low method

So far we have assumed that we can easily determine which are fixed and which are variable costs. But if we are given levels of activity and associated costs how can we separate these mixed costs into fixed and variable elements? One simple method is known as the *high-low* method. In the case of Brentline Hospital, we will use the following records of maintenance costs and patient-days for the first seven months of the year to estimate the fixed and variable elements of maintenance costs:

Month	Activity level: patient-days	Maintenance cost incurred
January	5,600	£7,900
February	7,100	8,500
March	5,000	7,400
April	6,500	8,200
May	7,300	9,100
June	8,000	9,800
July	6,200	7,800

The high-low method

To analyse mixed costs with the high-low method, one begins by identifying the period with the lowest level of activity and the period with the highest level of activity. The difference in cost observed at the two extremes is divided by the change in activity between the extremes in order to estimate the variable cost per unit of activity.

Since total maintenance cost at Brentline Hospital appears generally to increase as the activity level increases, it is likely that some variable cost element is present. Using the high-low method, we first identify the periods with the highest and lowest activity – in this case, June and March. We then use the activity and cost data from these two periods to estimate the variable cost component as follows:

	Patient-days	Maintenance cost incurred
High activity level (June)	8,000	£9,800
Low activity level (March)	5,000	7,400
Change	3,000	£2,400

$$\text{Variable cost} = \frac{\text{Change in cost}}{\text{Change in activity}} = \frac{£2400}{3000} = £0.80 \text{ per patient day}$$

Having determined that the variable rate for maintenance cost is 80 pence per patient-day, we can now determine the amount of fixed cost. This is done by taking total cost at *either* the high *or* the low activity level and

deducting the variable cost element. In the computation below, total cost at the high activity level is used in computing the fixed cost element:

Fixed cost element = Total cost − Variable cost element
= £9,800 − (£0.80 per patient-day × per 8,000 patient-days)
= £3,400

Both the variable and fixed cost elements have now been isolated. The cost of maintenance can be expressed as £3,400 per month plus 80 pence per patient-day.

The cost of maintenance can also be expressed in terms of the equation for a straight line as follows:

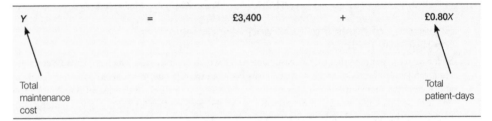

Y	=	£3,400	+	£0.80X
Total maintenance cost				Total patient-days

Although there are other more sophisticated ways of measuring cost functions, the high-low method is a quick and easy approach.

Summary

- CVP analysis involves finding the most favourable combination of variable costs, fixed costs, selling price, sales volume, and mix of products sold.

- Trade-offs are possible between types of costs, as well as between costs and selling price, and between selling price and sales volume.

- Sometimes these trade-offs are desirable, and sometimes they are not. CVP analysis provides the manager with a powerful tool for identifying those courses of action that will improve profitability.

- The concepts developed in this chapter represent *a way of thinking* rather than a mechanical set of procedures. That is, to put together the optimum combination of costs, selling price and sales volume, the manager must be trained to think in terms of the unit contribution margin, the break-even point, the CM ratio, the sales mix, and the other concepts developed in this chapter.

- These concepts are dynamic in that a change in one will trigger changes in others – changes that may not be obvious on the surface.

Key terms

Break-even point The level of sales at which profit is zero. The break-even point can also be defined as the point where total sales equals total expenses or as the point where total contribution margin equals total fixed expenses (p. 45).

Contribution margin method A method of computing the break-even point in which the fixed expenses are divided by the contribution margin per unit (p. 51).

Contribution margin ratio (CM ratio) The contribution margin as a percentage of total sales (p. 47).

Cost–volume–profit (CVP) graph The relations between revenues, costs and level of activity in an organization presented in graphic form (p. 52).

Degree of operating leverage A measure, at a given level of sales, of how a percentage change in sales volume will affect profits. The

degree of operating leverage is computed by dividing contribution margin by profit (p. 57).

High-low method A technique for separating mixed costs into fixed and variable components (p. 61).

Incremental analysis An analytical approach that focuses only on those items of revenue, cost and volume that will change as a result of a decision (p. 49)

Margin of safety The excess of budgeted (or actual) sales over the break-even volume of sales (p. 54).

Operating leverage A measure of how sensitive profit is to a given percentage change in sales. It is computed by dividing the contribution margin by profit (p. 57).

Sales mix The relative proportions in which a company's products are sold. Sales mix is computed by expressing the sales of each product as a percentage of total sales (p. 58).

Endnotes

1 Wilke (1994).

2 Reed and Schafer (2010).

3 See Lord (1995) for an extensive discussion of the impact of cost structure on the degree of operating leverage.

When you have read this chapter, log on to the Online Learning Centre for *Management Accounting for Business Decisions* at **www.mcgraw-hill.co.uk/ textbooks/seal**, where you'll find multiple choice questions, practice exams and extra study tools for management accounting.

Assessment

Questions

connect

3–1   What is meant by a product's CM ratio? How is this ratio useful in planning business operations?

3–2   Company A's cost structure includes costs that are mostly variable, whereas Company B's cost structure includes costs that are mostly fixed. In a time of increasing sales, which company will tend to realize the most rapid increase in profits? Explain.

3–3   What is meant by the term *operating leverage*?

3–4   A 10 per cent decrease in the selling price of a product will have the same impact on profit as a 10 per cent increase in the variable expenses. Do you agree? Why or why not?

3–5   What is meant by the term *break-even point*?

3–6   Name three approaches to break-even analysis. Briefly explain how each approach works.

3–7   In response to a request from your immediate supervisor, you have prepared a CVP graph portraying the cost and revenue characteristics of your company's product and operations. Explain how the lines on the graph and the break-even point would change if (a) the selling price per unit decreased, (b) fixed costs increased throughout the entire range of activity portrayed on the graph, and (c) variable costs per unit increased.

3–8   Al's Car Wash charges £4 to wash a car. The variable costs of washing a car are 15 per cent of sales. Fixed expenses total £1,700 monthly. How many cars must be washed each month for Al to break even?

3–9   What is meant by the margin of safety?

3–10 Companies X and Y are in the same industry. Company X is highly automated, whereas Company Y relies primarily on labour to make its products. If sales and total expenses in the two companies are about the same, which would you expect to have the lower margin of safety? Why?

3–11 What is meant by the term sales mix? What assumption is usually made concerning sales mix in CVP analysis?

3–12 Explain how a shift in the sales mix could result in both a higher break-even point and a lower profit.

Exercises

connect

E3–1   Time allowed: 20 minutes

Menlo Company manufactures and sells a single product. The company's sales and expenses for the last quarter follow:

	Total	Per unit
Sales	£450,000	£30
Less variable expenses	180,000	12
Contribution margin	270,000	£18
Less fixed expenses	216,000	
Profit	£54,000	

Required

1 What is the quarterly break-even point in units sold and in sales pounds?
2 Without resorting to computations, what is the total contribution margin at the break-even point?
3 How many units would have to be sold each quarter to earn a target profit of £90,000? Use the unit contribution method. Verify your answer by preparing a contribution profit and loss account at the target level of sales.
4 Refer to the original data. Compute the company's margin of safety in both pound and percentage terms.
5 What is the company's CM ratio? If sales increase by £50,000 per quarter and there is no change in fixed expenses, by how much would you expect quarterly profit to increase? (Do not prepare a profit and loss account; use the CM ratio to compute your answer.)

E3–2 ⏱ Time allowed: 20 minutes

Lindon Company is the exclusive distributor for an automotive product. The product sells for £40 per unit and has a CM ratio of 30%. The company's fixed expenses are £180,000 per year.

Required

1 What are the variable expenses per unit?
2 Using the equation method:
   (a) What is the break-even point in units and sales pounds?
   (b) What sales level in units and in sales pounds is required to earn an annual profit of £60,000?
   (c) Assume that by using a more efficient shipper, the company is able to reduce its variable expenses by £4 per unit. What is the company's new break-even point in units and sales pounds?
3 Repeat Question 2 above using the unit contribution method.

E3–3 ⏱ Time allowed: 25 minutes

The Hartford Symphony Guild is planning its annual dinner-dance. The dinner-dance committee has assembled the following expected costs for the event:

Dinner (per person)	£18
Favours and programme (per person)	2
Band	2,800
Rental of ballroom	900
Professional entertainment during intermission	1,000
Tickets and advertising	1,300

The committee members would like to charge £35 per person for the evening's activities.

Required

1 Compute the break-even point for the dinner-dance (in terms of the number of persons that must attend).
2 Assume that last year only 300 persons attended the dinner-dance. If the same number attend this year, what price per ticket must be charged in order to break even?
3 Refer to the original data (£35 ticket price per person). Prepare a CVP graph for the dinner-dance from a zero level of activity up to 900 tickets sold. Number of persons should be placed on the horizontal (x) axis, and pounds should be placed on the vertical (z) axis.

E3–4   Time allowed: 15 minutes

Magic Realm Ltd has developed a new fantasy board game. The company sold 15,000 games last year at a selling price of £20 per game. Fixed costs associated with the game total £182,000 per year, and variable costs are £6 per game. Production of the game is entrusted to a printing contractor. Variable costs consist mostly of payments to this contractor.

Required

1   Prepare a profit and loss account for the game last year and compute the degree of operating leverage.
2   Management is confident that the company can sell 18,000 games next year (an increase of 3,000 games, or 20 per cent, over last year). Compute:
3   (a) The expected percentage increase in profit for next year.
      (b) The expected total pound profit for next year. (Do not prepare a profit and loss account; use the degree of operating leverage to compute your answer.)

E3–5   Time allowed: 20 minutes

Miller Company's most recent profit and loss account is shown below:

	Total	Per unit
Sales (20,000 units)	£300,000	£15.00
Less variable expenses	180,000	9.00
Contribution margin	120,000	£6.00
Less fixed expenses	70,000	
Profit	£50,000	

Required

Prepare a new profit and loss account under each of the following conditions (consider each case independently):

1   The sales volume increases by 15%.
2   The selling price decreases by £1.50 per unit, and the sales volume increases by 25%.
3   The selling price increases by £1.50 per unit, fixed expenses increase by £20,000, and the sales volume decreases by 5%.
4   The selling price increases by 12%, variable expenses increase by 60 pence per unit, and the sales volume decreases by 10%.

E3–6   Time allowed: 20 minutes

Fill in the missing amounts in each of the eight case situations below. Each case is independent of the others. (*Hint:* One way to find the missing amounts would be to prepare a contribution profit and loss account for each case, enter the known data, and then compute the missing items.)

    (a) Assume that only one product is being sold in each of the four following case situations:

Case	Units sold	Sales	Variable expenses	Contribution margin per unit	Fixed expenses	Net profit (loss)
1	15,000	£180,000	£120,000	£?	£50,000	£?
2	?	100,000	?	10	32,000	8,000
3	10,000	?	70,000	13	?	12,000
4	6,000	300,000	?	?	100,000	(10,000)

(b) Assume that more than one product is being sold in each of the four following case situations:

Case	Sales	Variable expenses	Contribution margin (per cent)	Average fixed expenses	Net profit (loss)
1	£500,000	£?	20	£?	£7,000
2	400,000	260,000	?	100,000	?
3	?	?	60	130,000	20,000
4	600,000	420,000	?	?	(5,000)

E3–7 ⏱ Time allowed: 25 minutes

Olongapo Sports Corporation is the distributor in the Philippines of two premium golf balls – the Flight Dynamic and the Sure Shot. Monthly sales and the contribution margin ratios for the two products follow:

	Product		
	Flight Dynamic	Sure Shot	Total
Sales	P150,000	P250,000	P400,000
CM ratio	80%	36%	?

Fixed expenses total P183,750 per month (the currency in the Philippines is the peso, which is denoted by P).

Required

1 Prepare a profit and loss account for the company as a whole. Use the format shown in Exhibit 3.3 and carry computations to one decimal place.
2 Compute the break-even point for the company based on the current sales mix.
3 If sales increase by P100,000 a month, by how much would you expect profit to increase? What are your assumptions?

E3–8 ⏱ Time allowed: 25 minutes

Outback Outfitters manufactures and sells recreational equipment. One of the company's products, a small camp stove, sells for £50 per unit. Variable expenses are £32 per stove, and fixed expenses associated with the stove total £108,000 per month.

Required

1 Compute the break-even point in number of stoves and in total sales pounds.
2 If the variable expenses per stove increase as a percentage of the selling price, will it result in a higher or a lower break-even point? Why? (Assume that the fixed expenses remain unchanged.)
3 At present, the company is selling 8,000 stoves per month. The sales manager is convinced that a 10 per cent reduction in the selling price would result in a 25% increase in monthly sales of stoves. Prepare two contribution profit and loss accounts, one under present operating conditions, and one as operations would appear after the proposed changes. Show both total and per unit data on your statements.
4 Refer to the data in Question 3 above. How many stoves would have to be sold at the new selling price to yield a minimum profit of £35,000 per month?

P3–9 Basic CVP analysis; graphing

⏱ Time allowed: 60 minutes

The Fashion Shoe Company operates a chain of women's shoe shops around the country. The shops carry many styles of shoes that are all sold at the same price. Sales personnel in the shops are paid a substantial commission on each pair of shoes sold (in addition to a small basic salary) in order to encourage them to be aggressive in their sales efforts.

The following cost and revenue data relate to Shop 48 and are typical of one of the company's many outlets:

Per pair of shoes	
Sales price	£30.00
Variable expenses:	
Invoice cost	£13.50
Sales commission	4.50
Total variable expenses	£18.00

Annual	
Fixed expenses:	
Advertising	£30,000
Rent	20,000
Salaries	100,000
Total fixed expenses	£150,000

Required

1. Calculate the annual break-even point in pound sales and in unit sales for Shop 48.
2. Prepare a CVP graph showing cost and revenue data for Shop 48 from a zero level of activity up to 20,000 pairs of shoes sold each year. Clearly indicate the break-even point on the graph.
3. If 12,000 pairs of shoes are sold in a year, what would be Shop 48's profit or loss?
4. The company is considering paying the store manager of Shop 48 an incentive commission of 75 pence per pair of shoes (in addition to the salesperson's commission). If this change is made, what will be the new break-even point in pound sales and in unit sales?
5. Refer to the original data. As an alternative to (4) above, the company is considering paying the store manager 50 pence commission on each pair of shoes sold in excess of the break-even point. If this change is made, what will be the shop's profit or loss if 15,000 pairs of shoes are sold?
6. Refer to the original data. The company is considering eliminating sales commissions entirely in its shops and increasing fixed salaries by £31,500 annually. If this change is made, what will be the new break-even point in pound sales and in unit sales for Shop 48? Would you recommend that the change be made? Explain.

P3–10 Basics of CVP analysis; cost structure

⏱ Time allowed: 60 minutes

Due to erratic sales of its sole product – a high-capacity battery for laptop computers – PEM Ltd has been experiencing difficulty for some time. The company's profit and loss account for the most recent month is given below:

Sales (19,500 units × £30)	£585,000
Less variable expenses	409,500
Contribution margin	175,500
Less fixed expenses	180,000
Net loss	£(4,500)

Required

1 Compute the company's CM ratio and its break-even point in both units and pounds.
2 The president believes that a £16,000 increase in the monthly advertising budget, combined with an intensified effort by the sales staff, will result in an £80,000 increase in monthly sales. If the president is right, what will be the effect on the company's monthly profit or loss? (Use the incremental approach in preparing your answer.)
3 Refer to the original data. The sales manager is convinced that a 10% reduction in the selling price, combined with an increase of £60,000 in the monthly advertising budget, will cause unit sales to double. What will the new profit and loss account look like if these changes are adopted?
4 Refer to the original data. The Marketing Department thinks that a fancy new package for the laptop computer battery would help sales. The new package would increase packaging costs by 75 pence per unit. Assuming no other changes, how many units would have to be sold each month to earn a profit of £9,750?
5 Refer to the original data. By automating certain operations, the company could reduce variable costs by £3 per unit. However, fixed costs would increase by £72,000 each month.
6 (a) Compute the new CM ratio and the new break-even point in both units and pounds.
   (b) Assume that the company expects to sell 26,000 units next month. Prepare two profit and loss accounts, one assuming that operations are not automated and one assuming that they are. (Show data on a per unit and percentage basis, as well as in total, for each alternative.)
   (c) Would you recommend that the company automate its operations? Explain.

P3–11 Sales mix assumptions; break-even analysis

Time allowed: 35 minutes

Gold Star Rice Ltd of Thailand, exports Thai rice throughout Asia. The company grows three varieties of rice – Fragrant, White and Loonzain. (The currency in Thailand is the baht, which is denoted by B.) Budgeted sales by product and in total for the coming month are shown below:

	Product							
	White		Fragrant		Loonzain		Total	
Percentage of total sales	20%		52%		28%		100%	
Percentage of sales	B150,000	100%	B390,000	100%	B210,000	100%	B750,000	100%
Less variable expenses	108,000	72%	78,000	20%	84,000	40%	270,000	36%
Contribution margin	B 42,000	28%	B312,000	80%	B126,000	60%	480,000	64%
Less fixed expenses							449,280	
Profit							B30,720	

Break-even sales: $\frac{\text{Fixed Expenses, B449,280}}{\text{CM Ratio, 0.64}} = \text{B702,000}$

As shown by these data, profit is budgeted at B30,720 for the month and break-even sales at B702,000.

Assume that actual sales for the month total B750,000 as planned. Actual sales by product are: White, B300,000; Fragrant, B180,000; and Loonzain, B270,000.

Required

1 Prepare a contribution profit and loss account for the month based on actual sales data. Present the profit and loss account in the format shown above.
2 Compute the break-even sales for the month based on your actual data.
3 Considering the fact that the company met its B750,000 sales budget for the month, the managing director is shocked at the results shown on your profit and loss account in Question 1 above. Prepare a brief memo for the MD explaining why both the operating results and break-even sales are different from what was budgeted.

P3–12 Basics of CVP analysis

Time allowed: 20 minutes
Feather Friends Ltd makes a high-quality wooden birdhouse that sells for £20 per unit. Variable costs are £8 per unit, and fixed costs total £180,000 per year.

Required

Answer the following independent questions:
1 What is the product's CM ratio?
2 Use the CM ratio to determine the break-even point in sales pounds.
3 Due to an increase in demand, the company estimates that sales will increase by £75,000 during the next year. By how much should profit increase (or net loss decrease) assuming that fixed costs do not change?
4 Assume that the operating results for last year were:

Sales	£400,000
Less variable expenses	160,000
Contribution margin	240,000
Less fixed expenses	180,000
Profit	£60,000

  (a) Compute the degree of operating leverage at the current level of sales.
  (b) The MD expects sales to increase by 20% next year. By what percentage should profit increase?
5 Refer to the original data. Assume that the company sold 18,000 units last year. The sales manager is convinced that a 10% reduction in the selling price, combined with a £30,000 increase in advertising, would cause annual sales in units to increase by one-third. Prepare two contribution profit and loss accounts, one showing the results of last year's operations and one showing the results of operations if these changes are made. Would you recommend that the company do as the sales manager suggests?
6 Refer to the original data. Assume again that the company sold 18,000 units last year. The president does not want to change the selling price. Instead, he wants to increase the sales commission by £1 per unit. He thinks that this move, combined with some increase in advertising, would increase annual sales by 25%. By how much could advertising be increased

with profits remaining unchanged? Do not prepare a profit and loss account; use the incremental analysis approach.

P3–13 The case of the elusive contribution margin

⏱ Time allowed: 30 minutes

The Shirt Works sells a large variety of tee shirts and sweat shirts. Steve Hooper, the owner, is thinking of expanding his sales by hiring local high school students, on a commission basis, to sell sweat shirts bearing the name and mascot of the local high school.

These sweat shirts would have to be ordered from the manufacturer six weeks in advance, and they could not be returned because of the unique printing required. The sweat shirts would cost Mr Hooper £8 each with a minimum order of 75 sweat shirts. Any additional sweat shirts would have to be ordered in increments of 75.

Since Mr Hooper's plan would not require any additional facilities, the only costs associated with the project would be the costs of the sweat shirts and the costs of the sales commissions. The selling price of the sweat shirts would be £13.50 each. Mr Hooper would pay the students a commission of £1.50 for each shirt sold.

Required

1 To make the project worth while, Mr Hooper would require a £1,200 profit for the first three months of the venture. What level of sales in units and in pounds would be required to reach this target profit? Show all computations.
2 Assume that the venture is undertaken and an order is placed for 75 sweat shirts. What would be Mr Hooper's break-even point in units and in sales pounds? Show computations and explain the reasoning behind your answer.

P3–14 Sensitivity analysis of profit; changes in volume

⏱ Time allowed: 30 minutes

Minden Company introduced a new product last year for which it is trying to find an optimal selling price. Marketing studies suggest that the company can increase sales by 5,000 units for each £2 reduction in the selling price. The company's present selling price is £70 per unit, and variable expenses are £40 per unit. Fixed expenses are £540,000 per year. The present annual sales volume (at the £70 selling price) is 15,000 units.

Required

1 What is the present yearly profit or loss?
2 What is the present break-even point in units and in pound sales?
3 Assuming that the marketing studies are correct, what is the maximum profit that the company can earn yearly? At how many units and at what selling price per unit would the company generate this profit?
4 What would be the break-even point in units and in pound sales using the selling price you determined in Question 3 above (e.g., the selling price at the level of maximum profits)? Why is this break-even point different from the break-even point you computed in Question 2 above?

P3–15 Graphing; incremental analysis; operating leverage

⏱ Time allowed: 60 minutes

Angie Silva has recently opened The Sandal Shop in Brisbane, Australia, a store that specializes in fashionable sandals. Angie has just received a degree in business and she is anxious to apply the principles she has learned to her business. In time, she hopes to open a chain of sandal shops. As a first step, she has prepared the following analysis for her new store:

Sales price per pair of sandals	£40
Variable expenses per pair of sandals	16
Contribution margin per pair of sandals	£24
Fixed expenses per year:	
Building rental	£15,000
Equipment depreciation	7,000
Selling	20,000
Administrative	18,000
Total fixed expenses	£60,000

Required

1 How many pairs of sandals must be sold each year to break even? What does this represent in total pound sales?

2 Angie has decided that she must earn at least £18,000 the first year to justify her time and effort. How many pairs of sandals must be sold to reach this target profit?

3 Angie now has two salespersons working in the store – one full time and one part time. It will cost her an additional £8,000 per year to convert the part-time position to a full-time position. Angie believes that the change would bring in an additional £25,000 in sales each year. Should she convert the position? Use the incremental approach (do not prepare a profit and loss account).

4 Refer to the original data. During the first year, the store sold only 3,000 pairs of sandals and reported the following operating results:

Sales (3,000 pairs)	£120,000
Less variable expenses	48,000
Contribution margin	72,000
Less fixed expenses	60,000
Profit	£12,000

5 (a) What is the store's degree of operating leverage?

   (b) Angie is confident that with a more intense sales effort and with a more creative advertising programme she can increase sales by 50% next year. What would be the expected percentage increase in profit? Use the degree of operating leverage to compute your answer.

P3–16 Sales mix; commission structure; break-even point

⏱ Time allowed: 60 minutes

Carbex Ltd produces cutlery sets out of high-quality wood and steel. The company makes a standard cutlery set and a deluxe set and sells them to retail department stores throughout the country. The standard set sells for £60, and the deluxe set sells for £75.

The variable expenses associated with each set are given below (in cost per set):

	Standard	Deluxe
Production costs	£ 15.00	£30.00
Sales commissions (15% of sales price)	9.00	11.25
The company's fixed		
Advertising	£105,000	
Depreciation	21,700	
Administrative	63,000	

Salespersons are paid on a commission basis to encourage them to be aggressive in their sales efforts. Mary Parsons, the financial vice president, watches sales commissions carefully and has noted that they have risen steadily over the last year. For this reason, she was shocked to find that even though sales have increased, profits for the current month – May – are down substantially from April. Sales, in sets, for the last two months are given below:

	Standard	Deluxe	Total
April	4,000	2,000	6,000
May	1,000	5,000	6,000

Required

1 Prepare a profit and loss account for April and a profit and loss account for May. Use the contribution format, with the following headings:

	Standard		Deluxe		Total	
Amount	Percentage	Amount	Percentage	Amount	Percentage
Sales etc.						

Place the fixed expenses only in the Total column. Carry percentage computations to one decimal place. Do not show percentages for the fixed expenses.

2 Explain why there is a difference in profit between the two months, even though the same total number of sets was sold in each month.

3 What can be done to the sales commissions to optimize the sales mix?

4 (a) Using April's figures, what was the break-even point for the month in sales pounds?

  (b) Has May's break-even point gone up or down from that of April? Explain your answer without calculating the break-even point for May.

P3–17 Various CVP questions: break-even point; cost structure; target sales

⏱ Time allowed: 60 minutes

Northwood Company manufactures basketballs. The company has a standard ball that sells for £25. At present, the standard ball is manufactured in a small plant that relies heavily on direct labour workers. Thus, variable costs are high, totalling £15 per ball.

Last year, the company sold 30,000 standard balls, with the following results:

Sales (30,000 standard balls)	£750,000
Less variable expenses	450,000
Contribution margin	300,000
Less fixed expenses	210,000
Profit	£90,000

Required

1 Compute (a) the CM ratio and the break-even point in balls (b), and the degree of operating leverage at last year's level of sales.

2 Due to an increase in labour rates, the company estimates that variable costs will increase by £3 per ball next year. If this change takes place and the selling price per ball remains constant at £25, what will be the new CM ratio and break-even point in balls?

3   Refer to the data in Question 2 above. If the expected change in variable costs takes place, how many balls will have to be sold next year to earn the same profit (£90,000) as last year?

4   Refer again to the data in Question 2 above. The managing director feels that the company must raise the selling price on the standard balls. If Northwood Company wants to maintain the same CM ratio as last year, what selling price per ball must it charge next year to cover the increased labour costs?

5   Refer to the original data. The company is discussing the construction of a new, automated plant to manufacture the standard balls. The new plant would slash variable costs per ball by 40%, but it would cause fixed costs to double in amount per year. If the new plant is built, what would be the company's new CM ratio and new break-even point in balls?

6   Refer to the data in Question 5 above.

7   (a) If the new plant is built, how many balls will have to be sold next year to earn the same profit (£90,000) as last year?

    (b) Assume the new plant is built and that next year the company manufactures and sells 30,000 balls (the same number as sold last year). Prepare a contribution profit and loss account and compute the degree of operating leverage.

    (c) If you were a member of top management, would you have voted in favour of constructing the new plant? Explain.

P3–18 Changing levels of fixed and variable costs

Time allowed: 30 minutes

Neptune Company produces toys and other items for use in beach and resort areas. A small, inflatable toy has come onto the market that the company is anxious to produce and sell. Enough capacity exists in the company's plant to produce 16,000 units of the toy each month. Variable costs to manufacture and sell one unit would be £1.25, and fixed costs associated with the toy would total £35,000 per month.

The company's Marketing Department predicts that demand for the new toy will exceed the 16,000 units that the company is able to produce. Additional manufacturing space can be rented from another company at a fixed cost of £1,000 per month. Variable costs in the rented facility would total £1.40 per unit, due to somewhat less efficient operations than in the main plant. The new toy will sell for £3 per unit.

Required

1   Compute the monthly break-even point for the new toy in units and in total pound sales. Show all computations in good form.

2   How many units must be sold each month to make a monthly profit of £12,000?

3   If the sales manager receives a bonus of 10 pence for each unit sold in excess of the break-even point, how many units must be sold each month to earn a return of 25% on the monthly investment in fixed costs?

Chapter 2
Cost terms and concepts

▶ LO Learning **objectives**

After studying Chapter 2, you should be able to:
1 Understand the need for costing for external financial reporting
2 Identify each of the three basic cost elements involved in the manufacture of a product
3 Distinguish between product costs and period costs and give examples of each
4 Understand the basics of cost behaviour
5 Identify and give examples of variable costs and fixed costs
6 Define cost classifications used in making decisions: differential costs, opportunity costs and sunk costs

Concepts **in Context**

This chapter introduces issues concerned with the classification of costs. These issues may be controversial. For example, the British Broadcasting Corporation (BBC) has been accused of concealing the true costs of its individual channels by reporting the cost of items such as news gathering, marketing and publicity under separate headings instead of allocating them as overheads to each channel. It was alleged that the corporation wished to reduce the apparent costs both of expanding into digital broadcasting and the budget of BBC1, the channel that competes with the main commercial broadcasters. The BBC responded by claiming that the new format reflected the corporation's internal reporting system and that the new format was 'more transparent'.[1]

© Anthony Baggett

In introductory financial accounting, you learn that firms prepare periodic financial reports for creditors, shareholders and others to show the financial condition of the firm and the firm's earnings performance over some specified interval. Since firms are generally legally obliged to produce financial statements, many organizations may only produce cost data for such *financial reporting* purposes. The financial accounting concepts of cost classification will concern us in the first part of the chapter.

Later in this chapter, we will also consider other ways of looking at costs. For example, how do costs *behave* especially with changes in the level of activity? Which costs are fixed and which are variable and over what range of activity level?

Finally, we will explore different concepts of costs classified according to the principle of 'decision-relevance'. The decision-relevance approach may suggest that the costs collected for finance reporting purposes may not be either appropriate or sufficient for decision-making purposes.[2]

LO 1 Costing for financial reporting purposes: an example from manufacturing

Manufacturing costs

Costs are associated with all types of organizations – business, non-business, manufacturing, retail and service. Generally, the kinds of costs incurred and the way in which these costs are classified depends on the type of organization involved. Management accounting is as applicable to one type of organization as to another. The focus in this chapter is on manufacturing companies, since their basic activities include most of the activities found in other types of business organizations. Manufacturing companies are involved in acquiring raw materials, producing finished goods, marketing, distributing, billing and almost every other business activity. Therefore, an understanding of costs in a manufacturing company can be very helpful in understanding costs in other types of organizations. Most manufacturing companies divide manufacturing costs into three broad categories: direct materials, direct labour, and manufacturing overhead. A discussion of each of these categories follows.

LO 2 Direct materials

The materials that go into the final product are called raw materials. This term is somewhat misleading, since it seems to imply unprocessed natural resources like wood pulp or iron ore. Actually, raw materials refer to any materials that are used in the final product; and the finished product of one company can become the raw materials of another company. Direct materials are those materials that become an integral part of the finished product and that can be physically and conveniently traced to it. Sometimes it isn't worth the effort to trace the costs of relatively insignificant materials to the end products. Such minor items would include the solder used to make electrical connections in a TV. Materials such as solder and glue are called indirect materials and are included as part of manufacturing overhead, which is discussed later in this section.

Direct labour

The term direct labour is reserved for those labour costs that can easily (i.e., physically and conveniently) be traced to individual units of product. Direct labour is sometimes called *touch labour*, since direct labour workers typically touch the product while it is being made. The labour costs of assembly-line workers, for example, would be direct labour costs, as would the labour costs of carpenters, bricklayers and machine operators.

Labour costs that cannot be physically traced to the creation of products, or that can be traced only at great cost and inconvenience, are termed indirect labour and treated as part of manufacturing overhead, along with indirect materials. Indirect labour includes the labour costs of caretakers, supervisors, materials handlers and night security guards. Although the efforts of these workers are essential to production, it would either be impractical or impossible accurately to trace their costs to specific units of product. Hence, such labour costs are treated as indirect labour.

Manufacturing overhead

Manufacturing overhead, the third element of manufacturing cost, includes all costs of manufacturing except direct materials and direct labour. Manufacturing overhead includes items such as indirect materials; indirect labour; maintenance and repairs on production equipment; and heat and light, property taxes, depreciation and insurance on manufacturing facilities. A company also incurs costs for heat and light, property taxes, insurance, depreciation and so forth, associated with its selling and administrative functions, but these costs are not included as part of manufacturing overhead. Only those costs associated with *operating the factory* are included in the manufacturing overhead category.

Various names are used for manufacturing overhead, such as *indirect manufacturing cost, factory overhead*, and *factory burden*. All of these terms are synonymous with *manufacturing overhead*.

Manufacturing overhead combined with direct labour is called conversion cost. This term stems from the fact that direct labour costs and overhead costs are incurred in the conversion of materials into finished products. Direct labour combined with direct materials is called prime cost.

Non-manufacturing costs

Generally, non-manufacturing costs are subclassified into two categories:

1 Marketing or selling costs
2 Administrative costs

Marketing or selling costs include all costs necessary to secure customer orders and get the finished product or service into the hands of the customer. These costs are often called *order-getting* and *order-filling costs*. Examples of marketing costs include advertising, shipping, sales travel, sales commissions, sales salaries and costs of finished goods warehouses.

Administrative costs include all executive, organizational and clerical costs associated with the *general management* of an organization rather than with manufacturing, marketing or selling. Examples of administrative costs include executive compensation, general accounting, secretarial, public relations and similar costs involved in the overall general administration of the organization *as a whole*.

Product costs versus period costs

LO 3

In addition to the distinction between manufacturing and non-manufacturing costs, there are other ways to look at costs. For instance, they can also be classified as either product costs or period costs. To understand the difference between product costs and period costs, we must first refresh our understanding of the matching principle from financial accounting.

Generally, costs are recognized as expenses on the *profit and loss account* (sometimes alternatively known as the *income statement*)[3] in the period that benefits from the cost. For example, if a company pays for liability insurance in advance for two years, the entire amount is not considered an expense of the year in which the payment is made. Instead, half of the cost would be recognized as an expense each year. This is because both years – not just the first – benefit from the insurance payment. The unexpensed portion of the insurance payment is carried on the balance sheet as an asset called prepaid insurance. You should be familiar with this type of *accrual* from your financial accounting course.

The *matching principle* is based on the accrual concept and states that *costs incurred to generate a particular revenue should be recognized as expenses in the same period that the revenue is recognized*. This means that if a cost is incurred to acquire or make something that will eventually be sold, then the cost should be recognized as an expense only when the sale takes place – that is, when the benefit occurs. Such costs are called *product costs*.

Product costs

For financial accounting purposes, product costs include all the costs that are involved in acquiring or making a product. In the case of manufactured goods, these costs consist of direct materials, direct labour and manufacturing overhead. Product costs are viewed as 'attaching' to units of product as the goods are

purchased or manufactured, and they remain attached as the goods go into stock awaiting sale. So, initially, product costs are assigned to a stock account on the balance sheet. When the goods are sold, the costs are released from stock as expenses (typically called cost of goods sold) and matched against sales revenue. Since product costs are initially assigned to stocks, they are also known as *stock-related costs*.

We want to emphasize that product costs are not necessarily treated as expenses in the period in which they are incurred. Rather, as explained above, they are treated as expenses in the period in which the related products *are sold*. This means that a product cost such as direct materials or direct labour might be incurred during one period but not treated as an expense until a following period when the completed product is sold.

Period costs

Period costs are all the costs that are not included in product costs. These costs are expensed on the profit and loss account in the period in which they are incurred, using the usual rules of accrual accounting you have already learned in financial accounting. Period costs are not included as part of the cost of either purchased or manufactured goods. Sales commissions and office rent are good examples of the kind of costs we are talking about. Neither commissions nor office rent are included as part of the cost of purchased or manufactured goods. Rather, both items are treated as expenses on the profit and loss account in the period in which they are incurred. Thus, they are said to be period costs.

As suggested above, *all selling and administrative expenses are considered to be period costs*. Therefore, advertising, executive salaries, sales commissions, public relations, and other non-manufacturing costs discussed

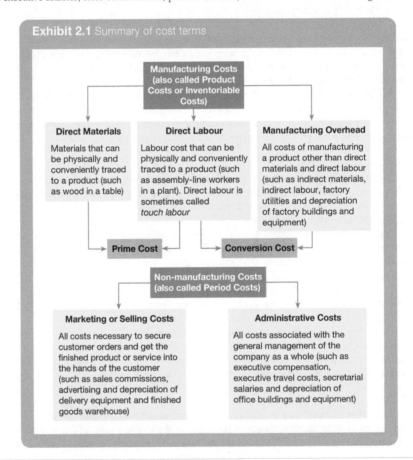

Exhibit 2.1 Summary of cost terms

Manufacturing Costs (also called Product Costs or Inventoriable Costs)

Direct Materials

Materials that can be physically and conveniently traced to a product (such as wood in a table)

Direct Labour

Labour cost that can be physically and conveniently traced to a product (such as assembly-line workers in a plant). Direct labour is sometimes called *touch labour*

Manufacturing Overhead

All costs of manufacturing a product other than direct materials and direct labour (such as indirect materials, indirect labour, factory utilities and depreciation of factory buildings and equipment)

Prime Cost   **Conversion Cost**

Non-manufacturing Costs (also called Period Costs)

Marketing or Selling Costs

All costs necessary to secure customer orders and get the finished product or service into the hands of the customer (such as sales commissions, advertising and depreciation of delivery equipment and finished goods warehouse)

Administrative Costs

All costs associated with the general management of the company as a whole (such as executive compensation, executive travel costs, secretarial salaries and depreciation of office buildings and equipment)

earlier would all be period costs. They will appear on the profit and loss account as expenses in the period in which they are incurred.

Exhibit 2.1 contains a summary of the cost terms that we have introduced so far.

Product costs – a closer look

To understand product costs more fully, it will be helpful at this point to look briefly at the flow of costs in a manufacturing company. By doing so, we will be able to see how product costs move through the various accounts and affect the balance sheet and the profit and loss account in the course of producing and selling products.

Exhibit 2.2 illustrates the flow of costs in a manufacturing company. Raw materials purchases are recorded in the Raw Materials inventory account. When raw materials are used in production, their costs are transferred to the Work in Progress inventory account as direct materials. Notice that direct labour cost and manufacturing overhead cost are added directly to Work in Progress. Work in Progress can be viewed most simply as an assembly line where workers are stationed and where products slowly take shape as they move from one end of the assembly line to the other. The direct materials, direct labour and manufacturing overhead costs added to Work in Progress in Exhibit 2.2 are the costs needed to complete these products as they move along this assembly line.

Notice from the exhibit that as goods are completed, their cost is transferred from Work in Progress into Finished Goods. Here the goods await sale to a customer. As goods are sold, their cost is then transferred from Finished Goods into Cost of Goods Sold. It is at this point that the various material, labour and overhead costs that are required to make the product are finally treated as expenses.

Stock/inventory-related costs

As stated earlier, product costs are often called stock-related (or inventoriable[4]) costs. The reason is that these costs go directly into inventory accounts as they are incurred (first into Work in Progress and then into Finished Goods), rather than going into expense accounts. Thus, they are termed **stock-related costs**. *This is a key concept in management accounting, since such costs can end up on the balance sheet as assets if goods are only*

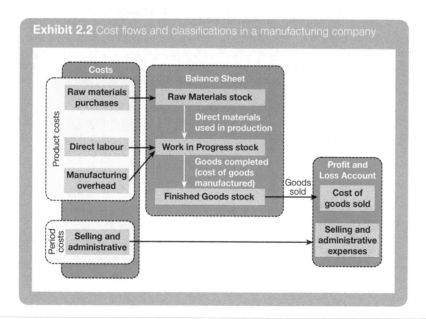

Exhibit 2.2 Cost flows and classifications in a manufacturing company

partially completed or are unsold at the end of a period. At the end of the period, the materials, labour and overhead costs that are associated with the units in the Work in Progress and Finished Goods stock accounts will appear on the balance sheet as part of the company's assets. As explained earlier, these costs will not become expenses until later when the goods are completed and sold.

Focus on Business Practice
The full cost of the 2010 Gulf of Mexico oil spill

© M

When management accountants talk about the full costs of a product or service this usually means that all costs – materials, labour and a portion of overhead – are included in the cost of the product/service. In more basic terms, this means that whatever the cost object is, accountants ensure that the cost calculated includes as many costs as possible (if not all). Consider for a moment an event like the oil spill from a BP-owned well in the Gulf of Mexico in 2010. How could an accountant begin to work out the full cost of this environmental disaster? The first thing to do would be to try to think of all the costs which might arise. Prior to this oil spill, the Exxon Valdez tanker leak off Alaska in 1989 was the biggest oil spill in the US. The full cost of the clean up then was $4 billion, more than 600 times what the oil lost was worth at the time. In the Gulf of Mexico case, which at the time of writing is still ongoing, a picture of the full costs of the disaster is beginning to emerge. The first cost is the cost of the 3 million or so litres of oil per day being lost. The clean-up and containment costs are in the order of $5–10 million per day. As of early June 2010, BP themselves had incurred costs of $1.43 billion in clean-up, claims and other costs. Lawsuits to the tune of $25 billion have been filed against BP and related companies. Lost tourism and fishing in and around the Gulf area accounts for $8–12 billion in cost. In addition to the mentioned costs, the costs of extra personnel and administrative staff involved might also be included. While this example does not portray a product or service, it does highlight the difficulties faced by management accountants in calculating any full cost. This does not mean they abandon efforts, however, as in most cases a reasonably accurate full cost figure can be determined.[5]

Exercise: Look up other examples of cases where large-scale damage has been caused by an industrial or environmental type accident/disaster. Try to find out the full costs to the company and/or the community/environment.

As shown in Exhibit 2.2, selling and administrative expenses are not involved in the manufacture of a product. For this reason, they are not treated as product costs but rather as period costs that go directly into expense accounts as they are incurred.

Thus far, we have been mainly concerned with classifications of manufacturing costs for the purpose of determining inventory valuations on the balance sheet and cost of goods sold on the profit and loss account of external financial reports. There are, however, many other purposes for which costs are used, and each

Exhibit 2.3 Summary of cost classifications

Purpose of cost classification	Cost classifications
Preparing external financial statements	• Product costs (inventoriable)
	• Direct materials
	• Direct labour
	• Manufacturing overheads
	• Period costs (expensed)
	• Non-manufacturing costs
	• Marketing or selling costs
	• Administrative costs
Predicting cost behaviour in response to changes in activity	• Variable cost (proportional to activity)
	• Fixed cost (constant in total)
Assigning costs to cost objects such as departments or products	• Direct cost (can easily be traced)
	• Indirect cost (cannot easily be traced; must be allocated)
Making decisions	• Differential cost (differs between alternatives)
	• Sunk cost (past cost not affected by a decision)
	• Opportunity cost (forgone benefit)

purpose requires a different classification of costs. We will consider several different purposes for cost classifications in the remaining sections of this chapter. These purposes and the corresponding cost classifications are summarized in Exhibit 2.3. To maintain focus, we suggest that you refer back to this exhibit frequently as you progress through the rest of this chapter.

Cost classifications for predicting cost behaviour

LO 4

Quite frequently, it is necessary to predict how a certain cost will behave in response to a change in activity. Cost behaviour means how a cost will react or respond to changes in the level of business activity. As the activity level rises and falls, a particular cost may rise and fall as well – or it may remain constant. For planning purposes, a manager must be able to anticipate which of these will happen; and if a cost can be expected to change, the manager must know by how much it will change. To help make such distinctions, costs are often categorized as variable or fixed.

Variable cost

LO 5

A variable cost is a cost that varies, in total, in direct proportion to changes in the level of activity. The activity can be expressed in many ways, such as units produced, units sold, miles driven, beds occupied, lines of print, hours worked, and so forth. A good example of a variable cost is direct materials. The cost of direct materials used during a period will vary, in total, in direct proportion to the number of units that are produced. To illustrate this idea, consider the example of a car factory. Each car requires one battery. As the output of cars increases and decreases, the number of batteries used will increase and decrease proportionately. If car production goes up 10%, then the number of batteries used will also go up 10%. The concept of a variable cost is shown in graphic form in Exhibit 2.4.

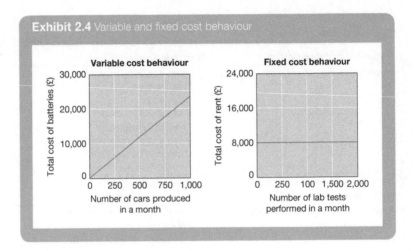

Exhibit 2.4 Variable and fixed cost behaviour

It is important to note that when we speak of a cost as being variable, we mean the *total* cost rises and falls as the activity level rises and falls. This idea is presented below, assuming that a battery costs £24:

Number of cars produced	Cost per battery	Total variable cost-batteries
1	£24	£24
500	24	12,000
1,000	24	24,000

One interesting aspect of variable cost behaviour is that a variable cost is constant if expressed on a *per unit* basis. Observe from the tabulation above that the per unit cost of batteries remains constant at £24 even though the total amount of cost involved increases and decreases with activity.

There are many examples of costs that are variable with respect to the products and services provided by a company. In a manufacturing company, variable costs include items such as direct materials and some elements of manufacturing overhead such as lubricants, shipping costs and sales commissions. For the present we will also assume that direct labour is a variable cost, although as we shall see later, direct labour may act more like a fixed cost in many situations. In a merchandising company, variable costs include items such as cost of goods sold, commissions to salespersons and billing costs. In a hospital, the variable costs of providing healthcare services to patients would include the costs of the supplies, drugs, meals and, perhaps, nursing services.

The activity causing changes in a variable cost need not be how much output is produced or sold. For example, the wages paid to employees at a video outlet will depend on the number of hours the shop is open and not strictly on the number of videos rented. In this case, we would say that wage costs are variable with respect to the hours of operation. Nevertheless, when we say that a cost is variable, we ordinarily mean it is variable with respect to the volume of revenue-generating output – in other words, how many units are produced and sold, how many videos are rented, how many patients are treated and so on.

Fixed cost

A fixed cost is a cost that remains constant, in total, regardless of changes in the level of activity. Unlike variable costs, fixed costs are not affected by changes in activity. Consequently, as the activity level rises and falls, the fixed costs remain constant in total amount unless influenced by some outside force, such as price changes. Rent is a good example of a fixed cost. Suppose a hospital rents a machine for £8,000 per month that tests blood samples for the presence of leukaemia cells. The £8,000 monthly rental cost will be sustained regardless of the number of tests that may be performed during the month. The concept of a fixed cost is shown in graphic form in Exhibit 2.4.

Very few costs are completely fixed. Most will change if there is a large enough change in activity. For example, suppose that the capacity of the leukaemia diagnostic machine at the hospital is 2,000 tests per month. If the clinic wishes to perform more than 2,000 tests in a month, it would be necessary to rent an additional machine, which would cause a jump in the fixed costs. When we say a cost is fixed, we mean it is fixed within some *relevant range*. The relevant range is the range of activity within which the assumptions about variable and fixed costs are valid. For example, the assumption that the rent for diagnostic machines is £8,000 per month is valid within the relevant range of 0 to 2,000 tests per month.

Fixed costs can create difficulties if it becomes necessary to express the costs on a per unit basis. This is because if fixed costs are expressed on a per unit basis, they will react inversely with changes in activity. In the hospital, for example, the average cost per test will fall as the number of tests performed increases. This is because the £8,000 rental cost will be spread over more tests. Conversely, as the number of tests performed in the clinic declines, the average cost per test will rise as the £8,000 rental cost is spread over fewer tests. This concept is illustrated in the table below:

Monthly rental cost	Number of tests performed	Average cost per test
£8,000	10	£800
8,000	500	16
8,000	2,000	4

Note that if the hospital performs only ten tests each month, the rental cost of the equipment will average £800 per test. But if 2,000 tests are performed each month, the average cost will drop to only £4 per test. More will be said later about the problems created for both the accountant and the manager by this variation in unit costs.

Examples of fixed costs include straight-line depreciation, insurance, property taxes, rent, supervisory salaries, administrative salaries and advertising.

A summary of both variable and fixed cost behaviour is presented in Exhibit 2.5.

Exhibit 2.5 Summary of variable and fixed cost behaviour

	Behaviour of the cost (within the relevant range)	
Cost	In total	Per unit
Variable cost	Total variable cost increases and decreases in proportion to changes in the activity level.	Variable costs remain constant per unit.
Fixed cost	Total fixed cost is not affected by changes in the activity level within the relevant range.	Fixed costs decrease per unit as the activity level rises and increases per unit as the activity level falls.

Focus on Business Practice

The cost of phone calls

© Neustockimages

Because of national and European regulation of the telecommunications industry, considerable research has been published on calculating the cost of providing telecommunications such as phone, text and other forms of communication. In a recent report, the UK regulator discussed the way that these costs have been calculated using many of the terms used in this and subsequent chapters (direct cost, variable cost, common cost allocation, overheads, avoidable costs, and so on…). As Exhibit 2.6 shows, they have estimated cost behaviour for different types of calls and networks. The exhibit shows how the cost structure varies between different types of traffic and networks. Much of the debate between the regulators and providers concerns the *allocation* of 'common costs' rather than direct costs which may be estimated using economic cost models.

Exercise: Note how the discussions of fair phone tariffs combine the *technological character* of telecommunications, which helps to explain cost behaviour, with *commercial* decisions based on marketing and accounting issues.

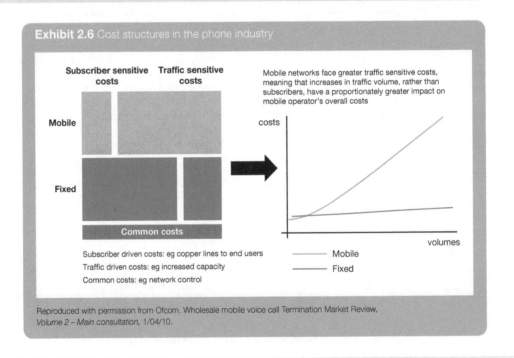

Exhibit 2.6 Cost structures in the phone industry

Subscriber driven costs: eg copper lines to end users
Traffic driven costs: eg increased capacity
Common costs: eg network control

Reproduced with permission from Ofcom. Wholesale mobile voice call Termination Market Review, *Volume 2 – Main consultation*, 1/04/10.

The contribution format

Once the manager has separated costs into fixed and variable elements, what is done with the data? We have already answered this question somewhat by showing how a cost formula can be used to predict costs. To answer this question more fully would require most of the remainder of this text, since much of what the manager does rests in some way on an understanding of cost behaviour. One immediate and very significant application of the ideas we have developed, however, is found in a new profit statement format known as the contribution approach. The unique thing about the contribution approach is that it provides the manager with a profit statement geared directly to cost behaviour.

Why a new profit and loss statement format?

The *traditional approach* to the profit and loss statement is not organized in terms of cost behaviour. Rather, it is organized in a 'functional' format – emphasizing the functions of production, administration and sales in the classification and presentation of cost data. No attempt is made to distinguish between the behaviour of costs included under each functional heading. Under the heading 'Administrative expense', for example, one can expect to find both variable and fixed costs lumped together.

Although a profit and loss statement prepared in the functional format may be useful for external reporting purposes, it has serious limitations when used for internal purposes. Internally, the manager needs cost data organized in a format that will facilitate planning, control and decision making. These tasks are much easier when cost data are available in a fixed and variable format. The contribution approach to the profit and loss statement has been developed in response to this need.

The contribution approach

Exhibit 2.7 illustrates the contribution approach to the profit and loss statement with a simple example, along with the traditional approach discussed above.

Notice that the contribution approach separates costs into fixed and variable categories, first deducting variable expenses from sales to obtain what is known as the *contribution margin*. The contribution margin is

Exhibit 2.7 Comparison of the contribution profit statement with the traditional profit statement

Traditional approach (costs organized by function)			Contribution approach (costs organized by behaviour)		
Sales		£12,000	Sales		£12,000
Less cost of goods sold		6,000*	Less variable expenses:		
Gross margin		6,000	Variable production	£2,000	
Less operating expenses:			Variable selling	600	
Selling	£3,100*		Variable administrative	400	3,000
Administrative	1,900*	5,000	Contribution margin		9,000
Net profit		£1,000	Less fixed expenses:		
			Fixed production	4,000	
			Fixed selling	2,500	
			Fixed administrative	1,500	8,000
			Net profit		£1,000

*Contains both variable and fixed expenses. This is the profit statement for a manufacturing company; thus, when the profit statement is placed in the contribution format, the 'cost of goods sold' figure is divided between variable production costs and fixed production costs. If this were the profit statement for a *merchandising* company (which simply purchases completed goods from a supplier), then the cost of goods sold would *all* be variable.

the amount remaining from sales revenues after variable expenses have been deducted. This amount *contributes* towards covering fixed expenses and then towards profits for the period.

The contribution approach to the profit and loss statement is used as an internal planning and decision-making tool. Its emphasis on costs by behaviour facilitates cost–volume–profit analysis, which we will tackle in Chapter 3. The approach is also very useful in appraising management performance, in segmented reporting of profit data, and in budgeting. Moreover, the contribution approach helps managers organize data pertinent to all kinds of special decisions such as product-line analysis, pricing, use of scarce resources, and make or buy analysis. All of these topics are covered in later chapters.

Managers use costs organized by behaviour as a basis for many decisions. To facilitate this use, the profit statement can be prepared in a contribution format. The contribution format classifies costs on the profit and loss statement by cost behaviour (i.e., variable versus fixed) rather than by the functions of production, administration, and sales.

Cost classifications for decision-relevance

Costs are an important feature of many business decisions. In making decisions, it is essential to have a firm grasp of the concepts *differential cost, opportunity cost* and *sunk cost.*

Differential cost and revenue

Decisions involve choosing between alternatives. In business decisions, each alternative will have certain costs and benefits that must be compared to the costs and benefits of the other available alternatives. A difference in costs between any two alternatives is known as a **differential cost**. A difference in revenues between any two alternatives is known as **differential revenue**.

A differential cost is also known as an **incremental cost**, although technically an incremental cost should refer only to an increase in cost from one alternative to another; decreases in cost should be referred to as *decremental costs*. Differential cost is a broader term, encompassing both cost increases (incremental costs) and cost decreases (decremental costs) between alternatives.

The accountant's differential cost concept can be compared to the economist's marginal cost concept. In speaking of changes in cost and revenue, the economist employs the terms *marginal cost* and *marginal revenue*. The revenue that can be obtained from selling one more unit of product is called marginal revenue, and the cost involved in producing one more unit of product is called marginal cost. The economist's marginal concept is basically the same as the accountant's differential concept applied to a single unit of output.

Differential costs can be either fixed or variable. To illustrate, assume that Nature Way Cosmetics is thinking about changing its marketing method from distribution through retailers to distribution by door-to-door direct sale. Present costs and revenues are compared to projected costs and revenues in the following table:

	Retailer distribution (present)	Direct sale distribution (proposed)	Differential costs and revenues
Revenues (V)	£700,000	£800,000	£100,000
Cost of goods sold (V)	350,000	400,000	50,000
Advertising (F)	80,000	45,000	(35,000)
Commissions (V)	0	40,000	40,000
Warehouse depreciation (F)	50,000	80,000	30,000
Other expenses (F)	60,000	60,000	0
Total	540,000	625,000	85,000
Profit	£160,000	£175,000	£15,000

V = Variable; F = Fixed

According to the above analysis, the differential revenue is £100,000 and the differential costs total £85,000, leaving a positive differential profit of £15,000 under the proposed marketing plan.

The decision of whether Nature Way Cosmetics should stay with the present retail distribution or switch to door-to-door direct selling could be made on the basis of the profits of the two alternatives. As we see in the above analysis, the profit under the present distribution method is £160,000, whereas the profit under door-to-door direct selling is estimated to be £175,000. Therefore, the door-to-door direct distribution method is preferred, since it would result in £15,000 higher profit. Note that we would have arrived at exactly the same conclusion by simply focusing on the differential revenues, differential costs and differential profit, which also show a £15,000 advantage for the direct selling method.

In general, only the differences between alternatives are relevant in decisions. Those items that are the same under all alternatives and that are not affected by the decision can be ignored. For example, in the Nature Way Cosmetics example above, the 'Other expenses' category, which is £60,000 under both alternatives, can be ignored, since it has no effect on the decision. If it were removed from the calculations, the door-to-door direct selling method would still be preferred by £15,000.

Opportunity cost

Opportunity cost is the potential benefit that is given up when one alternative is selected over another. To illustrate this important concept, consider the following examples:

Example 1

Vicki has a part-time job that pays her £100 per week while attending college. She would like to spend a week at the beach during spring break, and her employer has agreed to give her the time off, but without pay. The £100 in lost wages would be an opportunity cost of taking the week off to be at the beach.

Example 2

Suppose that Tesco is considering investing a large sum of money in land that may be a site for a future shop. Rather than invest the funds in land, the company could invest the funds in high-grade securities. If the land is acquired, the opportunity cost will be the investment income that could have been realized if the securities had been purchased instead.

Example 3

Steve is employed with a company that pays him a salary of £20,000 per year. He is thinking about leaving the company and going to university. Since going to university would require that he give up his £20,000 salary, the forgone salary would be an opportunity cost of seeking further education.

Opportunity cost is not usually entered in the accounting records of an organization, but it is a cost that must be explicitly considered in every decision a manager makes. Virtually every alternative has some opportunity cost attached to it. In Example 3 above, for instance, if Steve decides to stay at his job, there still is an opportunity cost involved: it is the greater income that could be realized in future years as a result of returning to university.

Sunk cost

A sunk cost is a cost *that has already been incurred* and that cannot be changed by any decision made now or in the future. Since sunk costs cannot be changed by any decision, they are not differential costs. Therefore, they can and should be ignored when making a decision.

To illustrate a sunk cost, assume that a company paid £50,000 several years ago for a special-purpose machine. The machine was used to make a product that is now obsolete and is no longer being sold. Even though in hindsight the purchase of the machine may have been unwise, no amount of regret can undo that decision. And it would be folly to continue making the obsolete product in a misguided attempt to 'recover' the original cost of the machine. In short, the £50,000 originally paid for the machine has already been incurred and cannot be a differential cost in any future decisions. For this reason, such costs are said to be sunk and should be ignored in decisions.

We will explore some applications of relevant cost principles further in Chapter 4 when making a number of important business decisions such as replacing equipment, make-or-buy, special orders and dealing with capacity constraints.

Focus on Business Practice

Cost considerations at a retail florist

© Catherine Yeulet

Terri, the owner of a retail florist shop, has been trying to decide for some time whether she should continue to use a local courier service to deliver flowers to customers or buy a delivery van and use one of her employees to make the deliveries. At a recent family dinner, she brought up the subject of the delivery van with her brother-in-law, who fancies himself as an expert on all management subjects. He grabbed this opportunity to impress on Terri his understanding of costs.

In rapid-fire succession, Terri's brother-in-law told her that the fees paid to the courier to deliver flowers are a variable cost and a period cost, but the costs of the flowers are product costs rather than period costs, even though the flower costs are also variable costs. On the other hand, the depreciation of the delivery van would be a fixed cost and a period cost. And while the fuel for the truck would be a variable cost and a differential cost, the wages of the person making the deliveries would be a fixed cost, not a differential cost, and would involve an opportunity cost. At this point, Terri excused herself, pleading that she had to help in the kitchen. Terri felt that her brother-in-law's comments were more confusing than helpful, but she knew that she could no longer put off the decision about the delivery van.

Exercise: Referring to Exhibit 2.3, which costs *should* be considered in this decision?

Focus on Business Practice

Hotel accounting and costs

© Elena Elisseeva

In a recent project, an author was undertaking research into management accounting in the hospitality industry. He noted that many hotels saw room costs in terms of servicing the room and the ongoing expense of maintaining the fixtures and fittings. They did not have an operational measure of the biggest fixed cost of all – the cost of the land and buildings. In the short run, this approach seemed logical as the managers could reduce some of the costs of servicing the rooms through better labour scheduling but they could not (in the short-term) *avoid* the fixed costs of the building itself.

Exercise: In what sense are room servicing costs *variable* in that they vary with activity levels? What other room-related costs are also variable?

Summary

- In this chapter, we have looked at some of the ways in which managers classify costs. How the costs will be used – for preparing external reports, predicting cost behaviour, assigning costs to cost objects, or decision making – will dictate how the costs will be classified.

- For purposes of valuing stocks and determining expenses for the balance sheet and profit and loss account, costs are classified as either product costs or period costs. Product costs are assigned to stocks and are considered assets until the products are sold. At the point of sale, product costs become costs of goods sold on the profit and loss account. In contrast, following the usual accrual practices, period costs are taken directly to the profit and loss account as expenses in the period in which they are incurred.

- For purposes of predicting cost behaviour – how costs will react to changes in activity – managers commonly classify costs into two categories – variable and fixed. Variable costs, in total, are strictly proportional to activity. Thus, the variable cost per unit is constant. Fixed costs, in total, remain at the same level for changes in activity that occur within the relevant range. Thus, the average fixed cost per unit decreases as the number of units increases.

- For purposes of assigning costs to cost objects such as products or departments, costs are classified as direct or indirect. Direct costs can conveniently be traced to the cost objects. Indirect costs cannot conveniently be traced to cost objects.

- For purposes of making decisions, the concepts of differential costs and revenue, opportunity cost and sunk cost are of vital importance. Differential cost and revenue are the cost and revenue items that differ between alternatives. Opportunity cost is the benefit that is forgone when one alternative is selected over another. Sunk cost is a cost that occurred in the past and cannot be altered. Differential cost and opportunity cost should be considered carefully in decisions. Sunk cost is always irrelevant in decisions and should be ignored.

- These various cost classifications are *different* ways of looking at costs. A particular cost, such as the cost of cheese in a cheese burger, could be a manufacturing cost, a product cost, a variable cost, a direct cost, and a differential cost – all at the same time.

Key terms

Administrative costs All executive, organizational and clerical costs associated with the general management of an organization rather than with manufacturing, marketing or selling (p. 17).

Contribution approach A profit statement format that is geared to cost behaviour in that costs are separated into variable and

fixed categories rather than being separated according to the functions of production, sales and administration (p. 25).

Contribution margin The amount remaining from sales revenue after all variable expenses have been deducted (p. 25).

Conversion cost Direct labour cost plus manufacturing overhead cost (p. 17).

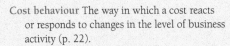

Cost behaviour The way in which a cost reacts or responds to changes in the level of business activity (p. 22).

Differential cost Any cost that differs between alternatives in a decision-making situation. In managerial accounting, this term is synonymous with avoidable cost and relevant cost. Also see Incremental cost (p. 26).

Differential revenue The difference in revenue between any two alternatives (p. 26).

Direct labour Those factory labour costs that can easily be traced to individual units of product. Also called touch labour (p. 16).

Direct materials Those materials that become an integral part of a finished product and can conveniently be traced into it (p. 16).

Fixed cost A cost that remains constant, in total, regardless of changes in the level of activity within the relevant range. If a fixed cost is expressed on a per unit basis, it varies inversely with the level of activity (p. 23).

Incremental cost An increase in cost between two alternatives. Also see Differential cost (p. 26).

Indirect labour The labour costs of caretakers, supervisors, materials handlers, and other factory workers that cannot conveniently be traced directly to particular products (p. 16).

Indirect materials Small items of material such as glue and nails. These items may become an integral part of a finished product but are traceable to the product only at great cost or inconvenience (p. 16).

Manufacturing overhead All costs associated with manufacturing except direct materials and direct labour (p. 16).

Marketing or selling costs All costs necessary to secure customer orders and get the finished product or service into the hands of the customer (p. 17).

Opportunity cost The potential benefit that is given up when one alternative is selected over another (p. 27).

Period costs Those costs that are taken directly to the profit and loss account as expenses in the period in which they are incurred or accrued; such costs consist of selling (marketing) and administrative expenses (p. 17).

Prime cost Direct materials cost plus direct labour cost (p. 17).

Product costs All costs that are involved in the purchase or manufacture of goods. In the case of manufactured goods, these costs consist of direct materials, direct labour, and manufacturing overhead. Also see Stock-related costs (p. 17).

Raw materials Any materials that go into the final product (p. 16).

Relevant range The range of activity within which assumptions about variable and fixed cost behaviour are valid (p. 23).

Stock-related costs (also known as inventoriable costs) Synonym for product costs (p. 19).

Sunk cost Any cost that has already been incurred and that cannot be changed by any decision made now or in the future (p. 27).

Variable cost A cost that varies, in total, in direct proportion to changes in the level of activity. A variable cost is constant per unit (p. 21).

Endnotes

1 *Financial Management*, September 2003, p. 4.

2 These issues are discussed thoroughly in Johnson and Kaplan (1987).

3 See note 4.

4 In many countries, such as the US, 'stock' is known as 'inventory'. With globalization of capital markets and accounting, terms such as *stock* and *inventory* are increasingly used interchangeably. Other examples of interchangeable terms are *profit* (UK) = *net*

income (US), *debtors* (UK) = *accounts receivable* (US) and *creditors* (UK) = *accounts payable* (US), *work in progress* (UK) = *work in process* (US).

5 http://moneymorning.com/2010/05/10/gulf-oil-spill-2/; http://news.bbc.co.uk/2/hi/americas/8666276.stm; http://www.rte.ie/business/2010/0610/bp.html

When you have read this chapter, log on to the Online Learning Centre for *Management Accounting for Business Decisions* at **www.mcgraw-hill.co.uk/textbooks/seal**, where you'll find multiple choice questions, practice exams and extra study tools for management accounting.

Assessment

Questions

2–1 What are the three major elements of product costs in a manufacturing company?

2–2 Distinguish between the following: (a) direct materials, (b) indirect materials, (c) direct labour, (d) indirect labour, and (e) manufacturing overhead.

2–3 Explain the difference between a product cost and a period cost.

2–4 Why are product costs sometimes called stock-related costs? Describe the flow of such costs in a manufacturing company from the point of incurrence until they finally become expenses on the profit and loss account.

2–5 What is meant by the term *cost behaviour*?

2–6 'A variable cost is a cost that varies per unit of product, whereas a fixed cost is constant per unit of product.' Do you agree? Explain.

2–7 How do fixed costs create difficulties in costing units of product?

2–8 Why is manufacturing overhead considered an indirect cost of a unit of product?

2–9 Define the following terms: differential cost, opportunity cost, and sunk cost.

2–10 Only variable costs can be differential costs. Do you agree? Explain.

Exercises

E2–1 ⏱ Time allowed: 15 minutes
The following are a number of cost terms introduced in the chapter:

Variable cost	Product cost
Fixed cost	Sunk cost
Prime cost	Conversion cost
Opportunity cost	Period cost

Choose the term or terms above that most appropriately describe the cost identified in each of the following situations. A cost term can be used more than once.

1 Lake Company produces a bag that is very popular with college students. The cloth going into the manufacture of the bag would be called direct materials and classified as a _____ cost. In terms of cost behaviour, the cloth could also be described as a _____ cost.

2 The direct labour cost required to produce the bags, combined with the manufacturing overhead cost involved, would be known as _____ cost.

3 The company could have taken the funds that it has invested in production equipment and invested them in interest-bearing securities instead. The interest forgone on the securities would be called _____ cost.

4 Taken together, the direct materials cost and the direct labour cost required to produce bags would be called _____ cost.

5 The company used to produce a smaller bag that was not very popular. Some three hundred of these smaller bags are stored in one of the company's warehouses. The amount invested in these bags would be called a _____ cost.

6 The bags are sold through agents who are paid a commission on each bag sold. These commissions would be classified by Lake Company as a _____ cost. In terms of cost behaviour, commissions would be classified as a _____ cost.

7 Depreciation on the equipment used to produce the bags would be classified by Lake Company as a _____ cost. However, depreciation on any equipment used by the company in selling and administrative activities would be classified as _____ cost. In terms of cost behaviour, depreciation would probably be classified as a _____ cost.

8 A _____ cost is also known as a stock-related cost, since such costs go into the Work in Progress stock account and then into the Finished Goods stock account before appearing on the profit and loss account as part of cost of goods sold.

9 The salary of Lake Company's managing director would be classified as a _____ cost, since the salary will appear on the profit and loss account as an expense in the time period in which it is incurred.

10 Costs can often be classified in several ways. For example, Lake Company pays £5,000 rent each month on its factory building. The rent would be part of manufacturing overhead. In terms of cost behaviour, it would be classified as a _____ cost. The rent can also be classified as a _____ cost and as part of _____ cost.

E2–2 ⏱ Time allowed: 10 minutes

A product cost is also known as a stock-related cost. Classify the following costs as either product (stock-related) costs or period (non-stock-related) costs in a manufacturing company:

1 Depreciation on salespersons' cars
2 Rent on equipment used in the factory
3 Lubricants used for maintenance of machines
4 Salaries of finished goods warehouse personnel
5 Soap and paper towels used by factory workers at the end of a shift
6 Factory supervisors' salaries
7 Heat, water and power consumed in the factory
8 Materials used in boxing units of finished product for shipment overseas (units are not normally boxed)
9 Advertising outlays
10 Workers' compensation insurance on factory employees
11 Depreciation on chairs and tables in the factory lunchroom
12 The salary of the switchboard operator for the company
13 Depreciation on a Lear Jet used by the company's executives
14 Rent on rooms at a West Country resort for holding of the annual sales conference
15 Attractively designed box for packaging breakfast cereal.

E2–3 Time allowed: 10 minutes

Below are a number of costs that are incurred in a variety of organizations:

1 X-ray film used in the radiology lab at Queens Medical Centre in Nottingham
2 The costs of advertising a Madonna rock concert in London
3 Depreciation on the Planet Hollywood restaurant building in Hong Kong
4 The electrical costs of running a roller-coaster at Blackpool
5 Property taxes on a local cinema
6 Commissions paid to salespersons at McGraw-Hill
7 Property insurance on a Coca-Cola bottling plant
8 The costs of synthetic materials used to make Nike running shoes
9 The costs of shipping Panasonic televisions to retail shops
10 The cost of leasing an ultra-scan diagnostic machine at St Thomas's hospital in London.

Required

Classify each cost as being variable or fixed with respect to the number of units of product or services sold by the organization. Set out your answers as below.

Cost Item	Cost behaviour	
	Variable	Fixed

Place an X in the appropriate column for each cost to indicate whether the cost involved would be variable or fixed with respect to the number of units of products or services sold by the organization.

E2–4 Time allowed: 20 minutes

The following cost and stock data are taken from the accounting records of Mason Company for the year just completed:

Costs incurred:		
Direct labour cost		£70,000
Purchases of raw materials		118,000
Indirect labour		30,000
Maintenance, factory equipment		6,000
Advertising expense		90,000
Insurance, factory equipment		800
Sales salaries		50,000
Rent, factory facilities		20,000
Supplies		4,200
Depreciation, office equipment		3,000
Depreciation, factory equipment		19,000

	Beginning of the Year	End of the Year
Stocks:		
Raw materials	£7,000	£15,000
Work in progress	10,000	5,000
Finished goods	20,000	35,000

Required

1 Prepare a schedule of cost of goods manufactured in good form
2 Prepare the cost of goods sold section of Mason Company's profit and loss account for the year

E2–5 ⏱ **Time allowed:** 15 minutes

Below are listed various costs that are found in organizations:

1 Hamburger buns in a McDonald's outlet
2 Advertising by a dental office
3 Apples processed and canned by Del Monte Corporation
4 Shipping canned apples from a Del Monte plant to customers
5 Insurance on a Bausch & Lomb factory producing contact lenses
6 Insurance on IBM's corporate headquarters
7 Salary of a supervisor overseeing production of circuit boards at Hewlett-Packard
8 Commissions paid to *Encyclopaedia Britannica* salespersons
9 Depreciation of factory lunchroom facilities at an ICI plant
10 Steering wheels installed in BMWs.

Required

Classify each cost as being either variable or fixed with respect to the number of units sold. Also classify each cost as either a selling and administrative cost or a product cost. Prepare your answer sheet as shown below.

Cost item	Cost behaviour		Selling and administrative cost	Product cost
	Variable	Fixed cost		

Place an X in the appropriate columns to show the proper classification of each cost.

P2–6 Cost identification

Problems

⏱ Time allowed: 30 minutes

connect

Wollongong Group Ltd of New South Wales, Australia, acquired its factory building about ten years ago. For several years the company has rented out a small annex attached to the rear of the building. The company has received a rental income of £30,000 per year on this space. The renter's lease will expire soon and, rather than renewing the lease, the company has decided to use the space itself to manufacture a new product.

Direct materials cost for the new product will total £80 per unit. To have a place to sell finished units of product, the company will rent a small warehouse nearby. The rental cost will be £500 per month. In addition, the company must rent equipment for use in producing the new product; the rental cost will be £4,000 per month. Workers will be hired to manufacture the new product, with direct labour cost amounting to £60 per unit. The space in the annex will continue to be depreciated on a straight-line basis, as in prior years. This depreciation is £8,000 per year.

Advertising costs for the new product will total £50,000 per year. A supervisor will be hired to oversee production; her salary will be £1,500 per month. Electricity for operating machines will be £1.20 per unit. Costs of shipping the new product to customers will be £9 per unit.

To provide funds to purchase materials, meet payrolls and so forth, the company will have to liquidate some temporary investments. These investments are presently yielding a return of about £3,000 per year.

Required

Prepare an answer sheet with the following column headings:

Name of the cost	Variable cost	Fixed cost	Product cost			Period (selling and administrative) cost	Opportunity cost	Sunk cost
			Direct materials	Direct labour	Manufacturing overhead			

List the different costs associated with the new product decision down the extreme left column (under Name of the cost). Then place an X under each heading that helps to describe the type of cost involved. There may be Xs under several column headings for a single cost (for example, a cost may be a fixed cost, a period cost and a sunk cost; you would place an X under each of these column headings opposite the cost).

P2–7 Supply missing production and cost data

Time allowed: 30 minutes

Supply the missing data in the following cases. Each case is independent of the others.

	Case			
	1	2	3	4
Direct materials	£4,500	£6,000	£5,000	£3,000
Direct labour	?	3,000	7,000	4,000
Manufacturing overhead	5,000	4,000	?	9,000
Total manufacturing costs	18,500	?	£20,000	?
Beginning work in progress stock	2,500	?	3,000	?
Ending work in progress stock	?	1,000	4,000	3,000
Cost of goods manufactured	£18,000	£14,000	£?	£?
Sales	£30,000	£21,000	£36,000	£40,000
Beginning finished goods stock	1,000	2,500	?	2,000
Cost of goods manufactured	?	?	?	17,500
Goods available for sale	?	?	?	?

(continued)

Ending finished goods stock	?	1,500	4,000	3,500
Cost of goods sold	17,000	?	18,500	?
Gross margin	13,000	?	17,500	?
Operating expenses	?	3,500	?	?
Profit	£4,000	£ ?	£5,000	£9,000

P2–8 Cost classification

⏱ Time allowed: 20 minutes

Various costs associated with the operation of a factory are given below:
1 Electricity used in operating machines
2 Rent on a factory building
3 Cloth used in drapery production
4 Production superintendent's salary
5 Cost of labourers assembling a product
6 Depreciation of air purification equipment used in furniture production
7 Caretaker salaries
8 Peaches used in canning fruit
9 Lubricants needed for machines
10 Sugar used in soft-drink production
11 Property taxes on the factory
12 Cost of workers painting a product
13 Depreciation on cafeteria equipment
14 Insurance on a building used in producing TV sets
15 Picture tubes used in TV sets.

Required

Classify each cost as being either variable or fixed with respect to the number of units produced and sold. Also indicate whether each cost would typically be treated as a direct cost or an indirect cost with respect to units of product. Prepare your answer sheet as shown below:

	Cost behaviour		To units of product	
Cost Item	Variable	Fixed	Direct	Indirect
Example: Factory insurance		X		X

P2–9 Cost identification

⏱ Time allowed: 40 minutes

The Dorilane Company specializes in producing a set of wooden patio furniture consisting of a table and four chairs. The set enjoys great popularity, and the

company has ample orders to keep production going at its full capacity of 2,000 sets per year. Annual cost data at full capacity follow:

To units of product	Product cost
Factory labour, direct	£118,000
Advertising	50,000
Factory supervision	40,000
Property taxes, factory building	3,500
Sales commissions	80,000
Insurance, factory	2,500
Depreciation, office equipment	4,000
Lease cost, factory equipment	12,000
Indirect materials, factory	6,000
Depreciation, factory building	10,000
General office supplies (billing)	3,000
General office salaries	60,000
Direct materials used (wood, bolts, etc.)	94,000
Utilities, factory	20,000

Required

1 Prepare an answer sheet with the column headings shown below. Enter each cost item on your answer sheet, placing the pound amount under the appropriate headings. As examples, this has been done already for the first two items in the list above. Note that each cost item is classified in two ways: first, as variable or fixed, with respect to the number of units produced and sold; and second, as a selling and administrative cost or a product cost. (If the item is a product cost, it should be classified as being either direct or indirect as shown.)

2 Total the pound amounts in each of the columns in 1 above. Compute the cost to produce one patio set.

3 Assume that production drops to only 1,000 sets annually. Would you expect the cost per set to increase, decrease, or remain unchanged? Explain. No computations are necessary.

4 Refer to the original data. The managing director's brother-in-law has considered making himself a patio set and has priced the necessary materials at a building supply shop. The brother-in-law has asked the managing director if he could purchase a patio set from the Dorilane Company 'at cost', and the managing director agreed to let him do so.

 (a) Would you expect any disagreement between the two men over the price the brother-in-law should pay? Explain. What price does the managing director probably have in mind? The brother-in-law?

 (b) Since the company is operating at full capacity, what cost term used in the chapter might be justification for the managing director to charge the full, regular price to the brother-in-law and still be selling 'at cost'?

	Cost behaviour		Selling or administrative cost	Product cost	
Cost item	Variable	Fixed		Direct	Indirect*
Factory labour, direct	£118,000			£118,000	
Advertising		£50,000	£50,000		

*To units of product.

P2–10 Cost classification

⏱ Time allowed: 25 minutes

Listed below are a number of costs typically found in organizations:

1   Property taxes, factory
2   Boxes used for packaging detergent
3   Salespersons' commissions
4   Supervisor's salary, factory
5   Depreciation, executive cars
6   Workers assembling computers
7   Packing supplies for shipments
8   Insurance, finished goods warehouses
9   Lubricants for machines
10 Advertising costs
11 'Chips' used in producing calculators
12 Shipping costs on merchandise sold
13 Magazine subscriptions, factory lunchroom
14 Thread in a garment factory
15 Billing costs
16 Executive life insurance
17 Ink used in textbook production
18 Fringe benefits, assembly-line workers
19 Yarn used in sweater production
20 Receptionist, executive offices.

Required

Prepare an answer sheet with column headings as shown below. For each cost item, indicate whether it would be variable or fixed with respect to the number of units produced and sold; and then whether it would be a selling cost, an administrative cost, or a manufacturing cost. If it is a manufacturing cost, indicate whether it would typically be treated as a direct cost or an indirect cost with respect to units of product. Three sample answers are provided for illustration.

Cost Item	Variable or fixed	Selling cost	Administrative cost	Manufacturing (product) cost	
				Direct	Indirect
Direct labour	V			X	
Executive salaries	F		X		
Factory rent	F				X

P2–11 Cost identification

⏱ Time allowed: 20 minutes

Tracy Beckham began dabbling in pottery several years ago as a hobby. Her work is quite creative, and it has been so popular with friends and others that she has decided to quit her job with an aerospace firm and manufacture pottery full time. The salary from Tracy's aerospace job is £2,500 per month.

Tracy will rent a small building near her home to use as a place for manufacturing the pottery. The rent will be £500 per month. She estimates that the cost of clay and glaze will be £2 for each finished piece of pottery. She will hire workers to produce the pottery at a labour rate of £8 per pot. To sell her pots, Tracy feels that she must advertise heavily in the local area. An advertising agency states that it will handle all advertising for a fee of £600 per month. Tracy's brother will sell the pots; he will be paid a commission of £4 for each pot sold. Equipment needed to manufacture the pots will be rented at a cost of £300 per month.

Tracy has already paid some start-up fees associated with her business. These fees amounted to £500. A small room has been located in a tourist area that Tracy will use as a sales office. The rent will be £250 per month. A phone installed in the room for taking orders will cost £40 per month. In addition, a recording device will be attached to the phone for taking after-hours messages.

Tracy has some money in savings that is earning interest of £1,200 per year. These savings will be withdrawn and used to get the business going. For the time being, Tracy does not intend to draw any salary from the new company.

Required

1 Prepare an answer sheet with the following column headings:

Name of the cost	Variable cost	Fixed cost	Product cost			Period (selling and administrative) cost	Opportunity cost	Sunk cost
			Direct materials	Direct labour	Manufacturing overhead			

List the different costs associated with the new company down the extreme left column (under Name of cost). Then place an X under each heading that helps to describe the type of cost involved. There may be Xs under several column headings for a single cost. (That is, a cost may be a fixed cost, a period cost, and a sunk cost; you would place an X under each of these column headings opposite the cost.)

Under the Variable cost column, list only those costs that would be variable with respect to the number of units of pottery that are produced and sold.

2 All the costs you have listed above, except one, would be differential costs between the alternatives of Tracy producing pottery or staying with the aerospace firm. Which cost is not differential? Explain.

P2–12 Cost behaviour; manufacturing statement; unit costs

Time allowed: 40 minutes

Visic Company, a manufacturing firm, produces a single product. The following information has been taken from the company's production, sales, and cost records for the just completed year.

Production in units	29,000
Sales in units	?
Ending finished goods stock in units	?
Sales in pounds	£1,300,000
Costs:	
Advertising	105,000
Entertainment and travel	40,000
Direct labour	90,000
Indirect labour	85,000
Raw materials purchased	480,000
Building rent (production uses 80% of the space administrative and sales offices use the rest)	40,000
Utilities, factory	108,000
Royalty paid for use of production patent, £1.50 per unit produced	?
Maintenance, factory	9,000
Rent for special production equipment, per year plus £0.30 per unit produced	£7,000 ?
Selling and administrative salaries	210,000
Other factory overhead costs	6,800
Other selling and administrative expenses	17,000

Stocks:	Beginning of year	End of year
Raw materials	£20,000	£30,000
Work in progress	50,000	40,000
Finished goods	0	?

The finished goods stock is being carried at the average unit production cost for the year. The selling price of the product is £50 per unit.

Required

1 Prepare a schedule of goods manufactured for the year.
2 Compute the following:
    (a) The number of units in the finished goods stock at the end of the year
    (b) The cost of the units in the finished goods stock at the end of the year.
3 Prepare a profit and loss account for the year.

Chapter 8
Profit planning and controlling: budgeting

 LO Learning **objectives**

After studying Chapter 8, you should be able to:
1 Understand why organizations budget and the processes they use to create budgets
2 Understand the inter-relationships and components that make up a master budget
3 Prepare a budgeted profit and loss statement and a budgeted balance sheet on static and flexible bases
4 Review some criticisms of budgeting and possible responses
5 Review the concept of zero-based budgeting

Concepts **in Context**

After an initial boom, many early dotcom companies have now failed. One reason seems to be that some companies thought that the old business practices such as budgeting were obsolete. The emphasis was on speed, being the first-mover and working out detailed business plans as the business developed. Frequently, many companies squandered their start-up resources before they had established a sustainable business. The collapse of dotcoms and the high tech sector around the turn of the millennium seemed to suggest that the disciplines of planning and control inherent in budgeting should not just be the concern of 'fuddy-duddy', bricks-and-mortar organizations.[1]

© Axaulya

In this chapter, we focus our attention on those steps taken by business organizations to achieve their desired levels of profits – a process that is generally called profit planning. We shall see that profit planning is accomplished through the preparation of a number of budgets, which, when brought together, form an integrated business plan known as the master budget. The master budget is an essential management tool that communicates management's plans throughout the organization, allocates resources and co-ordinates activities.

LO 1 The basic framework of budgeting

Definition of budgeting

A budget is a detailed plan for the acquisition and use of financial and other resources over a specified time period. It represents a plan for the future expressed in formal quantitative terms. The act of preparing a budget is called *budgeting*. The use of budgets to control a firm's activities is known as *budgetary control*.

The *master budget* is a summary of a company's plans that sets specific targets for sales, production, distribution and financing activities. It generally culminates in a *cash budget*, a *budgeted profit and loss account*, and a *budgeted balance sheet*. In short, it represents a comprehensive expression of management's plans for the future and how these plans are to be accomplished.

Personal budgets

Nearly everyone budgets to some extent, even though many of the people who use budgets do not recognize what they are doing as budgeting. For example, most people make estimates of their income and plan expenditures for food, clothing, housing and so on. As a result of this planning, people restrict their spending to some predetermined, allowable amount. While they may not be conscious of the fact, these people clearly go through a budgeting process. Income is estimated, expenditures are planned, and spending is restricted in accordance with the plan. Individuals also use budgets to forecast their future financial condition for purposes such as purchasing a home, financing college education, or setting aside funds for retirement. These budgets may exist only in the mind of the individual, but they are budgets nevertheless.

The budgets of a business firm serve much the same functions as the budgets prepared informally by individuals. Business budgets tend to be more detailed and to involve more work, but they are similar to the budgets prepared by individuals in most other respects. Like personal budgets, they assist in planning and controlling expenditures; they also assist in predicting operating results and financial condition in future periods.

Advantages of budgeting

Managers who have never tried budgeting are usually quick to state that budgeting is a waste of time. These managers may argue that even though budgeting may work well in some situations, it would never work well in their companies because operations are too complex or because there are too many uncertainties. In reality, however, managers who argue this way usually will be deeply involved in planning (albeit on an informal basis). These managers will have clearly defined thoughts about what they want to accomplish and when they want it accomplished. The difficulty is that unless they have some way of communicating their thoughts and plans to others, the only way their companies will ever attain the desired objectives will be through accident. In short, even though companies may attain a certain degree of success without budgets, they never attain the heights that could have been reached with a co-ordinated system of budgets.

Companies realize many benefits from a budgeting programme. Among these benefits are the following:

1 Budgets provide a means of *communicating* management's plans throughout the organization.
2 Budgets force managers to *think about* and plan for the future. In the absence of the necessity to prepare a budget, too many managers would spend all their time dealing with daily emergencies.
3 The budgeting process provides a means of *allocating resources* to those parts of the organization where they can be used most effectively.
4 The budgeting process can uncover potential *bottlenecks* before they occur.

5 Budgets *co-ordinate* the activities of the entire organization by integrating the plans of the various parts. Budgeting helps to ensure that everyone in the organization is pulling in the same direction.

6 Budgets define goals and objectives that can serve as *benchmarks* for evaluating subsequent performance.

The impact of computers on budgeting

In the past, some managers have avoided budgeting because of the time and effort involved in the budgeting process. It can be argued that budgeting is actually 'free' in that the manager's time and effort are more than offset by greater profits. Moreover, with the advent of computer spreadsheets, *any* company – large or small – can implement and maintain a budgeting programme at minimal cost. Budgeting lends itself well to readily available spreadsheet application programs.

Focus on Business Practice

Budgeting in banking firms

© Joshua Hodge Photography

Consider the following situation encountered by one of the authors at a mortgage banking firm. For years, the company operated with virtually no system of budgets whatever. Management contended that budgeting was not well suited to the firm's type of operation. Moreover, management pointed out that the firm was already profitable. Indeed, outwardly the company gave every appearance of being a well-managed, smoothly operating organization. A careful look within, however, disclosed that day-to-day operations were far from smooth, and often approached chaos. The average day was nothing more than an exercise in putting out one brush fire after another.

The Cash account was always at crisis levels. At the end of a day, no one ever knew whether enough cash would be available the next day to cover required loan closings. Departments were uncoordinated, and it was not uncommon to find that one department was pursuing a course that conflicted with the course pursued by another department. Employee morale was low, and turnover was high. Employees complained bitterly that when a job was well done, nobody ever knew about it. The company was bought out by a new group who required that an integrated budgeting system be established to control operations. Within one year, significant changes were evident. Brush fires were rare. Careful planning virtually eliminated the problems that had been experienced with cash, and departmental efforts were co-ordinated and directed towards predetermined overall company goals. Although the employees were wary of the new budgeting programme initially, they became 'converted' when they saw the positive effects that it brought about. The more efficient operations caused profits to jump dramatically. Communication increased throughout the organization. When a job was well done everybody knew about it. As one employee stated, 'For the first time, we know what the company expects of us.'

Exercise: One of the key issues that emerged after the recent collapse of the Bradford & Bingley bank was the poor state of the bank's financial controls. How did that contribute to the wider banking problems that became known as the *credit crunch*?[2]

Choosing a budget period

Operating budgets are ordinarily set to cover a one-year period. The one-year period should correspond to the company's fiscal year so that the budget figures can be compared with the actual results. Many companies divide their budget year into four quarters. The first quarter is then subdivided into months, and monthly budget figures are established. These *near-term* figures can often be established with considerable accuracy. The last three quarters are carried in the budget as quarterly totals only. As the year progresses, the figures for the second quarter are broken down into monthly amounts, then the third-quarter figures are broken down, and so forth. This approach has the advantage of requiring periodic review and reappraisal of budget data throughout the year.

Continuous, perpetual or *rolling budgets* are used by a significant number of organizations. A continuous or perpetual budget is a 12-month budget that rolls forward one month (or quarter) as the current month (or quarter) is completed. In other words, one month (or quarter) is added to the end of the budget as each month (or quarter) comes to a close. This approach keeps managers focused on the future at least one year ahead. Advocates of continuous budgets argue that with this approach there is less danger that managers will become too focused on short-term results as the year progresses.

The self-imposed or participative budget

The success of a budget programme will be determined in large part by the way in which the budget is developed. The most successful budget programmes involve managers with cost control responsibilities in preparing their own budget estimates – rather than having a budget imposed from above. This approach to preparing budget data is particularly important if the budget is to be used to control and evaluate a manager's activities. If a budget is imposed on a manager from above, it will probably generate resentment and ill will rather than co-operation and increased productivity.

This budgeting approach, in which managers prepare their own budget estimates – called a *self-imposed budget* – is generally considered to be the most effective method of budget preparation. A self-imposed budget or participative budget is a budget that is prepared with the full co-operation and participation of managers at all levels. Exhibit 8.1 illustrates this approach to budget preparation.

A number of advantages are commonly cited for such self-imposed budgets:

1   Individuals at all levels of the organization are recognized as members of the team whose views and judgements are valued by top management.
2   The person in direct contact with an activity is in the best position to make budget estimates. Therefore, budget estimates prepared by such persons tend to be more accurate and reliable.

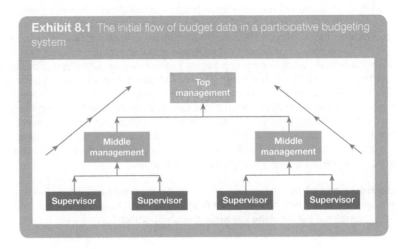

Exhibit 8.1 The initial flow of budget data in a participative budgeting system

3   People are more likely to work at fulfilling a budget that they have participated in setting than they are to work at fulfilling a budget that is imposed from above.

4   A self-imposed budget contains its own unique system of control in that if people are not able to meet budget specifications, they have only themselves to blame. On the other hand, if a budget is imposed from above, they can always say that the budget was unreasonable or unrealistic to start with, and therefore was impossible to meet.

Once self-imposed budgets are prepared, are they subject to any kind of review? The answer is yes. Budget estimates prepared by lower-level managers cannot necessarily be accepted without question by higher levels of management. If no system of checks and balances is present, self-imposed budgets may be too loose and allow too much 'budgetary slack'. The result will be inefficiency and waste. Therefore, before budgets are accepted, they must be carefully reviewed by immediate superiors. If changes from the original budget seem desirable, the items in question are discussed and modified as necessary by mutual consent.

In essence, all levels of an organization should work together to produce the budget. Since top management is generally unfamiliar with detailed, day-to-day operations, it should rely on subordinates to provide detailed budget information. On the other hand, top management has a perspective on the company as a whole that is vital in making broad policy decisions in budget preparation. Each level of responsibility in an organization should contribute in the way that it best can in a *co-operative* effort to develop an integrated budget document.

We have described an ideal budgetary process that involves self-imposed budgets prepared by the managers who are directly responsible for revenues and costs. Most companies deviate from this ideal. Typically, top managers initiate the budget process by issuing broad guidelines in terms of overall target profits or sales. Lower-level managers are directed to prepare budgets that meet those targets. The difficulty is that the targets set by top managers may be unrealistically high or may allow too much slack. If the targets are too high and employees know they are unrealistic, motivation will suffer. If the targets allow too much slack, waste will occur. And, unfortunately, top managers are often not in a position to know whether the targets they have set are appropriate. Admittedly, however, in a pure self-imposed budgeting system, lower-level managers may be tempted to build into their budgets a great deal of budgetary slack and there may be a lack of direction. Nevertheless, because of the motivational advantages of self-imposed budgets, top managers should be cautious about setting inflexible targets or otherwise imposing limits on the budgeting process.

The matter of human relations

Whether or not a budget programme is accepted by lower management personnel will be reflective of (first) the degree to which top management accepts the budget programme as a vital part of the company's activities, and (second) the way in which top management uses budgeted data.

If a budget programme is to be successful, it must have the complete acceptance and support of the persons who occupy key management positions. If lower or middle management personnel sense that top management is lukewarm about budgeting, or if they sense that top management simply tolerates budgeting as a necessary evil, then their own attitudes will reflect a similar lack of enthusiasm. Budgeting is hard work, and if top management is not enthusiastic about and committed to the budget programme, then it is unlikely that anyone else in the organization will be either.

In administering the budget programme, it is particularly important that top management not use the budget as a club to pressure employees or as a way to find someone to blame for a particular problem. This type of negative emphasis will simply breed hostility, tension and mistrust rather than greater co-operation and productivity. Unfortunately, research suggests that the budget is often used as a pressure device and that great emphasis is placed on 'meeting the budget' under all circumstances.[3] Rather than being used as a pressure device, the budget should be used as a positive instrument to assist in establishing goals, in measuring operating results, and in isolating areas that are in need of extra effort or attention. Any misgivings that employees have about a budget programme can be overcome by meaningful involvement at all levels and by proper use of the programme over a period of time. Administration of a budget programme requires a great deal of insight and sensitivity on the part of management. The ultimate object must be to develop the realization that the budget is designed to be a positive aid in achieving both individual and company goals.

Management must keep clearly in mind that the human dimension in budgeting is of key importance. It is easy for the manager to become preoccupied with the technical aspects of the budget programme to the exclusion of the human aspects. Indeed, the use of budget data in a rigid and inflexible manner is the greatest single complaint of persons whose performance is being evaluated through the budget process.[4] Management should remember that the purposes of the budget are to motivate employees and to co-ordinate efforts. Preoccupation with the pounds and pence in the budget, or being rigid and inflexible in budget administration, can only lead to frustration of these purposes.

The budget committee

A standing budget committee will usually be responsible for overall policy matters relating to the budget programme and for co-ordinating the preparation of the budget itself. This committee generally consists of the managing director; directors in charge of various functions such as sales, production and purchasing; and the controller. Difficulties and disputes between segments of the organization in matters relating to the budget are resolved by the budget committee. In addition, the budget committee approves the final budget and receives periodic reports on the progress of the company in attaining budgeted goals.

Disputes can (and do) erupt over budget matters. Because budgets allocate resources, the budgeting process, to a large extent, determines which departments get more resources and which get relatively less. Also, the budget sets the benchmarks by which managers and their departments will be at least partially evaluated. Therefore, it should not be surprising that managers take the budgeting process very seriously and invest considerable energy and even emotion in ensuring that their interests, and those of their departments, are protected. Because of this, the budgeting process can easily degenerate into an inter-office brawl in which the ultimate goal of working together towards common goals is forgotten.

Running a successful budgeting programme that avoids inter-office battles requires considerable inter-personal skills in addition to purely technical skills. But even the best inter-personal skills will fail if, as discussed earlier, top management uses the budget process inappropriately as a club or as a way to find blame.

Focus on Business Practice

The game of budgeting

© P_Wei

Budgeting is often an intensely political process in which managers jockey for resources and relaxed goals for the upcoming year. One group of consultants describes the process in this way: Annual budgets 'have a particular urgency in that they provide the standard and most public framework against which managers are assessed and judged. It is, therefore, not surprising that budget-setting is taken seriously...Often budgets are a means for managers getting what they want. A relaxed budget will secure a relatively easy twelve months, a tight one means that their names will constantly be coming up in the monthly management review meeting. Far better to shift the burden of cost control and financial discipline to someone else. Budgeting as an intensely political exercise is conducted with all the sharper managerial skills not taught at business school, such as lobbying and flattering superiors, forced haste, regretted delay, hidden truth, half-truths, and lies.'[5]

Exercise: Why might an organization that has a high level of *trust* between managerial levels achieve a better quality of budgeting than those where mistrust is the rule?

The master budget inter-relationships

LO 2

The master budget consists of a number of separate but interdependent budgets. Exhibit 8.2 provides an overview of the various parts of the master budget and how they are related.

The sales budget

A sales budget is a detailed schedule showing the expected sales for the budget period; typically, it is expressed in both pounds and units of product. An accurate sales budget is the key to the entire budgeting process. All other parts of the master budget are dependent on the sales budget in some way, as illustrated in Exhibit 8.2. Thus, if the sales budget is sloppily done, then the rest of the budgeting process is largely a waste of time.

The sales budget will help determine how many units will have to be produced. Thus, the *production budget* is prepared after the sales budget. The production budget in turn is used to determine the budgets for manufacturing costs including the *direct materials budget*, the *direct labour budget*, and the *manufacturing overhead budget*. These budgets are then combined with data from the sales budget and the selling and administrative expense budget to determine the cash budget. In essence, the sales budget triggers a chain reaction that leads to the development of the other budgets.

As shown in Exhibit 8.2, the selling and administrative expense budget is both dependent on and a determinant of the sales budget. This reciprocal relationship arises because sales will in part be determined by the funds committed for advertising and sales promotion.

The cash budget

Once the operating budgets (sales, production, and so on) have been established, the cash budget and other financial budgets can be prepared. A cash budget is a detailed plan showing how cash resources will be acquired and used over some specified time period. Observe from Exhibit 8.2 that all of the operating budgets have an impact on the cash budget. In the case of the sales budget, the impact comes from the planned cash receipts to be received from sales. In the case of the other budgets, the impact comes from the planned cash expenditures within the budgets themselves.

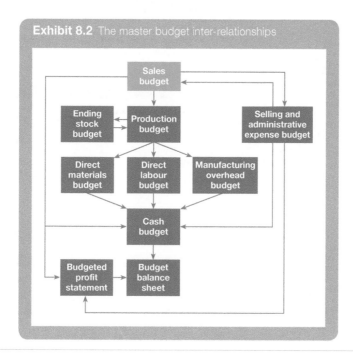

Exhibit 8.2 The master budget inter-relationships

Sales forecasting – a critical step

The sales budget is usually based on the company's *sales forecast*. Sales from prior years are commonly used as a starting point in preparing the sales forecast. In addition, the manager may examine the company's unfilled back orders, the company's pricing policy and marketing plans, trends in the industry and general economic conditions. Sophisticated statistical tools may be used to analyse the data and to build models that are helpful in predicting key factors influencing the company's sales.

Preparing the master budget

The sales budget

The sales budget is the starting point in preparing the master budget. As shown earlier in Exhibit 8.2, all other items in the master budget, including production, purchases, stocks and expenses, depend on it in some way.

The sales budget is constructed by multiplying the budgeted sales in units by the selling price. Schedule 1 contains the sales budget for Hampton Freeze Ltd for the year 2011, by quarters. Notice from the schedule that the company plans to sell 100,000 cases of ice lollies during the year, with sales peaking in the third quarter.

Schedule 1

Hampton Freeze Ltd.
Sales budget
for the year ended 31 December 2011

	Quarter				
	1	2	3	4	Year
Budgeted sales in units (cases of lollies)	10,000	30,000	40,000	20,000	100,000
Selling price per unit	× £20	× £20	× £20	× £20	× £20
Total sales	£200,000	£600,000	£800,000	£400,000	£2,000,000

Schedule of expected cash collections

	1	2	3	4	Year
Debtors, beginning balance*	£90,000				£90,000
First-quarter sales (£200,000 × 70%, 30%)†	140,000	60,000			200,000
Second-quarter sales (£600,000 × 70%, 30%)		420,000	180,000		600,000
Third-quarter sales (£800,000 × 70%, 30%)			560,000	240,000	800,000
Fourth-quarter sales (£400,000 × 70%)‡				280,000	280,000
Total cash collections	£230,000	£480,000	£740,000	£520,000	£1,970,000

* Cash collections from last year's fourth-quarter sales. See the beginning-of-year balance sheet on page 190.

†Cash collections from sales are as follows: 70 per cent collected in the quarter of sale, and the remaining 30 per cent collected in the following year.

‡Uncollected fourth-quarter sales appear as debtors on the company's end-of-year balance sheet (see Schedule 10 on page 194).

A schedule of expected *cash collections*, such as the one that appears in Schedule 1 for Hampton Freeze, is prepared after the sales budget. This schedule will be needed later to prepare the cash budget. Cash collections consist of collections on sales made to customers in prior periods plus collections on sales made in the current budget period. At Hampton Freeze, experience has shown that 70% of sales are collected in the quarter in which the sale is made and the remaining 30% are collected in the following quarter. So, for example, 70% of the first quarter sales of £200,000 (or £140,000) is collected during the first quarter and 30% (or £60,000) is collected during the second quarter.

The production budget

The production budget is prepared after the sales budget. The production budget lists the number of units that must be produced during each budget period to meet sales needs and to provide for the desired ending stock. Production needs can be determined as follows:

Budgeted sales in units	XXXX
Add desired ending stock	XXXX
Total needs	XXXX
Less beginning stock	XXXX
Required production	XXXX

Schedule 2 contains the production budget for Hampton Freeze.

Note that production requirements for a quarter are influenced by the desired level of the ending stock. Stocks should be carefully planned. Excessive stocks tie up funds and create storage problems. Insufficient stocks can lead to lost sales or crash production efforts in the following period. At Hampton Freeze, management believes that an ending stock equal to 20% of the next quarter's sales strikes the appropriate balance.

Schedule 2

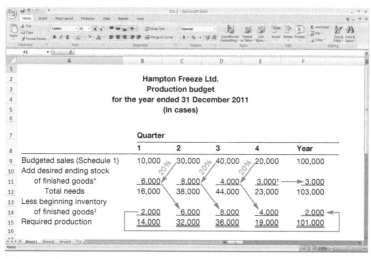

Hampton Freeze Ltd.
Production budget
for the year ended 31 December 2011
(in cases)

	Quarter 1	2	3	4	Year
Budgeted sales (Schedule 1)	10,000	30,000	40,000	20,000	100,000
Add desired ending stock of finished goods*	6,000	8,000	4,000	3,000†	3,000
Total needs	16,000	38,000	44,000	23,000	103,000
Less beginning inventory of finished goods‡	2,000	6,000	8,000	4,000	2,000
Required production	14,000	32,000	36,000	19,000	101,000

* 20 per cent of next quarter's sales.
†Estimated.
‡The same as the prior quarter's *ending* stock.

The direct materials budget

Returning to Hampton Freeze's budget data, after the production requirements have been computed, a *direct materials budget* can be prepared. The direct materials budget details the raw materials that must be purchased to fulfil the production budget and to provide for adequate stocks. The required purchases of raw materials are computed as follows:

Raw materials needed to meet the production schedule	XXXXX
Add desired ending stock of raw materials	XXXXX
Total raw materials needs	XXXXX
Less beginning stock of raw materials	XXXXX
Raw materials to be purchased	XXXXX

Preparing a budget of this kind is one step in a company's overall material requirements planning (MRP). MRP is an operations management tool that uses a computer to help manage materials and stocks. The objective of MRP is to ensure that the right materials are on hand, in the right quantities, and at the right time to support the production budget. The detailed operation of MRP is covered in most operations management books.

Schedule 3 contains the direct materials budget for Hampton Freeze. The only raw material included in that budget is high fructose sugar, which is the major ingredient in ice lollies other than water. The remaining raw materials are relatively insignificant and are included in variable manufacturing overhead. Notice that materials requirements are first determined in units (kilos, litres, and so on) and then translated into pounds by multiplying by the appropriate unit cost. Also note that the management of Hampton Freeze desires to maintain ending stocks of sugar equal to 10% of the following quarter's production needs.

The direct materials budget is usually accompanied by a schedule of expected cash disbursements for raw materials. This schedule is needed to prepare the overall cash budget. Disbursements for raw materials consist of payments for purchases on account in prior periods plus any payments for purchases in the current budget period. Schedule 3 contains such a schedule of cash disbursements.

The direct labour budget

The direct labour budget is also developed from the production budget. Direct labour requirements must be computed so that the company will know whether sufficient labour time is available to meet production needs. By knowing in advance just what will be needed in the way of labour time throughout the budget year, the company can develop plans to adjust the labour force as the situation may require. Firms that neglect to budget run the risk of facing labour shortages, or having to hire and lay off at awkward times. Erratic labour policies lead to insecurity and inefficiency on the part of employees.

To compute direct labour requirements, the number of units of finished product to be produced each period (month, quarter, and so on) is multiplied by the number of direct labour-hours required to produce a single unit. Many different types of labour may be involved. If so, then computations should be by type of labour needed. The direct labour requirements can then be translated into expected direct labour costs. How this is done will depend on the labour policy of the firm. In Schedule 4, the management of Hampton Freeze has assumed that the direct labour force will be adjusted as the work requirements change from quarter to quarter. In that case, the total direct labour cost is computed by simply multiplying the direct labour-hour requirements by the direct labour rate per hour as was done in Schedule 4.

However, many companies have employment policies or contracts that prevent them from laying off and rehiring workers as needed. Suppose, for example, that Hampton Freeze has fifty workers who are classified as direct labour and each of them is guaranteed at least 480 hours of pay each quarter at a rate of £7.50 per hour. In that case, the minimum direct labour cost for a quarter would be as follows:

50 workers × 480 hour × £7.50 = £180,000

Note that in Schedule 4 the direct labour costs for the first and fourth quarters would have to be increased to a £180,000 level if Hampton Freeze's labour policy did not allow it to adjust the workforce at will.

Schedule 3

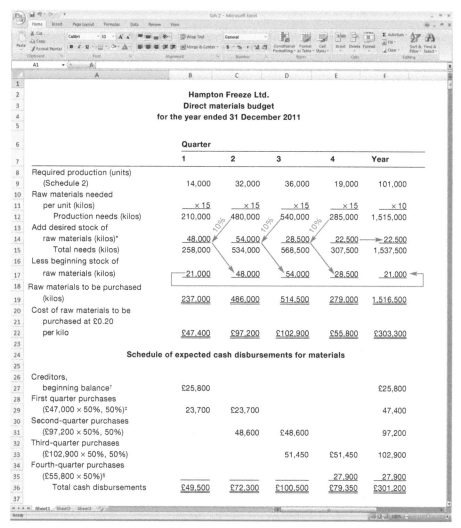

The spreadsheet shows:

Hampton Freeze Ltd.
Direct materials budget
for the year ended 31 December 2011

	Quarter				
	1	2	3	4	Year
Required production (units) (Schedule 2)	14,000	32,000	36,000	19,000	101,000
Raw materials needed per unit (kilos)	×15	×15	×15	×15	×10
Production needs (kilos)	210,000	480,000	540,000	285,000	1,515,000
Add desired stock of raw materials (kilos)*	48,000	54,000	28,500	22,500	22,500
Total needs (kilos)	258,000	534,000	568,500	307,500	1,537,500
Less beginning stock of raw materials (kilos)	21,000	48,000	54,000	28,500	21,000
Raw materials to be purchased (kilos)	237,000	486,000	514,500	279,000	1,516,500
Cost of raw materials to be purchased at £0.20 per kilo	£47,400	£97,200	£102,900	£55,800	£303,300

Schedule of expected cash disbursements for materials

Creditors, beginning balance†	£25,800				£25,800
First quarter purchases (£47,000 × 50%, 50%)‡	23,700	£23,700			47,400
Second-quarter purchases (£97,200 × 50%, 50%)		48,600	£48,600		97,200
Third-quarter purchases (£102,900 × 50%, 50%)			51,450	£51,450	102,900
Fourth-quarter purchases (£55,800 × 50%)§				27,900	27,900
Total cash disbursements	£49,500	£72,300	£100,500	£79,350	£301,200

*10 per cent of the next quarter's production needs. For example, the second-quarter production needs are 480,000 kilos. Therefore, the desired ending inventory for the first quarter would be 10 per cent × 480,000 kilos – 48,000 kilos. The ending stock of 22,500 kilos for the fourth quarter is estimated.

†Cash payments for last year's fourth-quarter material purchases. See the beginning-of-year balance sheet on page 190.

‡Cash payments for purchases are as follows: 50 per cent paid for in the quarter of purchase, and the remaining 50 per cent paid for in the following quarter.

§Unpaid fourth-quarter purchases appear as creditors on the company's end-of-year balance sheet (see Schedule 10 on page 194).

The manufacturing overhead budget

The manufacturing overhead budget provides a schedule of all costs of production other than direct materials and direct labour. Schedule 5 shows the manufacturing overhead budget for Hampton Freeze.

Schedule 4

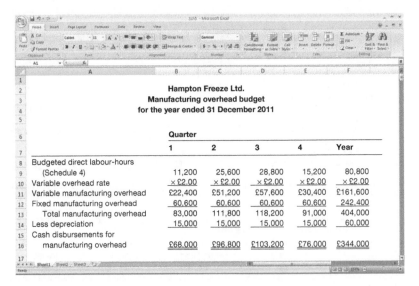

Hampton Freeze Ltd.
Direct labour budget
for the year ended 31 December 2011

	Quarter				
	1	2	3	4	Year
Units (cases) to be produced (Schedule 2)	14,000	32,000	36,000	19,000	101,000
Direct labour time per unit (hours)	×0.8	×0.8	×0.8	×0.8	×0.8
Total hours of direct labour time needed	11,200	25,600	28,800	15,200	80,800
Direct labour cost per hour	×£7.50	×£7.50	×£7.50	×£7.50	×£7.50
Total direct labour cost*	£84,000	£192,000	£216,000	£114,000	£606,000

*This schedule assumes that the direct labour workforce will be fully adjusted to the workload (i.e., 'total hours of direct labour time needed') each quarter.

Schedule 5

Hampton Freeze Ltd.
Manufacturing overhead budget
for the year ended 31 December 2011

	Quarter				
	1	2	3	4	Year
Budgeted direct labour-hours (Schedule 4)	11,200	25,600	28,800	15,200	80,800
Variable overhead rate	×£2.00	×£2.00	×£2.00	×£2.00	×£2.00
Variable manufacturing overhead	£22,400	£51,200	£57,600	£30,400	£161,600
Fixed manufacturing overhead	60,600	60,600	60,600	60,600	242,400
Total manufacturing overhead	83,000	111,800	118,200	91,000	404,000
Less depreciation	15,000	15,000	15,000	15,000	60,000
Cash disbursements for manufacturing overhead	£68,000	£96,800	£103,200	£76,000	£344,000

Note how the production costs are separated into variable and fixed components. The variable component is £2 per direct labour-hour. The fixed component is £60,600 per quarter.

The last line of Schedule 5 for Hampton Freeze shows its budgeted cash disbursements for manufacturing overhead. Since some of the overhead costs are not cash outflows, the total budgeted manufacturing overhead costs must be adjusted to determine the cash disbursements for manufacturing overhead. At Hampton Freeze, the only significant non-cash manufacturing overhead cost is depreciation, which is £15,000 per quarter. These non-cash depreciation charges are deducted from the total budgeted manufacturing overhead to determine the expected cash disbursements. Hampton Freeze pays all overhead costs involving cash disbursements in the quarter incurred.

The finished goods stock budget

Schedules 1–5 contain all of the data needed to compute unit product costs. This computation is needed for two reasons: first, to determine cost of goods sold on the budgeted profit and loss account; and second, to know what amount to put on the balance sheet stock account for unsold units. The carrying cost of the unsold units is computed on the **finished goods stock budget**.

The unit product cost computations are shown in Schedule 6. For Hampton Freeze, the absorption costing unit product cost is £13 per case of ice lollies – consisting of £3 of direct materials, £6 of direct labour and £4 of manufacturing overhead. For convenience, the manufacturing overhead is applied to units of product on the basis of direct labour-hours. The budgeted carrying cost of the expected ending stock is £39,000.

The selling and administrative expense budget

The **selling and administrative expense budget** lists the budgeted expenses for areas other than manufacturing. In large organizations, this budget would be a compilation of many smaller, individual budgets submitted by department heads and other persons responsible for selling and administrative expenses. For example, the marketing manager in a large organization would submit a budget detailing the advertising expenses for each budget period.

Schedule 6

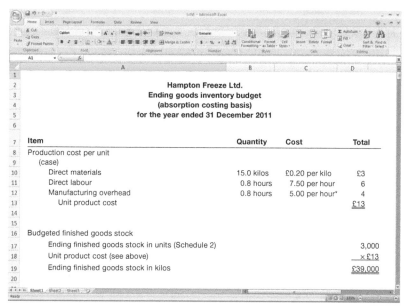

Hampton Freeze Ltd.
Ending goods inventory budget
(absorption costing basis)
for the year ended 31 December 2011

Item	Quantity	Cost	Total
Production cost per unit			
(case)			
Direct materials	15.0 kilos	£0.20 per kilo	£3
Direct labour	0.8 hours	7.50 per hour	6
Manufacturing overhead	0.8 hours	5.00 per hour*	4
Unit product cost			£13
Budgeted finished goods stock			
Ending finished goods stock in units (Schedule 2)			3,000
Unit product cost (see above)			× £13
Ending finished goods stock in kilos			£39,000

*£404,000 ÷ 80,800 hours = £5.

Schedule 7 contains the selling and administrative expense budget for Hampton Freeze.

Schedule 7

	Quarter				
Hampton Freeze Ltd. Selling and administrative expense budget for the year ended 31 December 2011					
	1	**2**	**3**	**4**	**Year**
Budgeted sales in units (cases)	10,000	30,000	40,000	20,000	100,000
Variable selling and administrative expense per unit*	× £1.80	× £1.80	× £1.80	× £1.80	× £1.80
Variable expense	£18,000	£54,000	£72,000	£36,000	£180,000
Fixed selling and administrative expenses:					
Advertising	20,000	20,000	20,000	20,000	80,000
Executive salaries	55,000	55,000	55,000	55,000	220,000
Insurance		1,900	37,750		39,650
Property taxes				18,150	18,150
Depreciation	10,000	10,000	10,000	10,000	40,000
Total	85,000	86,900	122,750	103,150	397,800
Total selling and administrative expenses	103,000	140,900	194,750	139,150	577,800
Less depreciation	10,000	10,000	10,000	10,000	40,000
Cash disbursements for selling and administrative expenses	£93,000	£130,900	£184,750	£129,150	£537,800

*Commissions, clerical and shipping.

The cash budget

As illustrated in Exhibit 8.2, the cash budget pulls together much of the data developed in the preceding steps. It is a good idea to restudy Exhibit 8.2 to get the big picture firmly in mind before moving on.

The cash budget is composed of four major sections:

1 The receipts section.
2 The disbursements section.
3 The cash excess or deficiency section.
4 The financing section.

The receipts section consists of a listing of all of the cash inflows, except for financing, expected during the budget period. Generally, the major source of receipts will be from sales.

The disbursements section consists of all cash payments that are planned for the budget period. These payments will include raw materials purchases, direct labour payments, manufacturing overhead costs, and so on, as contained in their respective budgets. In addition, other cash disbursements such as equipment purchases, dividends and other cash withdrawals by owners are listed. For instance, we see in Schedule 8 that management plans to spend £130,000 during the budget period on equipment purchases and £32,000 on dividends to the owners. This is additional information that does not appear on any of the earlier schedules.

The cash excess or deficiency section is computed as follows:

Cash balance, beginning	XXXX
Add receipts	XXXX
Total cash available before financing	XXXX
Less disbursements	XXXX
Excess (deficiency) of cash available over disbursements	XXXX

Schedule 8

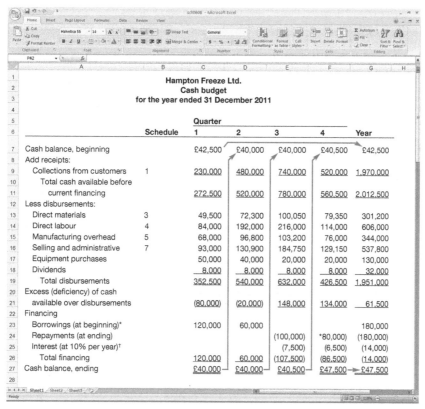

Hampton Freeze Ltd.
Cash budget
for the year ended 31 December 2011

		Quarter				
	Schedule	1	2	3	4	Year
Cash balance, beginning		£42,500	£40,000	£40,000	£40,500	£42,500
Add receipts:						
Collections from customers	1	230,000	480,000	740,000	520,000	1,970,000
Total cash available before current financing		272,500	520,000	780,000	560,500	2,012,500
Less disbursements:						
Direct materials	3	49,500	72,300	100,050	79,350	301,200
Direct labour	4	84,000	192,000	216,000	114,000	606,000
Manufacturing overhead	5	68,000	96,800	103,200	76,000	344,000
Selling and administrative	7	93,000	130,900	184,750	129,150	537,800
Equipment purchases		50,000	40,000	20,000	20,000	130,000
Dividends		8,000	8,000	8,000	8,000	32,000
Total disbursements		352,500	540,000	632,000	426,500	1,951,000
Excess (deficiency) of cash available over disbursements		(80,000)	(20,000)	148,000	134,000	61,500
Financing						
Borrowings (at beginning)*		120,000	60,000			180,000
Repayments (at ending)				(100,000)	*80,000)	(180,000)
Interest (at 10% per year)†				(7,500)	(6,500)	(14,000)
Total financing		120,000	60,000	(107,500)	(86,500)	(14,000)
Cash balance, ending		£40,000	£40,000	£40,500	£47,500	£47,500

*The company requires a minimum cash balance of £40,000. Therefore, borrowing must be sufficient to cover the cash deficiency of £80,000 in quarter 1 and to provide for the minimum cash balance of £40,000. All borrowings and all repayments of principal are in round £1,000 amounts.

† The interest payments relate only to the principal being repaid at the time it is repaid. For example, the interest in quarter 3 relates only to the interest due on the £100,000 principal being repaid from quarter 1 borrowing: £100,00 × ¾ × 10 per cent = £7,500. The interest paid in quarter 4 is computed as follows:

£20,000 × 10 per cent × 1 year	£2,000
£60,000 × 10 per cent × ¾	4,500
Total interest paid	£6,500

If there is a cash deficiency during any budget period, the company will need to borrow funds. If there is a cash excess during any budget period, funds borrowed in previous periods can be repaid or the idle funds can be placed in short-term or other investments.

The financing section provides a detailed account of the borrowings and repayments projected to take place during the budget period. It also includes a detail of interest payments that will be due on money borrowed. Generally speaking, the cash budget should be broken down into time periods that are as short as feasible. There can be considerable fluctuations in cash balances that would be hidden by looking at a longer time period. While a monthly cash budget is most common, many firms budget cash on a weekly or even daily basis. The quarterly cash budget for Hampton Freeze can be further refined as necessary. This budget appears in Schedule 8; it is assumed that an open line of credit can be arranged with the bank that can be used as needed to bolster the company's cash position. It is also assumed that the interest on any loans taken out with this line of credit would carry an interest rate of 10% per year. For simplicity, it is assumed that all borrowings and repayments are in round £1,000 amounts and that all borrowing occurs at the beginning of a quarter and all repayments are made at the end of a quarter.

In the case of Hampton Freeze, all loans have been repaid by year-end. If all loans are not repaid and a budgeted profit and loss account or balance sheet is being prepared, then interest must be accrued on the unpaid loans. This interest will *not* appear on the cash budget (since it has not yet been paid), but it will appear as part of interest expense on the budgeted profit and loss account and as a liability on the budgeted balance sheet.

A budgeted profit and loss account can be prepared from the data developed in Schedules 1–8. The budgeted profit and loss account is one of the key schedules in the budget process. It shows the company's planned profit for the upcoming budget period, and it stands as a benchmark against which subsequent company performance can be measured. Schedule 9 contains the budgeted profit and loss account for Hampton Freeze.

Schedule 9

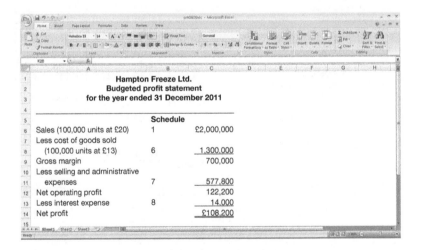

Hampton Freeze Ltd.
Budgeted profit statement
for the year ended 31 December 2011

	Schedule	
Sales (100,000 units at £20)	1	£2,000,000
Less cost of goods sold		
(100,000 units at £13)	6	1,300,000
Gross margin		700,000
Less selling and administrative		
expenses	7	577,800
Net operating profit		122,200
Less interest expense	8	14,000
Net profit		£108,200

The budgeted balance sheet

The budgeted balance sheet is developed by beginning with the current balance sheet and adjusting it for the data contained in the other budgets. Hampton Freeze's budgeted balance sheet is presented in Schedule 10. Some of the data on the budgeted balance sheet has been taken from the company's end of-year balance sheet for 2010 which appears below:

Hampton Freeze Ltd		
Balance sheet		
31 December 2010		
Assets		
Current assets:		
Cash	£42,500	
Debtors	90,000	
Raw materials stock (21,000 kilos)	4,200	
Finished goods stock (2,000 cases)	26,000	
Total current assets		£162,700
Plant and equipment:		
Land	80,000	
Buildings and equipment	700,000	
Accumulated depreciation	(292,000)	
Plant and equipment, net		488,000
Total assets		£650,700
Liabilities and shareholders' equity		
Current liabilities:		
Creditors (raw materials)		£25,800
Shareholders' equity:		
Common stock, no par	£175,000	
Retained earnings	449,900	
Total shareholders' equity		624,900
Total liabilities and shareholders' equity		£650,700

Flexible budgeting: expanding the budgeted profit and loss account

The master budget profit and loss account in Schedule 9 focuses on a single level of activity and has been prepared using absorption costing. Some managers prefer an alternative format that focuses on a *range of activity* and that is prepared using the contribution approach. An example of a master budget profit and loss account using this alternative format is presented in Exhibit 8.3.

A statement such as that in Exhibit 8.3 is flexible, since it is geared to more than one level of activity. If, for example, the company planned to sell 2,000 units during a period but actually sold only 1,900 units, then the budget figures at the 1,900-unit level would be used to compare against actual costs and revenues. Other columns could be added to the budget as needed by simply applying the budget formulas provided. In short, a master budget profit and loss account in this expanded format can be very useful in planning and controlling operations.

Schedule 10

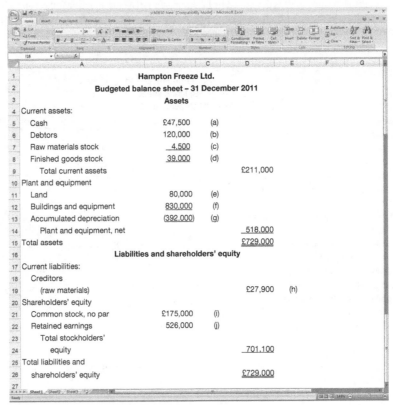

	A	B	C	D	E	F	G
1	**Hampton Freeze Ltd.**						
2	**Budgeted balance sheet – 31 December 2011**						
3	**Assets**						
4	Current assets:						
5	Cash	£47,500	(a)				
6	Debtors	120,000	(b)				
7	Raw materials stock	4,500	(c)				
8	Finished goods stock	39,000	(d)				
9	Total current assets			£211,000			
10	Plant and equipment						
11	Land	80,000	(e)				
12	Buildings and equipment	830,000	(f)				
13	Accumulated depreciation	(392,000)	(g)				
14	Plant and equipment, net			518,000			
15	Total assets			£729,000			
16	**Liabilities and shareholders' equity**						
17	Current liabilities:						
18	Creditors						
19	(raw materials)			£27,900	(h)		
20	Shareholders' equity						
21	Common stock, no par	£175,000	(i)				
22	Retained earnings	526,000	(j)				
23	Total stockholders'						
24	equity			701,100			
25	Total liabilities and						
26	shareholders' equity			£729,000			
27							

Explanation of 31 December 2011 balance sheet figures:

a The ending cash balance, as projected by the cash budget in Schedule 8.

b 30% of fourth-quarter sales, from Schedule 1 (£400,000 × 30 per cent = £120,000).

c From Schedule 3, the ending raw materials stock will be 22,500 kilos. This material costs £0.20 per kilo. Therefore, the ending stock in kilos will be 22,500 kilos × £0.20 = £4,500.

d From Schedule 6.

e From the 31 December 2010 balance sheet (no change).

f The 31 December 2010 balance sheet indicated a balance of £700,000. During 2011, £130,000 additional equipment will be purchased (see Schedule 8), bringing the 31 December 2011 balance to £830,000.

g The 31 December 2010 balance sheet indicated a balance sheet of £292,000. During 2011, £100,000 of depreciation will be taken (£60,000 on Schedule 5 and £40,000 on Schedule 7), bringing the 31 December 2011 balance to £392,000.

h One-half of the fourth-quarter raw materials purchases, from Schedule 3.

i From the 31 December 2010 balance sheet (no change).

j	31 December 2010 balance	£449,000
	Add net profit, from Schedule 9	108,200
		558,100
	Deduct dividends paid, from Schedule 8	32,000
	31 December 2011 balance	£526,100

Exhibit 8.3 Flexible budget profit statement

Example company
Master budget profit statement

	Budget formula (per unit)	Sales in units		
		1,900	2,000	2,100
Sales	£75.00	£142,500	£150,000	£157,500
Less variable expenses:				
Direct materials	12.00	22,800	24,000	25,200
Direct labour	31.00	58,900	62,000	65,100
Variable manufacturing overhead	7.50	14,250	15,000	15,750
Variable selling and administrative	4.00	7,600	8,000	8,400
Total variable expenses	54.50	103,550	109,000	114,450
Contribution margin	£20.50	38,950	41,000	43,050
Less fixed expenses:				
Fixed manufacturing overhead		18,000	18,000	18,000
Fixed selling administrative		9,000	9,000	9,000
Total fixed expenses		27,000	27,000	27,000
Net profit		£11,950	£14,000	£16,050

Some criticisms of budgeting as a performance management system

LO 4

For many, if not most businesses, the budget is a key planning and control mechanism with many desirable characteristics. Yet budgeting has come in for much criticism in recent years. It has been described by Jan Wallander as 'an unnecessary evil' and Jack Welch as the 'bane of corporate America'.[6] Such criticisms of budgeting are easier to appreciate when looked at in the wider context of performance management systems. Furthermore, not only may we consider some organizational problems caused by budgeting but we can see that there are alternative, or at least supplementary, control models suggested by the performance management perspective.

One common criticism is that budgets produce a particular type of constrained management style, they concentrate on easy to measure events and they are *too historically based*. The last point is often linked to the view that budgets tend to be *incrementalist*. Particularly in not-for-profit organizations in the public sector, discussions about changes to budgets concentrate on marginal or incremental increases or decreases in particular departmental budgets. The problem with incrementalism is that activities become institutionalized through the budget and there is a reluctance to ask questions about fundamental purposes.

Another criticism is that budgeting makes organizations *inflexible* and *unable to respond to uncertainty*. Budgeting is seen as being *mechanistic* with *rigid, formalized* and *tightly coupled* systems. Budgeting-led

organizations may be slow to recognize changes in the market and also slow to react to changes even when they have been noticed. Other criticisms of budgeting are that it is *too time consuming*, it tends to *focus on cost control* rather than value creation, it tends to be *top down*, it encourages *gaming* and *opportunism*, it reinforces departmental *barriers* and it *hinders knowledge sharing*. Overall it makes *people feel undervalued*.[7]

Much of the criticism of budgeting is driven by a changing business environment, especially the belief that competition in modern markets has increased the importance of *intellectual capital* relative to physical or tangible capital.[8] In order to respond to this new competitive challenge, it is argued that companies need to adopt a *network* rather than a hierarchical, departmental structure. A network model may still use budgets for cash forecasting but not for cost control. The aim is to avoid 'actual versus budget' reports and concentrate on relative performance. These alternative approaches draw on other forms of management control such as benchmarking and the mix of financial and non-financial measures found in approaches such as the balanced scorecard.

Reform or abandon budgeting?

Given the criticisms of budgeting, what is the appropriate response? Currently, there seems to be two main practice-led approaches. One approach is to improving budgeting and the other is to abandon it.[9] If we review the criticisms of budgeting there seems to be two main issues. One issue concerns the question of *predictability*. It could be argued that budgets work well if managers' predictions are reliable because the budget can then represent a viable plan. Conversely, budgets tend to work badly in conditions of great uncertainty and turbulent environments.[10] The other issue concerns *organizational* and *time-frame problems*. It is argued that budgeting fosters a centralizing and stifling atmosphere as well as a possible mismatch between operational strategies and annual reporting cycles. These organizational problems tend to reduce the ability of units and employees to use their initiative as they lack empowerment.

When it is advocated that organizations abandon budgeting, it may mean that budgets are still used for financial purposes but, crucially, not for *performance evaluation*. The aim is to avoid the annual performance trap associated with budgeting by working with what have been called 'relative performance contracts with hindsight'.[11] The significance of the term 'relative' is that performance is benchmarked against *internal* or *external comparators* rather than against historical standards such as last year's results. The term 'with hindsight' means that rather than referring to fixed targets set at the *beginning* of the period, 'targets are adjusted by looking back and incorporating the actual operating and economic circumstances during the period'.[12] Managerial and employee rewards tend to be based on subjective and group criteria with an 'objective to engender a philosophy doing what is best for the firm in the light of current circumstance and to promote teamwork'.[13]

 ## Zero-based budgeting

One way to reform budgeting is known as zero-based budgeting. Under a zero-based budget, managers are required to justify all budgeted expenditures, not just changes in the budget from the previous year. The baseline is zero rather than last year's budget. A zero-based budget requires considerable documentation. In addition to all the schedules in the usual master budget, the manager must prepare a series of 'decision packages' in which all the activities of the department are ranked according to their relative importance and the cost of each activity is identified. Higher-level managers can then review the decision packages and cut back in those areas that appear to be less critical or whose costs do not appear to be justified.

Under zero-based budgeting, the review is performed every year. Critics of zero-based budgeting charge that properly executed zero-based budgeting is too time consuming and too costly to justify on an annual basis. In addition, it is argued that annual reviews soon become mechanical and that the whole purpose of

Focus on Business Practice

Base budget review

© Mark Evans

Public sector managers have tried to move away from the more traditional incremental approach by introducing priority-led budgeting and base budget review. With priority-led budgeting, budget holders are encouraged to take an investment view, (e.g. spend more now to save later) based on a three year rather than annual perspective. With base budget review, managers do not start with a blank sheet of paper (an extreme view of zero-based budgeting) but are required to take a line-by-line approach and ask 'Do we need that line and do we need that much money?'[14]

Exercise: Consider the impact of employment contracts which seem to make labour costs in the public sector more 'fixed' than in the private sector.

zero-based budgeting is then lost. Whether or not an organization should use an annual review is a matter of judgement. In some situations annual zero-based reviews may be justified; in other situations they may not because of the time and cost involved. However, most managers would at least agree that, on occasion, zero-based reviews can be very helpful.

Summary

- Our purpose has been to present an overview of the budgeting process and to show how the various operating budgets relate to each other.

- We have seen how the sales budget forms the foundation for profit planning. Once the sales budget has been set, the production budget and the selling and administrative budget can be prepared since they depend on how many units are to be sold.

- The production budget determines how many units are to be produced, so after it is prepared, the various manufacturing cost budgets can be prepared. All of these various budgets feed into the cash budget and the budgeted profit and loss account and balance sheet.

- There are many connections between these various parts of the master budget. For example, the schedule of expected cash collections, which is completed in connection with the sales budget, provides data for both the cash budget and the budgeted balance sheet.

- Although budgeting is a very widespread practice, it has come in for some criticism and some suggestions for reform and even calls the abandonment of budgeting as a performance control system.

Key terms

Budget committee A group of key management persons who are responsible for overall policy matters relating to the budget programme and for co-ordinating the preparation of the budget (p. 182).

Cash budget A detailed plan showing how cash resources will be acquired and used over some specific time period (p. 183).

Constrained management style A management approach that concentrates on easy to measure events and lacks flexibility (p. 195).

Continuous or perpetual budget A 12-month budget that rolls forward one month as the current month is completed (p. 180).

Direct labour budget A detailed plan showing labour requirements over some specific time period (p. 186).

Direct materials budget A detailed plan showing the amount of raw materials that must be purchased during a period to meet both production and stock needs (p. 186).

Finished goods stock budget A budget showing the cost expected to appear on the balance sheet for unsold units at the end of a period (p. 189).

Manufacturing overhead budget A detailed plan showing the production costs, other than direct materials and direct labour, that will be incurred over a specified time period (p. 187).

Master budget A summary of a company's plans in which specific targets are set for sales, production, distribution, and financing activities and that generally culminates in a cash budget, budgeted profit and loss account, and budgeted balance sheet (p. 183).

Material requirements planning (MRP) An operations management tool that uses a computer to help manage materials and stocks (p. 186).

Participative budget *See* Self-imposed budget (p. 180).

Production budget A detailed plan showing the number of units that must be produced during a period in order to meet both sales and stock needs (p. 185).

Sales budget A detailed schedule showing the expected sales for coming periods; these sales are typically expressed in both pounds and units (p. 183).

Self-imposed budget A method of preparing budgets in which managers prepare their own budgets. These budgets are then reviewed by the manager's supervisor, and any issues are resolved by mutual agreement (p. 180).

Selling and administrative expense budget A detailed schedule of planned expenses that will be incurred in areas other than manufacturing during a budget period (p. 189).

Zero-based budgeting A method of budgeting in which managers are required to justify all costs as if the programmes involved were being proposed for the first time (p. 196)

Endnotes

1 Bates, Rizvi, Tewari and Vardan (2001).

2 See, e.g., Aldrick (2008).

3 Carruth, McClendon and Ballard (1983).

4 Hope and Hope (1997).

5 Wildavsky (1975).

6 Wildavsky (1975).

7 Neely, Sutcliff and Heyns (2001).

8 Hope and Hope (1997).

9 Hansen, Otley and Van der Stede (2003).

10 Wallander (1999).

11 Hansen *et al.* (2003), p. 101.

12 Hansen *et al.* (2003), p. 101.

13 Hansen *et al.* (2003), p. 102.

14 Seal and Ball (2008).

When you have read this chapter, log on to the Online Learning Centre for *Management Accounting for Business Decisions* at **www.mcgraw-hill.co.uk/textbooks/seal**, where you'll find multiple choice questions, practice exams and extra study tools for management accounting.

Assessment

8–1 What is a budget? What is budgetary control?
8–2 Discuss some of the major benefits to be gained from budgeting.
8–3 What is a master budget? Briefly describe its contents.
8–4 Why is the sales forecast the starting point in budgeting?
8–5 Describe the flow of budget data in an organization. Who are the participants in the budgeting process, and how do they participate?
8–6 What is a self-imposed/participatory budget? What are the major advantages of self-imposed budgets? What caution must be exercised in their use?
8–7 How can budgeting assist a firm in its employment policies?
8–8 'The principal purpose of the cash budget is to see how much cash the company will have in the bank at the end of the year.' Do you agree? Explain.
8–9 How does zero-based budgeting differ from traditional budgeting?

E8–1 Time allowed: 20 minutes
Silver Company makes a product that has peak sales in May of each year. These peak sales are shown in the company's sales budget for the second quarter given below:

	April	May	June	Total
Budgeted sales	£300,000	£500,000	£200,000	£1,000,000

From past experience, the company has learned that 20% of a month's sales are collected in the month of sale, that another 70% is collected in the month following sale, and that the remaining 10% is collected in the second month following sale. Bad debts are negligible and can be ignored. February sales totalled £230,000 and March sales totalled £260,000.

Required
1 Prepare a schedule of expected cash collections from sales, by month and in total, for the second quarter.
2 Assume that the company will prepare a budgeted balance sheet as of 30 June. Compute the debtors as of that date.

E8–2 Time allowed: 10 minutes
Down Under Products Ltd of Australia has budgeted sales of its popular boomerang for the next four months as follows:

	Sales in units
April	50,000
May	75,000
June	90,000
July	80,000

The company is now in the process of preparing a production budget for the second quarter. Past experience has shown that end-of-month stock levels must equal 10% of the following month's sales. The stock at the end of March was 5,000 units.

Required
Prepare a production budget for the second quarter. In your budget, show the number of units to be produced each month and for the quarter in total.

E8–3 Time allowed: 15 minutes
Three grams of musk oil are required for each bottle of Mink Caress, a very popular perfume made by a small company in western Siberia. The cost of the musk oil is 150 roubles per gram. (Siberia is located in Russia, whose currency is the rouble.) Budgeted production of Mink Caress is given below by quarters for Year 2 and for the first quarter of Year 3.

	Year 2 quarter				Year 3 quarter
	First	Second	Third	Fourth	First
Budgeted production, in bottles	60,000	90,000	150,000	100,000	70,000

Musk oil has become so popular as a perfume base that it has become necessary to carry large inventories as a precaution against stock-outs. For this reason, the stock of musk oil at the end of a quarter must be equal to 20% of the following quarter's production needs. Some 36,000 grams of musk oil will be on hand to start the first quarter of Year 2.

Required
Prepare a materials purchases budget for musk oil, by quarter and in total, for Year 2. At the bottom of your budget, show the amount of purchases in roubles for each quarter and for the year in total.

E8–4 Time allowed: 25 minutes
You have been asked to prepare a December cash budget for Ashton Company, a distributor of exercise equipment. The following information is available about the company's operations:
1 The cash balance on 1 December will be £40,000.
2 Actual sales for October and November and expected sales for December are as follows:

	October	November	December
Cash sales	£65,000	£70,000	£83,000
Sales on account	400,000	525,000	600,000

Sales on account are collected over a three-month period in the following ratio: 20% collected in the month of sale, 60% collected in the month following sale, and 18% collected in the second month following sale. The remaining 2% is uncollectable.

3   Purchases of stock will total £280,000 for December and 30% of a month's stock purchases are paid during the month of purchase. The accounts payable remaining from November's stock purchases total £161,000, all of which will be paid in December.

4   Selling and administrative expenses are budgeted at £420,000 for December. Of this amount, £50,000 is for depreciation.

5   A new web server for the Marketing Department costing £76,000 will be purchased for cash during December, and dividends totalling £9,000 will be paid during the month.

6   The company must maintain a minimum cash balance of £20,000. An open line of credit is available from the company's bank to bolster the cash position as needed.

Required

1   Prepare a schedule of expected cash collections for December.
2   Prepare a schedule of expected cash disbursements during December to suppliers for materials for stock purchases.
3   Prepare a cash budget for December. Indicate in the financing section any borrowing that will be needed during the month.

Problems

connect

P8–5 Production and purchases budgets

⏱ Time allowed: 40 minutes

Pearl Products Limited of Shenzhen, China, manufactures and distributes toys throughout South East Asia. Three cubic centimetres (cc) of solvent H300 are required to manufacture each unit of Supermix, one of the company's products. The company is now planning raw materials needs for the third quarter, the quarter in which peak sales of Supermix occur. To keep production and sales moving smoothly, the company has the following stock requirements:

1   The finished goods stock on hand at the end of each month must be equal to 3,000 units of Supermix plus 20% of the next month's sales. The finished goods stock on 30 June is budgeted to be 10,000 units.

2   The raw materials stock on hand at the end of each month must be equal to one-half of the following month's production needs for raw materials. The raw materials stock on 30 June is budgeted to be 54,000 cc of solvent H300.

3   The company maintains no work in progress stocks.

A sales budget for Supermix for the last six months of the year follows.

	Budgeted sales in units
July	35,000
August	40,000
September	50,000
October	30,000
November	20,000
December	10,000

Required

1 Prepare a production budget for Supermix for the months July–October.
2 Examine the production budget that you prepared in Question 1 above. Why will the company produce more units than it sells in July and August, and fewer units than it sells in September and October?
3 Prepare a budget showing the quantity of solvent H300 to be purchased for July, August and September, and for the quarter in total.

P8–6 Evaluating a company's budget procedures

⏱ Time allowed: 30 minutes

Springfield Corporation operates on a calendar-year basis. It begins the annual budgeting process in late August, when the managing director establishes targets for the total pound sales and net income before taxes for the next year.

The sales target is given to the Marketing Department, where the marketing manager formulates a sales budget by product line in both units and pounds. From this budget, sales quotas by product line in units and pounds are established for each of the corporation's sales districts.

The marketing manager also estimates the cost of the marketing activities required to support the target sales volume and prepares a tentative marketing expense budget.

The operations manager uses the sales and profit targets, the sales budget by product line, and the tentative marketing expense budget to determine the pound amounts that can be devoted to manufacturing and corporate office expense. The operations manager prepares the budget for corporate expenses, and then forwards to the Production Department the product-line sales budget in units and the total pound amount that can be devoted to manufacturing.

The production manager meets with the factory managers to develop a manufacturing plan that will produce the required units when needed within the cost constraints set by the operations manager. The budgeting process usually comes to a halt at this point because the Production Department does not consider the financial resources allocated to be adequate.

When this standstill occurs, the director of finance, the operations manager, the marketing manager and the production manager meet to determine the final budgets for each of the areas. This normally results in a modest increase in the total amount available for manufacturing costs, while the marketing expense and corporate office expense budgets are cut. The total sales and profit figures proposed by the managing director are seldom changed. Although the participants are seldom pleased with the compromise, these budgets are final. Each executive then develops a new detailed budget for the operations in his or her area.

None of the areas has achieved its budget in recent years. Sales often run below the target. When budgeted sales are not achieved, each area is expected to cut costs so that the managing director's profit target can still be met. However, the profit target is seldom met because costs are not cut enough. In fact, costs often run above the original budget in all functional areas. The managing director is disturbed that Springfield has not been able to meet the sales and profit targets. He hired a consultant with considerable experience with companies in Springfield's industry. The consultant reviewed the budgets

for the past four years. He concluded that the product-line sales budgets were reasonable and that the cost and expense budgets were adequate for the budgeted sales and production levels.

Required

1 Discuss how the budgeting process as employed by Springfield Corporation contributes to the failure to achieve the managing director's sales and profit targets.
2 Suggest how Springfield Corporation's budgeting process could be revised to correct the problem.
3 Should the functional areas be expected to cut their costs when sales volume falls below budget? Explain your answer.

(CMA, adapted)

Chapter

12

Management of Working Capital

Chapter contents

 Learning objectives

After studying this chapter you will be able to:

- Define working capital and explain its importance in relation to solvency, overtrading and profitability
- Explain how to manage receivables and calculate the financial implications of different policies for managing receivables
- Discuss the control of inventories and apply the economic order quantity (EOQ) model
- Explain how to plan, control and manage cash, and how to manage and avoid cash crises
- Understand the role of control and management of payables

12.1 Introduction

The planning and management of working capital is an important part of the financing of a business. High levels of inventories and receivables tie up large amounts of finance; reductions in inventories and receivables, and increases in payables, provide extra finance for the business.

12.2 Definition and Importance of Working Capital

A large part of a company's capital is usually tied up in assets such as buildings and machinery for a period of years. But companies also need some capital to finance short-term assets such as inventories and receivables, and there is a need for some cash for day-to-day operations. The amount of long-term capital available after financing non-current assets is known as 'working capital', which may be defined as:

$$\text{Long-term funds} - \text{non-current assets} = \text{working capital}$$

From the statement of financial position in Illustration 12.1 we can see that working capital in year 1 was:

$$\text{Year 1}\quad 85,000 + 110,000 - 140,000 = £55,000$$
$$\text{Year 2}\quad 88,000 + 135,000 - 138,000 = £85,000$$

The more usual definition of working capital is:

$$\text{Current assets} - \text{current liabilities} = \text{working capital}$$

From the statement of financial position above we can see that working capital is:

$$\text{Year 1}\quad 175,000 - 120,000 = £55,000$$
$$\text{Year 2}\quad 145,000 - 60,000 = £85,000$$

The two definitions appear to be different, but provided all items on the statement of financial position are classified under the same five headings, the two approaches will produce the same figure.

Although most businesses finance their inventories and receivables partly from their long-term funds, current assets are also partly financed by payables and other current liabilities. In year 2 Solverham (Illustration 12.1) had inventories of £70,000; £60,000 of this was financed by current liabilities. In some companies, particularly retailers, inventories are wholly financed by short-term creditors.

How much working capital should a business have?

There is usually a relationship between a company's turnover, and the amount of working capital it has. In Chapter 4, ratios 14, 15 and 16 express inventories, receivables and payables in relation to the amount of (cost of) sales. As turnover increases we can expect working capital to increase in proportion. If turnover goes up by 25 per cent, it does not mean that the amount of cash coming into the business immediately goes up by 25 per cent: there is likely to be an increase in inventories and receivables (partly financed by an increase in creditors).

But companies should not simply watch working capital drift upwards: there is a need for proper planning and control. There is, however, no ideal level for working capital. It is a question of balancing (a) *solvency* against (b) *profitability*, that is, risk against reward.

A company that is very safe in terms of solvency will have lots more current assets than current liabilities. There will always be more than enough current assets, either in the form of cash or receivables (and even inventories) that will soon become cash, to meet short-term liabilities as they fall due. This short-term financial strength can be expressed in the form of *current ratios* and *liquidity ratios*. In Illustration 12.2, the first of the four companies (Alice Ltd) has most working capital, the strongest current ratio (3 : 1), and the strongest liquidity ratio (2 : 1). The fourth company (Dora Ltd) has the least working capital: a negative amount! Dora also has a very low current ratio (0.17 : 1) and a very low liquidity ratio (0.1 : 1).

Definition and importance of working capital

297

ILLUSTRATION 12.1

Statements of financial position of Solverham Company Ltd as at 31 December

	Year 1	Year 2
	£000	£000
Non-current assets (at cost)	200	220
Provision for depreciation	(60)	(82)
Net book value	140	138
Current assets		
Inventories	95	70
Receivables	80	50
Cash	–	25
	175	145
Total assets	315	283
Current liabilities		
Payables	40	60
Overdraft	80	–
	120	60
Non-current liabilities		
12% debentures	110	135
Equity		
Share capital	50	50
Retained earnings	35	38
	85	88
Total liabilities plus equity	315	283

A company that is more concerned with profitability than with appearing to be solvent will concentrate on keeping down the amount of working capital. In order to maximize return on capital employed companies need not only to maximize profits or returns, but also to minimize capital employed (ROCE) in relation to profits. Other things being equal, companies that manage with the least working capital are likely to be the ones that are most profitable.

Each of the four companies in Illustration 12.2 has the same amount of non-current assets, and the same amount of profit. The only differences between the companies are the amounts of working capital. As working capital decreases, so the ROCE increases. The company with the lowest amount of working capital (Dora Ltd has £50,000 *negative* working capital) has the highest ROCE.

In terms of solvency or liquidity, however, Dora looks very weak. There are payables of £60,000, but current assets amount to only £10,000. Few businesses would have such a pattern of working capital (perhaps a florist's shop; inventories would be low because fresh flowers do not keep for long). Retailers tend to sell mostly on a cash basis, and so a low receivables figure is to be expected. Retailers buy mostly on credit and so a significant creditors' figure is normal.

Although there is no 'normal' level of working capital, we can see that higher levels of working capital are associated with higher levels of solvency; and lowering levels of working capital can increase profitability.

ILLUSTRATION 12.2

	Alice Ltd £000	Bertha Ltd £000	Colin Ltd £000	Dora Ltd £000
Non-current assets	150	150	150	150
Current assets				
Inventories	100	50	100	4
Receivables	150	80	150	2
Bank/cash	50	10	–	4
	300	140	250	10
Current liabilities				
Payables	100	80	200	60
Overdraft	–	–	50	–
	100	80	250	60
Working capital	200	60	–	(50)
Net assets = capital employed	350	210	150	100
Profit	35	35	35	35
Return on capital employed	10%	16.7%	23.3%	35%

Overtrading

Having too little working capital is associated with 'overtrading'. This occurs when a company is trying to do too much business with too little long-term capital. If a company is generating lots of cash, and manages its working capital carefully, it may survive and prosper even if it appears to be overtrading. But having insufficient liquid resources (or access to them) to meet liabilities as they fall due is fatal for businesses.

The problem can start with a major outflow of cash, perhaps to buy additional non-current assets or another business; to repay a loan; or paying too much out as dividends. It is sometimes the result of success: rapid expansion can lead to a rapid outflow of cash (inventories, receivables and non-current assets: all increase) before the cash comes in from customers. High levels of inflation make the problem worse: the amount of cash required to replace assets increases in line with inflation.

Overtrading can also be the result of failure. A company that makes substantial losses is likely to find that cash is haemorrhaging out of the business. A mild case of overtrading is easily treated with various tactics to bring in cash more quickly. Receivables can be pressed to pay more quickly; inventories can be reduced by control of new purchases and by extra efforts to clear inventory; and payments to creditors may be delayed.

A cash shortage, and the effects of reducing inventories and receivables, and increasing payables, soon show up in reducing a company's current ratio. A trend of falling current ratios is a matter for concern.

In a serious case of overtrading the symptoms get worse, and attempts to deal with it can lead to further deterioration. The overdraft limit can often be increased, but if an increased limit is breached, the bank soon loses patience with a business that seems unable to manage its cash. If a company reduces its inventories too much it will soon find that it is losing business because it is unable to supply what its customers want. Customers will go elsewhere, if they are pushed too hard to pay their bills too quickly. Trade payables will usually put up with a little delay, but most will not tolerate repeated or increased delays. If a company cannot pay its bills without excessive delay it soon finds that it is unable to obtain supplies on credit. If it is to continue in business it has to find cash to buy supplies, which makes the original problem worse.

Many of us have been in shops where the signs of overtrading are obvious. There is very little on the shelves because suppliers are no longer willing to sell to them on credit. Each day the shopkeeper hopes to bring in a few hundred pounds from customers so that they can go to their local cash and carry to replace what they have sold; they cannot buy very much because they have to use some of the cash to pay off some of the amounts due to whichever creditors are pressing hardest.

Often it is a wages bill that precipitates the crisis, especially at the stage when the bank is no longer willing to honour cheques because the business has (again!) exceeded its overdraft limit. At this stage desperate measures are needed. When difficulties first arise, surplus assets are sold off to raise cash. Towards the end it even has to sell essential assets, and sell off stocks at ridiculously low prices, just to bring in some cash to survive another day. At this stage the business has little chance of survival.

It is not difficult to spot the early symptoms of overtrading, and good financial planning and management can avoid a crisis. The usual problem is trying to do too much with too little money, especially where there is too little long-term finance. Solutions include raising more long-term capital, and careful management of working capital and profitability, with a particular emphasis on cash budgeting so that crises can be identified and averted before they become critical to survival (see Example 12.1).

A manufacturer buys goods on credit, uses those goods in production, sells those goods and then sells those goods. At each stage in this process, there is a time gap. It takes time between buying goods and production, between production and selling the goods, and the objective is to minimize the gap between each stage. Additionally, there is a time delay from each stage in its effect on cash. A business will try to minimize the time between paying for goods it has purchased to manufacture and sell and receipts of cash from its customers. In order to optimize its management of working capital and the effect of these time delays on its bank balance, it must control its stockholding and production process, its credit control by managing its receivables and the positive effect on its bank balance in paying its suppliers.

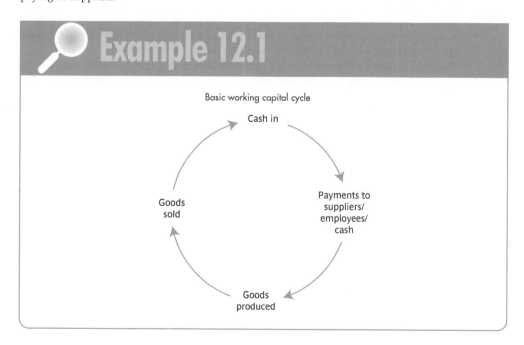

Example 12.1

Basic working capital cycle

Managing receivables

Financial managers may prefer to minimize the amounts tied up in receivables (debtors). This minimizes the requirements for external funding. If receivables are reduced, cash is brought into the business more quickly; the amount of capital employed is reduced; and profitability is increased.

Some businesses sell on a cash-only basis: there are no receivables. Some (such as mail order companies) require customers to pay in advance: their receivables can be negative. Others (particularly service providers such as airlines) require part of full payment in advance; this reduces the amount tied up in receivables.

Offering credit facilities to customers may be an important part of marketing strategy, and it is usually essential when supplying governments and other major organizations. But it has its costs: bad debts, administration of customers' accounts, credit control (chasing customers to pay on time), and the cost of capital (money tied up in receivables may be used more effectively elsewhere). If a company is partly financed by an overdraft that costs 10 per cent per annum, and the level of their receivables is £100,000, then the cost of financing those debtors is £10,000 per annum. It is worth calculating whether the costs of offering credit facilities are justified by the contribution earned by the additional business generated.

If a business decides that it will sell on credit, the following steps should be taken to encourage customers to pay on time, and to minimize losses through bad debts.

Accepting credit customers

It would be foolish to sell on credit to every Tom, Dick and Harry; there are always a few dodgy customers who will not pay up. There are various ways of deciding who is likely to be creditworthy:

1 *Personal judgement and the impression someone creates* – This is still important and no amount of investigation or calculation can eliminate the need for personal judgement. Even the most reputable companies and individuals (and even countries' governments) get into financial difficulties and are unable to pay their bills. But we should not rely on a smart suit and a flashy car being the guarantee of financial strength; they can be financed by excessive borrowing. A visit to a customer's premises can be revealing: many businesses with impressive internet sites and publicity are operated from a backroom above a shop, or a teenager's bedroom.

2 *Bankers' references* – Although they may say very little that is useful, with current money-laundering regulations, the mere fact that someone has a bank account is some indication that they exist, and have an address (or they did when they opened the account).

3 *Business annual reports and accounts* – These can be checked before accepting a credit customer, and show what liabilities a business already had, and indicate their financial strength and ability to pay liabilities as they fall due. It is also worth calculating their payables' ratio: how long they seem to take to pay existing creditors. It may be easier to rely on a credit rating agency to do the assessment.

4 *Ask other creditors how reliable a company is in paying its bills* – This can be done formally, by taking up trade references. It may be more revealing if done informally, through business contacts. Often it becomes widely known when a particular company becomes a slow payer.

5 *Credit-rating agencies* – Agencies such as Experian, Moodies and Standard and Poor provide information on the creditworthiness of individuals and firms; it can be done immediately by telephone or the internet.

How much credit to allow

The amount of credit allowed to customers should be limited in four ways:

1 *Time* – It is important to be clear about how long customers are allowed to pay, perhaps within 30 days. It is wise to have a contract with the agreed terms for payment, with penalties for delay.

Definition and importance of working capital **301**

2 *Amount of money* – There should be a credit limit for each customer, based on their size and creditworthiness. It could be millions of pounds for a government body, but perhaps only £100 for a student!

3 *Maximum for an individual receivable* – Many businesses rely too heavily on one or two major customers. If one such customer does not pay up, the business may go bankrupt. It is important for a business to know that there is not an individual receivable owing an amount large enough to bring the business down if they do not pay.

4 *Maximum total receivables figure* – It may be prudent to estimate the maximum total receivables figure that the business can afford to finance. Profitable expansion usually looks attractive, but if it involves additional working capital that the business cannot afford, it could be very risky.

Collecting in the money

The first step in collecting the money from trade receivables is to send out the paperwork promptly and correctly, and for it to be clear when payment is due. Small businesses are often lax about this: proprietors are often more keen on their product or service than they are on paperwork. Larger businesses usually have fairly tight – sometimes aggressive –credit control systems.

When payments come in, it is necessary to check carefully the amounts received; some customers are good at disputing invoices, delaying payments and taking discounts to which they are not entitled.

Offering cash discounts for prompt payment can be an effective way of encouraging customers to pay within, say, 14 days. But the cost of offering such discounts needs to be carefully calculated. A 10 per cent discount may encourage customers to pay up, say, one month early. But a 10 per cent discount for one month is very expensive – equivalent to 120 per cent per annum! Even a discount of 4 per cent may prove too expensive, as shown in Example 12.2. More modest discounts of, say, 1 per cent, may not be enough incentive for early payment. It might be more cost-effective to employ a competent credit controller to chase debtors to pay up promptly. Another approach is to charge interest on late payments.

It is important to have a credit control system that carefully monitors the payment record of customers, and what has been done about late payers. It is usual to produce an 'age analysis' of receivables, showing little detail where the sale took place only a month or two previously. But where

Last year the Vinelia Building Company's turnover was £12m. All sales were made on credit. Their receivables figure was £3m at the statement of financial position date and that figure was typical of the figure throughout the year.

The company usually has a large overdraft and their cost of capital is 15 per cent per annum. The sales director recommends offering customers a 4 per cent discount for prompt payment and estimates that this would halve the receivables figure.

The costs and benefits of this proposal would be as follows:

Annual cost of discount: 4% × £12m	£480,000
Reduction in receivables: £1.5m	
Annual interest savings on reduction 15% × £1.5m	£225,000

The cost of offering the discount is more than the saving in interest.

Example 12.3

The Vinelia Building Company (as in Example 12.2) is considering employing a credit controller and instituting more effective procedures for collecting money from receivables. The annual cost of doing this is expected to be £40,000. If the average period taken by receivables to pay their bills is reduced from three months to two and a half months, would this expense be justified?

> Reduction in receivables: half of one month's sales = 500,000
> Annual saving in interest £500,000 × 15% = 75,000

Additional expenditure of £40,000 a year is justified if it has the effect of reducing the average level of receivables by £500,000, and reducing interest costs by £75,000 a year.

amounts have been outstanding for more than two or three months, the amounts and dates should be carefully detailed for each customer, together with what action had been taken, and what promises and payments have been received. The financial costs and benefits of a credit control system can be seen in Example 12.3.

When payments do not come in on time the next step is a prompt and polite reminder. Problems arise when customers have still not paid a few weeks after the due date. There are three main approaches to get customers to pay up:

1 *Phoning them, following up promises to pay and visiting them* – Sales staff are not usually keen on the sordid business of asking their customers for money. But continuing to supply customers who do not pay can be fatal to a business.

2 *Withdrawing supplies to customers* – Sometimes it may be best to negotiate a compromise: supplies will continue if the customer pays for them on delivery, and begins to pay off some of the amounts due for previous supplies.

3 *Threatening legal action* – The threat should be enough to frighten most customers into paying promptly. Legal action can be very expensive, but threats are cheap: a routine letter (that appears to come) from solicitors may be cost effective.

The costs and benefits of different approaches

The costs of having receivables include:

1 cost of capital;
2 administration;
3 bad debts;
4 discount allowed.

Companies need to evaluate the costs and benefits involved in different strategies. Sometimes they may want to increase sales by offering more attractive payment terms. If we know the contribution/sales ratio of a company[1] we can estimate the additional profits that will be brought in by an increase

---

[1] Contribution as a percentage of sales, as explained in Section 17.2.

Example 12.4

The Tightar Company specializes in surfacing driveways and minor roads. It has a strict credit control policy because it is short of funds, and depends on an overdraft that has an interest rate of 18 per cent per annum.

It does not undertake work for public institutions or building contractors because such customers are slow to pay, taking on average 10 weeks.

The company's annual turnover is £520,000, and its average receivables figure at any one time is £30,000.

The direct costs of surfacing a driveway amount to 40 per cent of the selling price.

Would it be worth extending its average credit period to 10 weeks if it could double turnover?

Direct costs as a proportion of turnover	40%	
Contribution as a proportion of turnover	60%	
Proposed additional sales	£520,000	
Additional contribution (60%)		£312,000
Existing receivables figure		£ 30,000
New receivables figure	$\dfrac{10 \text{ weeks}}{52 \text{ weeks}} \times £1,040,000 =$	£200,000
Increase in receivables		£ 170,000
Annual cost of increase in receivables	18% × £170,000 =	£ 30,600

It is worth while to pay interest on the necessary additional borrowings because the cost of the interest is substantially lower than the additional contribution generated.

in sales. We can also estimate the amount by which receivables will be increased by offering more attractive credit terms. If we also know the company's cost of capital, we can estimate the annual cost of an increase in debtors. We can then calculate if it appears to be worth while to offer more generous credit terms to customers, as shown in Example 12.4.

Factoring and invoice discounting

A business can outsource or subcontract almost any activity, including the management of receivables. With factoring, most of the money tied up in receivables (typically 75–80 per cent) can be turned into cash immediately. The factoring company provides the money, and charges interest for so doing; it also takes over the administration of the client's sales accounting, invoicing and credit control, for which they also charge a fee, typically of between 0.75 per cent and 2 per cent of turnover. These costs may be more than offset by savings in the business's own administration, and advantages in getting the money in more quickly so that it can be used for other, more profitable purposes. Factoring is likely to be particularly appropriate in small, rapidly growing businesses, where the business has relatively little expertise in credit control and the factor is likely to be more efficient and effective, with economies of scale in carrying out its specialist activity. Using a factor can mean that cash from debtors becomes readily available as the business expands; otherwise, the need to finance working capital can be a significant constraint on growth: increased sales usually require increases in inventory and receivables that are only partly financed by payables. Factoring can be a way of financing growth.

Factoring can be done confidentially so that customers do not know that a company's receivables are being collected by a third party. A business should be careful to calculate the costs and benefits of using a factor: it may seem to be more expensive, but if it is more effective in the long run, it may prove to be more economical. It usually has to be a long-term arrangement: once a business becomes reliant on getting the cash in quickly by using a factor, it is difficult to go back and establish a replacement source of finance, and to set up a credit control function again. Another disadvantage of factoring is that, sometimes, the factor may be unwilling to take on particular types of customer where it anticipates problems.

Invoice discounting is usually a short-term way of using receivables to make cash available quickly. In effect, the receivables are 'sold' to a financial institution that provides around 75 per cent of the amount immediately. The client (not the financial institution) continues with the administration of receivables and continues to bear any risks of bad debts. This usually applies only to selected receivables, and can be a useful source of short-term finance.

Managing inventories

Inventories of raw materials, work in progress and finished goods can be reduced by careful budgeting and planning, and the use of techniques such as the EOQ.

It is always handy to have lots of stuff in stock just in case it might be needed. But holding stock is a very expensive business. There are all the costs involved in providing storage space, including rent, rates, lighting, heating, insurance, security and administration. But the most substantial costs of holding stocks are:

1 *The cost of capital* – A company's cost of capital might typically be between 10–15 per cent per annum. This means that, just in terms of the cost of capital, it costs between £10,000 and £15,000 a year to have average inventory of £100,000.

2 *Obsolescence* – Clothes go out of fashion; publications go out of date; and technological items are soon superseded. Stocks of computers, software or mobile phones that are only a year or two old are worth very little. Inventories of goods for sale, and even raw materials and components, rapidly become out of date.

3 *Physical deterioration* – Inventories physically deteriorate – or even disappear – in various ways. Some things are eaten by rats and other creatures; some things evaporate, go mouldy, or become unusable in a variety of ways.

Holding inventories is expensive, typically costing perhaps 25 per cent per annum. A company that on average holds an inventory of £100,000 is likely to incur costs of about £25,000 a year. In order to maximize profitability, there is pressure to reduce inventory levels. Various approaches are used to achieve this.

Where inventory of finished goods appears to be excessive, there has presumably been a mismatch between the sales budget and the production budget – too much has been produced. This can be tackled by using appropriate control information more quickly, and considering special offers to clear existing inventories.

It is also worth concentrating only on the most valuable items in stock. Sometimes as much as 90 per cent of the value of inventory may be in only 10 per cent of the items. It may not be worth bothering too much about lots of small items of little value.

Economic order quantity (EOQ)

Various quantitative techniques are available for effective management of inventories. If the aim is to keep inventories at as low a level as practicable, there is a need to order small quantities at frequent intervals. But every time an order is placed, there are significant administrative costs: placing the order, checking what has been received, and checking and paying invoices. The administrative costs of ordering suggest that it would be better to order larger quantities less frequently. It is possible to balance these two factors, as shown in Example 12.5.

Definition and importance of working capital   **305**

Example 12.5

The Chemvee company uses 10,000 special purpose disks each year, and pays 50 pence each for them. The administration cost associated with each order is £200, and annual stockholding costs are estimated at 25 per cent per annum. Calculate the EOQ.

$$EOQ = \sqrt{\frac{2 \times \text{annual demand} \times \text{ordering cost}}{\text{Price per unit} \times \text{stockholding cost}}}$$

$$= \sqrt{(2 \times 10,000 \times 200) \div (50p \times 0.25)}$$

$$= \sqrt{4,000,000 \div 0.125} = 5,657$$

The EOQ is 5,657 units.

If the company orders 5,657 units at a time it will have to order (10,000 ÷ 5,657 = 1.77) just less than twice a year: about once in 29 weeks. The average annual ordering cost will be 1.77 × £200 = £354 per annum.

When it receives each new order it will have 5,657 units in inventory that will be gradually whittled down to zero units. On average it will have half of 5,657 units in inventory (2,828½ each costing 50 pence) amounting to £1,414. Annual stockholding costs amount to 25 per cent of the amount of inventory (0.25 × £1,414 =) £354.

We can see that the EOQ is the quantity at which the annual inventory holding cost is equal to the annual ordering cost. If the company ordered more often, the annual cost of ordering would increase. If it ordered larger amounts, the annual inventory holding cost would increase.

A formula such as this is useful in drawing attention to two of the key variables in determining inventory levels, and providing rough guidelines. In practice it might be difficult to determine ordering costs and stockholding costs with the accuracy inherent in the use of the formula. Even annual demand may not be so predictable. A more serious weakness of the EOQ formula is that it ignores quantity discounts. It is often possible to negotiate price reductions in return for more substantial order quantities.

Just in time

The just-in-time approach to inventory planning and control is that goods are purchased or produced only when they are needed. A fine line is drawn so that inventories are neither too high, with the associated stockholding costs, or too low, so that customers cannot be supplied. A just-in-time policy is only suitable when there is reliable sales forecasting and when supply of materials and production are fast and reliable. Supermarkets have fresh bread delivered every day, just in time to meet customers' demand. Similarly, manufacturers can have components delivered just in time to meet production schedules; this minimizes the amounts of inventories held. It depends on managing good quality relationships with suppliers. Traditional managers may be tempted to keep large inventories 'just in case' they are needed. But the pressures of financial management lead to the use of a variety of approaches to minimizing inventory levels.

Managing cash

Planning and control of cash (and bank) is an essential part of financing a business. New and rapidly expanding businesses are often short of cash; unplanned overdrafts can incur very high rates of interest. In serious cases the bank may withdraw support and the business is then unable to meet its liabilities. In some businesses, excessive amounts of cash can be a problem and lead to underperformance. The business may earn interest on its deposits at modest rates (currently 4 or 5 per cent per annum),

but shareholders expect their funds to be used more profitably. Sometimes companies have large hoards of cash that they keep to be ready to buy another business; sometimes companies have surplus funds and they do not seem to know what to do with them; and sometimes these surplus funds are returned to shareholders as extra dividends, or the company buys up its own shares on the market and cancels them.

Careful planning and control of cash should ensure that sufficient long-term funds are available to finance all long-term assets; that additional funds are retained or raised to meet planned high levels of investment whether in non-current assets or acquiring other businesses; and that working capital is properly planned and financed, partly from current liabilities. Overdrafts are an appropriate source of finance to meet temporary or seasonal requirements. Cash budgeting is an essential tool of financial management, and businesses should plan their financing requirements over a three- to five-year period. Cash budgeting is dealt with in Chapter 7 and the main approaches to raising finance are outlined in this chapter. Liquidity problems become apparent in interpreting financial statements, as shown in Chapter 4, and cash flow statements can be used to review a company's performance, as shown in Chapter 7.

Where a company has liquidity problems, the ideal solution may be to raise more equity finance (by issuing shares); but a number of approaches suggested below may minimize the problem in the short term.

Liquidity problems can be minimized by good housekeeping. Prompt banking of all receipts will minimize cash shortages and interest charges. Centralized banking should ensure that any cash shortages in one part of the business are offset by surpluses elsewhere. Payments should not be made ahead of schedule and sending a cheque rather than using a bank transfer helps to retain funds within the business for a few more days. But customers should be encouraged to pay by the fastest means. Creditors should be paid at the time of the month when the business normally has most money in the bank, not at the same time as it pays wages and salaries. It is also important to maintain good relationships with bankers, letting them see budgets, and keeping within agreed limits; the role of bankers can be vital when times are tough. Careful planning and monitoring can avoid liquidity problems.

Where there are more serious liquidity problems, the business may need to take emergency measures that could include a desperate trip to the bank. Banks are always willing to help if they are sure that the customer will repay (and has assets as security), but can make high charges in situations that look risky, and may refuse to help if they have no confidence in the management of the business. Delaying payments to payables may be necessary. Receivables can be encouraged to pay more quickly. Selling off stocks at low prices will bring in cash, at the expense of profits. Capital expenditure can be postponed or cancelled. Surplus assets can be sold off: many businesses have some assets that are underutilized. Sometimes large companies, in times of crisis, suddenly appear to discover that they have expensive head office buildings in the centre of London, or country houses, or sports grounds (or even executive jets) that they do not really need. Smaller businesses can consider transferring their main administrative office to the spare bedroom at home! And businesses can free up cash by selling off company cars and using taxis or bicycles instead, especially when the only realistic alternative is bankruptcy. It may be possible or necessary to defer the payment of taxes; this can usually be negotiated with HM Revenue and Customs, although, of course, interest will be payable. The payment of dividends can also be delayed, or reduced, or cancelled, although it looks better if this is planned in advance.

Some short-term crisis measures can do more harm than good, especially if there is an underlying problem, such as overtrading. But tackling a problem promptly and harshly is better than undue optimism – a key cause of business failure.

Managing payables

To some extent inventories and receivables are financed by payables, and such trade credit is an attractive source of finance. It is cost-free, and the amount of payables tends to increase in line with increases in sales, inventories and receivables. When a company has short-term liquidity problems,

Definition and importance of working capital
307

the easiest thing to do is to delay paying trade payables. This does not cause much of a problem if it is only for a week or two, especially if, after a short-term blip, the company goes back to paying its payables on time. But there is a danger that a company may be unable to resume normal payment periods, and that further delays will occur if it becomes too heavily dependent on creditors as a source of short-term funding.

Excessive delay in paying creditors is not cost-free. Payables soon lose patience with slow payers and are likely to cut off supplies, take legal action or add interest to the amount due. If supplies are cut off because of slow (or non-) payment, it may be difficult to get supplies on credit elsewhere, especially if a company gets a reputation as being a poor payer.

There is much to be said for cultivating good relationships with suppliers, keeping to the terms of the contract, and concentrating on the quality of the relationship including payment. A company that delays making payments is in a weak position when it comes to negotiating improvements in the quality of goods or service received from suppliers.

In some businesses, such as retailers, the amount of payables is greater than the total of current assets; in this case short-term creditors are, in effect, financing some of the company's long-term assets. But a 'normal' working capital cycle would show that inventories represent a number of days' sales; receivables represent a number of days' sales; and this is only partly offset by the number of days' sales represented by payables (see Example 12.6).

Example 12.6

Ground Limited is in business as a frozen food manufacturer. Figures from the annual accounts are as follows:

	20X2	20X1
	£000	£000
Sales	3,427	2,981
Cost of goods sold	2,124	1,789
Inventory	500	374
Trade receivables	492	324
Trade payables	218	347

Chapter 4, ratios 14, 15 and 16 express inventories, receivables and payables in relation to the amount of (cost of) sales. These three ratios for the two years are as follows:

	20X2	20X1
	days	days
Inventory period	86	76
Trade receivables period	52	40
Trade payables period	(37)	(71)
Working capital period	101	45

So, although the sales have increased, the working capital period has more than doubled and this is likely to put a strain on the ability of the business to survive with its existing level of capital.

308   CHAPTER 12 Management of working capital

 Summary

Working capital is the inventory, receivables, cash and payables tied up in the day-to-day operations of the business. It is vital for the optimal effectiveness of the business that there is neither too much money tied up in working capital nor too little. If there is too much in working capital that will be a drain on cash; it will affect the possibility of investing in new projects and buying new non-current assets or other businesses. On the other hand, if there is too little working capital, this is likely to affect relationships with suppliers; result in the inability to supply customers; and could result in overtrading and the collapse of the business. In this chapter, we have examined these issues, looked at the working capital cycle, how to optimize the quantity and reordering of inventory, the management of cash, credit control of receivables and issues relating to paying suppliers. These procedures and considerations will increase the company's efficiency.

Review of key points

- Working capital is usually measured as current assets minus current liabilities.
- Insufficient working capital is likely to be associated with liquidity problems; excessive working capital restricts profitability.
- Receivables should be managed to minimize bad debts and to encourage debtors to pay up quickly.
- The cost-effectiveness of different ways of managing debtors should be assessed.
- Carrying excessive inventories is expensive for companies.
- Careful planning and control of cash is essential.
- Trade payables should be paid in accordance with agreed terms; some companies prefer the short-term financial advantage of delaying paying their creditors.
- Calculations and estimates can be made of the costs and benefits of different policies for managing each element of working capital.

 Self-testing questions

1 Why might a company want high levels of working capital?

2 Can a company operate with zero or negative levels of working capital?

3 How would you detect overtrading, and why does it matter?

4 What steps can be taken to speed up the collection of receivables? Why might a company deliberately allow an increase in the time taken for receivables to pay?

5 What factors are taken into consideration in the conventional model for calculating economic order quantities (EOQs)?

6 How can a company avoid having liquidity crises?

7 The Congle Company uses 40,000 wongles a year. Each wongle costs £1.25 to buy; stockholding costs are estimated to be 32 per cent per annum of the cost of the inventory held; each order costs £20 to place. What ordering quantity will minimize costs? How many orders will be placed each

Assessment questions   309

year? How often will goods be delivered, and what is the average inventory level? What is the annual stockholding cost?

8 Fleshwick Traders has a large overdraft on which interest of 17 per cent per annum is being charged. The directors are considering offering cash discounts to customers to encourage prompt payment. Annual sales, all on credit, amount to £365,000, and the receivables figure at present is £90,000. The sales director considers that a discount of 2.5 per cent for settlement in 10 days would be taken up by about one-third of their customers. The finance director thinks that a larger discount would be required to achieve this result. Assuming that the sales level remained constant:

a Would it be worth offering the discount if the sales director is right?

b What is the largest discount the company could offer without a reduction in profits?

c Assume that each £1 of sales contributes 20 pence to non-current costs and profits. If the company decided to offer a 5 per cent cash discount for payment in 10 days, and it is taken up by one-third of its customers, how large an increase in sales would be required to maintain profits?

9 Stokeypokey Wholesalers Ltd is proposing to set up a branch in Northern Ireland. Experience elsewhere suggests that sales will start off at £100,000 a month in January, and then increase by £100,000 a month until reaching £400,000 in April. Then sales will increase by £80,000 a month until they reach £640,000 in July. In August sales are expected to reach £700,000 a month and remain at that level until the end of the year. Customers are expected to pay two months after the sales are made.

The cost of purchases is 80 per cent of the sales figure, and they are paid for in the month following the purchase. In January purchases will amount to £240,000; then, each month they purchase the amount of goods required for the following month.

Rent of £100,000 per quarter is payable at the beginning of January, and then in March, June, September and December. Other expenses, payable in the month that they are incurred, are expected to amount to £10,000 per month for the first four months; they will increase to £15,000 a month in May, and then to £16,000 a month in August–December.

The only capital expenditure is for purchase of fittings, with £50,000 payable in January and £50,000 in September. Depreciation is at 10 per cent per annum, with a full year's depreciation being charged in the first year.

The Northern Ireland branch starts business with an interest-free loan of £1 million from Stokeypokey Wholesalers, which is put into a separate bank account.

a Prepare a summarized income statement for the first year of business.

b Prepare a statement of financial position as at the end of the first year.

c Prepare a cash budget showing receipts and payments for each month for the year.

d Comment on the results, highlighting key learning points.

Assessment questions

1 How can a company operate with minimum levels of working capital?

2 Working capital should be managed to maximize profitability. Explain and comment.

3 What steps can be taken to minimize bad debts?

4 What are the main limitations of the EOQ model?

5 The Scottish Cake Company has annual sales of £1,200,000. Annual non-current costs are £150,000 and last year's profit was £50,000. At the year end the receivables figure was £100,000.

  The company has been offered a contract for supplying cakes to the Swaysco Supermarket Group in England. Sales would be £300,000 in a year, and Swaysco would require three months' credit. The Scottish Cake Company's cost of capital is estimated at 15 per cent per annum. Is the proposed expansion worth while if all customers are given three months' credit? Is the proposed expansion worth while if only Swaysco is given three months' credit?

6 The summarized statement of financial position of the Warmel Trading Company as at 31 December last year was as follows:

	£	£
Non-current assets		3,000,000
Current assets		
Inventories	500,000	
Trade receivables	600,000	
Cash	10,000	1,110,000
Total assets		4,110,000
Current liabilities		
Trade payables		110,000
Equity		4,000,000
Total liabilities and equity		4,110,000

Last year sales amounted to £3,600,000 and net profit before tax was £600,000. The company's target ROCE is 15 per cent. It is estimated that variable costs amount to 50 per cent of sales, and that non-current costs amount to £1,200,000 per annum.

The purchasing manager is concerned about the very small amount of cash available and that the company may be unable to meet its current liabilities as they fall due.

The financial accountant says that the level of receivables is too high, and proposes to appoint a credit controller at an annual cost of £25,000. He reckons that by doing this the amount of receivables could be halved.

The sales manager believes that many customers are put off by the strict credit control policies, and would like to allow three months' credit to customers. If this policy was adopted he reckons that sales would increase by at least 10 per cent. The finance director estimates that such a policy would result in receivables taking, on average, four months to pay, that inventory and payables would each increase by 10 per cent, and that bad debts would increase by £18,000 per annum.

Required:

a Evaluate the comments made by:
  i the purchasing manager;
  ii the financial accountant;
  iii the sales manager and finance director.
b What would be your recommendation and why?

7 The following information has been extracted from the most recent annual report and accounts of Greyhound Leather Manufacturers Ltd:

Income statement	Year 1	Year 2
	£000	£000
Sales	20,000	22,000
Cost of sales	16,000	17,800
Gross profit	4,000	4,200
Operating profit	2,000	2,050
Net profit after tax	1,500	1,300
Statement of financial position		
Non-current assets	6,200	12,680
Inventories		
Raw materials	1,600	2,000
Work in progress	400	420
Finished goods	2,000	2,500
Receivables	5,000	3,200
Bank	2,000	–
Total assets	17,200	20,800
Current liabilities		
Payables	2,200	2,800
Overdraft	–	2,000
	2,200	4,800
Equity	15,000	16,000
Total liabilities and equity	17,200	20,800

a The finance director is pleased with the management of working capital, but the chairman is more concerned about profitability. Making use of appropriate calculations, you are required to analyse the financial management of the company and comment on the two points of view expressed.

b What is meant by the working capital cycle? Illustrate your answer with appropriate calculations for Greyhound Leather Manufacturers Ltd.

c What steps can a company take to improve inventory turnover?

d The company uses one million hides of leather a year, which it buys for £16 each. Stockholding costs are estimated to be 25 per cent per annum of the cost of the items in inventory. Administration costs for placing and receiving an order are estimated to be £50. How many hides should the company order at a time (i.e. calculate the EOQ)?

e Illustrate the financial effects of implementing the EOQ in practice and suggest its limitations.

8 The directors of Woebun Standard Components plc have been very successful in persuading their customers to pay, on average, in one month. However, they believe that this policy is restricting sales and that sales would increase by 15 per cent if the average collection period for receivables was allowed to increase from one month to two months.

312 CHAPTER 12 Management of working capital

The selling price of the component is £40 per unit and variable costs per unit are £30. Annual sales revenue is £6m. A sales increase of 15 per cent would lead to an increase in inventory of £400,000 and an increase in trade payables of £100,000.

Woebun expects a ROCE of 27 per cent per annum.

a On purely financial grounds, should the company allow its customers to enjoy the extended credit period of two months?

b Assess the practicability and financial viability of restricting the two months' credit to new customers only.

c What are the main causes and symptoms of *overtrading*? To what extent and in what ways can effective management of debtors avoid the problems of overtrading?

9 The Bonjarron Decorating Company uses 14,400 large-size cans of white gloss paint in a year. It uses different suppliers and on average pays £20 per can. It has limited storage space and reckons that the annual stockholding costs amount to 20 per cent of the cost of the stocks held. Administration costs amount to £50 per order placed.

a Calculate the EOQ.

b For what reasons might the company use (i) a much higher, or (ii) a much lower, ordering quantity?

Group activities and discussion questions

1 Many small businesses may be seen as 'overtrading'. Accountants are too conservative about such things. To be successful, a rapidly expanding small business needs to sail close to the wind. Discuss these views.

2 Large businesses should not have working capital problems. It is easy for them to borrow large sums on a long-term basis. The problem for large businesses is not working capital; it is excessive gearing. Discuss.

3 Discuss the effects on 'just in time' of increasing proportions of manufacturing (for the UK) taking place in Eastern Europe, Africa and Asia.

4 Can working capital, like manufacturing, be 'outsourced'? Could a company operate with zero or negative capital employed, make some profits, and therefore have a ROCE of infinity?

5 Large companies can bully small customers to pay up promptly, while they need not bother paying their own bills on time. Small companies have to pay up promptly if they are to continue to receive supplies, but they cannot force large customers to pay them promptly if they are to continue to make sales. Discuss these views.

6 How does cash budgeting for a business differ from the way in which you do your own, personal cash budgeting. Should it differ? (Other than the amounts of money being very different!)

7 Distinguish between factoring and invoice discounting. Explain the circumstances in which a company considering these two forms of finance would be likely to prefer factoring rather than invoice discounting.

Accounting in context

313

Accounting in context

Discuss and comment on the following extract from the press with reference to alternative ways of controlling a company's working capital, such as using a company's assets to finance its operations.

Struggling to find credit? Invoice finance may be for you

Banks are pushing invoice finance as an alternative to overdrafts.

By Richard Tyler

"Giving a small business an overdraft is like handing a child a loaded gun," a leading business banker has told MPs in the Commons.

Without sensing that he might have said the wrong thing, the banker went on to advocate invoice finance as "a highly inexpensive form of finance if used properly".

Official surveys show demand from small businesses for overdrafts remains on the increase, with 35pc of firms applying in 2010 compared with only a quarter in 2007.

Banks, however, are less keen about overdrafts, as this banker speaking on condition of anonymity made clear. The part-nationalised banks – Royal Bank of Scotland and Lloyds Banking Group – may have pledged not to withdraw or alter the terms of agreed borrowing facilities before they mature, but that is not stopping them encouraging customers to shift onto other forms of finance.

While traditional bank lending to small businesses is still declining, lending against assets, like a company's invoices, is growing. They rose by 9pc to £12.4bn in the first quarter of 2011, according to the latest figures from the Asset Based Lending Association.

The shift comes as the cost to the banks of providing overdrafts increases as they have to hold more capital against the facilities even if they are not drawn down by customers.

The banks are also working harder to reduce bad debts on their loan books and prefer to monitor a customer's trading performance and reasons for needing credit, which invoice financing allows while an overdraft does not.

A significant change in the law in 2005 also meant that an overdraft is now classed as a fixed rather than a floating charge on a company's assets. If a company goes bust, its overdraft provider falls behind other preferential creditors in the queue to recover any remaining cash.

For small businesses keen to borrow to finance growth, asking for the right kind of finance has become more essential as banks remain highly selective about which ones they back.

A survey for the Business Department found that in 2010 more than a third of all small businesses needing finance were turned down by their bank, up from only 14pc before the financial crisis took hold.

Invoice finance works with a finance supplier auditing a company's customer base and setting credit limits on the amounts it is prepared to advance against business done with those customers.

Companies pay a fee when they draw down a percentage of the value of an invoice up until the date it is paid by the customer. The outstanding percentage of the invoice is then collected – either by the company's credit department (invoice discounting) or by the finance provider (factoring) directly – minus further fees and any insurance charges.

The latest ABFA statistics show that more than 41,000 companies used asset based finance in March, down 2pc year on year. [...]

Source: The Telegraph, 13 June 2011.

314   CHAPTER 12 Management of working capital

References and further reading

Atkinson, A., R. Kaplan, E. Matsumura and M. Young (2012) *Management Accounting* (6th edn.). Harlow: Pearson.

Dyson, J.R. (2010) *Accounting for Non-accounting Students* (8th edn.). Upper Saddle River, NJ: FT Prentice Hall.

Proctor, R. (2009) *Managerial Accounting for Business Decisions* (3rd edn.). Harlow: Pearson.

Seal, W., R.H. Garrison and E.W. Nooreen (2011) *Management Accounting* (4th edn.). Maidenhead: McGraw-Hill.

When you have read this chapter, log on to the Online Learning Centre website at *www.mcgraw-hill.co.uk/textbooks/leiwy* to explore chapter-by-chapter test questions, further reading and more online study tools.

Chapter 10
Long-term decision making: capital investment appraisal

 LO Learning **objectives**

After studying Chapter 10, you should be able to:
1 Determine the acceptability of an investment project using the net present value method
2 Determine the acceptability of an investment project using the internal rate of return method
3 Compare the net present value and internal rate of return methods
4 Determine the payback period for an investment
5 Compute the simple rate of return for an investment

Concepts **in Context**

Neil is a commercial manager working in a large hotel chain. His job is to appraise possible sites for new hotels. He has data for each town and city on transport, businesses, and tourism as well as on competitor hotels in the area. His team uses these data to estimate future guest volumes and revenues. The projected net cash flows are then analysed using investment appraisal techniques in order to evaluate the financial viability of a new hotel.

© Jay Spooner

The term 'investment decision making' or, alternatively, 'capital budgeting', is used to describe how managers plan significant outlays on projects that have long-term implications such as the purchase of new equipment and the introduction of new products. Most companies have many more potential projects than can actually be funded. Hence, managers must carefully select those projects that promise the greatest future return. How well managers make these capital budgeting decisions is a critical factor in the long-run profitability of the company.

Capital budgeting involves *investment* – a company must commit funds now in order to receive a return in the future. Investments are not limited to shares and bonds. Purchase of inventory or equipment is also an investment. For example, Wetherspoons makes an investment when it opens a new pub/restaurant. Eon makes an investment when it installs a new computer to handle customer billing. Jaguar makes an investment when it redesigns a model and must retool its production lines. All of these investments are characterized by a commitment of funds today in the expectation of receiving a return in the future in the form of additional cash inflows or reduced cash outflows.

Focus on Business Practice

Investing in renewable energy

Renewable energy projects are in vogue with investors and energy firms. Wind farms are increasingly common, particularly in remote upland areas and offshore. Energy and utility companies who invest in wind energy projects do incur high development costs – in the region of £1 million per megawatt of electricity. Debt finance is typically available for such projects, helped by guaranteed cash flows over 15–20 years from energy sales to utility companies. The return on investment is thus dependent on the price agreed in the longer term, as ongoing running costs are low compared to initial investment costs. Take for example the London Array, a proposed project to construct the world's largest offshore wind farm in the Thames estuary. The estimated investment cost of the project in early 2009 was £3 billion. However, the global economic recession and falling electricity prices has seen one backer (Royal Dutch Shell) withdraw from the project. In May 2009, two other firms behind the project, German energy concern Eon and Danish firm Dong Energy, joined forces with Abu Dhabi firm Masdar to sign contracts for a £2 billion investment. Work on the project will be in two phases, starting in 2011.[1]

© TebNad

Exercise: Using the internet or other sources, find the costs and savings from installing a domestic wind turbine in your own home.

Capital budgeting – planning investments

Typical capital budgeting decisions

What types of business decisions require capital budgeting analysis? Virtually any decision that involves an outlay now in order to obtain some return (increase in revenue or reduction in costs) in the future. Typical capital budgeting decisions include:

1 Cost reduction decisions. Should new equipment be purchased to reduce costs?

2   Expansion decisions. Should a new plant, warehouse, or other facility be acquired to increase capacity and sales?

3   Equipment selection decisions. Which of several available machines would be the most cost effective to purchase?

4   Equipment replacement decisions. Should old equipment be replaced now or later?

The time value of money

As stated earlier, business investments commonly promise returns that extend over fairly long periods of time. Therefore, in approaching capital budgeting decisions, it is necessary to employ techniques that recognize *the time value of money*. A pound today is worth more than a pound a year from now. The same concept applies in choosing between investment projects. Those projects that promise returns earlier in time are preferable to those that promise returns later in time.

The capital budgeting techniques that recognize the two above characteristics of business investments most fully are those that involve discounted cash flows. We will spend most of this chapter illustrating the use of discounted cash flow methods in making *capital budgeting decisions*.

Discounted cash flows – the net present value method

There are two approaches to making capital budgeting decisions by means of discounted cash flows. One is the *net present value* method, and the other is the *internal rate of return method* (sometimes called the *time-adjusted rate of return method*). The net present value method is discussed in this section; the internal rate of return method is discussed in the next section.

The net present value method illustrated

Under the net present value method, the present value of all cash inflows is compared to the present value of all cash outflows that are associated with an investment project. The difference between the present value of these cash flows, called the **net present value**, determines whether or not the project is an acceptable investment. To illustrate, let us assume the following data:

- Harper Company is contemplating the purchase of a machine capable of performing certain operations that are now performed manually. The machine will cost £5,000, and it will last for five years. At the end of the five-year period, the machine will have a zero scrap value. Use of the machine will reduce labour costs by £1,800 per year. Harper Company requires a minimum return of 20% before taxes on all investment projects.

Should the machine be purchased? Harper Company must determine whether a cash investment now of £5,000 can be justified if it will result in a £1,800 reduction in cost each year over the next five years. It may appear that the answer is obvious since the total cost savings is £9,000 (5 × £1,800). However, the company can earn a 20% return by investing its money elsewhere. It is not enough that the cost reductions cover just the original cost of the machine; they must also yield at least a 20% return or the company would be better off investing the money elsewhere.

To determine whether the investment is desirable, it is necessary to discount the stream of annual £1,800 cost savings to its present value and then to compare this discounted present value with the cost of the new machine. Since Harper Company requires a minimum return of 20% on all investment projects, this rate is used in the discounting process. Exhibit 10.1 shows how this analysis is done.

According to the analysis, Harper Company should purchase the new machine. The present value of the cost savings is £5,384, as compared to a present value of only £5,000 for the investment required (cost of the machine). Deducting the present value of the investment required from the present value of the cost savings gives a net present value of £384. Whenever the net present value is zero or greater, as in

Exhibit 10.1 Net present value analysis of a proposed project

Initial cost			£5,000	
Life of the project (years)			5	
Annual cost savings			£1,800	
Salvage value			0	
Required rate of return			20%	

Item Year	Year(s)	Amount of cash flow	20% factor	Present value of cash flows
Annual cost savings	1–5	£1,800	2.991*	£5,384
Initial investment	Now	(5,000)	1.000	(5,000)
Net present value				£384

*From Exhibit 10A.4 in Appendix 10A at the end of the chapter.

our example, an investment project is acceptable. Whenever the net present value is negative (the present value of the cash outflows exceeds the present value of the cash inflows), an investment project is not acceptable. In sum:

If the net present value is ...	Then the project is ...
Positive	Acceptable, since it promises a return greater than a required rate of return
Zero	Acceptable, since it promises a return equal to the required rate of return
Negative	Not acceptable, since it promises a return less than the required rate of return

A full interpretation of the solution would be as follows: The new machine promises more than the required 20% rate of return. This is evident from the positive net present value of £384. Harper Company could spend up to £5,384 for the new machine and still obtain the minimum required 20% rate of return. The net present value of £384, therefore, shows the amount of 'cushion' or 'margin of error'. One way to look at this is that the company could underestimate the cost of the new machine by up to £384, or overestimate the net present value of the future cash savings by up to £384, and the project would still be financially attractive.

Emphasis on cash flows

In capital budgeting decisions, the focus is on cash flows and not on accounting profit. The reason is that accounting profit is based on accrual concepts that ignore the timing of cash flows into and out of an organization. From a capital budgeting standpoint the timing of cash flows is important, since a pound received today is more valuable than a pound received in the future. Therefore, even though the accounting profit figure is useful for many things, it is not used in discounted cash flow analysis. Instead of determining accounting profit, the manager must concentrate on identifying the specific cash flows associated with an investment project.

What kinds of cash flows should the manager look for? Although the specific cash flows will vary from project to project, certain types of cash flows tend to recur, as explained in the following paragraphs.

Typical cash outflows

Most projects will have an immediate cash outflow in the form of an initial investment in equipment or other assets. Any salvage value realized from the sale of old equipment can be recognized as a cash inflow or as a reduction in the required investment. In addition, some projects require that a company expand its working capital. Working capital is current assets (cash, debtors and stock) less current liabilities. When a company takes on a new project, the balances in the current asset accounts will often increase. For example, opening a new Tesco store would require additional cash in sales registers, increased debtors for new customers, and more stock to fill the shelves. These additional working capital needs should be treated as part of the initial investment in a project. Also, many projects require periodic outlays for repairs and maintenance and for additional operating costs. These should all be treated as cash outflows for capital budgeting purposes.

Typical cash inflows

On the cash inflow side, a project will normally either increase revenues or reduce costs. Either way, the amount involved should be treated as a cash inflow for capital budgeting purposes. (In regard to this point, notice that so far as cash flows are concerned, *a reduction in costs is equivalent to an increase in revenues*.) Cash inflows are also frequently realized from salvage of equipment when a project is terminated. In addition, upon termination of a project, any working capital that was tied up in the project can be released for use elsewhere and should be treated as a cash inflow. Working capital is released, for example, when a company sells off its stock or collects its receivables. (If the released working capital is not shown as a cash inflow at the termination of a project, then the project will go on being charged for the use of the funds forever!)

In summary, the following types of cash flows are common in business investment projects:

Cash outflows:
Initial investment (including installation costs)
Increased working capital needs
Repairs and maintenance
Incremental operating costs.
Cash inflows:
Incremental revenues
Reduction in costs
Salvage value
Release of working capital

Recovery of the original investment

When computing the present value of a project, depreciation is not deducted for two reasons.

First, depreciation is not a current cash outflow. Second, as discussed above, discounted cash flow methods of making capital budgeting decisions focus on *cash flows*. Although depreciation is a vital concept in computing profit for financial statements, it is not relevant in an analytical framework that focuses on cash flows. A second reason for not deducting depreciation is that discounted cash flow methods *automatically* provide for return of the original investment, thereby making a deduction for depreciation unnecessary.

Simplifying assumptions

In working with discounted cash flows, at least two simplifying assumptions are usually made.

The first assumption is that all cash flows other than the initial investment occur at the end of a period. This is somewhat unrealistic in that cash flows typically occur somewhat uniformly throughout a period. The purpose of this assumption is just to simplify computations.

The second assumption is that all cash flows generated by an investment project are immediately reinvested. It is further assumed that the reinvested funds will yield a rate of return equal to the discount rate. Unless these conditions are met, the return computed for the project will not be accurate.

Choosing a discount rate

To use the net present value method, we must choose some rate of return for discounting cash flows to their present value. The firm's cost of capital is usually regarded as the most appropriate choice for the discount rate. The cost of capital is the average rate of return the company must pay to its long-term creditors and shareholders for the use of their funds. The mechanics involved in cost of capital computations are covered in finance texts and will not be considered here.

LO 2 Discounted cash flows – the internal rate of return method

The internal rate of return (or time-adjusted rate of return) can be defined as the interest yield promised by an investment project over its useful life. It is sometimes referred to simply as the yield on a project. The internal rate of return is computed by finding the discount rate that equates the present value of a project's cash outflows with the present value of its cash inflows. In other words, the internal rate of return is that discount rate which will cause the net present value of a project to be equal to zero.

The internal rate of return method illustrated

To illustrate the internal rate of return method, let us assume the following data:

* Glendale School is considering the purchase of a large tractor-pulled lawn mower. At present, the lawn is mowed using a small hand-pushed petrol mower. The large, tractor-pulled mower will cost £16,950 and will have a useful life of ten years. It will have only a negligible scrap value, which can be ignored. The tractor-pulled mower would do the job much more quickly than the old mower and would result in a labour saving of £3,000 per year.

To compute the internal rate of return promised by the new mower, we must find the discount rate that will cause the net present value of the project to be zero. How do we do this? The simplest and most direct approach *when the net cash inflow is the same every year* is to divide the investment in the project by the expected net annual cash inflow. This computation will yield a factor from which the internal rate of return can be determined. The formula is as follows:

$$\text{Factor of the internal rate of return} = \frac{\text{Investment required}}{\text{Net annual cash flow}} \tag{1}$$

The factor derived from formula (1) is then located in the present value tables to see what rate of return it represents. Using formula (1) and the data for Glendale School's proposed project, we get:

$$\frac{\text{Investment required}}{\text{Net annual cash flow}} = \frac{£16,950}{£3,000} = 5.650$$

Thus, the discount factor that will equate a series of £3,000 cash inflows with a present investment of £16,950 is 5.650. Now we need to find this factor in Exhibit 10A.4 in Appendix 10A to see what rate of return it represents. We should use the 10-period line in Exhibit 10A.4 since the cash flows for the project continue for 10 years. If we scan along the 10-period line, we find that a factor of 5.650 represents a 12% rate of return. Therefore, the internal rate of return promised by the mower project is 12%. We can verify this by computing the project's net present value using a 12% discount rate. This computation is made in Exhibit 10.2.

Notice from Exhibit 10.2 that using a 12% discount rate equates the present value of the annual cash inflows with the present value of the investment required in the project, leaving a zero net present value. The 12% rate therefore represents the internal rate of return promised by the project.

Exhibit 10.2 Evaluation of the mower purchase using a 12% discount rate

		Initial cost	£16,950
		Life of the project (years)	10
		Annual cost savings	£3,000
		Salvage value	0

Item	Year(s)	Amount of cash flow	20% factor	Present value of cash flows
Annual cost savings	1–10	£3,000	5.650*	£16,950
Initial investment	Now	(16,950)	1.000	(16,950)
Net present value				£0

*From Exhibit 10A.4 in Appendix 10A.

Salvage value and other cash flows

The technique just demonstrated works very well if a project's cash flows are identical every year. But what if they are not? For example, what if a project will have some salvage value at the end of its life in addition to the annual cash inflows? Under these circumstances, a trial-and-error process is necessary to find the rate of return that will equate the cash inflows with the cash outflows. This trial-and-error process can be carried out by hand, or it can be carried out by means of computer software programs such as spreadsheets that perform the necessary computations in seconds. In short, erratic or uneven cash flows should not prevent a manager from determining a project's internal rate of return.

Using the internal rate of return

Once the internal rate of return has been computed, what does the manager do with the information? The internal rate of return is compared to the company's *required rate of return*. The required rate of return is the minimum rate of return that an investment project must yield to be acceptable. If the internal rate of return is *equal* to or *greater than* the required rate of return, then the project is acceptable. If it is less than the required rate of return, then the project is rejected. Quite often, the company's cost of capital is used as the required rate of return. The reasoning is that if a project cannot provide a rate of return at least as great as the cost of the funds invested in it, then it is not profitable.

In the case of the Glendale School example used earlier, let us assume that the district has set a minimum required rate of return of 15% on all projects. Since the large mower promises a rate of return of only 12%, it does not clear this hurdle and would therefore be rejected as a project.

The cost of capital as a screening tool

As we have seen in preceding examples, the cost of capital often operates as a screening device, helping the manager screen out undesirable investment projects. This screening is accomplished in different ways, depending on whether the company is using the internal rate of return method or the net present value method in its capital budgeting analysis.

When the internal rate of return method is used, the cost of capital is used as the hurdle rate that a project must clear for acceptance. If the internal rate of return of a project is not great enough to clear the cost of capital hurdle, then the project is ordinarily rejected. We saw the application of this idea in the Glendale School example, where the hurdle rate was set at 15%.

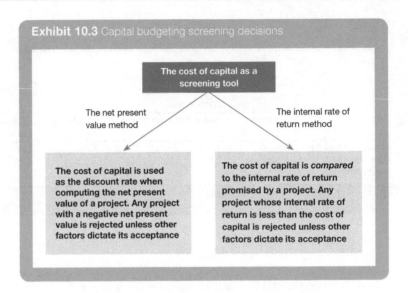

Exhibit 10.3 Capital budgeting screening decisions

The cost of capital as a screening tool

The net present value method

The internal rate of return method

The cost of capital is used as the discount rate when computing the net present value of a project. Any project with a negative net present value is rejected unless other factors dictate its acceptance

The cost of capital is *compared* to the internal rate of return promised by a project. Any project whose internal rate of return is less than the cost of capital is rejected unless other factors dictate its acceptance

When the net present value method is used, the cost of capital is the discount rate used to compute the net present value of a proposed project. Any project yielding a negative net present value is rejected unless other factors are significant enough to require its acceptance. The use of the cost of capital as a screening tool is summarized in Exhibit 10.3.

 LO 3

Comparison of the net present value and the internal rate of return methods

The net present value method has several important advantages over the internal rate of return method.

First, the net present value method is often simpler to use. As mentioned earlier, the internal rate of return method may require hunting for the discount rate that results in a net present value of zero. This can be a very laborious trial-and-error process, although it can be automated to some degree using a computer spreadsheet.

Second, a key assumption made by the internal rate of return method is questionable. Both methods assume that cash flows generated by a project during its useful life are immediately reinvested elsewhere. However, the two methods make different assumptions concerning the rate of return that is earned on those cash flows. The net present value method assumes the rate of return is the discount rate, whereas the internal rate of return method assumes the rate of return is the internal rate of return on the project. Specifically, if the internal rate of return of the project is high, this assumption may not be realistic. It is generally more realistic to assume that cash inflows can be reinvested at a rate of return equal to the discount rate – particularly if the discount rate is the company's cost of capital or an opportunity rate of return. For example, if the discount rate is the company's cost of capital, this rate of return can actually be realized by paying off the company's creditors and buying back the company's stock with cash flows from the project. In short, when the net present value method and the internal rate of return method do not agree concerning the attractiveness of a project, it is best to go with the net present value method. Of the two methods, it makes the more realistic assumption about the rate of return that can be earned on cash flows from the project.

Focus on Business Practice

Investment appraisal in software engineering

According to an editorial in *IEEE Software* in 2004, software engineers view the term 'return on investment' (ROI) with suspicion, due mainly to its (mis-)use by many software vendors trying to increase sales of their product. One of the issues faced in evaluating investments in software (bought or in-house developed) is that accurate cash flows representing the costs and revenues/cost savings of any proposed software project as a 'must have'. Identifying all cash flow associated with software is not an easy task. However, the authors propose that software engineers should acquaint themselves with the

© Matthew Barnett

investment evaluation techniques like net present value, as in many businesses software is strategically important and must undergo rigorous investment appraisal. This knowledge can help software engineers in two ways. First, it may help them to understand the strategic nature of the software they are working on. Second, it may help them do their own investment analysis on whether software should be upgraded/modified versus completely rewritten.[2]

Exercise: Do you think it is necessary to evaluate investment in software which is viewed as a 'must have' for an organization? For example, no bank could trade nowadays without ATMs and internet banking.

Other approaches to capital budgeting decisions

Discounted cash flow methods have gained widespread acceptance as decision-making tools. Other methods of making capital budgeting decisions are also used, however, and are preferred by some managers. In this section, we discuss two such methods known as *payback* and *simple rate of return*.

The payback method

The payback method centres on a span of time known as the payback period. The payback period can be defined as the length of time that it takes for a project to recoup its initial cost out of the cash receipts that it generates. This period is sometimes referred to as 'the time that it takes for an investment to pay for itself'. The basic premise of the payback method is that the more quickly the cost of an investment can be recovered, the more desirable is the investment.

The payback period is expressed in years. *When the net annual cash inflow is the same every year*, the following formula can be used to compute the payback period:

$$\text{Payback period} = \frac{\text{Investment required}}{\text{Net annual cash flow}^*} \tag{2}$$

*If new equipment is replacing old equipment, this becomes incremental net annual cash inflow.

To illustrate the payback method, assume the following data:

- York Company needs a new milling machine. The company is considering two machines: machine A and machine B. Machine A costs £15,000 and will reduce operating costs by £5,000 per year. Machine B costs only £12,000 but will also reduce operating costs by £5,000 per year.

Which machine should be purchased according to the payback method?

$$\text{Machine A payback period} = \frac{£15,000}{£5,000} = 3.0 \text{ years}$$

$$\text{Machine B payback period} = \frac{£12,000}{£5,000} = 2.4 \text{ years}$$

According to the payback calculations, York Company should purchase machine B, since it has a shorter payback period than machine A.

Evaluation of the payback method

The payback method is not a true measure of the profitability of an investment. Rather, it simply tells the manager how many years will be required to recover the original investment. Unfortunately, a shorter payback period does not always mean that one investment is more desirable than another.

To illustrate, consider again the two machines used in the example above. Since machine B has a shorter payback period than machine A, it *appears* that machine B is more desirable than machine A. But, if we add one more piece of data, this illusion quickly disappears. Machine A has a projected 10-year life, and machine B has a projected 5-year life. It would take two purchases of machine B to provide the same length of service as a single purchase of machine A. Under these circumstances, machine A would be a much better investment than machine B, even though machine B has a shorter payback period. Unfortunately, the payback method has no inherent mechanism for highlighting differences in useful life between investments. Such differences can be very important, and relying on payback alone may result in incorrect decisions.

A further criticism of the payback method is that it does not consider the time value of money. A cash inflow to be received several years in the future is weighed equally with a cash inflow to be received right now. To illustrate, assume that for an investment of £8,000 you can purchase either of the two following streams of cash inflows:

Year	0	1	2	3	4	5	6	7	8
Stream 1		0	0	0	£8,000	£2,000	£2,000	£2,000	£2,000
Stream 2		£2,000	£2,000	£2,000	£2,000	£8,000	0	0	0

Which stream of cash inflows would you prefer to receive in return for your £8,000 investment? Each stream has a payback period of 4.0 years. Therefore, if payback alone were relied on in making the decision, you would be forced to say that the streams are equally desirable. However, from the point of view of the time value of money, stream 2 is much more desirable than stream 1.

On the other hand, under certain conditions the payback method can be very useful. For one thing, it can help identify which investment proposals are in the 'ballpark'. That is, it can be used as a screening tool to help answer the question, 'Should I consider this proposal further?' If a proposal does not provide a payback within some specified period, then there may be no need to consider it further. In addition, the payback period is often of great importance to new firms that are 'cash poor'. When a firm is cash poor, a project with a short payback period but a low rate of return might be preferred over another project with a high rate of return but a long payback period. The reason is that the company may simply need a faster return of its cash investment. And finally, the payback method is sometimes used in industries where products become obsolete very rapidly – such as consumer electronics. Since products may last only a year or two, the payback period on investments must be very short.

Payback and uneven cash flows

When the cash flows associated with an investment project change from year to year, the simple payback formula that we outlined earlier is no longer usable, and the computations involved in deriving the payback period can be fairly complex. Consider the following data:

Year	Investment	Cash inflow
1	£4,000	£1,000
2		0
3		2,000
4	2,000	1,000
5		500
6		3,000
7		2,000
8		2,000

What is the payback period on this investment? The answer is 5.5 years, but to obtain this figure it is necessary to track the unrecovered investment year by year. The steps involved in this process are shown in Exhibit 10.4. By the middle of the sixth year, sufficient cash inflows will have been realized to recover the entire investment of £6,000 (£4,000 + £2,000).

The simple/accounting rate of return method

The simple rate of return method is another capital budgeting technique that does not involve discounted cash flows. The method is also known as the accounting rate of return, the unadjusted rate of return, and the financial statement method.

Unlike the other capital budgeting methods that we have discussed, the simple rate of return method does not focus on cash flows. Rather, it focuses on accounting profit. The approach is to estimate the revenues that will be generated by a proposed investment and then to deduct from these revenues all of the

Exhibit 10.4 Payback and uneven cash flows

Year	(1) Beginning unrecovered investment	(2) Additional Investment	(3) Total Unrecovered Investment (1) + (2)	(4) Cash inflow	(5) Ending unrecovered Investment (3) – (4)
1	£4,000		£4,000	£1,000	£3,000
2	3,000		3,000	0	3,000
3	3,000		3,000	2,000	1,000
4	1,000	£2,000	3,000	1,000	2,000
5	2,000		2,000	500	1,500
6	1,500		1,500	3,000	0
7	0		0	2,000	0
8	0		0	2,000	0

projected operating expenses associated with the project. This profit figure is then related to the initial investment in the project, as shown in the following formula:

$$\text{Simple rate of return} = \frac{\begin{array}{c}\text{Incremental revenues} - \text{Incremental expenses}\\\text{including depreciation} = \text{Incremental net profit}\end{array}}{\text{Initial investment}^*} \qquad (3)$$

*The investment should be reduced by any salvage from the sale of old equipment. Or, if a cost reduction project is involved, formula (3) becomes:

$$\text{Simple rate of return} = \frac{\text{Cost savings} - \text{Depreciation on new equipment}}{\text{Initial investment}^*} \qquad (4)$$

*The investment should be reduced by any salvage from the sale of old equipment.

- Brigham Tea Ltd is a processor of a non-tannic acid tea. The company is contemplating purchasing equipment for an additional processing line. The additional processing line would increase revenues by £90,000 per year. Incremental cash operating expenses would be £40,000 per year. The equipment would cost £180,000 and have a nine-year life. No salvage value is projected.

Required
1 Compute the simple rate of return.
2 Compute the internal rate of return and compare it to the simple rate of return.

Solution
1 By applying the formula for the simple rate of return found in equation (3), we can compute the simple rate of return:

$$\text{Simple rate of return} = \frac{\left[\begin{array}{c}£90,000\\\text{incremental}\\\text{revenues}\end{array}\right] - \left[\begin{array}{c}£40,000\text{ cash operating}\\\text{expenses} + £20,000\\\text{depreciation}\end{array}\right]}{£180,000\text{ initial investment}}$$

$$= \frac{£30,000}{£180,000}$$

$$= 16.7\%$$

2 The rate computed in (1) above, however, is far below the internal rate of return of approximately 24%:

$$\text{Factor of the internal rate of return} = \frac{£180,000}{£50,000} = 3.600$$

*£30,000 profit + £20,000 depreciation = £50,000; or the annual cash inflow can be computed as £90,000 increased revenues − £40,000 cash expenses = £50,000.

By scanning across the nine-year line in Exhibit 10A.4 in Appendix 10A, we can see that the internal rate of return is approximately 24%.

- Midshires Farms Ltd hires people on a part-time basis to sort eggs. The cost of this hand-sorting process is £30,000 per year. The company is investigating the purchase of an egg-sorting machine that would cost £90,000 and have a 15-year useful life. The machine would have negligible salvage value, and it would cost £10,000 per year to operate and maintain. The egg-sorting equipment currently being used could be sold now for a scrap value of £2,500.

Required

Compute the simple rate of return on the new egg-sorting machine.

A cost reduction project is involved in this situation. By applying the formula for the simple rate of return found in equation (4), we can compute the simple rate of return as follows:

Solution

$$\text{Simple rate of return} = \frac{£20,000^{*}\text{ cost savings} - £6,000^{\dagger}\text{ depreciation on new equipment}}{£90,000 - £2,500}$$

$$= 16.0\%$$

* £30,000 − £10,000 = £20,000 cost savings.

† £90,000 ÷ 15 years = £6,000 depreciation.

Criticisms of the simple rate of return

The most damaging criticism of the simple rate of return method is that it does not consider the time value of money. A pound received ten years from now is viewed as being just as valuable as a pound received today. Thus, the manager can be misled if the alternatives being considered have different cash flow patterns. For example, assume that project A has a high simple rate of return but yields the bulk of its cash flows many years from now. Another project, B, has a somewhat lower simple rate of return but yields the bulk of its cash flows over the next few years. Project A has a higher simple rate of return than project B; however, project B might in fact be a much better investment if the time value of money were considered.

Summary

- Investment decisions should take into account the time value of money since a pound today is more valuable than a pound received in the future. The net present value and internal rate of return methods both reflect this fact. In the net present value method, future cash flows are discounted to their present value so that they can be compared on a valid basis with current cash outlays.

- The difference between the present value of the cash inflows and the present value of the cash outflows is called the project's net present value. If the net present value of the project is negative, the project is rejected.

- The discount rate in the net present value method is usually a minimum required rate of return such as the company's cost of capital.

- The internal rate of return is the rate of return that equates the present value of the cash inflows and the present value of the cash outflows, resulting in a zero net present value. If the internal rate of return is less than the company's minimum required rate of return, the project is rejected.

- Some companies prefer to use either payback or the simple rate of return to evaluate investment proposals. The payback period is the number of periods that are required to recover the initial investment in the project. The simple rate of return is determined by dividing a project's accounting profit by the initial investment in the project.

Key terms

Capital budgeting The process of planning significant outlays on projects that have long-term implications, such as the purchase of new equipment or the introduction of a new product (p. 234).

Cost of capital The overall cost to an organization of obtaining investment funds, including the cost of both debt sources and equity sources (p. 238).

Internal rate of return The discount rate at which the net present value of an investment project is zero; thus, the internal rate of return represents the interest yield promised by a project over its useful life. This term is synonymous with time-adjusted rate of return (p. 238).

Net present value The difference between the present value of the cash inflows and the present value of the cash outflows associated with an investment project (p. 235).

Payback period The length of time that it takes for a project to recover its initial cost out of the cash receipts that it generates (p. 241).

Required rate of return The minimum rate of return that an investment project must yield to be acceptable (p. 239).

Simple rate of return The rate of return computed by dividing a project's annual accounting profit by the initial investment required (p. 243).

Time-adjusted rate of return This term is synonymous with internal rate of return (p. 238).

Working capital The excess of current assets over current liabilities (p. 237).

Yield A term synonymous with internal rate of return and time-adjusted rate of return (p. 238).

Endnotes

1 http://www.guardian.co.uk/business/2009/may/12/wind-farm-electricity-london-array; http://www.guardian.co.uk/business/2009/apr/08/london-array-seeks-bailout; http://www.seai.ie/Renewables/Wind_Energy/Wind_Farm_Development/Financing_wind_farms/

2 Erdogmus, Favaro and Strigel (2004).

When you have read this chapter, log on to the Online Learning Centre for *Management Accounting for Business Decisions* at **www.mcgraw-hill.co.uk/textbooks/seal**, where you'll find multiple choice questions, practice exams and extra study tools for management accounting.

Future value and present value tables

Appendix
10A

Exhibit 10A.1 Future value of £1; $F_n = P(1 + r)^n$

Periods	4%	6%	8%	10%	12%	14%	20%
1	1.040	1.060	1.080	1.100	1.120	1.140	1.200
2	1.082	1.124	1.166	1.210	1.254	1.300	1.440
3	1.125	1.191	1.260	1.331	1.405	1.482	1.728
4	1.170	1.263	1.361	1.464	1.574	1.689	2.074
5	1.217	1.338	1.469	1.611	1.762	1.925	2.488
6	1.265	1.419	1.587	1.772	1.973	2.195	2.986
7	1.316	1.504	1.714	1.949	2.211	2.502	3.583
8	1.369	1.594	1.851	2.144	2.476	2.853	4.300
9	1.423	1.690	1.999	2.359	2.773	3.252	5.160
10	1.480	1.791	2.159	2.594	3.106	3.707	6.192
11	1.540	1.898	2.332	2.853	3.479	4.226	7.430
12	1.601	2.012	2.518	3.139	3.896	4.818	8.916
13	1.665	2.133	2.720	3.452	4.364	5.492	10.699
14	1.732	2.261	2.937	3.798	4.887	6.261	12.839
15	1.801	2.397	3.172	4.177	5.474	7.138	15.407
20	2.191	3.207	4.661	6.728	9.646	13.473	38.338
30	3.243	5.744	10.063	17.450	29.960	50.950	237.380
40	4.801	10.286	21.275	45.260	93.051	199.880	1469.800

Exhibit 10A.2 Future value of an annuity of £1 in arrears; $F_n = \dfrac{(1 + r)_n - 1}{r}$

Periods	4%	6%	8%	10%	12%	14%	20%
1	1.000	1.000	1.000	1.000	1.000	1.000	1.000
2	2.040	2.060	2.080	2.100	2.120	2.140	2.220
3	3.122	3.184	3.246	3.310	3.374	3.440	3.640
4	4.247	4.375	4.506	4.641	4.779	4.921	5.368
5	5.416	5.637	5.867	6.105	6.353	6.610	7.442
6	6.633	6.975	7.336	7.716	8.115	8.536	9.930
7	7.898	8.394	8.923	9.487	10.089	10.730	12.916
8	9.214	9.898	10.637	11.436	12.300	13.233	16.499
9	10.583	11.492	12.488	13.580	14.776	16.085	20.799
10	12.006	13.181	14.487	15.938	17.549	19.337	25.959
11	13.486	14.972	16.646	18.531	20.655	23.045	32.150
12	15.026	16.870	18.977	21.385	24.133	27.271	39.580
13	16.627	18.882	21.495	24.523	28.029	32.089	48.497
14	18.282	21.015	24.215	27.796	32.393	37.581	59.196
15	20.024	23.276	27.152	31.773	37.280	43.842	72.035
20	29.778	36.778	45.762	57.276	75.052	91.025	186.690
30	56.085	79.058	113.283	164.496	241.330	356.790	1181.900
40	95.026	154.762	259.057	442.597	767.090	1342.000	7343.900

Exhibit 10A.3 Present value of £1; $F_n = \dfrac{F_n}{(1+r)^n}$

Period	4%	5%	6%	8%	10%	12%	14%	16%	18%	20%	22%	24%	26%	28%	30%	40%
1	0.962	0.952	0.926	0.943	0.909	0.893	0.877	0.862	0.847	0.833	0.820	0.806	0.794	0.781	0.769	0.714
2	0.925	0.907	0.857	0.890	0.826	0.797	0.769	0.743	0.718	0.684	0.672	0.650	0.630	0.610	0.592	0.510
3	0.889	0.864	0.794	0.840	0.751	0.712	0.675	0.641	0.609	0.579	0.551	0.524	0.500	0.477	0.455	0.364
4	0.855	0.823	0.735	0.792	0.683	0.636	0.592	0.552	0.516	0.482	0.451	0.423	0.397	0.373	0.350	0.260
5	0.822	0.784	0.681	0.747	0.621	0.567	0.519	0.476	0.437	0.402	0.370	0.341	0.315	0.291	0.269	0.186
6	0.790	0.746	0.630	0.705	0.564	0.507	0.456	0.410	0.370	0.335	0.303	0.275	0.250	0.227	0.207	0.133
7	0.760	0.711	0.583	0.665	0.513	0.452	0.400	0.352	0.314	0.279	0.249	0.222	0.198	0.178	0.159	0.095
8	0.731	0.677	0.540	0.627	0.467	0.404	0.351	0.305	0.266	0.233	0.204	0.179	0.157	0.139	0.123	0.068
9	0.703	0.645	0.500	0.592	0.424	0.361	0.308	0.263	0.225	0.194	0.167	0.144	0.125	0.108	0.094	0.048
10	0.676	0.614	0.463	0.558	0.386	0.322	0.270	0.227	0.191	0.162	0.137	0.116	0.099	0.085	0.073	0.035
11	0.650	0.585	0.429	0.527	0.350	0.287	0.237	0.195	0.162	0.135	0.112	0.094	0.079	0.066	0.056	0.025
12	0.625	0.557	0.397	0.497	0.319	0.257	0.208	0.168	0.137	0.112	0.092	0.076	0.062	0.052	0.043	0.018
13	0.601	0.530	0.368	0.469	0.290	0.229	0.182	0.145	0.116	0.093	0.075	0.061	0.050	0.040	0.033	0.013
14	0.577	0.505	0.340	0.442	0.263	0.205	0.160	0.125	0.099	0.078	0.062	0.049	0.039	0.032	0.025	0.009
15	0.555	0.481	0.315	0.417	0.239	0.183	0.140	0.108	0.084	0.065	0.051	0.040	0.031	0.025	0.020	0.006
16	0.534	0.458	0.292	0.394	0.218	0.163	0.123	0.093	0.071	0.054	0.042	0.032	0.025	0.019	0.015	0.005
17	0.513	0.436	0.270	0.371	0.198	0.146	0.108	0.080	0.060	0.045	0.034	0.026	0.020	0.015	0.012	0.003
18	0.494	0.416	0.250	0.350	0.180	0.130	0.095	0.069	0.051	0.038	0.027	0.021	0.016	0.012	0.009	0.002
19	0.476	0.396	0.232	0.331	0.164	0.116	0.083	0.060	0.043	0.031	0.023	0.017	0.012	0.009	0.007	0.002
20	0.456	0.377	0.215	0.312	0.149	0.104	0.073	0.051	0.037	0.026	0.019	0.014	0.010	0.007	0.005	0.001
21	0.439	0.359	0.199	0.294	0.135	0.093	0.064	0.044	0.031	0.022	0.015	0.011	0.008	0.006	0.004	0.001
22	0.422	0.342	0.184	0.278	0.123	0.083	0.056	0.038	0.026	0.018	0.013	0.009	0.006	0.004	0.003	0.001
23	0.406	0.326	0.170	0.262	0.112	0.074	0.049	0.033	0.022	0.015	0.010	0.007	0.005	0.003	0.002	
24	0.390	0.310	0.158	0.247	0.102	0.066	0.043	0.028	0.019	0.013	0.008	0.006	0.004	0.003	0.002	
25	0.375	0.295	0.146	0.233	0.092	0.059	0.038	0.024	0.016	0.010	0.007	0.005	0.003	0.002	0.001	
26	0.361	0.281	0.135	0.220	0.084	0.053	0.033	0.021	0.014	0.009	0.006	0.004	0.002	0.002	0.001	
27	0.347	0.268	0.125	0.207	0.076	0.047	0.029	0.018	0.011	0.007	0.005	0.003	0.002	0.001	0.001	
28	0.333	0.255	0.116	0.196	0.069	0.042	0.026	0.016	0.010	0.006	0.004	0.002	0.002	0.001	0.001	
29	0.321	0.243	0.107	0.185	0.063	0.037	0.022	0.014	0.008	0.005	0.003	0.002	0.001	0.001	0.001	
30	0.308	0.231	0.099	0.174	0.057	0.033	0.020	0.012	0.007	0.004	0.003	0.002	0.001	0.001		
40	0.208	0.142	0.046	0.097	0.022	0.011	0.005	0.003	0.001	0.001						

Exhibit 10A.4 Present value of an annuity of £1 in arrears; $P_n = \dfrac{1}{r}\left[1 - \dfrac{1}{(1+r)^n}\right]$

Period	4%	5%	6%	8%	10%	12%	14%	16%	18%	20%	22%	24%	26%	28%	30%	40%
1	0.962	0.952	0.943	0.926	0.909	0.893	0.877	0.862	0.847	0.833	0.820	0.806	0.781	0.794	0.769	0.714
2	1.886	1.859	1.833	1.783	1.736	1.690	1.647	1.605	1.566	1.528	1.492	1.457	1.424	1.392	1.361	1.224
3	2.775	2.723	2.673	2.577	2.487	2.402	2.322	2.246	2.174	2.106	2.042	1.981	1.923	1.868	1.816	1.589
4	3.630	3.546	3.465	3.312	3.170	3.037	2.914	2.798	2.690	2.589	2.494	2.404	2.320	2.241	2.166	1.879
5	4.452	4.330	4.212	3.993	3.791	3.605	3.433	3.274	3.127	2.991	2.864	2.745	2.635	2.532	2.436	2.035
6	5.242	5.076	4.917	4.623	4.355	4.111	3.889	3.685	3.498	3.326	3.167	3.030	2.885	2.759	2.643	2.168
7	6.002	5.786	5.582	5.206	4.868	4.564	4.288	4.039	3.812	3.605	3.416	3.242	3.083	2.937	2.802	2.263
8	6.733	6.463	6.210	5.747	5.335	4.968	4.639	4.344	4.078	3.837	3.619	3.421	3.421	3.076	2.925	2.331
9	7.435	7.108	6.802	6.247	7.759	5.328	4.946	4.607	4.303	4.031	3.786	3.566	3.366	3.184	3.019	2.379
10	8.111	7.722	7.360	6.710	6.145	5.650	5.216	4.833	4.494	4.192	3.923	3.682	3.465	3.629	3.092	2.414
11	8.760	8.306	7.887	7.139	6.495	5.988	5.453	5.029	4.656	4.327	4.035	3.776	3.544	3.335	3.147	2.438
12	9.385	8.863	8.384	7.536	6.814	6.194	5.660	5.197	4.793	4.430	4.127	3.851	3.606	3.387	3.190	2.456
13	9.986	9.394	8.853	7.904	7.103	6.424	5.842	5.342	4.910	4.533	4.203	3.912	3.656	3.427	3.223	2.468
14	10.563	9.899	9.295	8.244	7.367	6.628	6.002	5.468	5.008	4.611	4.265	3.962	3.695	3.459	3.249	2.477
15	11.118	10.380	9.712	8.559	7.606	6.811	6.142	5.575	5.092	4.675	4.315	4.001	3.726	3.483	3.268	2.484
16	11.652	10.838	10.106	8.851	7.824	6.974	6.265	5.669	5.162	4.730	4.357	4.033	3.751	3.503	3.283	2.489
17	12.166	11.274	10.477	9.122	8.022	7.120	6.373	5.749	5.222	4.775	4.391	4.059	3.771	3.518	3.295	2.492
18	12.659	11.690	10.828	9.372	8.201	7.250	6.467	5.818	5.273	4.812	4.419	4.080	3.786	3.529	3.304	2.494
19	13.134	12.085	11.158	9.604	8.365	7.366	6.550	5.877	5.316	4.844	4.442	4.097	3.799	3.539	3.311	2.496
20	13.590	12.462	11.470	9.818	8.514	7.469	6.623	5.929	5.353	4.870	4.460	4.110	3.808	3.546	3.316	2.497
21	14.029	12.821	11.764	10.017	8.649	7.562	6.687	5.973	5.384	4.891	4.476	4.121	3.186	3.551	3.320	2.498
22	14.451	13.163	12.042	10.201	8.772	7.645	6.743	6.011	5.410	4.909	4.499	4.130	3.822	3.556	3.323	2.498
23	14.857	13.489	12.303	10.371	8.883	7.718	6.792	6.044	5.432	4.295	4.499	4.137	3.827	3.559	3.325	2.499
24	15.247	13.799	12.550	10.529	8.985	7.784	6.835	6.073	5.451	4.937	4.507	4.143	3.831	3.562	3.327	2.499
25	15.622	14.094	12.783	10.675	9.077	7.843	6.873	6.097	5.467	4.948	4.514	4.147	3.834	3.564	3.329	2.499
26	15.983	14.375	13.003	10.810	9.161	7.896	6.906	6.118	5.480	4.956	4.520	4.151	3.837	3.566	3.330	2.500
27	16.330	14.643	13.211	10.935	9.237	7.943	6.935	6.136	5.492	4.964	4.525	4.154	3.839	3.567	3.331	2.500
28	16.663	14.898	13.406	11.051	9.307	7.984	6.961	6.152	5.502	4.970	4.528	4.157	3.840	3.568	3.331	2.500
29	16.984	15.141	13.591	11.158	9.370	8.022	6.983	6.166	5.510	4.975	4.531	4.159	3.841	3.569	3.332	2.500
30	17.292	15.373	13.765	11.258	9.427	8.055	7.003	6.177	5.517	4.979	4.534	4.160	3.842	3.569	3.332	2.500
40	19.793	17.159	15.046	11.925	9.779	8.244	7.105	6.234	5.548	4.997	4.544	4.166	3.846	3.571	3.333	2.500

Assessment

Questions

connect

10–1   Why can't accounting profit figures be used in the net present value and internal rate of return methods of making capital budgeting decisions?

10–2   Why are discounted cash flow methods of making capital budgeting decisions superior to other methods?

10–3   What is net present value? Can it ever be negative? Explain.

10–4   Identify two simplifying assumptions associated with discounted cash flow methods of making capital budgeting decisions.

10–5   If a firm has to pay interest of 14% on long-term debt, then its cost of capital is 14%. Do you agree? Explain.

10–6   What is meant by an investment project's internal rate of return? How is the internal rate of return computed?

10–7   Explain how the cost of capital serves as a screening tool when dealing with (a) the net present value method and (b) the internal rate of return method.

10–8   What is meant by the term *payback period*? How is the payback period determined?

10–9   How can the payback method be useful to the manager?

10–10 What is the major criticism of the payback and simple rate of return methods of making capital budgeting decisions?

Exercises

connect

E10–1 Consider each of the following situations independently. (Ignore income taxes.)

⏱ Time allowed: 10 minutes

1   In three years, when he is discharged from the Air Force, Steve wants to buy a power boat that will cost £8,000. What lump-sum amount must he invest now to have the £8,000 at the end of three years if he can invest money at:
(a) 10%?
(b) 14%?

2   Annual cash inflows that will arise from two competing investment projects are given below:

| | Investment | |
Year	A	B
1	£3,000	£12,000
2	6,000	9,000
3	9,000	6,000
4	12,000	3,000
	£30,000	£30,000

Each investment project will require the same investment outlay. You can invest money at an 18% rate of return. Compute the present value of the cash inflows for each investment.

3 Julie has just retired. Her company's retirement programme has two options as to how retirement benefits can be received. Under the first option, Julie would receive a lump sum of £150,000 immediately as her full retirement benefit. Under the second option, she would receive £14,000 each year for 20 years plus a lump-sum payment of £60,000 at the end of the 20-year period. If she can invest money at 12%, which option would you recommend that she accept? Use present value analysis.

E10–2 Time allowed: 15 minutes

Each of the following parts is independent. (Ignore income/corporation taxes.)

1 The Atlantic Medical Clinic can purchase a new computer system that will save £7,000 annually in billing costs. The computer system will last for eight years and have no salvage value. What is the maximum purchase price that the Atlantic Medical Clinic should be willing to pay for the new computer system if the clinic's required rate of return is:
   (a) 16%?
   (b) 20%?

2 The Caldwell *Herald* newspaper reported the following story:
   Frank Ormsby of Caldwell is the state's newest millionaire. By choosing the six winning numbers on last week's state lottery, Mr Ormsby has won the week's grand prize totalling £1.6 million. The State Lottery Commission has indicated that Mr Ormsby will receive his prize in 20 annual instalments of £80,000 each.
   (a) If Mr Ormsby can invest money at a 12% rate of return, what is the present value of his winnings?
   (b) Is it correct to say that Mr Ormsby is the 'state's newest millionaire'? Explain your answer.

3 Fraser Company will need a new warehouse in five years. The warehouse will cost £500,000 to build. What lump-sum amount should the company invest now to have the £500,000 available at the end of the five-year period? Assume that the company can invest money at:
   (a) 10%
   (b) 14%.

E10–3 Time allowed: 15 minutes

Perot Industries has £100,000 to invest. The company is trying to decide between two alternative uses of the funds. The alternatives are:

	Project	
	A	B
Cost of equipment required	£100,000	–
Working capital investment required	–	£100,000
Annual cash inflows	21,000	16,000
Salvage value of equipment in six years	8,000	–
Life of the project	6 years	6 years

The working capital needed for project B will be released at the end of six years for investment elsewhere. Perot Industries' discount rate is 14%.

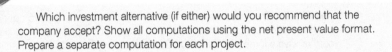

Which investment alternative (if either) would you recommend that the company accept? Show all computations using the net present value format. Prepare a separate computation for each project.

E10–4   Time allowed: 30 minutes

Complete the following cases (ignore income taxes).

1   Preston Company requires a minimum return of 14% on all investments. The company can purchase a new machine at a cost of £84,900. The new machine would generate cash inflows of £15,000 per year and have a 12-year useful life with no salvage value. Compute the machine's net present value. Is the machine an acceptable investment? Explain.

2   The Walton *Daily News* is investigating the purchase of a new auxiliary press that has a projected life of 18 years. It is estimated that the new press will save £30,000 per year in cash operating costs. If the new press costs £217,500, what is its internal rate of return? Is the press an acceptable investment if the company's required rate of return is 16%? Explain.

3   Refer to the data above for the Walton *Daily News*. How much would the annual cash inflows (cost savings) have to be for the new press to provide the required 16% rate of return? Round your answer to the nearest whole pound.

E10–5   Time allowed: 30 minutes

Solve the three following present value exercises:

1   The Cambro Foundation, a non-profit organization, is planning to invest £104,950 in a project that will last for three years. The project will provide cash inflows as follows:

Year 1	£30,000
Year 2	40,000
Year 3	?

Assuming that the project will yield exactly a 12% rate of return, what is the expected cash inflow for Year 3?

2   Lukow Products is investigating the purchase of a piece of automated equipment that will save £400,000 each year in direct labour and stock carrying costs. This equipment costs £2,500,000 and is expected to have a 15-year useful life with no salvage value. The company requires a minimum 20% return on all equipment purchases. Management anticipates that this equipment will provide intangible benefits such as greater flexibility, higher quality of output, and experience in automation. What pound value per year would management have to attach to these intangible benefits to make the equipment an acceptable investment?

3   The Matchless Dating Service has made an investment in video and recording equipment that costs £106,700. The equipment is expected to generate cash inflows of £20,000 per year. How many years will the equipment have to be used to provide the company with a 10% rate of return on its investment?

E10–6 Time allowed: 10 minutes

A piece of labour-saving equipment has just come onto the market that Mitsui Electronics Ltd could use to reduce costs in one of its plants in Japan. Relevant data relating to the equipment follow (currency is in thousands of yen, denoted by ¥).

Purchase cost of the equipment	¥432,000
Annual cost savings that will be provided by the equipment	¥90,000
Life of the equipment	12 years

Required

1 Compute the payback period for the equipment. If the company requires a payback period of four years or less, would the equipment be purchased?
2 Compute the simple rate of return on the equipment. Use straight-line depreciation based on the equipment's useful life. Would the equipment be purchased if the company requires a rate of return of at least 14%?

E10–7 Time allowed: 10 minutes

Nick's Novelties Ltd is considering the purchase of electronic pinball machines to place in amusement houses. The machines would cost a total of £300,000, have an eight-year useful life, and have a total salvage value of £20,000. Based on experience with other equipment, the company estimates that annual revenues and expenses associated with the machines would be as follows:

Revenues from use		£200,000
Less operating expenses:		
Commissions to amusement houses	£100,000	
Insurance	7,000	
Depreciation	35,000	
Maintenance	18,000	160,000
Profit		£40,000

Required (ignore taxes)

1 Assume that Nick's Novelties Ltd will not purchase new equipment unless it provides a payback period of four years or less. Would the company purchase the pinball machines?
2 Compute the simple rate of return promised by the pinball machines. If the company requires a simple rate of return of at least 12%, will the pinball machines be purchased?

Problems

connect

P10–8 Basic net present value analysis

Time allowed: 20 minutes

Joyce Mines of Ireland is contemplating the purchase of equipment to exploit a mineral deposit that is located on land to which the company has mineral rights. An engineering and cost analysis has been made, and it is expected that the following cash flows would be associated with opening and operating a mine in the area:

Cost of new equipment and timbers	€275,000
Working capital required	100,000
Net annual cash receipts	120,000*
Cost to construct new roads in three years	40,000
Salvage value of equipment in four years	€65,000

*Receipts from sales of ore, less out-of-pocket costs for salaries, utilities, insurance, and so forth.

It is estimated that the mineral deposit would be exhausted after four years of mining. At that point, the working capital would be released for reinvestment elsewhere. The company's discount rate is 20%.

Required (ignore taxes)
Determine the net present value of the proposed mining project. Should the project be accepted? Explain.

P10–9 Basic net present value analysis

⏱ Time allowed: 20 minutes

The Sweetwater Candy Company would like to buy a new machine that would automatically 'dip' chocolates. The dipping operation is currently done largely by hand. The machine the company is considering costs £120,000. The manufacturer estimates that the machine would be usable for 12 years but would require the replacement of several key parts at the end of the sixth year. These parts would cost £9,000, including installation. After 12 years, the machine could be sold for about £7,500.

The company estimates that the cost to operate the machine will be only £7,000 per year. The present method of dipping chocolates costs £30,000 per year. In addition to reducing costs, the new machine will increase production by 6,000 boxes of chocolates per year. The company realizes a contribution margin of £1.50 per box. A 20% rate of return is required on all investments.

Required (ignore taxes)
1 What are the net annual cash inflows that will be provided by the new dipping machine?
2 Compute the new machine's net present value. Use the incremental cost approach and round all pound amounts to the nearest whole pound.

P10–10 Simple rate of return; payback

⏱ Time allowed: 30 minutes

Paul Swanson has an opportunity to acquire a franchise from The Yogurt Place plc to dispense frozen yogurt products under The Yogurt Place name. Mr Swanson has assembled the following information relating to the franchise:
1 A suitable location in a large shopping mall can be rented for £3,500 per month.

2 Remodelling and necessary equipment would cost £270,000. The equipment would have an estimated 15-year life and an estimated £18,000 salvage value. Straight-line depreciation would be used, and the salvage value would be considered in computing depreciation deductions.

3 Based on similar outlets elsewhere, Mr Swanson estimates that sales would total £300,000 per year. Ingredients would cost 20% of sales.

4 Operating costs would include £70,000 per year for salaries, £3,500 per year for insurance, and £27,000 per year for utilities. In addition, Mr Swanson would have to pay a commission to The Yogurt Place plc of 12.5% of sales.

Rather than obtain the franchise, Mr Swanson could invest his funds in long-term corporate bonds that would yield a 12% annual return.

Required (ignore taxes)

1 Prepare a profit statement that shows the expected profit each year from the franchise outlet. Use the contribution format.

2 Compute the simple rate of return promised by the outlet. If Mr Swanson requires a simple rate of return of at least 12%, should he obtain the franchise?

3 Compute the payback period on the outlet. If Mr Swanson wants a payback of four years or less, should the outlet be opened?

P10–11   Net present value analysis of a new product

⏱ Time allowed: 50 minutes

Matheson Electronics has just developed a new electronic device which, when mounted on a car, will tell the driver how many miles the car is travelling per litre of petrol.

The company is anxious to begin production of the new device. To this end, marketing and cost studies have been made to determine probable costs and market potential. These studies have provided the following information:

1 New equipment would have to be acquired to produce the device. The equipment would cost £315,000 and have a 12-year useful life. After 12 years, it would have a salvage value of about £15,000.

2 Sales in units over the next 12 years are projected to be as follows:

Year	Sales in units
1	6,000
2	12,000
3	15,000
4–12	18,000

3 Production and sales of the device would require working capital of £60,000 to finance debtors, inventories and day-to-day cash needs. This working capital would be released at the end of the project's life.

4 The devices would sell for £35 each; variable costs for production, administration and sales would be £15 per unit.

5   Fixed costs for salaries, maintenance, property taxes, insurance and straight-line depreciation on the equipment would total £135,000 per year. (Depreciation is based on cost less salvage value.)

6   To gain rapid entry into the market, the company would have to advertise heavily. The advertising programme would be:

Year	Amount of yearly advertising
1–2	£180,000
3	150,000
4–12	120,000

7   Matheson Electronics' board of directors has specified that all new products must have a return of at least 14% to be acceptable.

Required (ignore taxes)

1   Compute the net cash inflow (cash receipts less yearly cash operating expenses) anticipated from sale of the device for each year over the next 12 years.

2   Using the data computed in Question 1 above and other data provided in the problem, determine the net present value of the proposed investment. Would you recommend that Matheson accepts the device as a new product?

P10–12 Opening a small business; net present value

⏱ Time allowed: 30 minutes

In eight years, John Duncan will retire. He has £150,000 to invest, and is exploring the possibility of opening a self-service car wash. The car wash could be managed in the free time he has available from his regular occupation, and it could be closed easily when he retires. After careful study, Mr Duncan has determined the following:

1   A building in which a car wash could be installed is available under an eight-year lease at a cost of £1,700 per month.

2   Purchase and installation costs of equipment would total £150,000. In eight years the equipment could be sold for about 10% of its original cost.

3   An investment of an additional £2,000 would be required to cover working capital needs for cleaning supplies, change funds, and so forth. After eight years, this working capital would be released for investment elsewhere.

4   Both a car wash and a vacuum service would be offered with a wash costing £1.50 and the vacuum costing 25 pence per use.

5   The only variable costs associated with the operation would be 23 pence per wash for water and 10 pence per use of the vacuum for electricity.

6   In addition to rent, monthly costs of operation would be: cleaning, £450; insurance, £75; and maintenance, £500.

7   Gross receipts from the car wash would be about £1,350 per week. According to the experience of other car washes, 70% of the customers using the wash would also use the vacuum.

Mr Duncan will not open the car wash unless it provides at least a 10% return, since this is the amount that could be earned by simply placing the £150,000 in high-grade securities.

Required (ignore taxes)

1 Assuming that the car wash will be open 52 weeks a year, compute the expected net annual cash receipts (gross cash receipts less cash disbursements) from its operation. (Do not include the cost of the equipment, the working capital, or the salvage value in these computations.)

2 Would you advise Mr Duncan to open the car wash? Show computations using the net present value method of investment analysis. Round all pound figures to the nearest whole pound.

P10-13 Simple rate of return; payback

Time allowed: 30 minutes

Sharkey's Fun Centre contains a number of electronic games as well as a miniature golf course and various rides located outside the building.

Paul Sharkey, the owner, would like to construct a water slide on one portion of his property. Mr Sharkey has gathered the following information about the slide:

1 Water slide equipment could be purchased and installed at a cost of £330,000. According to the manufacturer, the slide would be usable for 12 years after which it would have no salvage value.

2 Mr Sharkey would use straight-line depreciation on the slide equipment.

3 To make room for the water slide, several rides would be dismantled and sold. These rides are fully depreciated, but they could be sold for £60,000 to an amusement park in a nearby city.

4 Mr Sharkey has concluded that about 50,000 more people would use the water slide each year than have been using the rides. The admission price would be £3.60 per person (the same price that the Fun Centre has been charging for the rides).

5 Based on experience at other water slides, Mr Sharkey estimates that incremental operating expenses each year for the slide would be: salaries, £85,000; insurance, £4,200; utilities, £13,000; and maintenance, £9,800.

Required

1 Prepare a profit statement showing the expected profit each year from the water slide.

2 Compute the simple rate of return expected from the water slide. Based on this computation, should the water slide be constructed if Mr Sharkey requires a simple rate of return of at least 14% on all investments?

3 Compute the payback period for the water slide. If Mr Sharkey requires a payback period of five years or less, would the water slide be constructed?

P10–14 Simple rate of return; payback; internal rate of return

⏱ Time allowed: 30 minutes

Honest John's Used Cars plc has always hired students from the local university to wash the cars on the lot. Honest John is considering the purchase of an automatic car wash that would be used in place of the students. The following information has been gathered by Honest John's accountant to help Honest John make a decision on the purchase:

1   Payments to students for washing cars total £15,000 per year at present.
2   The car wash would cost £21,000 installed, and it would have a 10-year useful life. Honest John uses straight-line depreciation on all assets. The car wash would have a negligible salvage value in 10 years.
3   Annual out-of-pocket costs associated with the car wash would be: wages of students to operate the wash, keep the soap bin full and so forth, £6,300; utilities, £1,800; and insurance and maintenance, £900.
4   Honest John now earns a return of 20% on the funds invested in his stock of used cars. He feels that he would have to earn an equivalent rate on the car wash for the purchase to be attractive.

Required (ignore taxes)

1   Determine the annual savings that would be realized in cash operating costs if the car wash were purchased.
2   Compute the simple rate of return promised by the car wash. (*Hint:* Note that this is a cost reduction project.) Will Honest John accept this project if he expects a 20% return?
3   Compute the payback period on the car wash. Honest John (who has a reputation for being something of a penny-pincher) will not purchase any equipment unless it has a payback of four years or less. Will he purchase the car wash equipment?
4   Compute (to the nearest whole %) the internal rate of return promised by the car wash. Based on this computation, does it appear that the simple rate of return would normally be an accurate guide in investment decisions?

Chapter

11

Financing a Business

Chapter contents

✓ Learning objectives

After studying this chapter you will be able to:

- ✓ Describe the main sources of finance used by companies
- ✓ Appreciate the differences between the various sources, and evaluate the appropriateness of each in different circumstances
- ✓ Understand the advantages and disadvantages of high gearing
- ✓ Evaluate different dividend policies
- ✓ Understand how published accounts indicate companies' financing needs and policies
- ✓ Take an overall view of the financing of businesses, combining a number of different approaches

11.1 Introduction

Businesses own a variety of different assets, and statements of financial position show how these have been financed. There are non-current assets (such as land and buildings, plant and machinery, furniture and fittings), and current assets (such as inventories, receivables and cash). These have been financed from three main sources:

1 *The money or capital that was put into the business by its owners* – In a company this is the share capital which is part of 'equity' or shareholders' funds.

2 *Borrowing* – A company may borrow money on a long-term basis (e.g. by issuing debentures), and on a short-term basis (e.g. as a bank overdraft).

3 *Retained profits* – A successful company makes profits, some of which are paid out to shareholders as dividends; what is left is retained in the business, financing an increase in net assets.

When starting a business the owners usually put in a large amount of their own money ('equity') and/or borrow substantial sums. If the business is to expand, they will need to make profits, retaining some within the business. There are, however, other ways of financing the setting-up of a business, and its subsequent growth. Although businesses tend to own the premises that they occupy and the vehicles and equipment that they use, they may choose to lease them instead. Although many businesses finance inventories of goods, many find that, by buying on credit, they do not need to provide the finance themselves. Similarly, many businesses finance 'receivables' themselves, whereas others manage to get their customers to pay cash (so that there are few, if any, debtors) or even to require them to pay in advance. It can be very expensive to finance a manufacturing facility (factory premises, plant and machinery; inventories of raw materials, components, work in progress and finished goods); an alternative is to subcontract (or 'outsource') the manufacturing, perhaps to a country where these things cost less, leaving the subcontractor to provide the finance.

The three main sources of finance to a business (share capital, borrowing and retained profits, as shown in Illustration 11.1) are examined in the first three parts of this chapter. But it is always worth considering other ways of financing. Careful control of working capital can substantially reduce financing requirements, and ways of doing this are examined in the fourth part of the chapter. Finally, 'other sources of finance' are considered, including other ways of doing business that reduce the need for external finance. In most situations a combination of different ways of financing the business is used.

In this instance the three long-term sources of finance are each £1,000, making a total of £3,000. There is also short-term funding (current liabilities, or payables) of £800. The £800 has financed most of the current assets; perhaps their inventory of goods has been financed by the company's trade payables. The £3,000 has financed all the long-term assets, leaving £200 for working capital.

11.2 Share Capital

Share capital is perhaps the most important source of finance for companies, and it is mostly 'ordinary' share capital. There are other types of shares, including a variety of preference shares.

Ordinary shares

When a company is established it issues a number of ordinary shares. With a small, new company, they may be issued only to a few family members. The shareholders are the owners of the company. They also bear most of the risk. If the company gets into financial difficulties, all the creditors have to be repaid before anything is returned to the shareholders. Shareholders can lose everything that they put into a company, but their liability is limited to that amount. There can be no call on the shareholders' personal assets to pay any amounts due to creditors; that is the nature of limited liability.

ILLUSTRATION 11.1

The three main sources of finance are shown in the following simplified company statement of financial position:

	£
Non-current assets	
Property, plant and equipment	2,600
Current assets	
Inventories, receivables and cash	1,200
Total assets	3,800
Liabilities and equity	
Current liabilities	
Payables	800
Non-current liabilities	
Debentures	1,000
Total liabilities	1,800
Equity	
Share capital	1,000
Retained earnings	1,000
	2,000
Total liabilities and equity	3,800

A company may start off as a small, private limited company, with a restricted number of shares. If it grows and wants more shareholders it becomes a public limited company. Very large plcs may become listed on a stock market (such as the London Stock Exchange) to raise additional finance from many more shareholders, with an Initial Public Offering (IPO) of shares.

The initial nominal (or par) value of the shares may be £1 each (or 50 pence, or 10 pence, or any amount). In a successful expanding company the market value of shares is likely to increase. New shareholders will not be invited to buy shares at an old, low price. New shares are normally issued at a premium, as shown in Example 11.1, where additional £1 shares are issued for £2.50; the premium is £1.50 per share.

There is no requirement for a company to pay dividends on ordinary shares. In a very small company, where there are only two or three shareholders, they may easily agree what dividends, if any, are to be paid. In large, listed companies the directors normally propose a dividend for approval by shareholders at the annual general meeting. There is usually an interim dividend paid part-way through the year, and a final dividend after the year end. Companies sometimes decide not to pay a dividend, perhaps because they have been making losses, or have some other financial problem. In 2011 British Airways (now part of ICAG) did not pay a dividend, and this has been the pattern in recent years. Similarly, Barratt Developments and many other companies do not pay dividends.

The fact that there is no requirement to pay a dividend may make ordinary shares seem to be an attractive, cost-free source of finance. But many shareholders, especially institutional shareholders (such as pension funds), expect and rely on a steady (and increasing) stream of income from dividends. The shareholders are the owners of the company, and directors who regularly disappoint shareholders are likely to find themselves out of a job. Many companies pay regular and increasing dividends.

Growing companies might not seek a full listing on the stock exchange to begin with. They may first invite a financial institution or venture capitalist to buy some shares. Companies such as venture capitalist 3i invest in growing companies that are not yet large enough for a stock market listing. The formalities, administrative burden and costs of a full stock market listing may be too much for

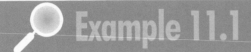

Share premium

Big Company agrees to pay £2,500,000 to take over Little Company. Big Company's shares are highly regarded by investors and their market value is £2.50. The £2,500,000 is paid not in cash, but by the issue of one million £1 shares.

The effect of this transaction is that Big Company's statement of financial position will show £1,000,000 of additional share capital, and £1,500,000 of share premium. The total, £2,500,000, was issued in exchange for assets (the Little Company).

Shares may be issued in exchange for cash or any assets.

companies of modest size and they are likely to seek a listing on the Alternative Investment Market (AIM). AIM is regulated by the London Stock Exchange (LSE) but has less demanding rules, and a listing is less costly than being on the LSE's Official List.

Companies often increase their share capital a little each year, especially when there is some sort of incentive scheme for directors and other staff that provides them with shares. But any significant increase in funding through the issue of shares is a major event for a company, and does not happen very often. Similarly, a company may, from time to time, buy back some of its own shares and so reduce share capital. Companies do not keep a supply of shares for investors to buy and sell: investors buy and sell shares from each other, usually via a stock exchange. Investors cannot go to Marks & Spencer and buy a few shares along with their new underwear and microwave dinner! They have to go via some sort of stockbroker, and there are lots of easy and flexible ways of buying and selling shares via a range of banks and other financial institutions, and on the internet.

Rights issue

When a company wants to raise substantial additional funds by issuing shares it often makes a *rights issue* to existing shareholders. This usually means that it offers new shares at a price lower than the current market price (see Example 11.2).

A *rights issue* is the normal way in which established companies raise additional funds and it is intended to be attractive to existing shareholders. If the current market price of a company's shares is £2, the right to buy more shares at £1.50 each sounds attractive. After the rights issue the total value of the company will, in theory, be worth the amount it was worth before the rights issue, plus the amount of money raised from the rights issue. In practice, if investors believe that the additional funds will be invested sufficiently profitably, the total value of the company will increase by more than the amount of cash raised.

If shareholders take up all the rights to which they are entitled, they will continue to own the same proportion of the company. The right to buy shares cheaply may look attractive, but the record of rights issues is mixed. Sometimes it seems that companies make rights issues because they are in financial difficulties. Sometimes it is a sign of success and additional funds are needed for expansion.

Bonus issue

A bonus issue (or a scrip issue) is quite different: it raises no additional funds, and so should not really be included in a chapter on sources of finance!

Many shareholders like receiving a bonus issue, although they really receive nothing. Most people would probably rather have two pieces of cake than one. But if the second piece of cake is created just by cutting the original piece of cake in half, there is no gain. In effect that is what a bonus issue does. A one-for-one bonus issue means that everyone has twice as many shares, but nothing has changed;

Example 11.2

The Right Company has one million ordinary shares with a nominal value of 50 pence each, and a market value of £2 each. The company decides to make a rights issue, offering existing shareholders one share for every five that they already hold, at a price of £1.50 per share.

Shareholders might choose to exercise their rights (by buying the additional shares), or to sell them.

After the rights issue the theoretical value of the company will be:

Existing one million shares at £2 each	£2,000,000
Cash raised from rights issue 200,000 at £1.50	300,000
	£2,300,000
Number of shares after issue	1,200,000

Theoretical share price after rights issue:

$$\frac{£2,300,000}{1,200,000} = £1.92$$

each still owns the same proportion of the same total. In Example 11.3 there was a 'two-for-one' bonus issue. For example, anyone who held 200 shares would be given an additional 400 shares, giving them a total of 600 shares. The total number of shares the company had therefore increased from 2m to 6m; share capital was increased by £4m; retained earnings were reduced by £4m. But the assets (and liabilities) of the company are unchanged.

In practice a bonus issue is more likely to be one new share for every three, or four, or five shares already held. Shareholders may think that they will still receive the same amount of dividend per share, and so they will be better off. Bonus issues are often associated with good performance, and optimism, which could lead to an increase in demand for the shares, and so an increase in share price and in the total value of the company.

One of the justifications for bonus issues is that it is often said that share prices higher than about £8 or £10 become less 'marketable': shareholders would rather buy five shares at £2 each than one share for £10. But there are plenty of successful companies where the share price is £10 or £20 or more.

Preference shares

Preference shareholders take less risk, and can expect less reward than ordinary shareholders. Preference shares have a fixed rate of dividend, perhaps 7 per cent. This means that for each £1 preference share, investors receive a 7 pence dividend each year. Sometimes a company might decide not to pay the preference dividend (perhaps when profits are low). But if no preference dividend is paid, then no ordinary dividend can be paid either. The preference shareholders have preference over ordinary shareholders with payment of dividends.

Preference shares are usually *cumulative*, which means that if the preference dividend is not paid in some years, all arrears of preference dividends must be paid before any ordinary dividends can be paid. But preference shares are not very popular for a number of reasons. Ordinary shareholders always have the prospect that the company might do really well, and there could be a substantial increase in profits, dividends and share price: they might make loads of money! Preference shareholders are more secure, but their level of dividend is fixed, whether the company does well or badly.

Example 11.3

Scriptease plc	Before bonus issue	After bonus issue
	£000	£000
Non-current assets	5,300	5,300
Current assets		
Inventories and receivables	3,000	3,000
Cash	500	500
Total assets	8,800	8,800
Trade payables	300	300
Equity		
Share capital (£1 shares)	2,000	6,000
Retained earnings	6,500	2,500
	8,800	8,800

Preference shares can be made more attractive if they are *participating* and/or if they are *convertible*. Participating preference shares can participate in higher levels of dividend when the company does well, and ordinary dividends rise above some predetermined level. Convertible preference shares can be more attractive: they can be converted to ordinary shares, at a predetermined rate (see Example 11.4). Since preference shares are generally redeemable at some future date, they are viewed more like liabilities than like equity and, as a result, IAS 32 requires that preference shares are classified as liabilities and since there is an obligation to pay the preference share dividend, such dividends are classified much like interest payments.

The prospect of a substantial capital gain if the company is successful can make convertible preference shares seem very attractive to investors; they get a decent dividend in the short term, with reasonable security. But the dividend is likely to be very expensive to the company, mainly because dividends (unlike interest) are not allowable as an expense to be charged against taxation. If we assume a corporation tax rate of 30 per cent, then a company needs to earn £10 profit to pay a

Example 11.4

The Fastgro company issues £1 ordinary shares at a premium of 50 pence per share. On the same date it issues 6 per cent convertible £1 preference shares giving the shareholders the right to convert three preference shares into one ordinary share at any date they choose.

In the early years preference shareholders are unlikely to give up three preference shares, worth about £3, for one ordinary share, worth £1.50. But if the company is successful, the market price of the ordinary shares might increase steadily to, say, £10 per share. An investor with 900,000 preference shares, worth about £900,000, could then convert them to 300,000 ordinary shares worth £3m; this would give a profit of over £2m!

£7 dividend. It is cheaper for the company to borrow money: a company earning £10 profit could pay £7 in interest and still have £3 (pre-tax) profit left for shareholders.

Interpretation of statements of financial position

When interpreting statements of financial position, for most purposes the total figure for 'equity' is used. Equity (or ordinary shareholders' funds) includes all ordinary shareholders' funds (share capital, share premium and all reserves/retained profits) except preference share capital. This figure is used in calculating gearing, and in calculating the net assets per share. It is also used in calculating the profitability of ordinary shareholders' funds: net profit after tax (and after deducting any preference share dividends) is expressed as a percentage of equity. It is usually a mistake (often made by students) to use the share capital figure instead of including all shareholders' funds.

The nominal value of shares is of little or no importance except perhaps in calculating the number of shares that make up share capital. Calculations of earnings per share (EPS), dividend per share and net assets per share are based on the number of ordinary shares.

11.3 Borrowing

Some very prudent individuals and businesses may think that it is dangerous to borrow: the business may not be able to meet the interest and repayments, and there is always the risk of insolvency if the business gets into difficulties. Those who want to minimize risk probably want to minimize borrowing. But if they are so risk averse, they should probably not go into business, and will probably never make much money.

It is safest and easiest to put your money in a bank, and earn a steady, low rate of interest, with little or no risk. But people invest in businesses because they think that it is worth the risk in order to earn more money. If banks are paying, say, 5 per cent interest, investors hope to earn more than that by investing in companies. Perhaps they expect a return on capital employed (ROCE) of 10 per cent or more. A business could argue that, if the cost of borrowing is less than the ROCE that they can earn, then the more they borrow, the more profit they will make. If you can borrow money at 7 per cent per annum, and invest it to earn 10 per cent per annum, then the more money you borrow, the more profit you will make, as shown in Example 11.5.

Example 11.5

Two companies in the same industry each have a return on capital employed of 10 per cent, and they are each able to borrow money at an interest rate of 7 per cent.

Prudent plc borrows an extra £1m	
Cost of additional borrowings: £1m at 7%	£70,000 per annum
Additional earnings: £1m at 10%	£100,000 per annum
Net additional earnings	£30,000 per annum
Profitable plc borrows an extra £100m	
Cost of additional borrowings £100m at 7%	£7,000,000 per annum
Additional earnings: £100b at 10%	£10,000,000 per annum
Net additional earnings	£3,000,000 per annum

Example 11.6

Low-geared company	Capital structure		Equity	100m
			10% debentures	£10m
				£110m

	Year 1	Year 2		
	£m	£m		
EBIT	10	12	+20%	
Interest	1	1		
Pre-tax profit	9	11		
Tax (say) 30%	2.7	3.3		
Profit after-tax	6.3	7.7	+22.2%	

High-geared company	Capital structure		Equity	£50m
			10% debentures	£60m
EBIT	10	12	+20%	£110m
Interest	6	6		
Pre-tax profit	4	6		
Tax (say) 30%	1.2	1.8		
Profit after-tax	2.8	4.2	+50%	

Borrowing can increase the return to shareholders, as is demonstrated in Example 11.6. Borrowing can also be relatively cheap, and is a cheaper source of finance than issuing ordinary shares because the interest is allowable as an expense for tax purposes; and because shareholders expect a higher return as they are taking more risk than lenders. But what they expect and what they get can be very different.

In both cases EBIT (earnings before interest and taxation) increased by 20 per cent between years 1 and 2, but the effect of gearing was a larger increase in the profit after-tax earned for the ordinary shareholders. In the low-geared company the return earned for ordinary shareholders increased by 22.2 per cent. In the high-geared company it increased by 50 per cent.

There are other good reasons for borrowing rather than issuing more shares. In a family-controlled company the existing shareholders and directors might not want to risk issuing more shares if it would result in new and different people becoming shareholders and controlling the company. In spite of what some textbooks say, directors do not always make rational economic decisions: many like to keep their positions of power and influence, even if (by not issuing more shares) they restrict the growth and profitability of the company. The costs involved in issuing shares also tend to be higher than the costs in obtaining loans.

Another advantage of borrowing is that it comes in many forms, and can be very flexible. It may be short or long term. The most flexible way of borrowing is through an overdraft. Interest rates are negotiable, and are usually a number of percentage points above base rate. Individuals with unauthorized overdrafts may find that they are charged with ridiculously high interest rates, perhaps even 10 or 15 points above base rate. A company ought to be able to negotiate an overdraft interest rate just a little above base rate. Some businesses are seasonal and need to borrow at particular times of the year.

A business such as a seaside hotel is likely to be flush with cash in October, after the holiday season; but by March they need short-term borrowings until the money starts coming in for the next holiday season. Many businesses have plenty of money in the middle of the month, but need to borrow at the end of the month, when wages and salaries are paid. Overdrafts are most appropriate for such short-term financing because interest is payable only for the actual days that the overdraft facility is used. There is no point in having a fixed loan throughout the year, and paying interest throughout the year, if the money is needed only for a few days each month, or for a few months each year.

Although overdrafts are supposed to be a short-term source of finance, many individuals and companies seem to have significant (and increasing!) overdrafts that go on for years. Banks are interested in converting overdrafts into fixed loans for a few years, if they can earn more interest by so doing. Businesses need to work out carefully how much it is appropriate to borrow with fixed-term loans and fixed interest rates, and how much it is appropriate to use overdraft facilities for.

Debentures are a form of long-term borrowing (typically 5–10 years), usually with a fixed rate of interest, which can be listed on a stock market. Investors can therefore sell them when they wish, and the company can choose to buy them back on the market, if they have nothing better to do with their money. Debentures are usually 'secured' on some assets of the company; perhaps on land and buildings; perhaps a floating charge on most of the assets of the company, including inventory and receivables. The effect is a bit like taking out a mortgage: if the company does not meet its payments as they fall due, the debenture holders can eventually get their money back by selling off the company's assets.

Debentures are sometimes 'convertible' into ordinary shares, which can make them very attractive to investors if it is expected that the company's shares will do very well in the future. Investors in a new or expanding business may be attracted by the security of a debenture with a reasonable interest rate to begin with, together with the possibility of conversion to ordinary shares (and increases in the share price, and increasing dividends) once the venture has proved to be successful.

The main attraction of borrowing is the idea that the more you borrow, the more profit you can make. It may be an attractive idea, but there are a number of problems with ever-increasing borrowings:

1 Borrowing may be no problem as long as the company can be sure of always having earnings above the required level of interest payments. But businesses tend to have good years and bad years; the economy tends to run in cycles; some industries are particularly cyclical; some industries run into bad patches, with bad luck and/or bad management. If in some years the company does not earn enough to make the necessary interest payments, lenders may repossess vital assets and force the business to curtail its activities or close down.

2 The more you get into debt, the more difficult it is to borrow more money. There is probably always someone, or some bank, that will lend to you, but as you get more into debt, the higher the interest rates become to compensate the lender for additional risk.

3 Lenders usually look for some sort of security. It is easy to borrow money secured on land and buildings. Lenders may be happy to take some sort of 'floating charge' on whatever other assets the company has. But when all assets have already been used as security, it is increasingly difficult to borrow more money.

4 Those who have already lent money to the company often lay down conditions to restrict the ability of the company to borrow more. These 'restrictive covenants' may specify that a company's total borrowing must not exceed some (small, e.g. 1 or 1.5) multiple of the amount of equity.

5 Companies that are heavily in debt may get a reputation as being 'high risk', and other businesses may be reluctant to do business with them. Sometimes investors steer clear because the risk is too great.

A good, old-fashioned view might be that a company should keep increasing its borrowing, as long as it can get away with it. Theory suggests that eventually lenders will see that the company has borrowed too much (gearing is too high), and they will start to charge higher interest rates. As borrowing increases, interest rates increase until eventually the cost of borrowing is higher than the return that the company can generate from the borrowings. High levels of borrowing are also associated with high risk, and this can affect the share price, especially if it starts to look as if the company is so heavily in debt that it might be forced into liquidation. There is, thus, in this traditional view, an optimal level of borrowing (although it is difficult to establish what this level is).

A different perspective was offered by following Modigliani and Miller (1958) who suggested that the level of gearing has no effect on share price. Even if the amount of borrowing changes, it is still the same business, with the same earnings stream and the same business risk. Modigliani and Miller's presentation is sophisticated, but it depends on a number of unrealistic assumptions; and it is often misinterpreted. Their emphasis is on the value of the company, which depends on the investments that they have, and the cash flows that they will generate; how the company is financed is a secondary issue. More recent work, recognizing the impact of taxation (interest is an allowable expense for taxation, and so the cost of borrowing is likely to be lower than the cost of equity), together with lower interest rates, and the actual behaviour of companies, suggest that there may be some optimal level of gearing; but this is hard to find, and views about acceptable levels of gearing change from time to time.

In practice, many companies seem to borrow as much as they can get away with. Some companies constantly need additional funds because of expansion and development. But some companies (like some individuals!) do not seem to be able to live within their means, and borrow until they go bust.

In Illustration 11.1 (p. 266) the company had total long-term funds of £3,000, of which £1,000 was borrowed. In other words, one-third of its long-term funding was borrowed, or its gearing ratio was $33\frac{1}{3}$ per cent. There is, of course, no 'correct' or 'best' level of borrowing; nor is there a single correct way of measuring gearing.[1] Companies that are able to borrow extensively are likely to have a steady, secure income stream so that they can be confident about being able to pay the necessary interest every year. They are also likely to have lots of good quality assets (particularly land and buildings) to offer as security to lenders. Companies in very cyclical industries should avoid high gearing, but many do not, and they get into financial difficulties. The airline industry is noticeably susceptible to epidemics of war, terrorism and disease, sudden and rapid rises in the price of oil and the recent economic downturn; many airlines are highly geared; and many found themselves in serious financial difficulties in recent years.

When the telecommunications industry was expanding and share prices were booming at the end of the twentieth century, many companies got away with very high levels of borrowing for a while. Then the business climate turned against them, and many share prices collapsed. BT had a debt mountain of £30bn which did not look too bad in relation to the market value of their equity when share prices were high. But in comparison with the statement of financial position value of equity it looked terrible. And when telecommunications share prices took a nosedive, the amount of debt looked unsustainable in relation to the market value of equity. BT has taken decisive action, and has substantially reduced the debt.

As interest rates have remained low in recent years, higher levels of gearing have become acceptable. Sometimes one company buys another company and finances the purchase almost entirely by borrowing; this is called a 'leveraged buy-out'.[2]

11.4 Retained Profits

A successful company makes profits that materialize in the form of additional cash or other net assets. The company may choose to pay out all its profits as dividends, in which case profits will not be a source of funds. Most companies choose to pay out a proportion (perhaps around 40 per cent) of their

---

[1] If borrowing is represented as D, and equity is represented as E, gearing can be measured by taking D as a percentage of D + E; or as a percentage of E. D is sometimes taken to include overdrafts; sometimes it refers only to long-term borrowing.

[2] The purchase of another business can, instead, be financed by issuing additional ordinary shares.

profits as dividends; the rest are retained and used to finance the business. Obviously, the more profit a company makes, the greater is the potential for using retained profits as a source of finance. Raising finance through retained profits depends on how profitable the business is. It also depends on the company's dividend policy.

Dividend policy

In deciding how much dividend to pay, or what proportion of profits are to be paid out as dividends, companies need to consider some important matters. Dividend policy usually requires striking a balance between (a) paying out *all* profits as dividends, and (b) paying *no* dividends at all.

Pay out all profits as dividends

There is a case for paying out all profits as dividends: profits belong to the shareholders, not the directors. The directors might see retained profits as being too easy a source of finance, and not bother to ensure that they are reinvested in the company properly and profitably. As profits are earned, they may simply disappear into higher levels of inventories and receivables, or even cars and 'conference centres' for the comfort of directors.

Many companies find themselves with surplus funds that they invest in disastrous diversification (ad)ventures or waste on more or less (un)successful takeover bids and mergers. Northern Rock lost millions of pounds attempting to move from its secure base in retail banking into areas of wholesale banking where it had no experience. Marks & Spencer lost millions of pounds in spreading its operations overseas, and then withdrawing. Marconi wasted millions of pounds investing in overpriced telecommunications companies just before they collapsed. Some companies have a history of merging with others, and then demerging, or selling off the bits they no longer want (e.g. Kingfisher, Hays, Debenhams). The evidence so far suggests that a takeover is more likely to destroy shareholder value than to create it.

There are, of course, plenty of exceptions: well-managed companies that succeed in reinvesting retained profits year after year and which have a good record in increasing profits and dividends; some even succeed in increasing their return on capital employed, and, with a bit of luck, the company's share price. There are also many companies where the directors know that they are unable to do this. GEC sat on mountains of cash rather than risk wasting it on ill-advised investments. Other companies, knowing that there are limited opportunities for successful investment of surplus funds, simply return them to shareholders as special dividends; or they use the money to buy their own shares on the market and cancel them.[3]

Many companies, or their directors, cannot be trusted to invest retained profits successfully. But there are good reasons for not expecting companies to pay out all their profits as dividends:

1 Rising prices, or inflation, usually mean that companies need to retain some of their profits, not for expansion, but merely to maintain the existing level of operations. More funds are required to finance receivables (as selling prices increase); to finance inventories (as replacement costs increase) and to replace non-current assets as the cost of these increases. Inflation in the UK in recent years has been very low, and the cost of replacing many items (e.g. computers and electronic equipment) has actually fallen. But few businesses can afford to finance even their existing level of operations without retaining some profits.

2 Investors, particularly financial institutions, generally want to see dividends increasing steadily each year, preferably by rather more than the rate of inflation. Illustration 11.2 shows how company profits can fluctuate, but attempts are made to keep dividends steady.

3 Many companies boast that they have succeeded in increasing dividends every year since anyone can remember. Compared with dividend expectations, profits are less predictable, less controllable,

---

[3] This is a way of increasing EPS; even if total earnings do not increase, the number of shares decreases and so the EPS increases.

Retained profits   **285**

ILLUSTRATION 11.2

The EPS and the dividend per share of the Cycle Company for the last few years are shown below (in pence).

Year	1	2	3	4	5	6	7
EPS	100	134	60	116	180	10	191
Div	50	53	56	59	63	64	70
Cover	2	2.5	1.1	2.0	2.9	0.2	2.7

more cyclical, and more affected by one-off 'exceptional' items. Companies usually prefer to increase dividends only modestly in the very good years so that there is more scope for maintaining or increasing dividends in the lean years.

Pay out no dividends

There is a case for paying no dividends at all, even in successful companies. When a company is making serious losses, or when it has massive borrowings, scrapping the dividend for a year or two makes good sense. Companies at an early stage of their development need all the money that they can get hold of and so are not inclined to pay dividends. In the great dotcom and TMT[4] bubble of the late 1990s many companies did not pay dividends. A quick look at the *Financial Times* today will show which companies are not paying dividends; usually there are plenty of mining companies and pharmaceuticals and biotechnology companies that have not yet found their pot of gold or wonder drug, and are burning up cash in their efforts; there is unlikely to be a dividend until a worthwhile discovery has been developed.

If a company can invest the shareholders' money and earn a better rate of return than the shareholders can themselves, then there is a case for the company to keep the money, and not pay dividends. If the money stays within the company, the value of its shares should increase. If shareholders need some income, they can sell a few shares; and (they hope!) the value of their shares will increase because of all the retained profits being reinvested. If they sell a few shares they may have to pay capital gains tax; but for many shareholders the taxation of capital gains is lower than the taxation on income from dividends. Paying no dividends at all may suit some companies and some shareholders – sometimes.

Dividend policy in practice

When making a dividend decision, companies need to take into consideration a variety of often conflicting factors. First, from a legal perspective, a company can only distribute its retained profits. Second, it needs to have the cash in the bank in order to pay a dividend or an overdraft which will enable it to pay a dividend. Then, as will be seen in Chapter 14, if a company needs money to invest in attractive investment opportunities, that would tend to reduce its dividend payment since it needs that money for profitable investment. By the same token, if it has available cash but no significant investment opportunities, that would tend to argue in favour of paying a larger dividend. Furthermore, some companies tend to pay out a small dividend and that will attract shareholders who do not want a dividend but are attracted to companies which focus on growth, while other companies favour a high dividend policy which would tend to attract shareholders who are investing for high annual dividend income, perhaps the elderly.

Companies tend to follow a consistent dividend payout policy and so shareholders will be attracted to invest in companies with the dividend policy they prefer. Most companies do not opt for the extremes of no dividends, or 100 per cent distribution. Usually a proportion of profits is distributed. Listed companies typically pay out rather less than half of their profits as dividends. Recent figures for the FTSE 100 index and a number of companies are shown in Illustration 11.3.

---

[4] Technology, media and telecommunications.

286   CHAPTER 11 Financing a business

Company profits tend to fluctuate from year to year, not least because of 'exceptional' items such as profits or losses arising from the sale of non-current assets, or closing down part of the business. As shown in Illustration 11.2, it makes more sense to try to maintain a record of steady and increasing dividends, rather than to pay out the same proportion of profits each year. Some companies pay an extra 'special' dividend in a particularly good year. But most try to keep an upward trend, even when profits fall. And many seem to increase their dividends more than the underlying profits justify; this results in the dividend cover declining over a number of years, and the dividend begins to look less safe.

In making dividend decisions, companies need to consider what 'signal' any change in dividends gives to investors. A sudden reduction in dividends suggests that directors are not confident about future years. Companies also need to consider what cash is available to pay dividends and their plans for expansion, investment and borrowing.

11.5 Other Sources of Finance

Companies are assumed to need funds to finance the purchase of fixed assets and inventories, and to pay expenses until the profits come rolling in, in the form of cash. In addition there is a need to finance working capital, but careful management of working capital can also be seen as a source of finance. If receivables or inventories are reduced, or if the time taken to pay trade payables is increased, funds are freed up to use for other purposes. The management of working capital is dealt with in Chapter 12.

There are various ways of avoiding, or minimizing, the need to raise finance:

1 Non-current assets can be leased instead of buying them. Obviously this applies to premises, but most machinery, equipment and vehicles can be leased if necessary. It is sometimes possible to arrange for an initial rent-free period to minimize initial funding requirements. But most lessors will not rent out equipment to any Tom, Dick or Harry: the lessee usually needs to produce evidence that they are creditworthy.

2 Sale and leaseback. A business can raise finance by selling assets that it owns and wants to continue using through a finance company (such as a bank or insurance company), and then leasing the asset back from that company. This is often done with premises, and many chains of retail shops no longer own the freehold of their premises: they made a sale and leaseback arrangement. This can make sense both for the finance company and for the retailer. The finance company gets a guaranteed return in rental income at the going rate (say 5–7 per cent per annum); the retailer continues to use the premises and raises additional funds at a reasonable cost. The transaction will look good if the premises are sold for more than their book value: the profit contributes to an increase in EPS. This may be further boosted if the funds raised are used to increase profits, or to reduce the number of shares.

A cautious proprietor may prefer to retain the freehold of business premises; it can be used to provide security for loans where additional finance is needed.

3   Businesses often find that they have more non-current assets than they need, especially when they find themselves in financial difficulties. Warehouses can be 'rationalized': the company may find that it can manage with two instead of six, and raise substantial sums by selling off uneconomic premises.

4   Outsourcing or subcontracting some activities (e.g. computing, accounting, catering, manufacture, cleaning, transport – indeed, almost anything) may free up surplus assets that can be sold to raise funds. It can also be used to minimize the finance required for expansion.

5   Careful management of working capital can effectively reduce the financing needs of a business; reductions in working capital can produce additional cash.

6   Factoring or invoice discounting the company's trade receivables. These involve borrowing funds from a 'factor', usually a department of a bank, equivalent to an agreed percentage of trade receivables. Usually, the factor will manage the collection of those debts from customers, while in invoice discounting, the company itself will manage credit control.

7   Increasing profits also generates additional funds. This can be done both by reducing costs (e.g. eliminating a layer of management, or transferring production to Morocco or Vietnam), or by increasing sales (the volume of sales, and/or selling prices).

8   Reducing dividends, or even not paying dividends for a year or two, is another way of making more funds available.

9   Careful cash budgeting can also make more funds available when needed by delaying major payments at times when there is a particular shortage of cash. Sometimes the easiest way to deal with a cash shortage is to delay capital expenditure programmes.

Businesses rely mostly on funds contributed by their owners (sole proprietors, partners or shareholders); on borrowing money; and on generating profits that are ploughed back into the business. But there are more creative ways of financing businesses.

📖 Summary

The published financial statements of companies show how they have been financed, and indicate the balance between safety and solvency, on the one hand, and risk and profitability, on the other. The safest way of financing a company is to issue more shares, but this can be an expensive business, and shareholders expect a high return. Borrowing is in many ways easier and cheaper, but excessive gearing can lead to excessive risk, which can adversely affect share prices, and increase the cost of borrowing. Retained profits are also an attractive source of funds, and companies need to have dividend policies that strike a balance between keeping shareholders happy, and retaining profits to finance expansion, where such reinvestment is justified. High gearing can enhance profitability, particularly during a period of low interest rates; but it also increases risk. Similar issues arise with the management of working capital. Minimizing levels of inventories and receivables can minimize the need for external finance, and enhance return on capital employed. But lowering levels of working capital make companies look less solvent. There are various more creative ways of financing a business, and there are no 'correct' solutions. Policies on gearing, dividends and working capital change as circumstances change, and a combination of several different approaches to financing a company is usually appropriate.

288   CHAPTER 11 Financing a business

⇨ Review of key points

- The three main sources of funds for companies are share capital, borrowing and retained profits.
- There is no requirement to pay dividends to ordinary shareholders; they bear most of the risk of the business, and, if the business does well, will get substantial rewards.
- Borrowing can 'gear up' the return to the owners of the business, but excessive gearing is risky.
- Profits may be paid out to shareholders as dividends, or reinvested in the business as they are earned.
- Dividend policy strikes a balance between retaining funds within the business that are needed, and maintaining a payment record to satisfy shareholders.
- Much of business activity can be financed without using share capital, borrowing or retained profits.
- Published financials statements indicate the way in which a business has been financed, its dividend, gearing policies, and the effectiveness of its working capital management.

Self-testing questions

1 What are the three main sources of finance for businesses?
2 What are the main differences between preference shares and ordinary shares?
3 Explain the advantages and disadvantages of a company increasing its gearing.
4 You are given the following information about two companies:

Summarized statements of financial position as at 31 December

| | TimeBall Company | | DownsPier Company | |
| | Year 6 | Year 7 | Year 6 | Year 7 |
	£000	£000	£000	£000
Total assets	350	402.2	400	354.1
Liabilities and equity				
Liabilities				
Current liabilities	50	60	100	70
9% debentures	100	140	100	50
	150	200	200	120
Equity				
Share capital	100	100	100	115
Share premium	–	–	–	15
Retained profits	100	102.2	100	104.1
Total equity	200	202.2	200	234.1
Total liabilities and equity	350	402.2	400	354.1

Summarized income statements for year ended 31 December

Sales	100	110	100	95
Gross profit	40	44	40	41
Operating profit	20	21.6	20	17.5
Interest	9	12.6	9	4.5
Pre-tax profit	11	9	11	13
Taxation	3.3	2.7	3.3	3.9
Profit after-tax	7.7	6.3	7.7	9.1
Dividends	4	4.1	4	5
Retained profit for the year	3.7	2.2	3.7	4.1

a You are required to calculate for each company for each year:
   i capital gearing ratio;
   ii interest cover;
   iii dividend cover;
   iv proportion of profits paid out as dividends.
b Explain what each shows.
c Comment on the financial performance and position of the two companies making use of appropriate ratios.
5 Explain what factors affect a company's dividend distribution in a year.

 ## Assessment questions

1 Why might a company issue convertible preference shares rather than debentures?
2 The capital structure of two companies is as follows:

	Loborough plc	Hiborough plc
	£m	£m
Equity	180	50
11% debentures	20	150
	200	200

The EBIT of both companies was as follows:

Year 1	£19m
Year 2	£22.8m
Year 3	£15.2m

The rate of corporation tax on profits is 25 per cent.

a Calculate the net profit after-tax earned for ordinary shareholders for each year and for each company.

b Comment on the effect that gearing has had on the results.

3 The directors of the Palazine Company are seeking funding of £50m to finance an expansion programme. The summarized financial statements for the most recent year are set out below:

Income statement for the year ended 31 December year 6		£000
Sales		120,000
Cost of sales		90,000
Gross profit		30,000
Distribution costs	8,000	
Administration expenses	12,000	(20,000)
Operating profit		10,000
Debenture interest		(5,000)
Net profit before taxation		5,000
Taxation		(3,000)
Net profit after taxation		2,000
Dividends		(1,000)
Retained profit for year		1,000

Statement of financial position as at 31 December year 6		£000
Non-current assets		
Land and buildings (market value £55m)		45,000
Plant and machinery		18,000
Investments at cost (market value £30m)		45,000
		108,000
Current assets		
Inventories	8,000	
Receivables	5,000	
Cash	1,000	14,000
Total assets		122,000
Current liabilities		
Payables		24,000
Non-current liabilities		
10% debentures (secured)		50,000
Equity		
Share capital	30,000	
Retained earnings	18,000	48,000
		122,000

The following suggestions have been made for raising the additional finance. You are required to explain the effects of each of the suggestions and to comment on their practicability.

The company could:

i   issue more debentures;

ii   make a sale and leaseback arrangement on its premises;

iii   sell its investments (although some directors object to this as it would involve a loss of £15m);

iv   reduce inventories by one half;

v   halve the period that receivables are allowed to pay (all sales are on credit);

vi   extend the period for paying payables by 50 per cent;

vii   use the reserves;

viii   issue more ordinary shares;

ix   obtain a bank overdraft.

4 The earnings per share and the dividend per share of Uppen Down plc for the last few years are shown below (in pence):

	Year 1	Year 2	Year 3	Year 4	Year 5	Year 6	Year 7
EPS	20	25	18	30	10	13	24
Div	10	10.4	10.8	11.2	11.7	12.2	12.7
Share price	300	400	200	270	250	270	300

a You are required to calculate the dividend cover for each year; the proportion of profits that was distributed as dividends; and the dividend yield based on the share price at the year end given above.

b Comment on the company's dividend policy.

c Since the end of year 7 the dividend yield, as shown in the *Financial Times*, has increased to 10 per cent. What is this likely to indicate?

5 An extract of Sky High plc's statement of financial position as at 1 October 20x6 is given below:

	£000
Ordinary share capital @ £1 each	1,000
Revaluation reserve	2,500
Retained profits	3,200
	6,700

On 1 January 20x7, the company issued 1 right share for every 5 in issue for £4 each when the market price was £5.

a Show how the rights issue should be accounted for in the statement of financial position.

b Calculate the theoretical share price of Sky High plc after the rights issue. Explain why in reality the share price may differ from the theoretical price.

292 CHAPTER 11 Financing a business

 ## Group activities and discussion questions

1 What is the minimum amount of funding with which it is possible to start a business? Could a business be started with zero funds? What sort of business could each member of the group start, with little or no funding? Prepare a (very brief) business plan. Would it be necessary to raise substantial funding to develop the business so that it becomes large scale? How would you define 'large scale' (big enough to provide you with a suitable lifestyle; big enough for a stock market listing)?

2 Prepare a list of companies that are not currently paying dividends. (Look for shares with a zero yield in the *Financial Times*'s listing.) Why are these companies not paying dividends? Each member of the group could research a number of companies. Can the companies be classified into groups each with similar reasons for not paying dividends (e.g. developing new products/services; recent losses)?

3 Why are some companies high-geared, and others low-geared? Each member of the group should examine the statements of financial position of a number of companies, probably in different sectors. It may be easiest to do this using the companies' websites. The group should agree the way in which gearing should be measured (e.g. is short-term borrowing to be included with long-term borrowing?). Are utility companies more highly geared than retailers? Are breweries more highly geared than oil companies? Can you identify what factors seem to be associated with high gearing and low gearing?

4 Prepare a list of companies which have arranged bonus (scrip) issues in the last three months. (You can look at the *Financial Times* website for this information.) Note down the share price before and after the bonus issue and the market capitalization (shown in Monday's *Financial Times*) before and after the scrip issue. How much has the total value of the company (market capitalization) changed as a result of the bonus issue?

 ## Financial accounting in context

Discuss and comment on the following extract taken from the press with reference to the evolution in the sources of capital available to companies.

Companies challenged to quit bank addiction

Britain's businesses are being urged to unhook themselves from bank debt and make more use of alternative sources of finance.

By Richard Tyler

"It's been difficult for a CFO to go through the last three years that we have just had and not feel some element of stress. And yes, I am using English understatement," deadpans Philip Keller, chief financial officer of Intermediate Capital Group.

With £2bn to £2.5bn of borrowings outstanding at any one time, historically supplied by numerous syndicates of banks he didn't really know well, some stress is understandable. Yet Keller is among those treasurers taking their businesses through the corporate equivalent of The Priory. [...]

Dependency on banks when the banks themselves are far from healthy is one cause for the loss of corporate confidence, the Treasury argues. [...]

The Treasury is already planning to shoehorn £1bn of public money into co-investment funds that will lend directly to British companies. Bids from fund managers are due in February and the Treasury has allocated at least £150m to get the Business Finance Partnership scheme going.

It is likely to operate in a similar way to the M&G UK Companies Financing Fund, which raised £500m from Prudential – its parent – and over £900m from other insurance and pension funds, to lend directly to UK companies sums of between £30m and £100m, at rates of between 4pc and 6pc over Libor and maturities of typically around seven years.

A spokesman said the fund was gaining momentum after a slow start, backing nine companies such as Northgate, Stobart and Barratt Developments, since May 2010 with £780m in loans. The hope is that funds such as M&G's will be used by firms as a viable alternative source of finance. The attraction for mid-sized companies is that they don't have to secure a credit rating or subject themselves to the due diligence demanded of a bond issue on the public markets. The catch is that bank debt remains cheap for the right borrowers.

Martin O'Donovan, policy director at the Association of Corporate Treasurers, did some calculations on the relative cost of a bond issue over bank debt. He found that a company with a BBB rating could secure a £250m five-year bank loan at a rough margin of 1.1pc over Libor, which even he says is "surprisingly low". Arrangement fees of 0.75pc of the value of the loan and external advisory fees of roughly £50,000 all add up. As do new facility utilisation and commitment fees – the price now charged by banks for just having the facility without drawing on it fully. [. . .]

[M]id-sized companies should get used to the idea of paying a bit more to become less reliant on the banks. The savings from the longer refinancing cycle and the benefits of secure funds on long-term business planning should not be underestimated [...].

One company tackling its addiction head-on is Intermediate Capital Group, a senior debt and mezzanine finance provider to private equity deals. It borrows between £2bn and £2.5bn at any one time and so has to think about these things quite carefully. "Historically, that was bank finance but the world has changed dramatically," says Keller.

It means that whereas three years ago banks supplied two-thirds of ICG's finance, Keller expects that to settle at around 50pc in the future, with the bank debt all concentrated in around six banks rather than dozens in multiple syndicates.

The financial crisis is forcing ICG to innovate. It is used to tapping the US private-placement market, but has now begun exploring the UK – borrowing £75m in December from M&G and issuing a £35m retail bond to wealthy private investors via brokers such as Brewin Dolphin and Charles Stanley.

The M&G paper – with maturities ranging from five to seven years – helped Keller to manage the profile of ICG's debt. He doesn't want all its loans coming up for renewal at the same time. [. . .]

The likes of M&S and Tesco Bank can get retail bonds away relatively easily, but few had heard of ICG outside of the Square Mile. [. . .]

"The banks accept they are not able to lend to their favourite clients in the way they used to so they are starting to help."

In fact, if a bank can help a client to raise funds from private sources but retain its main facilities, then this could suit it down to the ground.

"It's a fact of life that the banks will want to lend less but eep all the goodies, the ancillary services," says Keller.

Source: The Sunday Telegraph, 29 January 2012

References and further reading

Boakes, K. (2010) *Reading and Understanding the Financial Times*. Upper Saddle River, NJ: FT Prentice Hall.

Financial Times (daily newspaper) www.ft.com

Hillier, D. and S. Ross et al. (2010) *Corporate Finance* (1st European edn.). Maidenhead: McGraw-Hill Education.

Investors Chronicle (weekly magazine).

McKenzie, W. (2010) *Financial Times Guide to Using and Interpreting Company Accounts* (4th edn.). Upper Saddle River, NJ: FT Prentice Hall.

Modigliani, F. and M. Miller (1958) The cost of capital, corporation finance and the theory of investment, *American Economic Review*, June, pp. 261–97.

Rees, B. (2011) *Financial Analysis* (3rd edn.). Upper Saddle River, NJ: FT Prentice Hall.

Vernimemen, P. et al. (2009) *Corporate Finance: Theory and Practice*. Chichester: Wiley.

www.londonstockexchange.com

When you have read this chapter, log on to the Online Learning Centre website at *www.mcgraw-hill.co.uk/textbooks/leiwy* to explore chapter-by-chapter test questions, further reading and more online study tools.

Chapter 11
Strategic management accounting and the balanced scorecard

 Learning **objectives**

After studying Chapter 11, you should be able to:
1   Define the concepts of strategy and strategic management accounting
2   Understand the impact of corporate strategy on management accounting
3   Understand some basic strategic models and their relationship with management accounting techniques
4   Understand how a balanced scorecard fits together and how it supports a company's strategy

Concepts **in Context**

The term strategic management accounting (SMA) has been used to describe the process of 'provision and analysis of management accounting data about a business and its competitors for use in developing and monitoring business strategy'.[1] We may illustrate the basic ideas of SMA by looking at one of the leading retailers in the United Kingdom, Tesco, which has tailored its key performance indicators to the economics of its business. For example, rather than maximize EVA, Tesco has realized that its main fixed assets are its stores. With this type of asset base, the company aims to reduce the cost of building good quality new stores through strategic partnering with construction companies. In order to check its market positioning, the company is constantly monitoring the prices of its merchandise relative to the prices charged by its main competitors. As well as promoting customer loyalty, it uses its store card as a database for targeting the specific needs of individual customers as revealed through their purchase patterns. It also keeps a close eye on non-financial indicators such as the length of queues at the check-outs.

© Joshua Hodge Photography

In this chapter we will review both short- and long-term financial planning but in the context of *strategic choice*. Strategic choice means that companies can *choose* which industries and products they want to compete in but it also means that different companies in the *same* industry may decide to adopt different strategies with quite different implications for management accounting and control. For example, a company's strategy may determine whether management will be concentrating on a tight control of costs, maintaining quality or generating new product ideas.

As more and more reliance is placed on bought-in goods and services, a higher proportion of costs are generated by a firm's suppliers, which suggests that major improvements in cost, quality and innovation are potentially available through the effective management of the firm's supply chain. In *strategic* as opposed to *traditional* management accounting, there is a recognition that managers may have some freedom to choose which industry they operate in, which technology is used and how the organization is structured. Thus, rather than passively adapting to given competitive, technological and organizational circumstances, strategic management accounting (SMA) helps managers make choices through information support. Strategic management accounting is also concerned with the *implementation* of strategies by setting up control systems that drive through the chosen strategies. For example, if a company wishes to pursue a low-cost strategy then traditional budgetary control may help implementation. However, few companies compete on price alone so additional performance measures may be non-financial, such as delivery or queuing time.

As described above, Tesco's approach in linking its goals and its management information systems demonstrates many of the principles of SMA. The company has decided how it is going to compete, reviewed its internal and external operations and chosen key performance indicators that enable it to monitor the development of its chosen business model. The search for data is driven by decision needs rather than by what is simply easily available.

Some basic techniques of strategic management accounting

SMA has an orientation towards the firm's environment. The relevant environment may be in its value chain, that is, its 'upstream' relations with suppliers and 'downstream' relations with its customers. The other relevant environment is its competitive position relative to both existing and potential competitors. Its competitive position will not just depend on price but on a marketing mix.

Sometimes SMA will use existing information and sometimes new information will be sought. For example, the increased emphasis on marketing may involve the use of techniques such as attribute costing that costs product attributes that appeal to customers, using brand value as a basis for managerial decisions and measuring the costs of quality. The competitive position is monitored through competitor cost assessment through estimates of competitors' costs based on an appraisal of facilities, technology, economies of scale, market share, volume, unit costs and return on sales. Strategic management accounting is also concerned with the long run through the use of target and life-cycle costing that looks at the costs incurred throughout the life of a product as it goes through various stages such as development and full production.

SMA and the concept of strategic positioning

Both the choice of strategic options and the ongoing search for strategic information may be informed by a variety of corporate strategy models. In short, a further development of SMA integrates the more outward and forward-looking aspects of the strategic intelligence approach with some well-known models of strategic choice.

Some strategic choice models involve deciding on a company's *strategic position*. For example, following Miles and Snow,[2] should the company be a defender concentrating on reducing costs and/or improving quality, a prospector continually searching for market opportunities or an analyser which combines the defender and prospector positions? Or, following Michael Porter,[3] should the company concentrate on cost leadership (aiming to be the lowest-cost producer in an industry) or product differentiation (maintain a price premium based on superior product quality)? Porter argues that: '[T]he worst strategic error is to be *stuck in the middle* or to try simultaneously to pursue all the strategies. This is a recipe for strategic mediocrity and below-average performance, because pursuing all strategies simultaneously means that a firm is not able to achieve any of them because of their inherent contradictions.'

The implications for management accounting of these positional strategies could be that a company that seeks cost leadership may use standard costing with flexible budgets for manufacturing cost control. With product cost being the key input to pricing decisions, it may also analyse costs of competitors in order to review its positioning. If the company is a differentiator then traditional costing may be less important, and more attention is paid to new product development and marketing expenditures.

Porter's generic strategy model may be linked to another of his innovations, the concept of the value chain. The value chain,[4] which is illustrated in Exhibit 11.1, consists of the major business functions that add value to a company's products and services. All these functions, from research and development through product design, manufacturing, marketing, distribution and customer service, are required to bring a product or service to the customer and generate revenues.

With value-chain analysis, the aim is to find linkages between value-creating activities, which result in lower costs and/or enhanced differentiation. John Shank's *strategic cost management*[5] approach shows how Porter's ideas on strategic positioning and gaining competitive advantage can have an impact on management accounting. Shank advocates a cost-driver analysis, which suggests that costs are driven by *structural* and *executional* factors. Structural drivers consider factors such as scale, scope, experience, technology and complexity, while executional drivers include factors such as work force involvement, quality management capacity utilization, plant lay-out efficiency, product configuration effectiveness, and exploitation of linkages.

Strategic investment appraisal: investment appraisal with strategic 'bolt-ons'?

In Chapter 10, we considered the various techniques of investment appraisal such as net present value (NPV) and internal rate of return. In principle, many strategic decisions, such as acquisitions or major marketing initiatives, could be analysed using these techniques by estimating and discounting future net cash flows and choosing the option that seems to give the highest return or largest NPV. Yet some advocates of more strategic approaches have argued that the conventional investment appraisal approach may set up business problems in a misleading way with an overemphasis on financial calculation leaving strategic issues either neglected or treated in an *ad hoc*, 'bolt-on' manner. John Shank argues that the NPV model follows four steps:

Step 1	Identifying spending proposals
Step 2	Quantitative analysis of incremental cash flows
Step 3	Qualitative issues that cannot be fitted into NPV are then treated in an *ad hoc* manner
Step 4	Decision – *Yes/No*

According to Shank, in conventional capital budgeting/investment appraisals, *Step 1* is hardly analysed since the investment proposals just appear out of thin air. *Step 2*, in contrast, gets a great deal of attention with

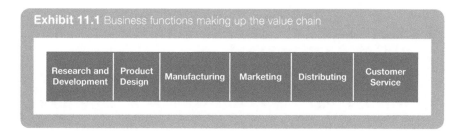

Exhibit 11.1 Business functions making up the value chain

Research and Development	Product Design	Manufacturing	Marketing	Distributing	Customer Service

elaborate considerations of relevant cash flows and sophisticated treatments of risk. *Step 3* is a 'step-child' concerned with 'soft-issues' that cannot be handled in *Step 2*. *Step 4*, the decision, *then generally flows out of Step 2*.

Shank[6] argues that the finance framework sets up strategic problems in a misleading way and argues that pure NPV analysis misses the richness of real business problems and is often merely set up to rationalize a prior decision. He illustrates the point with a case study, *Mavis Machines*.

The Mavis Machines case

Mavis Machines is a small metal working company producing drill bits for oil exploration. At present, the shop has four large manual lathes each operated by a skilled worker. The question facing the Managing Director of Mavis Machines is whether the company should install a numerically controlled lathe to replace all manual lathes. The numerical lathe would require only one operator but with different skills in computerized automation.

The decision can be set up using an NPV model and produces a very high rate of internal rate of return, as shown in Exhibit 11.2.

Exhibit 11.2 Summary of the quantitative analysis of the automation project in Mavis Machines

Net Investment

Purchase price		$680,000
Less:		
Trade-in value of old machines		(240,000)
Tax saving from trade-in (46%)		(108,000)
Book value	476,000	
Selling price	240,000	
Loss on resale	236,000	
Investment tax credit (10%)		(68,000)
Net		**($263,400)**

Annual cash savings

Labour – six operators (3/shift × 2 shifts) × $20,800 each		($124,800)
Factory space savings (no difference in cash flows)		0
Other cash savings (supplies, maintenance and power)		20,000
Total, pre-tax		$144,800
Less additional taxes (46%)		(60,600)
Cash saved – pre-tax	144,800	
Additional depreciation	(13,000)*	
Additional taxable income	131,800	
Annual after tax cash savings		**$84,200**
(ignoring inflation in savings in future years)		

*Old depreciation = $590 – $20/15 = $38,000
New depreciation = $680 – $68/12 = $51,000
Difference = $13,000

Summary of cash flows*
Period 0 (263,400) 12 year IRR = 32 + %, real
Periods 1–12 $84,200

---

*Ignoring the minor impact from the lost salvage values in year 12.

Reprinted from Management Accounting Research, 7/2, Shank, J., 'Analyzing technology investments – from NPV to Strategic Cost Management', 185–97, Copyright (1996), with permission from Elsevier.

The main cash savings stem from the need for fewer workers. However, other significant savings can be made in the net cost of the initial investment because of the healthy trade-in value of the relatively modern manual lathes. Indeed, 60% of the attractiveness of the project comes from the scrap value of the old machines, which suggests that the previous replacement decision might have been faulty. In an NPV approach other factors such as *flexibility, marketing* and *corporate image* are treated in rather an *ad hoc* manner.

An alternative strategic approach suggests a different perspective on the choice. Indeed when explicit strategic models are used to explore the issues the emphasis on a positive NPV in the financial analysis is eclipsed by other factors. *Competitive analysis* suggests that as a small machine shop, Mavis is best positioned as a *niche* player rather than a cost leader. The manual lathes and the skilled operators give it more product flexibility and greater security than one numerical lathe. Its strength lies in its flexibility to vary its products and sources of raw material. *Value chain analysis* suggested that it would lose both buyer and seller power because it would be more dependent only on those suppliers that could meet stringent quality requirements and would be more dependent on a single customer. There were also questions concerning the ease of maintenance of the new machine and the likely impact that firing eight workers out of a small workforce would have on morale and the firm's local reputation.

Strategic investment appraisal: an iterative model

Does the criticism of NPV by Shank and others mean that the material in Chapter 10 is of limited relevance for strategic decisions? Not according to Tomkins and Carr,[7] who suggest that strategic investment decisions may be modelled to include both financial and strategic analysis as shown in Exhibit 11.3. They suggest that a three-stage is followed:

1 The firm decides which markets to be in, by assessing both customer requirements and the relative ability of rivals to meet them. The firm will generate a number of investment possibilities based on product attributes related to volume of sales.

2 Analysis of the value chain assesses the means by which the attributes of the product can be delivered. This analysis will review possible suppliers and distributors as part of an iterative process to check on performance throughout the whole product life cycle.

3 The first two steps may then be modelled in terms of a cost and attribute driver analysis to see if the attributes can be delivered at an acceptable profit. The process is iterative in that a first assessment may suggest unacceptable low levels of profitability. The next assessment may then consider whether the profitability can be improved through piecemeal cost savings or whether existing delivery systems must be changed more radically through process re-engineering. Tomkins and Carr call this search for improvement, a process of 'probing' that uses discounted cash flow analysis but which also draws on an array of market, technological and other data.[8]

Modelling and monitoring strategy: the balanced scorecard and other non-financial measures

LO 4

So far in this chapter although we have discussed strategic choice, our focus on *financial metrics* of various sorts is arguably inappropriate for strategic decision making. We will now consider a very influential model, the *balanced scorecard*, which may be used by organizations to develop, implement and control strategy through a balanced use of financial and *non-financial* indicators. Rather than focus on an individual strategic investment, the balanced scorecard is concerned with the maintenance of an outward and forward-looking stance on a continuous and routine basis through a systematic process of monitoring and reporting on a variety of different performance dimensions.

A **balanced scorecard (BSC)** consists of an integrated set of performance measures that are derived from the company's strategy and that support the company's strategy throughout the organization.[9] A strategy is

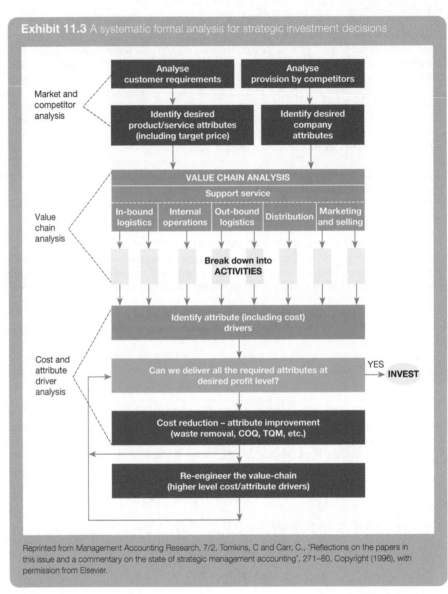

Exhibit 11.3 A systematic formal analysis for strategic investment decisions

Market and competitor analysis

Analyse customer requirements

Analyse provision by competitors

Identify desired product/service attributes (including target price)

Identify desired company attributes

Value chain analysis

VALUE CHAIN ANALYSIS

Support service

| In-bound logistics | Internal operations | Out-bound logistics | Distribution | Marketing and selling |

Break down into ACTIVITIES

Identify attribute (including cost) drivers

Cost and attribute driver analysis

Can we deliver all the required attributes at desired profit level?

YES → **INVEST**

Cost reduction – attribute improvement (waste removal, COQ, TQM, etc.)

Re-engineer the value-chain (higher level cost/attribute drivers)

Reprinted from Management Accounting Research, 7/2, Tomkins, C and Carr, C., 'Reflections on the papers in this issue and a commentary on the state of strategic management accounting', 271–80, Copyright (1996), with permission from Elsevier.

essentially a theory about how to achieve the organization's goals. For example, low-cost European carriers such as easyJet and Ryanair have copied Southwestern Airlines' strategy of offering passengers low prices and fun on short-haul jet service. The low prices result from the absence of costly frills such as meals and assigned seating. The fun is provided by flight attendants who go out of their way to entertain passengers with their antics. This is an interesting strategy. Southwestern Airlines consciously hires people who have a sense of humour and who enjoy their work. Hiring and retaining such employees probably costs no more – and may cost less – than retaining grumpy flight attendants who view their jobs as a chore. Southwestern Airlines' strategy is to build loyal customers through a combination of 'fun' – which does not cost anything to provide – and low prices that are possible because of the lack of costly frills offered by competing airlines. The theory is that low prices and fun[10] will lead to loyal customers, which, in combination with low costs, will lead to high profits. So far, this theory has worked.

Under the balanced scorecard approach, top management translates its strategy into performance measures that employees can understand and can do something about. For example, the amount of time passengers have to wait in line to have their baggage checked might be a performance measure for a supervisor in charge of the check-in counter at an airport. This performance measure is easily understood by the supervisor, and can be improved by the supervisor's actions.

Common characteristics of balanced scorecards

Performance measures used in the balanced scorecard approach tend to fall into the four groups illustrated in Exhibit 11.4: financial, customer, internal business processes, and learning and growth. Internal business processes are what the company does in an attempt to satisfy customers. For example, in a manufacturing company, assembling a product is an internal business process. In an airline, handling baggage is an internal business process. The basic idea is that learning is necessary to improve internal business processes; improving business processes is necessary to improve customer satisfaction; and improving customer satisfaction is necessary to improve financial results.

Note that the emphasis in Exhibit 11.4 is on *improvement* – not on just attaining some specific objective such as profits of £10 million. In the balanced scorecard approach, continual improvement is encouraged. In many industries, this is a matter of survival. If an organization does not continually improve, it will eventually lose out to competitors that do.

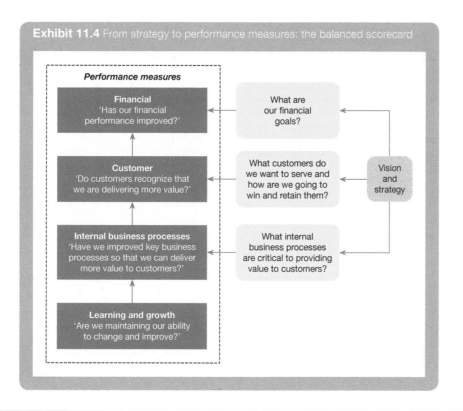

Exhibit 11.4 From strategy to performance measures: the balanced scorecard

Financial performance measures appear at the top of Exhibit 11.4. Ultimately, most companies exist to provide financial rewards to owners. There are exceptions. Some companies may have loftier goals, such as providing environmentally friendly products to consumers. However, even non-profit organizations must generate enough financial resources to stay in operation.

Ordinarily, top managers are responsible for the financial performance measures – not lower level managers. The supervisor in charge of checking in passengers can be held responsible for how long passengers have to queue. However, this supervisor cannot reasonably be held responsible for the entire company's profit. That is the responsibility of the airline's top managers.

Exhibit 11.5 lists some examples of performance measures that can be found on the balanced scorecards of companies. However, few companies, if any, would use all of these performance measures, and almost all companies would add other performance measures. Managers should carefully select the performance measures for their company's balanced scorecard, keeping the following points in mind. First and foremost, the performance measures should be consistent with, and follow from, the company's strategy. If the

Exhibit 11.5 Examples of performance measures for balanced scorecards

Customer perspective performance measure	Desired change
Customer satisfaction as measured by survey results	+
Number of customer complaints	–
Market share	+
Product returns as a percentage of sales	–
Percentage of customers retained from last period	+
Number of new customers	+
Internal business processes perspective performance measure	**Desired change**
Percentage of sales from new products	+
Time to introduce new products to market	–
Percentage of customer calls answered within 20 seconds	+
On-time deliveries as a percentage of all deliveries	+
Work in progress inventory as a percentage of sales	–
Unfavourable standard cost variances	–
Defect-free units as a percentage of completed units	+
Delivery cycle time*	–
Throughput time*	–
Manufacturing cycle efficiency*	+
Quality costs	–
Set-up time	–
Time from call by customer to repair of product	–
Percentage of customer complaints settled on first contact	+
Time to settle a customer claim	–
Learning and growth perspective performance measure	**Desired change**
Suggestions per employee	+
Value-added employee†	+
Employee turnover	–
Hours of in-house training per employee	+

*Explained later in this chapter.
†Value-added is revenue less externally purchased materials, supplies and services.

performance measures are not consistent with the company's strategy, people will find themselves working at cross-purposes. Second, the scorecard should not have too many performance measures. This can lead to a lack of focus and confusion.

While the entire organization will have an overall balanced scorecard, each responsible individual will have his or her own personal scorecard as well. This scorecard should consist of items the individual can personally influence that relate directly to the performance measures on the overall balanced scorecard. The performance measures on this personal scorecard should not be overly influenced by actions taken by others in the company or by events that are outside of the individual's control.

With those broad principles in mind, we will now take a look at how a company's strategy affects its balanced scorecard.

A company's strategy and the balanced scorecard

Returning to the performance measures in Exhibit 11.5, each company must decide which customers to target and what internal business processes are crucial to attracting and retaining those customers. Different companies, having different strategies, will target different customers with different kinds of products and services. Take the car industry as an example. BMW stresses engineering and handling; Volvo, safety; Jaguar, luxury detailing; and Toyota,[11] reliability. Because of these differences in emphases, a one-size-fits-all approach to performance measurement will not work even within this one industry. Performance measures must be tailored to the specific strategy of each company.

Suppose, for example, that Jaguar's strategy is to offer distinctive, richly finished luxury automobiles to wealthy individuals who prize handcrafted, individualized products. Part of Jaguar's strategy might be to create such a large number of options for details, such as leather seats, interior and exterior colour combinations, and wooden dashboards, that each car becomes virtually one of a kind. For example, instead of just offering tan or blue leather seats in standard cowhide, the company may offer customers the choice of an almost infinite palate of colours in any of a number of different exotic leathers. For such a system to work effectively, Jaguar would have to be able to deliver a completely customized car within a reasonable amount of time – and without incurring more cost for this customization than the customer is willing to pay. Exhibit 11.6 suggests how Jaguar might reflect this strategy in its balanced scorecard.

If the balanced scorecard is correctly constructed, the performance measures should be linked together on a cause-and-effect basis. Each link can then be read as a hypothesis in the form 'If we improve this performance measure, then this other performance measure should also improve.' Starting from the bottom of Exhibit 11.6, we can read the links between performance measures as follows. If employees acquire the skills to install new options more effectively, then the company can offer more options and the options can be installed in less time. If more options are available and they are installed in less time, then customer surveys should show greater satisfaction with the range of options available. If customer satisfaction improves, then the number of cars sold should increase. In addition, if customer satisfaction improves, the company should be able to maintain or increase its selling prices, and if the time to install options decreases, the costs of installing the options should decrease. Together, this should result in an increase in the contribution margin per car. If the contribution margin per car increases and more cars are sold, the result should be an increase in profits.

In essence, the balanced scorecard articulates a theory of how the company can attain its desired outcomes (financial, in this case) by taking concrete actions. While the strategy laid out in Exhibit 11.6 seems plausible, it should be regarded as only a theory that should be discarded if it proves to be invalid. For example, if the company succeeds in increasing the number of options available and in decreasing the time required to install options and yet there is no increase in customer satisfaction, the number of cars sold, the contribution margin per car, or profits, the strategy would have to be reconsidered. One of the advantages of the balanced scorecard is that it continually tests the theories underlying management's strategy. If a strategy is not working, it should become evident when some of the predicted effects (i.e. more car sales) do not occur. Without this feedback, management may drift on indefinitely with an ineffective strategy based on faulty assumptions.

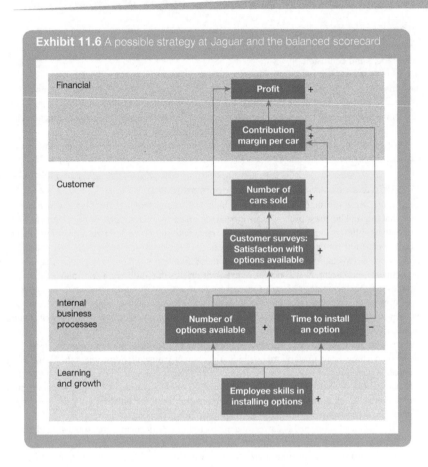

Exhibit 11.6 A possible strategy at Jaguar and the balanced scorecard

Advantages of timely feedback

Whatever performance measures are used, they should be reported on a frequent and timely basis. For example, data about defects should be reported to the responsible managers at least once a day so that action can quickly be taken if an unusual number of defects occurs. In the most advanced companies, any defect is reported *immediately*, and its cause is tracked down before any more defects can occur. Another common characteristic of the performance measures under the balanced scorecard approach is that managers focus on trends in the performance measures over time. The emphasis is on progress and *improvement* rather than on meeting any specific standard.

Some measures of internal business process performance

Most of the performance measures listed in Exhibit 11.5 are self-explanatory. However, three are not – *delivery cycle time, throughput time* and *manufacturing cycle efficiency* (MCE). These three important performance measures are discussed next.

Delivery cycle time

The amount of time between when an order is received from a customer to when the completed order is shipped is called the **delivery cycle time**. This time is clearly a key concern to many customers, who would like the delivery cycle time to be as short as possible. Cutting the delivery cycle time may give a company

Focus on Business Practice

A health service scorecard

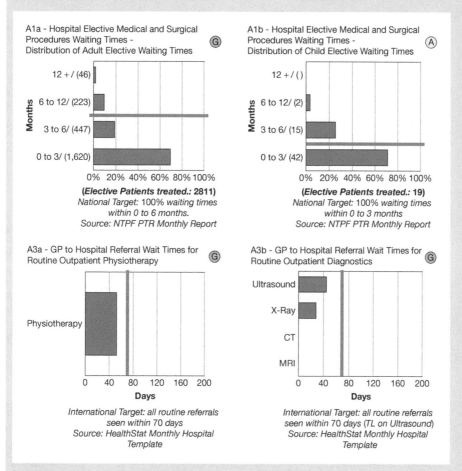

Many businesses and services use a balanced scorecard type system to report on key operating statistics and performance indicators. The Health Service Executive (HSE) is the state agency responsible for the running of the public health service in Ireland. It has over 100,000 employees and an annual budget of approximately €15 billion. The HSE uses a reporting system called HealthStat to monitor its performance in delivering health and care services.

HealthStat is described by the HSE as 'a comprehensive databank of performance information for Irish public health services'. To provide a comprehensive view of how services are delivered, HealthStat groups performance indicators under three headings: (1) Access – measuring waiting time for services; (2) Integration – checks that patients receive the correct services, in the right location and are informed about their treatment; and (3) Resources – whether a hospital or care facility is making best use of its financial and human resources. In total, 18 performance

metrics across these three headings are reported on a monthly basis. Each metric is compared to a national target – these targets have been set against best international practice and are regularly reviewed. Each month, a traffic-light type dashboard (green = better than target, amber = below target, but improving, red = well below target) is compiled and reported to clinical managers, hospitals and the HSE's board. The data are also released to the public via the HSE's website – see example above. According to the HSE, HealthStat, being the first unified reporting systems used by the HSE, provides all staff and managers with a platform to monitor and improve service delivery.[12]

Exercise: Looking at the example given, do you think these performance metrics take into account factors like quality of care received, willingness of medical professionals to communicate to patients and so on? Should such things be included in performance measurements?

a key competitive advantage – and may be necessary for survival – and therefore many companies would include this performance measure on their balanced scorecard.

Throughput (manufacturing cycle) time

The amount of time required to turn raw materials into completed products is called throughput time, or manufacturing cycle time. The relationship between the delivery cycle time and the throughput (manufacturing cycle) time is illustrated in Exhibit 11.7.

Note that, as shown in Exhibit 11.7, the throughput time, or manufacturing cycle time, is made up of process time, inspection time, move time and queue time. Process time is the amount of time in which work is actually done on the product. Inspection time is the amount of time spent ensuring that the product is not defective. Move time is the time required to move materials or partially completed products from workstation to workstation. Queue time is the amount of time a product spends waiting to be worked on, to be moved, to be inspected, or in storage waiting to be shipped.

As shown at the bottom of Exhibit 11.7, the only one of these four activities that adds value to the product is process time. The other three activities – inspecting, moving and queueing – add no value and should be eliminated as much as possible.

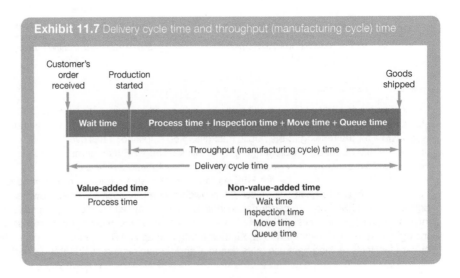

Exhibit 11.7 Delivery cycle time and throughput (manufacturing cycle) time

Manufacturing cycle efficiency (MCE)

Through concerted efforts to eliminate the non-value-added activities of inspecting, moving and queueing, some companies have reduced their throughput time to only a fraction of previous levels. In turn, this has helped to reduce the delivery cycle time from months to only weeks or hours. The throughput time, which is considered to be a key measure in delivery performance, can be put into better perspective by computing the manufacturing cycle efficiency (MCE). The MCE is computed by relating the value-added time to the throughput time. The formula is as follows:

$$MCE = \frac{\text{Value-added time}}{\text{Throughput (manufacturing cycle) time}}$$

If the MCE is less than 1, then non-value-added time is present in the production process. An MCE of 0.5, for example, would mean that half of the total production time consisted of inspection, moving and similar non-value-added activities. In many manufacturing companies, the MCE is less than 0.1 (10%), which means that 90% of the time a unit is in process is spent on activities that do not add value to the product. By monitoring the MCE, companies are able to reduce non-value-added activities and thus get products into the hands of customers more quickly and at a lower cost.

We would like to emphasize a few points concerning the balanced scorecard. First, the balanced scorecard should be tailored to the company's strategy; each company's balanced scorecard should be unique. The examples given in this chapter are just that – examples. They should not be interpreted as general templates to be fitted to each company. Second, the balanced scorecard reflects a particular strategy, or theory, about how a company can further its objectives by taking specific actions. The theory should be viewed as tentative and subject to change if the actions do not in fact lead to attaining the company's financial and other goals. If the theory (i.e. strategy) changes, then the performance measures on the balanced scorecard should also change. The balanced scorecard should be viewed as a dynamic system that evolves as the company's strategy evolves.[13,14]

The balanced scorecard should not be seen just as 'a four bucket' model[15] with four boxes that must be filled. Organizations may choose to have five main dimensions. For example, banks may wish to have an extra box labelled risk management. As we have seen recently with the world-wide 'credit crunch', banks that have failed to manage risk have suffered financially or even gone out of business completely.

Focus on Business Practice

Risk and the balanced scorecard

© slobo

The author was recently involved in a research project looking at the implementation of the balanced scorecard in a major European bank. The bank had 'customized' the scorecard by including 'risk' as a major objective. Relative to some of its competitors, this bank did seem to be better prepared for the credit crunch with a much less risky approach to lending. Another interesting feature of the bank was the way that each employee had a personal scorecard which was aligned to the local business unit through to corporate objectives. The scorecard implementation had a board level corporate champion and was 'owned' by both human resource and finance functions.[16]

Exercise: Not all performance indicators in the balanced scorecard are positively related. Consider in this example the potential trade-off between risk and financial return.

Summary

- Profit and shareholder value metrics may be used for business planning but they may not provide sufficient information for developing and implementing strategies.

- Strategic management accounting has evolved from the collection of competitor information to attempts to match management accounting systems with an organization's strategic position.

- A balanced scorecard consists of an integrated system of performance measures that are derived from and support the company's strategy. Different companies will have different balanced scorecards because they have different strategies. A well-constructed balanced scorecard provides a means for guiding the company and also provides feedback concerning the effectiveness of the company's strategy.

Key terms

Attribute costing Costing the product attributes that appeal to customers (p. 260).

Balanced scorecard (BSC) An integrated set of performance measures that is derived from and supports the organization's strategy (p. 263).

Cost leadership Aiming to be the lowest cost producer in an industry (p. 260).

Defender A company which concentrates on reducing costs and/or improving quality in existing markets/products (p. 260).

Delivery cycle time The amount of time required from receipt of an order from a customer to shipment of the completed goods (p. 268).

Executional drivers Cost factors such as work force involvement, quality management capacity utilization, plant lay-out efficiency, product configuration effectiveness, and exploitation of linkages (p. 261).

Life-cycle costing Analyses costs incurred throughout the life of a product from development through to full production (p. 260).

Manufacturing cycle efficiency (MCE) Process (value-added) time as a percentage of throughput time (p. 271).

Marketing mix Price is one element in product competitiveness together with product, promotion and place (p. 260).

Product differentiation Aims to maintain a price premium based on superior product quality (p. 261).

Prospector A company that is continually searching for market opportunities (p. 260).

Strategic choice Choosing not only which industries and products to compete in but also how a company plans to compete (p. 260).

Strategic management accounting The use of management accounting information to help managers choose where and how to compete (p. 260).

Structural drivers Factors such as scale, scope, experience, technology and complexity (p. 261).

Throughput time The amount of time required to turn raw materials into completed products (p. 270).

Value chain The major business functions that add value to a company's products and services (p. 261).

Endnotes

1 Simmonds (1981).

2 Miles and Snow (1978).

3 Porter (1980).

4 Porter (1985).

5 Shank (1996).

6 Shank (1996).

7 Tomkins and Carr (1996).

8 For a discussion of strategic investment appraisal see also Northcott and Alkaraan (2007).

9 The balanced scorecard concept was developed by Robert Kaplan and David Norton. For further details, see their articles Kaplan and Norton (1992) (1996a) (1996b), (1997) and (2004). In the 1960s, the French developed a concept similar to the balanced scorecard called Tableau de Bord or 'dashboard'. For details, see Lebas (1994).

10 Some low cost airlines have only copied the 'no-frills' and seem less concerned with 'fun'. There is also an emerging trend to encourage online check-in.

11 Of course, Toyota, *as a company*, is associated with the development of lean production, which, as we have seen is based on trying to achieve both low cost, reliability, and high quality specifications. It may not try to achieve all these characteristics *in a particular model*.

12 http://www.hse.ie/eng/staff/Healthstat/about/

13 Kaplan and Norton (1996b).

14 For a critical evaluation of the BSC see Norreklit (2000).

15 Ittner and Larcker (2003).

16 Ye and Seal (2009).

When you have read this chapter, log on to the Online Learning Centre for *Management Accounting for Business Decisions* at **www.mcgraw-hill.co.uk/textbooks/seal**, where you'll find multiple choice questions, practice exams and extra study tools for management accounting.

Assessment

11–1 Why is market share an important indicator to monitor?

11–2 What aspects of a competitor's costs should be analysed in a strategic assessment?

11–3 What sources are useful for strategic intelligence gathering?

11–4 What is the difference between a prospector and a defender company?

11–5 What is the difference between a cost leader and a product differentiator?

11–6 What are the three steps/dimensions that combine financial and strategic analysis as proposed by Tomkins and Carr?

11–7 What are the implications of the 'strategy as collision' model?

11–8 Why does the balanced scorecard include financial performance measures as well as measures of how well internal business processes are doing?

11–9 What is the difference between the delivery cycle time and the throughput time? What four elements make up the throughput time? Into what two classes can these four elements be placed?

11–10 Why does the balanced scorecard differ from company to company?

Exercises

E11–1 🕐 Time allowed: 20 minutes

Management of Mittel Rhein AG of Köln, Germany, would like to reduce the amount of time between when a customer places an order and when the order is shipped. For the first quarter of operations during the current year the following data were reported:

	Days
Inspection time	0.3
Wait time (from order to start of production)	14.0
Process time	2.7
Move time	1.0
Queue time	5.0

Required

1 Compute the throughput time, or velocity of production.
2 Compute the manufacturing cycle efficiency (MCE) for the quarter.
3 What percentage of the throughput time was spent in non-value-added activities?
4 Compute the delivery cycle time.

Problems

P11–2 Perverse effects of some performance measures

🕐 Time allowed: 30 minutes

There is often more than one way to improve a performance measure. Unfortunately, some of the actions taken by managers to make their performance look better may actually harm the organization. For example, suppose the marketing department is held responsible only for increasing the performance measure 'total revenues'. Increases in total revenues may be achieved by working harder and smarter, but they can also usually be achieved by simply cutting prices. The increase in volume from cutting prices almost always results in greater total revenues; however, it does not always lead to greater total profits. Those who design performance measurement systems need to keep in mind that managers who are under pressure to perform may take actions to improve performance measures that have negative consequences elsewhere.

Required

For each of the following situations, describe actions that managers might take to show improvement in the performance measure but which do not actually lead to improvement in the organization's overall performance.

1   Concerned with the slow rate at which new products are brought to market, top management of a consumer electronics company introduces a new performance measure – speed-to-market. The research and development department is given responsibility for this performance measure, which measures the average amount of time a product is in development before it is released to the market for sale.

2   The Chief Executive of a telephone company has been under public pressure from city officials to fix the large number of public pay phones that do not work. The company's repair people complain that the problem is vandalism and damage caused by theft of coins from coin boxes – particularly in high crime areas in the city. The Chief Executive says she wants the problem solved and has pledged to city officials that there will be substantial improvement by the end of the year. To ensure that this is done, she makes the managers in charge of installing and maintaining pay phones responsible for increasing the percentage of public pay phones that are fully functional.

3   A manufacturing company has been plagued by the chronic failure to ship orders to customers by the promised date. To solve this problem, the production manager has been given the responsibility of increasing the percentage of orders shipped on time. When a customer calls in an order, the production manager and the customer agree to a delivery date. If the order is not completed by that date, it is counted as a late shipment.

4   Concerned with the productivity of employees, the board of directors of a large multinational corporation has dictated that the manager of each subsidiary will be held responsible for increasing the revenue per employee of his or her subsidiary.

P11–3 Strategic analysis

Time allowed: 45 minutes

M-HK provides a passenger ferry service between two large cities separated by the mouth of a major river. The ferries are frequent, well-supported by passengers and cover the distance between the cities in one hour. M-HK also transports passengers and goods by water ferry to other cities located on the

river mouth. There are other ferry operators providing services between each of these locations besides M-HK.

Required

1. Explain what strategic information is required by M-HK's management in respect of customer demand, competition, competitiveness, and finance in order to plan its future ferry services. *(10 marks)*
2. Using the information in your answer to Question 1, discuss how M-HK's Chartered Management Accountant should provide reports to M-HK's senior management for operational and strategic planning purposes. *(15 marks)*

(Total = 25 marks)

CIMA Management Accounting – Business Strategy, May 2001

P11–4 Strategic analysis

⏱ Time allowed: 45 minutes

R is a large high-class hotel situated in a thriving city. It is part of a worldwide hotel group owned by a large number of shareholders. The majority of the shares are held by individuals, each holding a small number; the rest are owned by financial institutions.

The hotel provides full amenities, including a heated swimming pool, as well as the normal facilities of bars, restaurants and good-quality accommodation. There are many other hotels in the city which all compete with R. The city in which R is situated is old and attracts many foreign visitors, particularly in its summer season.

Required

1. State the main stakeholders with whom relationships need to be established and maintained by the management of R. Explain why it is important that relationships are developed and maintained with each of these stakeholders. *(10 marks)*
2. Explain how the management of R should carry out a benchmarking exercise on its services, and recommend ways in which the outcomes should be evaluated. *(15 marks)*
   Note: Do NOT describe different methods of benchmarking in answering this question. *(Total = 25 marks)*

CIMA Management Accounting – Business Strategy, May 2001

P11-5 Balanced scorecard

⏱ Time allowed: 45 minutes

The Royal Hotel Ltd is privately owned and situated in Keswick, an inland resort in the English Lake District. It is a medium-sized hotel with 50 bedrooms. Whilst high standards of building maintenance exist, the hotel has been conservatively managed by William Wordsworth, who owns 100% of its share capital. The hotel currently offers accommodation and restaurant facilities only, and has experienced little innovation in services offered during recent years.

William Wordsworth intends to retire in five years' time, so he has invited Pam Ayres to join him in partnership, with a view to her taking a controlling interest in the hotel on his retirement. She has recently qualified with a Master's Degree from the University of Birmingham, and has some knowledge of the latest approaches to the measurement of business performance. She has conducted a preliminary investigation of the hotel's performance over the past two years, to form a basis for taking a decision on joining William in partnership. The data she has gathered, based on the balanced scorecard approach to performance measurement, is presented in Appendix 1 and Appendix 2.

Appendix 1: Financial data

	Current year	Previous year
Estimated market value of the business	£2,000,000	£2,000,000
Turnover	£1,000,000	£950,000
Net profit	£200,000	£188,000
Current assets (cash, stock and credit card debtors)	£30,000	£25,000
Current liabilities (trade creditors)	£7,000	£10,000

Appendix 2: Non-financial data

Customer perspective

	Current year	Previous year
Room occupancy (during the 300 days the hotel is open each year)	55%	65%
Market share of overnight hotel accommodation in Keswick	4.33%	3.67%
Customer satisfaction rating (score maximum 100%)	55%	65%
Customers indicating they would return to the Royal Hotel if visiting Keswick again	25%	45%

Internal business processes

	Current year	Previous year
Audited percentage of procedures done according to job specification	75%	85%
Year on year employee retention rate	30%	50%
Customer rating of staff responsiveness (score maximum 100%)	60%	85%
Customer rating of staff competence (score maximum 100%)	50%	90%
Customer rating of staff courtesy (score maximum 100%)	60%	78%

Learning and growth perspective

	Current year	Previous year
Royal Hotel percentage of revenue from accommodation and restaurant	100%	100%
Keswick hotels industry average percentage of revenue from accommodation and restaurants	65%	75%
Average percentage of staff with hotel and restaurant qualifications	55%	65%

Required

1   Assess the financial performance of the Royal Hotel based only on the information provided in Appendix 1.
2   Explain why the information in Appendix 2 is likely to give a better indication of future success than the information in Appendix 1.
3   Using all the information at your disposal, assess the future prospects of the Royal Hotel, and advise Pam Ayres on the desirability of becoming a partner in the business

(Thanks to Alan Coad, University of Birmingham)